ENGINEERING MATHEMATICS

Volume 2

ENGINEERING MATHEMATICS

Volume 2

A. J. M. SPENCER
D. F. PARKER
D. S. BERRY
A. H. ENGLAND
T. R. FAULKNER
W. A. GREEN
J. T. HOLDEN
D. MIDDLETON
T. G. ROGERS

Department of Theoretical Mechanics
University of Nottingham

 VAN NOSTRAND REINHOLD COMPANY LIMITED

New York - Cincinnati - Toronto - London - Melbourne

ISBN 0 442 30206 1 cloth
ISBN 0 442 30208 8 paper

Library of Congress Catalog Card No. 76-45663

**Published by Van Nostrand Reinhold Company Ltd.,
Molly Millars Lane, Wokingham, Berkshire, England**

*Published in 1977 by Van Nostrand Reinhold Company
A Division of Litton Educational Publishing, Inc.,
450 West 33rd Street, New York, N.Y. 10001, U.S.A.*

*Van Nostrand Reinhold Limited
1410 Birchmount Road, Scarborough, Ontario, M1P 2E7*

*Van Nostrand Reinhold Limited
17 Queen Street, Mitcham, Victoria 3132, Australia*

Library of Congress Cataloging in Publication Data
Main entry under title:

Engineering mathematics
    Includes bibliographies and indexes.
    1. Engineering mathematics.   I. Spencer, Anthony
James Merrill.
TA330.E53   515'.14   76-45663
ISBN 0-442-30206-1 (V. 2)
ISBN 0-442-30208-8 pbk. (V. 2)

Typeset in IBM Press Roman by Preface Ltd., Salisbury, Wilts
Printed in Great Britain by Biddles Ltd., Guildford, Surrey
Production by Bucken Ltd.

Preface

This book is the second volume of a two-volume text on mathematics for engineering students in universities and polytechnics, for use in the second and subsequent years of a first degree course. The text is primarily designed to assist engineering undergraduates and their teachers, but we hope it may also prove of value to students of other disciplines that employ mathematics as a tool, to mathematicians who are interested in applications of their subject, and as a reference book for practising engineers and others.

The text is based on courses in mathematics given by the authors to the engineering students of the University of Nottingham. These courses have evolved over the last sixteen years, and have been developed in close consultation with our fellow teachers in the engineering departments of the University. In preparing the text, we have kept in mind the constraints imposed by the normal three or four year undergraduate course, and we believe that the choice of material in the two volumes is realistic in this respect. For completeness, some topics are pursued a little further than an engineering mathematics lecture course would normally take them, but all the material and examples should be within the grasp of a competent engineering undergraduate student. The greater part of Volume 1 forms a core of subjects which are included in most engineering courses. The remaining topics in Volume 1 and those in the present Volume, are more often studied as optional subjects. At Nottingham, almost all of the material in both volumes is taught to engineering students, although no single student studies all of the topics included. In our experience, this pattern of a core syllabus supplemented by a range of optional courses has proved to be a satisfactory way of meeting the varying needs of engineering students and their departments.

We have tried to give equal emphasis to both the analytical and the numerical aspects of engineering mathematics, so that the reader is encouraged to make use of whatever mathematical tool is best for the problem he has in hand. Until quite recently, engineering mathematics courses mainly comprised analysis. Most of this traditionally taught material is still essential, and it is not neglected in this text. However, recent trends have increased the importance of algebraic and numerical methods relative to analytical methods, and this is reflected in the list of contents of both volumes. Computer programming as such is not included because we feel that the teaching of this subject should be related to the computing facilities available to the student, and these vary greatly from one institution to another.

As far as possible within the space available, we have related the mathematics to its applications in engineering through illustrative examples and problems. The various topics have been approached in ways which we hope are relevant and useful to engineers. Since this is a book on the use of mathematics, we have made frequent use of intuitive arguments and have not attempted a standard of rigour which would be expected in a book designed for mathematics specialists. Nevertheless, we have tried to make our mathematical arguments accurate and precise. We have not hesitated to quote useful results without proof when we consider the proofs to be too difficult or too time-consuming for engineering undergraduates, but a short bibliography is appended to each chapter to assist the reader who wishes to pursue any topic further.

The text contains a large number of worked examples, many of which relate to engineering applications. A good selection of exercises on specific topics is given at the ends of sections. Each chapter concludes with a set of miscellaneous problems. These exercises and problems form an essential part of the text, and answers to them are given at the end of each volume. Many of the problems are taken from examination papers set for second and third year engineering students of the University of Nottingham in the period 1960–76, and we acknowledge the University's permission to make use of these questions.

Each chapter was first drafted by one or two of the authors, read and checked by several others, and then discussed and amended until a mutually agreed version was produced. The text is therefore a truly collaborative effort; no part of it is the sole work of any individual, and we share responsibility for the whole. Of course, this will not inhibit us from blaming each other for the slips and errors which no doubt still remain, despite all our efforts to eliminate them.

Among many who helped with the preparation of the manuscript, we particularly thank Mrs. Judy Hind who, as well as typing several chapters, gave us a great deal of assistance with the preparation of the final draft, dealing with correspondence, and in many other ways.

Finally, the rest of us gladly acknowledge our gratitude to David Parker who, in addition to his share of the writing, acted as our 'liaison officer' with the publishers, compelled us to (nearly) meet our deadlines, and generally organized and coordinated our activities. Without his strenuous and time-consuming efforts this book, if it had come into existence at all, would be much less consistent than it is.

Department of Theoretical Mechanics   A.J.M.S.   W.A.G.
University of Nottingham   D.F.P.   J.T.H.
September 1976   D.S.B.   D.M.
                                             A.H.E.   T.G.R.
                                             T.R.F.

The Greek Alphabet

α	A	alpha		ν	N	nu
β	B	beta		ξ	Ξ	xi
γ	Γ	gamma		o	O	omicron
δ	Δ	delta		π	Π	pi
ϵ	E	epsilon		ρ	P	rho
ζ	Z	zeta		σ	Σ	sigma
η	H	eta		τ	T	tau
θ	Θ	theta		υ	Υ	upsilon
ι	I	iota		ϕ, φ	Φ	phi
κ	K	kappa		χ	X	chi
λ	Λ	lambda		ψ	Ψ	psi
μ	M	mu		ω	Ω	omega

Contents

Appendix

CONTENTS OF VOLUME 1

CHAPTER 1

Linear Programming

1.1 INTRODUCTION

The general non-linear programming problem consists of maximizing (or minimizing) a non-linear function of n variables $x_1, x_2, \ldots, x_n$ subject to a set of inequality conditions. The function to be maximized is referred to as the *objective function*; if it is denoted by $f(x_1, \ldots, x_n)$ the problem becomes:

$$\text{maximize} \quad f(x_1, \ldots, x_n) \tag{1}$$

subject to the set of inequality conditions

$$
\begin{aligned}
& g_1(x_1, \ldots, x_n) \leqslant b_1, \\
& g_2(x_1, \ldots, x_n) \leqslant b_2, \\
& \ldots\ldots\ldots\ldots\ldots\ldots, \\
& g_k(x_1, \ldots, x_n) \leqslant b_k,
\end{aligned}
\tag{2}
$$

where k may be greater than, equal to or less than n. In addition it is normally required that the variables $x_1, \ldots, x_n$ are non-negative so that

$$x_1 \geqslant 0, x_2 \geqslant 0, \ldots, x_n \geqslant 0. \tag{3}$$

The constraints (2) and (3) define a region of n-dimensional space called the *feasible region*; any point $(x_1, x_2, \ldots, x_n)$ within and on the boundary of the feasible region is called a *feasible point* and satisfies the constraints (2) and (3). The mathematical problem consists of finding the feasible point (or points) at which the function $f(x_1, \ldots, x_n)$ takes its maximum value over all points of the feasible region. When stated in this generality, the problem is difficult to solve and requires the use of sophisticated numerical techniques. These form the subject of Chapter 2. However when the functions $f, g_1, \ldots, g_k$ are known to be *linear* functions of the n variables (or may be approximated by linear functions) the problem is much more tractable. The general *linear programming problem* with n variables and k constraints is

$$\text{maximize} \quad f = c_1 x_1 + c_2 x_2 + \ldots + c_n x_n \tag{4}$$

$$
\begin{aligned}
\text{subject to} \quad & g_1 = a_{11} x_1 + a_{12} x_2 + \ldots + a_{1n} x_n \leqslant b_1, \\
& g_2 = a_{21} x_1 + a_{22} x_2 + \ldots + a_{2n} x_n \leqslant b_2, \\
& \ldots\ldots\ldots\ldots\ldots\ldots\ldots\ldots\ldots\ldots\ldots\ldots, \\
& g_k = a_{k1} x_1 + a_{k2} x_2 + \ldots + a_{kn} x_n \leqslant b_k,
\end{aligned}
\tag{5}
$$

$$x_1 \geqslant 0, \quad x_2 \geqslant 0, \ldots, x_n \geqslant 0. \tag{6}$$

The constants b_i, c_j and a_{ij} for $i = 1, \ldots, k$, and $j = 1, \ldots, n$, are assumed to be known, so that the problem is to find the point $(x_1, \ldots, x_n)$, within the rather special type of feasible region defined by (5) and (6), at which the objective function (4) takes its maximum value. This chapter is concerned with the solution of this problem by both geometrical and algebraic procedures.

To put these techniques to use in a physical context requires the preliminary and skilled activity of building a mathematical model of the problem. Consider the following example:

EXAMPLE 1   A power station is supplied with coal from three collieries. The cost of a delivered tonne, the thermal units produced per tonne and the amounts available for transportation per day are given in the following table:

Colliery	A	B	C
Cost/tonne	4	5	2
Thermal units/tonne	3	2	1
Tonnes available/day	600	2000	600

If the handling capacity of coal at the power station is limited to 1800 tonnes per day and its heat requirements are at least 2700 thermal units per day, determine its purchasing policy so that it may operate at minimum cost.

This is a very crude model of one of the problems facing the manager of a power station. Let us suppose he is concerned entirely with running this power station to maximum efficiency and not fettered by restrictive contracts with any of the three collieries. The decision at his disposal is the number of tonnes of coal which should be purchased per day from each of the three collieries. Suppose x_1 tonnes/day are purchased from A, x_2 tonnes/day from B and x_3 tonnes/day from C, then the cost of coal purchased per day is

$$4x_1 + 5x_2 + 2x_3 .$$

The restrictions on amounts available are

$$x_1 \leqslant 600, \quad x_2 \leqslant 2000, \quad x_3 \leqslant 600 .$$

The total tonnage purchased per day is $x_1 + x_2 + x_3$ and this must not exceed the handling capacity at the power station, so that

$$x_1 + x_2 + x_3 \leqslant 1800 .$$

The thermal units available are $3x_1 + 2x_2 + x_3$ and since this must not be less than 2700 thermal units,

$$3x_1 + 2x_2 + x_3 \geqslant 2700 .$$

The optimization problem is to minimize the purchasing cost subject to the restrictions of the model, namely

$$\text{minimize} \quad 4x_1 + 5x_2 + 2x_3$$

subject to $x_1 \leqslant 600$, $x_2 \leqslant 2000$, $x_3 \leqslant 600$,

$$x_1 + x_2 + x_3 \leqslant 1800,$$

$$3x_1 + 2x_2 + x_3 \geqslant 2700.$$

The additional inequalities $x_1 \geqslant 0, x_2 \geqslant 0, x_3 \geqslant 0$ are also physically reasonable!

The fact that this is a *minimizing* problem and that one of the constraints is 'greater than or equal to' does not prevent this problem from joining the class of *linear programming problems* (4), (5), (6) after some minor manipulations which will be described later. What is important is that the model yields linear inequalities and a linear cost function. It is apparent that a more accurate model of this situation could be built which would involve a non-linear cost function and non-linear handling and thermal constraints (and perhaps other constraints besides). The art of model building consists of selecting the simplest model which will display the essential features of the physical situation. Since this problem has only three variables, it may be solved geometrically, but more typical linear programming problems (hereinafter referred to as L.P. problems) have variables and constraints numbering into the hundreds and such problems require numerical solution.

EXAMPLE 2   A contractor has to deliver various quantities of hardcore from two quarries to three separate sites, whose distances from each quarry are given in the following table which also gives the quantities required at each site and the quantities available at the quarries.

	Site 1	Site 2	Site 3	Quantity available
Quarry 1	9 miles	3 miles	6 miles	300 tonnes
Quarry 2	7 miles	12 miles	10 miles	720 tonnes
Quantity required	150 tonnes	350 tonnes	320 tonnes	

The transport cost is 10p per tonne per mile, on all routes. Determine the minimum cost of transporting the required hardcore, giving the amount of material transported from each quarry to each site.

In this problem the unknowns are the amounts of material transported from each quarry to each site. Denote the amount moving from quarry i to site j by x_{ij} tonnes where $i = 1, 2; j = 1, 2, 3$. Then there are six unknowns.

The amount removed from quarry 1 is $x_{11} + x_{12} + x_{13}$, and this must not exceed the quantity available. Hence

$$x_{11} + x_{12} + x_{13} \leqslant 300.$$

Similarly for quarry 2 the quantity removed satisfies

$$x_{21} + x_{22} + x_{23} \leqslant 720.$$

The quantity received at site 1 is $x_{11} + x_{21}$ and this must equal (or perhaps exceed)

150 tonnes:

$$x_{11} + x_{21} \geqslant 150 .$$

Similarly at sites 2 and 3

$$x_{12} + x_{22} \geqslant 350, \quad x_{13} + x_{23} \geqslant 320 .$$

Since transport costs have to be minimized, it might be expected that the amounts delivered to each site will not exceed the required quantities. This may be confirmed from the optimal solution but for present purposes it is convenient to leave these constraints as inequalities. The cost of delivery in pence is

$$10(9x_{11} + 3x_{12} + 6x_{13} + 7x_{21} + 12x_{22} + 10x_{23})$$

and this has to be minimized subject to the five constraints

$$
\begin{aligned}
x_{11} + x_{12} + x_{13} & & \leqslant 300 , \\
x_{21} + x_{22} + x_{23} & \leqslant 720 , \\
x_{11} \quad\quad + x_{21} & \geqslant 150 , \\
x_{12} \quad\quad + x_{22} & \geqslant 350 , \\
x_{13} \quad\quad + x_{23} & \geqslant 320 ,
\end{aligned}
$$

and the requirements

$$x_{ij} \geqslant 0 \quad i = 1, 2; \quad j = 1, 2, 3 .$$

This is a special type of L.P. problem referred to as a *transportation problem*. (In transportation problems the coefficients a_{ij} of the constraints (5) are either 0 or 1.) Obviously as the number of sites and quarries rises the size of the problem increases rapidly. For example, an oil company with 10 main depots and 600 filling stations is concerned with a transportation problem involving 6000 variables and 610 constraints representing storage capacities at the depots and estimated sales at the filling stations.

EXAMPLE 3   Andes Haulage Ltd. uses llamas and donkeys to transport alpaca rugs from Huancayo to Lima where they are sold to tourists at $25. A llama can carry 18 rugs and a donkey 15 rugs at these altitudes. En route a llama consumes 5 bales of hay and 4 bags of oats, a donkey 4 bales of hay and 5 bags of oats. Andes supply facilities have a total of 34 bales of hay and 30 bags of oats located in various villages along the route. Only 5 men are available to conduct the caravan, one man is needed per donkey, or, alternatively, can handle two llamas. What is the composition of the caravan which maximizes sales receipts?

The L.P. formulation of this problem is left as an exercise. If the number of llamas used is x_1 and the number of donkeys x_2, the optimal solution is $x_1 = 5\frac{5}{9}, x_2 = 1\frac{5}{9}$. The problem of getting 5/9ths of a llama and 5/9ths of a donkey across the Andes is insurmountable. The L.P. formulation of the problem was incomplete and needed the additional restriction that x_1 and x_2 were integers. This integer restriction changes the nature of the problem completely, and even a general L.P. technique such as the *simplex method* (§1.5) cannot handle this restriction. However the optimal L.P. solution does indicate the region in which the integer optimum lies, and consequently is useful even for integer L.P. problems.

A wide variety of optimization problems may be formulated in terms of linear programming. In particular, production scheduling and stock control for the oil refineries and mass production plants are conveniently performed by L.P. techniques. The transportation problem, optimal routing of ships, planes and aircrew and the optimal design of networks may be solved by the simplex method or more specialized L.P. methods. Many other types of problem such as blending or dietary problems, problems of financial investment, military and civilian manpower planning, have been successfully tackled using these methods. The original models were crude and the optimal predictions suspect, but many highly refined models have been produced, particularly by the oil industry, and are in daily use.

1.2 GEOMETRICAL METHODS OF SOLUTION

Lines, Planes and Inequalities

The equation $x_1 + 2x_2 = 100$ represents a straight line L in the x_1, x_2 plane which divides the plane into two regions (see Fig. 1.1). All points (x_1, x_2) satisfying the inequality $x_1 + 2x_2 \leqslant 100$ lie in the region on or below L, all points satisfying $x_1 + 2x_2 > 100$ lie in the region above L.

Points (x_1, x_2) satisfying the two constraints

$$x_1 + 2x_2 \leqslant 100, \quad 3x_1 + x_2 \leqslant 75$$

lie in the shaded region of Fig. 1.2. If we also suppose that $x_1 \geqslant 0$ and $x_2 \geqslant 0$, the region is further restricted to the quadrilateral *OABC*. Obviously additional linear inequalities will introduce more straight line boundaries into Fig. 1.2.

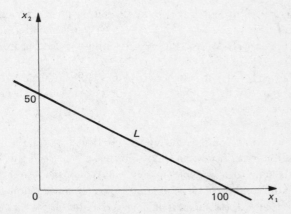

Fig. 1.1

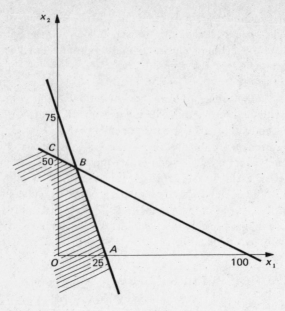

Fig. 1.2

Similar properties hold for inequalities in three variables. Every point (x_1, x_2, x_3) satisfying the constraint

$$3x_1 + 2x_2 + x_3 \leqslant 6$$

lies in the space on one side of the plane $3x_1 + 2x_2 + x_3 = 6$. For example it will be seen that points satisfying the constraints

$$3x_1 + 2x_2 + x_3 \leqslant 6,$$

$$x_1 \geqslant 0, \quad x_2 \geqslant 0, \quad x_3 \geqslant 0,$$

lie in the region (a tetrahedron) between the origin and the plane $3x_1 + 2x_2 + x_3 = 6$ which cuts the axes at the points $(2, 0, 0), (0, 3, 0), (0, 0, 6)$, (see Fig. 1.3). If further inequalities are introduced, for example $x_2 \leqslant \frac{1}{2}$, then this region of space will be further restricted.

It has been indicated in §1.1 that the constraints in L.P. problems are linear inequalities of the form

$$a_{11}x_1 + a_{12}x_2 + \ldots + a_{1n}x_n \leqslant b_1 .$$

Obviously, if the number n of variables in an L.P. problem is 2 or 3, it is possible to sketch the feasible region defined by the constraints, and hence solve an L.P. problem geometrically. If the number of variables exceeds 3 it is impossible to sketch the feasible region and the solution must be obtained using algebraic and numerical methods. The importance of the geometrical approach is that it gives a pictorial representation of the (more involved) algebraic methods.

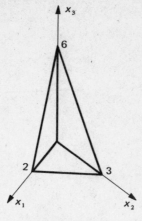

Fig. 1.3

The Geometrical Solution

The best way to illustrate this method is to consider a simple example. This example will be used throughout this chapter for illustration, and will be referred to as the standard problem.

EXAMPLE 1   A company produces two types of product, P_1 and P_2, on each of which the profit per unit is £1. If each unit of product P_1 takes 1 unit of machine time and 3 units of packing time to produce, and each unit of product P_2 takes 2 units of machine time and 1 unit of packing time to produce, and the capacity of the plant per day is 100 units of machine time and 75 units of packing time, what are the production rates which maximize the company's profit?

Suppose x_1 units of product P_1 and x_2 units of P_2 are produced per day. Note that x_1 and x_2 must be positive. Then the machine time used is $x_1 + 2x_2$ and the packing time used is $3x_1 + x_2$. The profit made is £$(x_1 + x_2)$ (assuming all production is sold). But there are constraints on the amounts of machine and packing time available. Hence the problem is to

maximize $x_1 + x_2$

subject to $x_1 + 2x_2 \leqslant 100$ (machine time),

$3x_1 + x_2 \leqslant 75$ (packing time),

$x_1 \geqslant 0, \quad x_2 \geqslant 0$ (positive production rates).

The feasible region is *OABC* of Fig. 1.4. The problem reduces to finding the maximum of $x_1 + x_2$ for points (x_1, x_2) in this region. Consider the line $x_1 + x_2 = c$. At each feasible point on this line the profit has the constant value c. This line is the contour line for the profit at 'height' c. On Fig. 1.4 the profit contour lines at heights $c = 25$ and $c = 50$ have been drawn. These are parallel straight lines. Hence, to maximize the

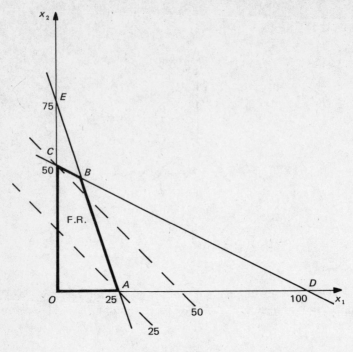

Fig. 1.4

profit, we must inspect the family of parallel lines $x_1 + x_2 = c$ which pass through the region $OABC$ (i.e. contain feasible points) to find the one for which c is a maximum. In this case the optimum line cuts the feasible region at B. Hence the maximum profit occurs at the corner B which is the point of intersection of the lines

$$x_1 + 2x_2 = 100 ,$$
$$3x_1 + x_2 = 75 ,$$

giving $x_1 = 10, x_2 = 45$. In this problem the optimum production rates are 10 of P_1 and 45 of P_2 giving a maximum profit of £$(10 + 45)$ = £55. Note that both machine and packing times are used completely.

EXAMPLE 2   Suppose that in the above problem the profit is changed to £4 per unit of P_1 and £1 per unit of P_2 but the constraints remain unchanged.

In this case we must maximize $4x_1 + x_2$ over the same feasible region $OABC$. By plotting the contours $(4x_1 + x_2 =$ constant$)$ of the objective function (see Fig. 1.5) the maximum is found to lie at the corner A, i.e., $x_1 = 25, x_2 = 0$ with optimum profit £100. In this case the packing constraint (AB) is satisfied but spare machine time is available as the optimum point A does not lie on CB.

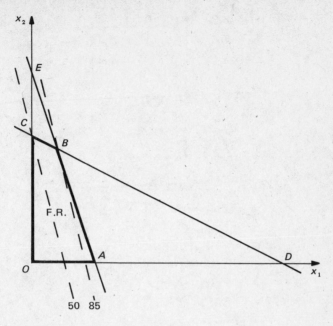

Fig. 1.5

It will be observed that unless the contours of the objective function are parallel to one of the constraints the optimum will always occur at a corner point of the feasible region. If an objective function contour is parallel to a constraint in two dimensions then it is possible that 2 corner points and every point on the constraint joining them will give the optimum. For instance, this is the case if we maximize $x_1 + 2x_2$ over the region $OABC$ of example 1. The optimum value is 100 and is achieved at B, at C and at all feasible points of BC. Similar results apply in three-dimensional problems.

EXAMPLE 3   Maximize $3x_1 + 4x_2 + 5x_3$

              subject to $x_1 + x_2 + x_3 \leqslant 1$,

$$x_1 \geqslant 0, \quad x_2 \geqslant 0, \quad x_3 \geqslant 0 .$$

The feasible region is the tetrahedron of Fig. 1.6. The objective function is constant on the planes $3x_1 + 4x_2 + 5x_3 = $ constant. The contour corresponding to the objective function having the value 2 is shown on Fig. 1.6. By considering what happens as this plane moves parallel to itself away from the origin, it is seen that the maximum occurs at the corner point $(0, 0, 1)$ giving the value 5.

If the feasible region is more involved it becomes difficult to visualize the moving plane of increasing profit, and the corner points themselves must be evaluated and checked individually.

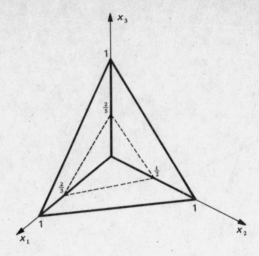

Fig. 1.6

EXAMPLE 4   Maximize $3x_1 + 4x_2 + 5x_3$

subject to $x_1 + x_2 + x_3 \leqslant 1,$

$$x_2 \qquad \leqslant \tfrac{1}{2},$$

$$4x_1 \qquad + 12x_3 \leqslant 3,$$

$$x_1 \geqslant 0, \quad x_2 \geqslant 0, \quad x_3 \geqslant 0.$$

The feasible region is shown on Fig. 1.7.

By evaluating the objective function at the corner points of Fig. 1.7 it will be found that the optimum occurs at $(\tfrac{3}{8}, \tfrac{1}{2}, \tfrac{1}{8})$ with the value $3\tfrac{3}{4}$.

So far the feasible regions have existed and been bounded. Obviously if a feasible region does not exist, so that there are no points which satisfy all of the constraints, the problem cannot be solved. For example, the constraints

$$x_1 + 2x_2 \leqslant 9,$$

$$-x_1 + x_2 \leqslant -10,$$

$$x_1 \geqslant 0, \quad x_2 \geqslant 0,$$

are inconsistent, so that there are no feasible points.

Alternatively, unbounded feasible regions can occur. Consider

$$x_1 - x_2 \leqslant 10,$$

$$x_1 \leqslant 15,$$

$$x_1 \geqslant 0, \quad x_2 \geqslant 0.$$

In this case the existence of a solution depends on the nature of the objective function. The maximum value of $3x_1 + x_2$ over this region is infinite. Infinite maxima are not to

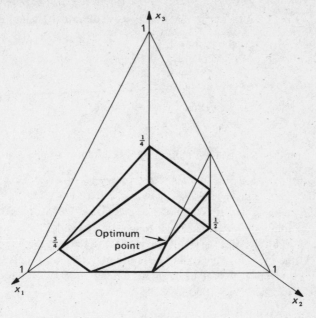

Fig. 1.7

be expected in physical problems. The maximum value of $x_1 - 2x_2$ is 5. Similar properties hold in problems with more variables. It will be appreciated that in the problems which can be solved geometrically the optimum will always occur at a corner point (even in the degenerate case when the contours of the objective function are parallel to a constraint, the optimum will occur at either one or several corner points and on the constraint joining them). However, as the number of constraints increases the number of corner points grows rapidly. For problems involving more than three variables or a larger number of constraints these geometrical methods become unwieldy and cease to have value except as pictorial representations of the problem. In order to solve these more realistic problems, the methods of linear algebra must be used and the relevant details are discussed in the next section.

Exercises

1. Sketch the feasible region defined by the set of inequalities

$$x_1 + x_2 \leqslant 10, \quad 4x_1 + x_2 \leqslant 24, \quad -x_1 + x_2 \leqslant 5, \quad x_1 - 3x_2 \leqslant 2,$$

$$x_1 \geqslant 0, \quad x_2 \geqslant 0 .$$

2. Find the maximum value of each of the following objective functions subject to the constraints of exercise 1: $x_2, \quad x_1, \quad 3x_1 + x_2, \quad x_1 - x_2$.

3. Find the maximum value of the function $x_1 + x_2$ subject to the constraints of exercise 1. What range of values of (x_1, x_2) may be chosen at that optimum?

4. Find the maximum values of the function $x_1 + x_2$ subject to each of the two sets of constraints

(a) $x_1 \leqslant 5$, $x_1 - 2x_2 \leqslant 3$, $x_1, x_2 \geqslant 0$,

(b) $x_1 \leqslant 5$, $x_1 - 2x_2 \geqslant 3$, $x_1, x_2 \geqslant 0$.

5. Sketch the feasible region specified by the constraints

$$x_1 + x_2 + x_3 \geqslant 1, \quad x_1 \leqslant \tfrac{1}{2}, \quad x_2 \leqslant 1, \quad x_3 \leqslant \tfrac{1}{2}, \quad x_1, x_2, x_3 \geqslant 0.$$

What is the maximum value of the function $x_1 + 2x_3$ subject to these constraints?

6. A manufacturer extracts lead and zinc from two types of scrap. Type A costs £6 per tonne and on the average yields 100 kg of lead and 100 kg of zinc per tonne. Type B, costing £10 per tonne, yields 100 kg of lead and 300 kg of zinc for each tonne processed. If the minimum daily sales are 3 tonnes of lead and 4 tonnes of zinc, how many tonnes of each type of scrap should be purchased to meet these requirements at lowest cost? If, due to improved extraction techniques, it becomes possible to produce twice as much lead from each type of scrap, should the purchasing policy be changed? *Note*: 1 tonne = 1 metric ton = 1000 kg.

7. Use geometrical methods to solve examples 1 and 3 of §1.1.

1.3 FINITE-DIMENSIONAL VECTOR SPACES

The methods of linear programming are based on the theories of matrices and finite-dimensional vector spaces. This section reviews the definitions and properties which are used in the remainder of the chapter. Matrix theory has been discussed in Chapter 8 of Volume 1.

The notation used is that the transpose of a matrix $\mathbf{A}$ is $\mathbf{A}^T$ and the inverse of any square non-singular matrix $\mathbf{B}$ is $\mathbf{B}^{-1}$. A unit matrix will be denoted by $\mathbf{I}$ and a zero matrix by $\mathbf{0}$. A $1 \times k$ matrix is called a row vector and a $k \times 1$ matrix is called a column vector. Note that the column vectors of the same order add, subtract and may be multiplied by a scalar according to the usual matrix rules. Thus if $\mathbf{X} = (x_1, \ldots, x_k)^T$, $\mathbf{Y} = (y_1, \ldots, y_k)^T$, then for example

$$\mathbf{X} \pm \mathbf{Y} = (x_1 \pm y_1, \ldots, x_k \pm y_k)^T \quad \text{and} \quad 7\mathbf{X} = (7x_1, \ldots, 7x_k)^T.$$

The set of all $k \times 1$ column vectors is said to form the k-dimensional *vector space* V_k, and the vectors themselves are called *elements* of V_k. An important set of elements of V_k is the set of *base vectors*

$$\mathbf{e}_1 = (1, 0, \ldots, 0)^T, \quad \mathbf{e}_2 = (0, 1, 0, \ldots, 0)^T, \quad \ldots, \quad \mathbf{e}_k = (0, \ldots, 0, 1)^T,$$

where each vector has k components. If $\mathbf{A}_1, \ldots, \mathbf{A}_n$ are elements of V_k and $\alpha_1, \ldots, \alpha_n$ are scalars, then the sum $\alpha_1 \mathbf{A}_1 + \ldots + \alpha_n \mathbf{A}_n$ is an element of V_k. The sum is referred to as a *linear combination* of the set $\mathbf{A}_1, \ldots, \mathbf{A}_n$.

Each vector element of V_k may be represented as a linear combination of the set of base vectors of V_k. If $\mathbf{X} = (x_1, x_2, \ldots, x_k)^T$, then

$$\mathbf{X} = x_1\mathbf{e}_1 + x_2\mathbf{e}_2 + \ldots + x_k\mathbf{e}_k.$$

This is not the only representation for $\mathbf{X}$, but it is the most convenient because of its simplicity. For example, in V_2 alternative representations for $(4, 5)^T$ are

$$\binom{4}{5} = 4\binom{1}{0} + 5\binom{0}{1} = 6\binom{1}{1} - \binom{2}{1}.$$

Further discussion on the representation of a vector in terms of a given set of vectors requires the concept of linearly independent or dependent sets of vectors.

A set of n column vectors $\mathbf{A}_1, \mathbf{A}_2, \ldots, \mathbf{A}_n$ (in the vector space V_k) is said to be *linearly dependent* if there exist constants $\alpha_1, \alpha_2, \ldots, \alpha_n$ *at least one of which is non-zero* such that

$$\alpha_1\mathbf{A}_1 + \alpha_2\mathbf{A}_2 + \ldots + \alpha_n\mathbf{A}_n = \mathbf{0}. \tag{7}$$

If the *only* values of $\alpha_1, \ldots, \alpha_n$ satisfying equations (7) are $\alpha_1 = 0, \alpha_2 = 0, \ldots,$ $\alpha_n = 0$, the set $\mathbf{A}_1, \mathbf{A}_2, \ldots, \mathbf{A}_n$ is said to be *linearly independent*. Note that a set of vectors is either linearly dependent or linearly independent.

For example, in V_2 the set $(1, 1)^T, (2, 1)^T$ is linearly independent since

$$\alpha_1\binom{1}{1} + \alpha_2\binom{2}{1} = \binom{\alpha_1 + 2\alpha_2}{\alpha_1 + \alpha_2} = \binom{0}{0}$$

implies $\alpha_1 = \alpha_2 = 0$. However, the set $(1, 1)^T, (2, 1)^T, (3, 1)^T$ is linearly dependent since

$$\binom{1}{1} - 2\binom{2}{1} + \binom{3}{1} = \binom{0}{0}.$$

The following properties (a) and (b) are proved in most linear algebra textbooks.

(a) In the k-dimensional space V_k a linearly independent set can contain *at most k vectors*. Thus, in V_2, any set containing three vectors is linearly dependent. However, not all sets of k vectors in V_k are linearly independent. A trivial example of a dependent set in V_2 is $(1, 1)^T, (5, 5)^T$.

A set of k linearly independent vectors in V_k is said to form a *basis* for the space V_k. For example, the set of the base vectors $\mathbf{e}_1, \ldots, \mathbf{e}_k$ is linearly independent and contains k vectors and so forms a basis for V_k. A vector space may have many different bases.

(b) Any vector in V_k can be expressed as a *linear combination* of the elements of a basis of V_k. The representation of a vector in terms of a given basis is unique.

EXAMPLE 1   The three vectors $(1, 1, 1)^T, (0, 1, 1)^T, (0, 0, 1)^T$ form a linearly independent set and hence a basis of V_3. Obviously a general vector $\mathbf{X} = (x_1, x_2, x_3)^T$ can be expressed in terms of this basis as

$$\begin{pmatrix} x_1 \\ x_2 \\ x_3 \end{pmatrix} = x_1\begin{pmatrix} 1 \\ 1 \\ 1 \end{pmatrix} + (x_2 - x_1)\begin{pmatrix} 0 \\ 1 \\ 1 \end{pmatrix} + (x_3 - x_2)\begin{pmatrix} 0 \\ 0 \\ 1 \end{pmatrix}. \tag{8}$$

The vectors $(1, 1, 1)^T, (0, 1, 1)^T, (0, 2, 1)^T$ are also linearly independent and form an alternative basis for V_3. Since a general vector $\mathbf{X}$ in V_3 can be represented as a linear combination of the elements of a basis, there exist constants $\alpha_1, \alpha_2, \alpha_3$ such that

$$\begin{pmatrix} x_1 \\ x_2 \\ x_3 \end{pmatrix} = \alpha_1 \begin{pmatrix} 1 \\ 1 \\ 1 \end{pmatrix} + \alpha_2 \begin{pmatrix} 0 \\ 1 \\ 1 \end{pmatrix} + \alpha_3 \begin{pmatrix} 0 \\ 2 \\ 1 \end{pmatrix}.$$

This gives rise to three equations for the three constants $\alpha_1, \alpha_2, \alpha_3$ namely

$$x_1 = \alpha_1, \quad x_2 = \alpha_1 + \alpha_2 + 2\alpha_3, \quad x_3 = \alpha_1 + \alpha_2 + \alpha_3.$$

The representation for $\mathbf{X}$ in terms of the second basis is

$$\mathbf{X} = x_1 \begin{pmatrix} 1 \\ 1 \\ 1 \end{pmatrix} + (2x_3 - x_1 - x_2) \begin{pmatrix} 0 \\ 1 \\ 1 \end{pmatrix} + (x_2 - x_3) \begin{pmatrix} 0 \\ 2 \\ 1 \end{pmatrix}. \tag{9}$$

Note that a vector has different representations in terms of different bases.

Change of Basis

Suppose the set of column vectors $\mathbf{A}_1, \ldots, \mathbf{A}_k$ of V_k is linearly independent. Then these vectors form a basis of V_k. Can we replace one vector in the basis by another vector $\mathbf{A}^*$? Let us assume $\mathbf{A}^*$ has the representation

$$\mathbf{A}^* = \lambda_1 \mathbf{A}_1 + \ldots + \lambda_k \mathbf{A}_k$$

in terms of the original basis. Supposing $\lambda_j \neq 0$, then $\mathbf{A}_j$ can be written as

$$\mathbf{A}_j = \frac{1}{\lambda_j}(\mathbf{A}^* - \lambda_1 \mathbf{A}_1 - \ldots - \lambda_{j-1}\mathbf{A}_{j-1} - \lambda_{j+1}\mathbf{A}_{j+1} - \ldots - \lambda_k \mathbf{A}_k). \tag{10}$$

It may be shown that the set of vectors $\mathbf{A}_1, \ldots, \mathbf{A}_{j-1}, \mathbf{A}_{j+1}, \ldots, \mathbf{A}_k, \mathbf{A}^*$ forms a basis provided $\lambda_j \neq 0$. If a general vector $\mathbf{X}$ has the representation

$$\mathbf{X} = \mu_1 \mathbf{A}_1 + \ldots + \mu_k \mathbf{A}_k$$

in terms of the original basis, its representation in terms of the new basis is easily found. As equation (10) gives the representation for $\mathbf{A}_j$ in terms of the new basis, this representation may be substituted into the form for $\mathbf{X}$ to give

$$\mathbf{X} = \mu_1 \mathbf{A}_1 + \ldots + \mu_{j-1}\mathbf{A}_{j-1} + \frac{\mu_j}{\lambda_j}(\mathbf{A}^* - \lambda_1 \mathbf{A}_1 - \ldots - \lambda_k \mathbf{A}_k)$$

$$+ \mu_{j+1}\mathbf{A}_{j+1} + \ldots + \mu_k \mathbf{A}_k$$

$$= \left(\mu_1 - \frac{\mu_j}{\lambda_j}\lambda_1\right) \mathbf{A}_1 + \ldots + \left(\mu_k - \frac{\mu_j}{\lambda_j}\lambda_k\right) \mathbf{A}_k + \frac{\mu_j}{\lambda_j}\mathbf{A}^*.$$

This is the representation for **X** in terms of the new basis

$$\mathbf{A}_1, \ldots, \mathbf{A}_{j-1}, \mathbf{A}'_{j+1}, \ldots, \mathbf{A}_k, \mathbf{A}^*.$$

EXAMPLE 2   The representation of $\mathbf{X} = (x_1, x_2, x_3)^T$ in terms of the basis $(1, 1, 1)^T$, $(0, 1, 1)^T$, $(0, 0, 1)^T$ of V_3 is given by equation (8). What is the representation in terms of the basis $(1, 1, 1)^T$, $(0, 1, 1)^T$, $(0, 2, 1)^T$?

It is necessary to find the representation for $(0, 2, 1)^T$ in terms of the original basis $(1, 1, 1)^T$, $(0, 1, 1)^T$, $(0, 0, 1)^T$. This is

$$\begin{pmatrix} 0 \\ 2 \\ 1 \end{pmatrix} = 0 \begin{pmatrix} 1 \\ 1 \\ 1 \end{pmatrix} + 2 \begin{pmatrix} 0 \\ 1 \\ 1 \end{pmatrix} - 1 \begin{pmatrix} 0 \\ 0 \\ 1 \end{pmatrix}.$$

Since $(0, 0, 1)^T$ is to be replaced in the original basis, this equation may be rearranged to express $(0, 0, 1)^T$ in terms of the new basis as

$$\begin{pmatrix} 0 \\ 0 \\ 1 \end{pmatrix} = 0 \begin{pmatrix} 1 \\ 1 \\ 1 \end{pmatrix} + 2 \begin{pmatrix} 0 \\ 1 \\ 1 \end{pmatrix} - \begin{pmatrix} 0 \\ 2 \\ 1 \end{pmatrix}.$$

On substituting for $(0, 0, 1)^T$ in the representation (8) for **X** in terms of the original basis, the expression becomes

$$\begin{pmatrix} x_1 \\ x_2 \\ x_3 \end{pmatrix} = x_1 \begin{pmatrix} 1 \\ 1 \\ 1 \end{pmatrix} + (x_2 - x_1) \begin{pmatrix} 0 \\ 1 \\ 1 \end{pmatrix} + 2(x_3 - x_2) \begin{pmatrix} 0 \\ 1 \\ 1 \end{pmatrix} - (x_3 - x_2) \begin{pmatrix} 0 \\ 2 \\ 1 \end{pmatrix}.$$

This will be seen to be the new representation (9) as derived in example 1.

These representations of the same vector in terms of different bases are particularly important when we deal with systems of simultaneous linear equations in which the number of unknowns exceeds the number of equations.

Consider the system of k equations in m unknowns

$$a_{11}x_1 + \ldots + a_{1m}x_m = h_1,$$

$$a_{21}x_1 + \ldots + a_{2m}x_m = h_2,$$

$$\cdots \cdots \cdots \cdots \cdots \cdots \cdots \cdots,$$

$$a_{k1}x_1 + \ldots + a_{km}x_m = h_k.$$

Let us denote the columns of the matrix **A** of coefficients a_{ij} by $\mathbf{A}_1, \ldots, \mathbf{A}_m$ so that $\mathbf{A}_r = (a_{1r}, \ldots, a_{kr})^T$ for $r = 1, 2, \ldots, m$, and let $\mathbf{X} = (x_1, \ldots, x_m)^T$, and $\mathbf{H} = (h_1, \ldots, h_k)^T$. The above system of equations may be written in either of the following forms

$$\mathbf{AX} = \mathbf{H}, \quad x_1\mathbf{A}_1 + x_2\mathbf{A}_2 + \ldots + x_m\mathbf{A}_m = \mathbf{H}.$$

The column vectors $A_1, A_2, \ldots, A_m, H$ are elements of the vector space V_k. The problem of solving the system of equations $AX = H$ is equivalent to the problem of representing the vector H as a linear combination of the vectors $A_1, \ldots, A_m$ in the vector space V_k. The existence and uniqueness of the solution of such systems has been examined in detail in §§8.7, 8.8 of Volume 1 and found to depend upon the rank of the matrix A. In §8.7 of Volume 1 the rank $r(A)$ has been defined in terms of non-singular sub-matrices of A. An equivalent definition of the rank of A may be given in terms of the column vectors $A_1, \ldots, A_m$ contained in the matrix A. The rank $r(A)$ is the largest number of vectors which may be selected from $A_1, \ldots, A_m$ to form a linearly independent set. For the above system of k equations in m unknowns it will be seen that the rank of A satisfies the inequalities $r(A) \leqslant m$ because there are only m column vectors, and $r(A) \leqslant k$ since a linearly independent set of vectors in the vector space V_k cannot contain more than k vectors.

If $r(A)$ is less than k then the set of column vectors $A_1, \ldots, A_m$ does not contain a linearly independent set which is large enough to form a basis for the space V_k. In this case it is not possible to represent a general vector H as a linear combination of these vectors. However we shall see that linear programming problems reduce to considering systems of linear equations in which the number of unknowns m exceeds the number of equations k and the matrix A is of rank k. In this case, since $m > k$ and $r(A) = k$, we may suppose (without loss of generality) that the first k column vectors of A are linearly independent and write the equations as

$$x_1 A_1 + \ldots + x_k A_k = H - x_{k+1} A_{k+1} - \ldots - x_m A_m = H_1 .$$

Since $A_1, \ldots, A_k$ form a basis for V_k, the k unknowns $x_1, \ldots, x_k$ may be found to satisfy this equation for arbitrary values of the right-hand side H_1, that is for arbitrary values of the parameters $x_{k+1}, x_{k+2}, \ldots, x_m$. When solving k equations in m unknowns we might expect $m - k$ unknowns to remain undetermined. A simple solution of the system is obtained by putting these undetermined variables equal to zero. By selecting different sets of k linearly independent vectors from $A_1, \ldots, A_m$ to form a basis, different solutions of the system may be produced.

EXAMPLE 3   The system

$$x_1 + 2x_2 + 3x_3 + 4x_4 = 1$$
$$5x_1 + 6x_2 + 7x_3 + 8x_4 = 2$$

may be written in vector form as

$$x_1 \begin{pmatrix} 1 \\ 5 \end{pmatrix} + x_2 \begin{pmatrix} 2 \\ 6 \end{pmatrix} + x_3 \begin{pmatrix} 3 \\ 7 \end{pmatrix} + x_4 \begin{pmatrix} 4 \\ 8 \end{pmatrix} = \begin{pmatrix} 1 \\ 2 \end{pmatrix} .$$

Since $(1, 5)^T, (2, 6)^T$ are linearly independent they form a basis for V_2. In this case the system may be solved for x_1 and x_2 by putting it in the form

$$x_1 \begin{pmatrix} 1 \\ 5 \end{pmatrix} + x_2 \begin{pmatrix} 2 \\ 6 \end{pmatrix} = \begin{pmatrix} 1 \\ 2 \end{pmatrix} - x_3 \begin{pmatrix} 3 \\ 7 \end{pmatrix} - x_4 \begin{pmatrix} 4 \\ 8 \end{pmatrix} .$$

The solution is

$$x_1 = -\tfrac{1}{2} + x_3 + 2x_4 \, ,$$
$$x_2 = \tfrac{3}{4} - 2x_3 - 3x_4 \, ,$$

for arbitrary values of x_3 and x_4. In particular, if $x_3 = 0$ and $x_4 = 0$ the system has the simple solution $x_1 = -\tfrac{1}{2}, x_2 = \tfrac{3}{4}, x_3 = x_4 = 0$, that is, $\mathbf{X} = (-\tfrac{1}{2}, \tfrac{3}{4}, 0, 0)^T$.

Obviously these equations could have been solved in terms of another pair of co-ordinates; for example, $\mathbf{X} = (0, -\tfrac{1}{4}, \tfrac{1}{2}, 0)^T$ is a solution in which the variables x_1 and x_4 have been taken to be zero and the basis is the linearly independent set $\mathbf{A}_2 = (2, 6)^T$ and $\mathbf{A}_3 = (3, 7)^T$. Such simple solutions determine the corner points of the feasible regions in linear programming problems.

Exercises

1. Show that the set of vectors $(1, 1, 1, 1)^T, (1, 1, 1, 0)^T, (1, 1, 0, 0)^T, (1, 0, 0, 0)^T$ forms a basis for V_4. Find the representation of $(1, 2, 3, 4)^T$ in terms of this basis.

2. Find the set of points (x_1, x_2, x_3, x_4) which have at most three non-zero coordinates and satisfy the system of equations

$$
\begin{aligned}
x_1 + x_2 + \quad x_3 \qquad &= 1 \, , \\
x_2 \qquad + x_4 &= \tfrac{1}{2} \, , \\
4x_1 \qquad + 12x_3 \qquad &= 3 \, .
\end{aligned}
$$

1.4 THE GENERAL LINEAR PROGRAMMING PROBLEM

The general L.P. problem is to find the point $(x_1, x_2, \ldots, x_n)$ at which the objective function

$$c_1 x_1 + c_2 x_2 + \ldots + c_n x_n \tag{11}$$

attains its maximum value subject to the set of k constraints

$$
\begin{aligned}
a_{11}x_1 + a_{12}x_2 + \ldots + a_{1n}x_n &\leqslant b_1 \, , \\
a_{21}x_1 + a_{22}x_2 + \ldots + a_{2n}x_n &\leqslant b_2 \, , \\
&\cdots\cdots\cdots\cdots \\
a_{k1}x_1 + a_{k2}x_2 + \ldots + a_{kn}x_n &\leqslant b_k \, ,
\end{aligned}
\tag{12}
$$

and non-negativity conditions

$$x_i \geqslant 0, \quad i = 1, 2, \ldots, n \, . \tag{13}$$

We refer to the variables $x_1, \ldots, x_n$ as the *structural* variables of the problem. The principal result governing the position of the optimum point is as follows.

OPTIMATILITY THEOREM   For the general programming problem of (11), (12) and (13), if the objective function attains its maximum at some finite point of the feasible region it will do so at a *corner point*.

Whilst this theorem is not proved in this text, some comments on its validity are required.

(a) The constraints (12), (13) define a *convex* feasible region, which is such that if points P and Q are in the feasible region the line PQ joining them lies entirely within the feasible region. Hence the feasible region has no re-entrant corners.

(b) The objective function is a linear function with 'plane' contours so that the optimum must occur on the boundary of the feasible region.

(c) It is possible for the objective to attain its maximum at more than one corner point. In this degenerate case the maximum will also occur at any feasible point on the 'plane' joining the optimum corners (see example 2 of §1.2).

Thus if the feasible region is bounded, the optimum will always occur at a corner point. If the feasible region is unbounded, then either the optimum is unbounded (a badly posed physical problem?) or it occurs at a (bounded) corner point of the feasible region.

The Augmented Problem

Since it is always easier to handle equality conditions, let us introduce into the first constraint of equation (12), viz.

$$a_{11}x_1 + \ldots + a_{1n}x_n \leqslant b_1 ,$$

a *slack variable* x_{n+1} to convert the inequality into an equality:

$$a_{11}x_1 + \ldots + a_{1n}x_n + x_{n+1} = b_1 .$$

As the inequality is 'less than or equal to' we must ensure the slack variable x_{n+1} is positive, so that $x_{n+1} \geqslant 0$. The value of the slack variable is the difference between the capacity of the constraint and what is actually used, so that it indicates how much slack there is in the first constraint. In particular, when $x_{n+1} = 0$, this resource is being fully utilized.

This procedure may be repeated by introducing the slack variable x_{n+r} into the rth constraint

$$a_{r1}x_1 + \ldots + a_{rn}x_n \leqslant b_r ,$$

for $r = 1, \ldots, k$ to give the equality

$$a_{r1}x_1 + \ldots + a_{rn}x_n + x_{n+r} = b_r, \quad r = 1, \ldots, k.$$

and the non-negativity conditions $x_{n+r} \geqslant 0, r = 1, \ldots, k$.

Note: When solving a problem it is convenient to denote the slack variables by $s_1, \ldots, s_k$, so that the slack s_3 is identified immediately with the third constraint, etc. For the theory the notation $x_{n+1}, \ldots, x_{n+k}$ is much tidier.

The L.P. problem corresponding to equations (11)–(13) now becomes the *augmented problem*:

maximize $\quad c_1 x_1 + \ldots + c_n x_n + 0 x_{n+1} + 0 x_{n+2} + \ldots + 0 x_{n+k}$ $\qquad$ (14)

subject to $\quad a_{11} x_1 + \ldots + a_{1n} x_n + x_{n+1} \qquad\qquad\qquad = b_1$,

$\qquad\qquad a_{21} x_1 + \ldots + a_{2n} x_n \qquad\quad + x_{n+2} \qquad\qquad = b_2$,

$$\cdots\cdots\cdots\cdots\cdots\cdots\cdots\cdots\cdots\cdots\cdots\cdots\cdots\cdots\cdots\cdots$$

$\qquad\qquad a_{k1} x_1 + \ldots + a_{kn} x_n \qquad\qquad\qquad + x_{n+k} = b_k$, $\qquad$ (15)

$x_1 \geqslant 0, x_2 \geqslant 0, \ldots, x_n \geqslant 0, x_{n+1} \geqslant 0, \ldots, x_{n+k} \geqslant 0$. $\qquad\qquad$ (16)

Note that the slack variables are included in equations (15) to give k equality conditions. The augmented problem has a total of $n + k$ variables (n structural variables and k slack variables) as compared with the n structural variables of the original problem so that the removal of the inequalities (12) has increased the number of variables by k. The k equality conditions (15) and $n + k$ inequalities (16) define the augmented feasible region for the $n + k$ variables $(x_1, \ldots, x_{n+k})$. For completeness the slack variables are inserted into the objective function (14) with zero multipliers. It can be shown that the corner points of the original feasible region transform into the corner points of the augmented feasible region and no new corner points are generated by the introduction of the slack variables (see example 1 following). Hence, by the Optimality Theorem, if a finite maximum of (14) exists it occurs at a corner point of the augmented feasible region.

Corner Points

We must now examine the character of a corner point of the augmented feasible region. A corner point has the $n + k$ coordinates $(x_1, \ldots, x_n, x_{n+1}, \ldots, x_{n+k})$ and hence requires $n + k$ linear equations to specify it. Thus a corner point is produced by satisfying *as equalities* $n + k$ of the constraints (15) and (16). However the constraints consist of the k equalities (15) and $n + k$ non-negativity conditions (16). Since precisely k of the equalities are those of (15), the remaining n must come from (16) and be of the form $x_r = 0$. Hence at a corner point of the augmented feasible region n of the coordinates must be zero. For a corner point to be feasible, the remaining k coordinates must be positive (or zero). Hence to find all feasible corner points of the augmented feasible region we must search for all solutions of (15) which have n of the variables zero and the remaining k variables positive (or zero). These solutions are called *basic feasible solutions* of (15) and (16). The set of all basic feasible solutions of the augmented feasible region corresponds exactly to the set of all *feasible corner points* of the original feasible region. This is best illustrated by an example.

EXAMPLE 1 $\quad$ In example 1 of §1.2 the constraints are

$x_1 + 2x_2 \leqslant 100$,

$3x_1 + x_2 \leqslant 75$,

$x_1 \geqslant 0, \quad x_2 \geqslant 0$.

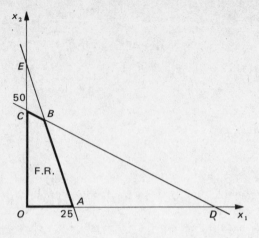

Fig. 1.8

The problem is augmented by introducing the slack variable x_3 into the first constraint and the slack variable x_4 into the second giving

$$x_1 + 2x_2 + x_3 \quad\;\; = 100 \,,$$
$$3x_1 + \;\; x_2 \quad\;\; + x_4 = 75 \,,$$
$$x_1 \geqslant 0, \quad x_2 \geqslant 0, \quad x_3 \geqslant 0, \quad x_4 \geqslant 0 \,.$$

The set of basic feasible solutions of these constraints may be enumerated by specifying in turn two zero coordinates in the set (x_1, x_2, x_3, x_4). These are

$$(0, 0, 100, 75), \quad (0, 50, 0, 25), (0, 75, -50, 0),$$
$$(100, 0, 0, -225), (25, 0, 75, 0), (10, 45, 0, 0) \,.$$

The four feasible points correspond respectively to the corner points O, C, A, B of the feasible region as illustrated on Fig. 1.8. The two non-feasible points (because of negative coordinates) correspond to the non-feasible corners E and D respectively.

To complete the solution of example 1, we must maximize $x_1 + x_2 + 0x_3 + 0x_4$ over the feasible region. Evaluating the objective function at the corners gives 0 at O, 50 at C, 25 at A, 55 at B. The optimum is at point B.

Note that the basic feasible solution corresponding to non-zero slack variables is easily calculated. Even for the general system of constraints (15) and (16) it is seen to be

$$x_1 = 0, x_2 = 0, \ldots, x_n = 0, \quad x_{n+1} = b_1, x_{n+2} = b_2, \ldots, x_{n+k} = b_k \,.$$

This point is feasible only if $b_r \geqslant 0$, for each $r = 1, 2, \ldots, k$. In the following we shall assume this to be the case. This point corresponds to the origin of the original feasible region — the 'holiday solution' for a firm in which every structural variable is zero so that there is no production and every resource is unused. We shall refer to it as the *slack variable solution*.

The number of corner points both feasible and non-feasible can be calculated from the number of ways of selecting the n zero variables at a corner from the total number of $n + k$ variables, which is $^{n+k}C_n \equiv (n + k)!/(n!k!)$.

In example 1 the number of variables n is 2 and the number of constraints k is 2 so that the number of corners is $4!/(2!2!) = 6$, of which 4 were feasible, 2 non-feasible. The number increases rapidly with the number of variables n and the number of constraints k. For $n = 3$ and $k = 6$, the number of corners is $9!/(3!6!) = 84$. It is not possible to estimate how many of these are feasible merely from a knowledge of n and k.

For a large number of variables and constraints it will be both very difficult and time-consuming to calculate all basic feasible solutions separately. The *simplex method* (described in the next section) starts from one basic feasible solution and by means of the calculations of the *simplex tableau* generates a second basic feasible solution for which the value of the objective function is greater. This process continues until the optimum is reached. Pictorially the process corresponds to moving from corner to corner around the boundary of the feasible region in such a way that the objective function is increased. Obviously those corner points not on this path between the starting corner and the optimum corner are avoided by this process.

Exercise

1. Determine the set of all basic feasible solutions of the augmented problem for the constraints

$$x_1 + 2x_2 \leqslant 6, \quad x_1 + x_2 \leqslant 4, \quad x_1, x_2 \geqslant 0 .$$

Sketch the feasible region and indicate the corner points obtained. What is the maximum of $x_1 + 3x_2$ over this region?

1.5 THE SIMPLEX METHOD

The augmented linear programming problem is to maximize

$$c_1 x_1 + \ldots + c_n x_n + 0x_{n+1} + 0x_{n+2} + \ldots + 0x_{n+k} \tag{17}$$

subject to

$$a_{11}x_1 + \ldots + a_{1n}x_n + x_{n+1} + 0x_{n+2} + \ldots + 0x_{n+k} = b_1 ,$$

$$a_{21}x_1 + \ldots + a_{2n}x_n + 0x_{n+1} + x_{n+2} + \ldots + 0x_{n+k} = b_2 , \tag{18}$$

$$\ldots \ldots \ldots \ldots \ldots \ldots \ldots \ldots \ldots \ldots \ldots \ldots \ldots \ldots \ldots$$

$$a_{k1}x_1 + \ldots + a_{kn}x_n + 0x_{n+1} + 0x_{n+2} + \ldots + x_{n+k} = b_k ,$$

$$x_i \geqslant 0 , \qquad i = 1, \ldots, n + k . \tag{19}$$

We can express the constraint equations (18) in vector form as

$$x_1 \mathbf{A}_1 + \ldots + x_n \mathbf{A}_n + x_{n+1} \mathbf{A}_{n+1} + \ldots + x_{n+k} \mathbf{A}_{n+k} = \mathbf{B} , \tag{20}$$

where the A_i, B are the columns

$$A_1 = (a_{11}, a_{21}, \ldots, a_{k1})^T$$
$$\ldots$$
$$A_n = (a_{1n}, a_{2n}, \ldots, a_{kn})^T$$
$$A_{n+1} = (1, 0, 0, \ldots, 0)^T = e_1$$
$$A_{n+2} = (0, 1, 0, \ldots, 0)^T = e_2 \tag{21}$$
$$\ldots$$
$$A_{n+k} = (0, 0, \ldots, 0, 1)^T = e_k$$
$$B = (b_1, b_2, \ldots, b_k)^T$$

and belong to the k-dimensional vector space V_k. Note that the vectors $A_{n+1}, \ldots, A_{n+k}$ are the base vectors for the space V_k. It is also convenient to denote the set of structural and slack variables by

$$X = (x_1, \ldots, x_{n+k})^T .$$

Let us assume that $A_1, \ldots, A_k$ are linearly independent vectors and so form a basis for the space V_k. Then on writing equations (18) in the form

$$x_1 A_1 + x_2 A_2 + \ldots + x_k A_k = B - x_{k+1} A_{k+1} - \ldots - x_{n+k} A_{n+k} \tag{22}$$

we can solve these equations to determine $x_1, \ldots, x_k$ uniquely in terms of B and the remaining variables on the right-hand side. This gives

$$X_B = E^{-1} B - x_{k+1} E^{-1} A_{k+1} - \ldots - x_{n+k} E^{-1} A_{n+k} \tag{23}$$

where $X_B = (x_1, \ldots, x_k)^T$, and $E = (A_1, \ldots, A_k)$ is the $k \times k$ non-singular matrix containing the basis. Note that the values of $x_{k+1}, \ldots, x_{n+k}$, may be chosen arbitrarily.

A corner point of the augmented feasible region is determined by satisfying the k *equality* constraints (18) and n equalities from (19). So far we have only satisfied the equations (18), and hence to find a corner point we must satisfy n equations from (19) of the form $x_r = 0$. Thus we can find a possible corner point by putting

$$x_{k+1} = 0, x_{k+2} = 0, \ldots, x_{n+k} = 0 \tag{24}$$

in equation (23) yielding

$$X_B = E^{-1} B = (\bar{x}_1, \bar{x}_2, \ldots, \bar{x}_k)^T . \tag{25}$$

Hence this basic solution is $X = (\bar{x}_1, \ldots, \bar{x}_k, 0, \ldots, 0)^T$. In general not all of the values $\bar{x}_1, \ldots, \bar{x}_k$ will be greater than zero. If the basic solution contains only non-negative variables, the solution is termed a *basic feasible solution*. This corresponds to a genuine corner point of the feasible region.

Note that on substituting equation (24) in equation (22) we see that $\bar{x}_1, \ldots, \bar{x}_k$ are merely the coefficients which express $\mathbf{B}$ as a linear combination of the basis $\mathbf{A}_1, \ldots, \mathbf{A}_k$. A basic solution may be found by using any linearly independent set of k vectors chosen from the set $\mathbf{A}_1, \ldots, \mathbf{A}_{n+k}$ to form a basis. Perhaps the most convenient set to select is the one corresponding to the slack variables which gives (on setting $x_1 = \ldots = x_n = 0$)

$$
x_{n+1} \begin{pmatrix} 1 \\ 0 \\ \vdots \\ \\ 0 \end{pmatrix} + x_{n+2} \begin{pmatrix} 0 \\ 1 \\ 0 \\ \vdots \\ 0 \end{pmatrix} + \ldots + x_{n+k} \begin{pmatrix} 0 \\ 0 \\ \vdots \\ 0 \\ 1 \end{pmatrix} = \begin{pmatrix} b_1 \\ b_2 \\ \vdots \\ \\ b_k \end{pmatrix}.
$$

Hence one basic solution is

$$
\mathbf{X} = (0, 0, \ldots, 0, b_1, b_2, \ldots, b_k)^T
$$

and is feasible provided $b_i \geqslant 0$, all i. This is the slack variable solution described in §1.4.

EXAMPLE 1   The constraints

$$
x_1 + 2x_2 \leqslant 100 ,
$$
$$
3x_1 + x_2 \leqslant 75 ,
$$

with $x_1, x_2 \geqslant 0$ yield the augmented constraints

$$
x_1 + 2x_2 + x_3 + 0x_4 = 100 ,
$$
$$
3x_1 + x_2 + 0x_3 + x_4 = 75 ,
$$

with $x_1, x_2, x_3, x_4 \geqslant 0$ so that

$$
x_1 \begin{pmatrix} 1 \\ 3 \end{pmatrix} + x_2 \begin{pmatrix} 2 \\ 1 \end{pmatrix} + x_3 \begin{pmatrix} 1 \\ 0 \end{pmatrix} + x_4 \begin{pmatrix} 0 \\ 1 \end{pmatrix} = \begin{pmatrix} 100 \\ 75 \end{pmatrix}.
$$

By selecting two linearly independent vectors to form a basis, different basic solutions may be generated; for example:

select $\mathbf{A}_3, \mathbf{A}_4$, put $x_1 = x_2 = 0$, then $\begin{pmatrix} 100 \\ 75 \end{pmatrix} = x_3 \begin{pmatrix} 1 \\ 0 \end{pmatrix} + x_4 \begin{pmatrix} 0 \\ 1 \end{pmatrix}$,

the solution is $(0, 0, 100, 75)^T$ and is feasible:

select $\mathbf{A}_2, \mathbf{A}_4$, put $x_1 = x_3 = 0$, then $\begin{pmatrix} 100 \\ 75 \end{pmatrix} = x_2 \begin{pmatrix} 2 \\ 1 \end{pmatrix} + x_4 \begin{pmatrix} 0 \\ 1 \end{pmatrix}$,

the solution is $(0, 50, 0, 25)^T$ and is feasible:

select $\mathbf{A}_1, \mathbf{A}_4$, put $x_2 = x_3 = 0$, then $\begin{pmatrix} 100 \\ 75 \end{pmatrix} = x_1 \begin{pmatrix} 1 \\ 3 \end{pmatrix} + x_4 \begin{pmatrix} 0 \\ 1 \end{pmatrix}$,

the solution $(100, 0, 0, -225)^T$ is basic but not feasible. Other points $(25, 0, 75, 0)^T$, $(10, 45, 0, 0)^T$, $(0, 75, -50, 0)^T$ may be generated similarly.

The *requirements* for the simplex method of solution of moving from corner to corner around the boundary of the feasible region are

(a) a method of generating an initial basic feasible solution without too much work — the slack variable solution forms a suitable starting point provided that b_i is non-negative for all values of $i = 1, \ldots, k$;

(b) a method of moving from one basic feasible solution to another, if possible increasing the objective function in the process.

Change of Basis

Assume a basic feasible solution has been found with the basis $\mathbf{A}_1, \mathbf{A}_2, \ldots, \mathbf{A}_k$. Then the solution is $\mathbf{X} = (\bar{x}_1, \bar{x}_2, \ldots, \bar{x}_k, 0, 0, \ldots, 0)^T$, where

$$\mathbf{B} = \bar{x}_1 \mathbf{A}_1 + \ldots + \bar{x}_k \mathbf{A}_k \quad \text{with} \quad \bar{x}_i \geqslant 0, \quad i = 1, \ldots, k. \tag{26}$$

Since another corner point may be found by a change of basis, let us introduce the vector $\mathbf{A}_r (r > k)$ into the basis and eliminate one vector from the basis, say $\mathbf{A}_j$. We can express $\mathbf{A}_r$ as a linear combination of the basis vectors as

$$\mathbf{A}_r = t_{1r} \mathbf{A}_1 + t_{2r} \mathbf{A}_2 + \ldots + t_{kr} \mathbf{A}_k, \tag{27}$$

so that the representation for $\mathbf{A}_j$ in terms of the new basis is

$$\mathbf{A}_j = \frac{1}{t_{jr}} [\mathbf{A}_r - t_{1r} \mathbf{A}_1 - \ldots - t_{kr} \mathbf{A}_k]$$
$$\underset{\text{no } j\text{th term}}{\uparrow}$$

provided that $t_{jr} \neq 0$. On substituting in equation (26) we find that the representation for $\mathbf{B}$ in terms of the new basis is

$$\mathbf{B} = \bar{x}_1 \mathbf{A}_1 + \ldots + \bar{x}_j [\mathbf{A}_r - t_{1r} \mathbf{A}_1 - \ldots - t_{kr} \mathbf{A}_k] \frac{1}{t_{jr}} + \ldots + \bar{x}_k \mathbf{A}_k,$$

$$= \left(\bar{x}_1 - \bar{x}_j \frac{t_{1r}}{t_{jr}} \right) \mathbf{A}_1 + \ldots + 0 \mathbf{A}_j + \ldots + \left(\bar{x}_k - \bar{x}_j \frac{t_{kr}}{t_{jr}} \right) \mathbf{A}_k + \bar{x}_j \frac{1}{t_{jr}} \mathbf{A}_r.$$

Hence the new basic solution is

$$\mathbf{X} = \left(\bar{x}_1 - \bar{x}_j \frac{t_{1r}}{t_{jr}}, \ldots, 0, \ldots, \bar{x}_k - \bar{x}_j \frac{t_{kr}}{t_{jr}}, 0, \ldots, 0, \frac{\bar{x}_j}{t_{jr}}, 0, \ldots, 0 \right)^T. \tag{28}$$
$$\qquad\qquad\quad \underset{j\text{th term}}{\uparrow} \qquad\qquad\qquad\qquad\qquad\qquad \underset{r\text{th term}}{\uparrow}$$

This solution is feasible provided that

$$\bar{x}_i - \bar{x}_j \frac{t_{ir}}{t_{jr}} \geqslant 0, \quad i = 1, \ldots, k,$$

and

$$\bar{x}_j \frac{1}{t_{jr}} \geqslant 0$$

where $\bar{x}_1, \ldots, \bar{x}_k$ are all non-negative.

Thus, when $\mathbf{A}_r$ is introduced into the basis, the vector $\mathbf{A}_j$, which is removed from the basis, must be chosen by the conditions

(a) $t_{jr} > 0$,

(b) $\dfrac{\bar{x}_j}{t_{jr}} \leqslant \dfrac{\bar{x}_i}{t_{ir}}$ for all i when $t_{ir} > 0$,

(29)

that is, we identify the vector $\mathbf{A}_j$ by finding the positive element t_{jr} which yields the minimum *positive* value from the ratios

$$\bar{x}_1/t_{1r}, \bar{x}_2/t_{2r}, \ldots, \bar{x}_k/t_{kr}.$$

The new solution will then be a basic feasible solution. The element t_{jr} selected by (29) is called the *pivot* element.

Note that the introduction of $\mathbf{A}_r$ into the basis and the elimination of $\mathbf{A}_j$ is equivalent to introducing x_r into the basic feasible solution and eliminating x_j from it.

EXAMPLE   The standard problem may be used to give a physical interpretation of conditions (29). The augmented constraints are

$$x_1 \begin{pmatrix} 1 \\ 3 \end{pmatrix} + x_2 \begin{pmatrix} 2 \\ 1 \end{pmatrix} + x_3 \begin{pmatrix} 1 \\ 0 \end{pmatrix} + x_4 \begin{pmatrix} 0 \\ 1 \end{pmatrix} = \begin{pmatrix} 100 \\ 75 \end{pmatrix}.$$

The solution with the basis $\mathbf{A}_1, \mathbf{A}_2$ is $(10, 45, 0, 0)^T$ and corresponds to B on Fig. 1.8. Let us introduce

$$\mathbf{A}_3 = \begin{pmatrix} 1 \\ 0 \end{pmatrix} = -\frac{1}{5} \begin{pmatrix} 1 \\ 3 \end{pmatrix} + \frac{3}{5} \begin{pmatrix} 2 \\ 1 \end{pmatrix}$$

into the basis. Since $t_{13} = -0.2$, $t_{23} = 0.6$, condition (29a) implies that $\mathbf{A}_3$ should replace $\mathbf{A}_2$ in the basis. From (28), the new solution is

$$\mathbf{X} = \left(10 - 45 \left(\frac{-0.2}{0.6} \right), \ 45 - 45, \ \frac{45}{0.6}, \ 0 \right)^T = (25, 0, 75, 0)^T.$$

Introducing $\mathbf{A}_3$ into the basis is equivalent to looking for a basic solution in which x_3 is non-zero. But x_3 is the slack variable corresponding to the constraint CB and is zero along CB. Hence, starting from B we must search for the new corner along the second constraint AE. Condition (29a) ensures that the move is to the feasible corner A.

As a second illustration, we reverse the process and start from the point A, with solution $(25, 0, 75, 0)^T$ corresponding to the basis $\mathbf{A}_1, \mathbf{A}_3$, and introduce $\mathbf{A}_2$ into the basis. Now

$$\mathbf{A}_2 = \begin{pmatrix} 2 \\ 1 \end{pmatrix} = \frac{1}{3} \begin{pmatrix} 1 \\ 3 \end{pmatrix} + \frac{5}{3} \begin{pmatrix} 1 \\ 0 \end{pmatrix}$$

so that $t_{12} = 0.3\dot{3}$, $t_{32} = 1.6\dot{6}$. Condition (29a) is satisfied, but to fulfil (29b) we must form the ratios

$$\frac{\bar{x}_1}{t_{12}} = \frac{25}{0.3\dot{3}}, \quad \frac{\bar{x}_3}{t_{32}} = \frac{75}{1.6\dot{6}}.$$

The second is the minimum and therefore we replace A_3 in the basis. Hence, from (28), the new solution is $X = (10, 45, 0, 0)^T$, as expected.

Note that in this case we have started from point A on Fig. 1.8 and looked for a new basic feasible solution in which x_2 is non-zero. The search is along the constraint AE and condition (29b) selects the *nearest* corner B. Any other corner points further along AE will not be feasible. A similar interpretation of conditions (29) is possible in more complicated problems.

Simplex Criterion

So far the vector to introduce into the basis has not been specially selected. We show that (except at the optimum point) it can always be chosen so that the objective function is increased. Suppose we have the basic feasible solution

$$(\bar{x}_1, \ldots, \bar{x}_k, 0, \ldots, 0)^T$$

corresponding to the basis $A_1, \ldots, A_k$. On introducing A_r into the basis and removing A_j (as detailed above), we find the new basic feasible solution (28)

$$\left(\bar{x}_1 - \bar{x}_j \frac{t_{1r}}{t_{jr}}, \ldots, 0, \ldots, \bar{x}_k - \bar{x}_j \frac{t_{kr}}{t_{jr}}, 0, \ldots, 0, \frac{\bar{x}_j}{t_{jr}}, 0, \ldots, 0 \right)^T.$$

The value of the objective function for the new basic feasible solution is

$$c_1 \left(\bar{x}_1 - \bar{x}_j \frac{t_{1r}}{t_{jr}} \right) + \ldots + c_k \left(\bar{x}_k - \bar{x}_j \frac{t_{kr}}{t_{jr}} \right) + c_r \frac{\bar{x}_j}{t_{jr}}$$

$$= \bar{z} - \frac{\bar{x}_j}{t_{jr}} (c_1 t_{1r} + \ldots + c_j t_{jr} + \ldots + c_k t_{kr} - c_r),$$

where $\bar{z} = c_1 \bar{x}_1 + \ldots + c_j \bar{x}_j + \ldots + c_k \bar{x}_k$ is the value of the objective function for the old basic feasible solution. As $\bar{x}_j / t_{jr}$ is positive, the objective function will be increased provided that

$$c_r - (c_1 t_{1r} + \ldots + c_j t_{jr} + \ldots + c_k t_{kr}) > 0. \tag{30}$$

Hence we choose to introduce into the basis the vector A_r for which the expression (30) is a *maximum*. This is the *simplex criterion*. We refer to the expression (30) as the *simplex coefficient* corresponding to the variable x_r. The negative of expression (30) is sometimes referred to as a *reduced cost*.

Note (a) if it is not possible to find a vector A_r for which the inequality (30) is satisfied, then it is not possible to find another corner point (basic feasible solution) for which the objective function is greater, i.e., we are at the optimum point;

(b) strictly we should try to maximize $(c_r - c_1 t_{1r} - \ldots - c_k t_{kr})\bar{x}_j/t_{jr}$, but this yields a more complicated numerical procedure which only slightly improves the rate of convergence of the simplex method.

The *simplex method* is then:

(1) Find an initial basic feasible solution (the slack variable solution?).
(2) From the remaining vectors $\mathbf{A}_r$ choose to introduce the one with the largest positive simplex coefficient (30).
(3) Choose the vector to eliminate from the basis by using the restrictions (29).
(4) Evaluate the new basic feasible solution and the objective function.
(5) Repeat the procedure until no positive values of the simplex coefficients (30) can be found.

To enable this method to be followed, we need to calculate the coefficients t_{ij} in the second and higher iterations without too much labour.

Suppose the first iteration has the basis $\mathbf{A}_1, \ldots, \mathbf{A}_k$; then each vector $\mathbf{A}_p$ can be represented in terms of this basis by

$$\mathbf{A}_p = \sum_{i=1}^{k} t_{ip} \mathbf{A}_i \quad \text{for each} \quad p = k+1, \ldots, n+k. \tag{31}$$

For the second iteration we need to express the general vector $\mathbf{A}_p$ in terms of the new basis $\mathbf{A}_1, \ldots, \mathbf{A}_{j-1}, \mathbf{A}_{j+1}, \ldots, \mathbf{A}_k, \mathbf{A}_r$. Since

$$\mathbf{A}_j = (\mathbf{A}_r - t_{1r}\mathbf{A}_1 - \ldots - t_{kr}\mathbf{A}_k)/t_{jr}, \tag{32}$$

this may be done by substituting equation (32) into equation (31) giving

$$\mathbf{A}_p = t_{1p}\mathbf{A}_1 + \ldots + \frac{t_{jp}}{t_{jr}}(\mathbf{A}_r - t_{1r}\mathbf{A}_1 - \ldots - t_{kr}\mathbf{A}_k) + \ldots + t_{kp}\mathbf{A}_k$$

$$= \left(t_{1p} - t_{1r}\frac{t_{jp}}{t_{jr}}\right)\mathbf{A}_1 + \ldots + \left(t_{kp} - t_{kr}\frac{t_{jp}}{t_{jr}}\right)\mathbf{A}_k + \frac{t_{jp}}{t_{jr}}\mathbf{A}_r. \tag{33}$$

$$\underset{\text{no } j\text{th term}}{\uparrow}$$

The coefficients in (33) are the values of t_{ip} in terms of the new basis.

The Simplex Tableau

The procedure described above is most conveniently carried out in the following tableau.

C_B	Basis	x_1 x_2 ... x_n x_{n+1} ... x_{n+k}	B.F.S.

Each tableau corresponds to a single basic feasible solution. As an example, consider the basic feasible solution $(\bar{x}_1, \bar{x}_2, \ldots, \bar{x}_k, 0, \ldots, 0)^T$ corresponding to the basis

$\mathbf{A}_1, \ldots, \mathbf{A}_k$. This is not the most convenient initial tableau, but corresponds to the calculations described above. The basic feasible solution is fed into the tableau in the following way.

(1) Insert into the Basis column the variables corresponding to the basis, in this case $x_1, \ldots, x_k$.

(2) Insert into the B.F.S. column the corresponding values of the basic feasible solution $x_1 = \bar{x}_1, x_2 = \bar{x}_2, \ldots, x_k = \bar{x}_k$.

(3) The main block of the tableau consists of the representations of the vectors $\mathbf{A}_p, p = 1, 2, \ldots, n + k$, in terms of the current basis, in this case $\mathbf{A}_1, \ldots, \mathbf{A}_k$. From equation (30), as $\mathbf{A}_p = \sum_{i=1}^{k} t_{ip} \mathbf{A}_i$, we insert in the x_p column the coefficients $t_{ip}, i = 1, 2, \ldots, k$.

(4) Place the coefficients c_i of the objective function above the x_i variables in the first row of the tableau. Also insert in the $\mathbf{C}_B$ column the coefficients of the objective function which correspond to the variables in the basic feasible solution.

This completes Tableau 1 apart from the last two lines.

TABLEAU 1

		c_1	c_r	c_n	c_{n+k}	
$\mathbf{C}_B$	Basis	x_1 $\cdots$	x_r $\cdots$	x_n $\cdots$	x_{n+k}	B.F.S.
c_1	x_1	t_{11}	t_{1r}	t_{1n}	$t_{1\,n+k}$	$\bar{x}_1$
$\vdots$	$\vdots$					$\vdots$
c_j	x_j	t_{j1}	t_{jr}	t_{jn}	$t_{j\,n+k}$	$\bar{x}_j$
$\vdots$	$\vdots$					$\vdots$
c_k	x_k	t_{k1}	t_{kr}	t_{kn}	$t_{k\,n+k}$	$\bar{x}_k$
	$\sum c_i t_{ip}$					$\sum c_i \bar{x}_i$ = O.F.
S.C. =	$c_p - \sum c_i t_{ip}$					

The Simplex Procedure

The simplex procedure for generating a second basic feasible solution with a greater profit is as follows:

(a) For each variable $x_p, p = 1, \ldots, n + k$, form the product $\sum_{i=1}^{k} c_i t_{ip}$ of the $\mathbf{C}_B$ column and the pth column of the tableau and insert the result beneath the pth column in the O.F. (objective function) row. Repeat for the B.F.S. column. This gives the value of the objective function for this corner point.

(b) To find the simplex coefficients (30) for each variable x_p, subtract from c_p the value in the O.F. row of the tableau and insert the result in the S.C. (simplex coefficient) row.

(c) Select the maximum of the positive simplex coefficients. Let us suppose it occurs in the x_r column; then we must introduce A_r into the basis.

(d) To determine the vector to eliminate from the basis, use conditions (29), i.e. find the minimum of $\bar{x}_i/t_{ir}$ for each *positive* element $t_{ir}, i = 1, \ldots, k$, of the x_r column. Suppose the minimum is $\bar{x}_j/t_{jr}$. *Comment:* we must now generate a new tableau by introducing x_r into the basic feasible solution and eliminating x_j from it. Mark the pivot element t_{jr}. We refer to the x_j row of Tableau 1 as the *pivot row*.

(e) The new tableau is generated by row operations on Tableau 1. We denote the equivalent elements in Tableau 2 by a dash so that $t_{ij} \to t'_{ij}$. In Tableau 2 set up the basis column replacing x_j by x_r and c_j by c_r in the C_B column.

(f) In Tableau 1 divide the pivot row (x_j row) by the pivot t_{jr} and insert the results in the x_r row of Tableau 2. Then the elements in this row are

$$t'_{rp} = t_{jp}/t_{jr} \quad \text{for } p = 1, \ldots, n + k, \quad \text{and} \quad \bar{x}'_r = \bar{x}_j/t_{jr}.$$

(g) To determine the new x_i row, evaluate the coefficient t_{ir}/t_{jr}. Then from (33)

$$t'_{ip} = t_{ip} - t_{jp}(t_{ir}/t_{jr}), \quad \bar{x}'_i = \bar{x}_i - \bar{x}_j(t_{ir}/t_{jr})$$

so that the new x_i row is equal to the old x_i row minus a constant multiple of the pivot row. This generates the new tableau (Tableau 2) corresponding to the basic feasible solution of (28).

TABLEAU 2

C_B	Basis	$x_1 \ldots$	x_p	$\ldots x_r \ldots x_{n+k}$	B.F.S.
c_1	x_1		$t_{1p} - t_{jp}(t_{1r}/t_{jr})$	0	$\bar{x}_1 - \bar{x}_j(t_{1r}/t_{jr})$
$\vdots$	$\vdots$			$\vdots$	
c_{j-1}	x_{j-1}			0	
c_r	x_r		t_{jp}/t_{jr}	1	$\bar{x}_j/t_{jr}$
c_{j+1}	x_{j+1}			0	
$\vdots$	$\vdots$			$\vdots$	
c_k	x_k			0	

This procedure may be repeated starting from Tableau 2 until a tableau is found with no positive simplex coefficients. This final tableau gives the optimal basic feasible solution.

Initial Tableau

The simplex procedure is simple to follow once an initial tableau has been found. The basis assumed here for Tableau 1, namely $A_1, \ldots, A_k$, is probably much too complicated in practice. The simplest possible basis (which generates a basic feasible solution) is required to form an initial tableau. Therefore the *slack variable solution* is selected to form the initial tableau as the basis consists of the base vectors $A_{n+1}, \ldots, A_{n+k}$ of (21). The corresponding basic solution $(0, \ldots, 0, b_1, \ldots, b_k)$ is feasible provided $b_i \geqslant 0$ for $i = 1, \ldots, k$. In this case, since the pth vector A_p has the representation

$$A_p = (a_{1p}, \ldots, a_{kp})^T = a_{1p}A_{n+1} + a_{2p}A_{n+2} + \ldots + a_{kp}A_{n+k}$$

in terms of the basis for each value $p = 1, \ldots, n$, the initial tableau is as shown.

INITIAL TABLEAU

		c_1		c_n	0	0	0	
C_B	Basis	x_1 $\ldots$		x_n	x_{n+1}	x_{n+2}	$\ldots x_{n+k}$	B.F.S.
0	x_{n+1}	a_{11}		a_{1n}	1	0	0	b_1
0	x_{n+2}	a_{21}		a_{2n}	0	1	0	b_2
0	x_{n+k}	a_{k1}		a_{kn}	0	0	1	b_k

It will be observed that the initial tableau is filled with the coefficients of the augmented constraints taken in order, and so forms a very simple starting point for the simplex procedure.

The simplex method is best illustrated by worked examples. Consider the standard example which is solved geometrically in §1.2.

EXAMPLE 1   Maximize $x_1 + x_2$

subject to $x_1 + 2x_2 \leqslant 100$,

$3x_1 + x_2 \leqslant 75$,

$x_1 \geqslant 0, \quad x_2 \geqslant 0$.

The augmented problem is:

maximize $x_1 + x_2 + 0x_3 + 0x_4$

subject to $x_1 + 2x_2 + x_3 + 0x_4 = 100$,

$3x_1 + x_2 + 0x_3 + x_4 = 75$,

$x_1, x_2, x_3, x_4 \geqslant 0$.

The initial tableau corresponding to the slack variable solution $\mathbf{X} = (0, 0, 100, 75)^T$ is Tableau 1 below.

TABLEAU 1

		1	1	0	0		
C_B	Basis	x_1	x_2	x_3	x_4	B.F.S.	
0	x_3	1	②	1	0	100	$R_1/2$
0	x_4	3	1	0	1	75	$R_2 - \frac{1}{2}R_1$
		0	0	0	0	0	= O.F.
	S.C. =	1	1	0	0		
			↑				

The simplex coefficients may be evaluated from the simplex procedure rules (a) and (b). In this case, as there are equal positive simplex coefficients, we may introduce either x_1 or x_2 into the solution; let us choose to introduce x_2. From rule (d) the variable to be eliminated corresponds to the minimum of $100/2, 75/1$. We therefore eliminate x_3. The pivot is 2. The row operations (f) and (g) to form the second tableau are shown next to the first tableau.

TABLEAU 2

		1	1	0	0		
C_B	Basis	x_1	x_2	x_3	x_4	B.F.S.	
1	x_2	$\frac{1}{2}$	1	$\frac{1}{2}$	0	50	$R_1 - \dfrac{\frac{1}{2}}{2\frac{1}{2}} R_2$
0	x_4	②½	0	$-\frac{1}{2}$	1	25	$R_2/2\frac{1}{2}$
		$\frac{1}{2}$	1	$\frac{1}{2}$	0	50	= O.F.
	S.C. =	$\frac{1}{2}$	0	$-\frac{1}{2}$	0		
		↑					

Tableau 2 corresponds to the basic feasible solution $(0, 50, 0, 25)^T$.

The simplex coefficients for the second tableau may be evaluated from rules (a) and (b). As the first coefficient is the only positive one, we introduce x_1. The variable to be eliminated corresponds to the minimum of $50/\frac{1}{2}, 25/2\frac{1}{2}$, so we eliminate x_4. The pivot is $2\frac{1}{2}$. The row operations to form the third tableau are shown next to the second tableau.

TABLEAU 3

		1	1	0	0	
C_B	Basis	x_1	x_2	x_3	x_4	B.F.S.
1	x_2	0	1	0.6	−0.2	45
1	x_1	1	0	−0.2	0.4	10
		1	1	0.4	0.2	55
S.C. =		0	0	−0.4	−0.2	

= O.F.

The simplex coefficients for Tableau 3 are zero or negative. Hence this is the optimal tableau. Reading from the tableau, the optimum lies at the point $x_1 = 10, x_2 = 45$, $x_3 = 0, x_4 = 0$ with the maximum value of the objective function equal to 55. Note that this solution follows the route $O \rightarrow C \rightarrow B$ around the feasible region of Fig. 1.9.

As an exercise the reader should start from the first tableau, introduce x_1 into the solution, and proceed to the optimum. Which path is followed?

EXAMPLE 2   Maximize $4x_1 + x_2$
            subject to $x_1 + 2x_2 \leqslant 100$,
                          $3x_1 + x_2 \leqslant 75$,
                          $x_1 \geqslant 0, \quad x_2 \geqslant 0$.

The augmented problem is:
    maximize $4x_1 + x_2 + 0x_3 + 0x_4$
    subject to $x_1 + 2x_2 + x_3 + 0x_4 = 100$,
                  $3x_1 + x_2 + 0x_3 + x_4 = 75$,
                  $x_1, x_2, x_3, x_4 \geqslant 0$.

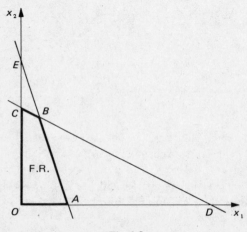

Fig. 1.9

The initial tableau corresponding to the slack variable solution $(0, 0, 100, 75)^T$ is Tableau 1 below.

TABLEAU 1

		4	1	0	0		
C_B	Basis	x_1	x_2	x_3	x_4	B.F.S.	
0	x_3	1	2	1	0	100	$R_1 - \frac{1}{3}R_2$
0	x_4	③	1	0	1	75	$R_2/3$
		0	0	0	0	0	= O.F.
	S.C. =	4	1	0	0		

Since the maximum simplex coefficient is 4, x_1 is introduced into the basic feasible solution. We eliminate the variable corresponding to the minimum of $100/1, 75/3$, i.e., we eliminate x_4. The pivot is 3. The row operations to give the second tableau are shown next to Tableau 1.

TABLEAU 2

		4	1	0	0		
C_B	Basis	x_1	x_2	x_3	x_4	B.F.S.	
0	x_3	0	$1\frac{2}{3}$	1	$-\frac{1}{3}$	75	
4	x_1	1	$\frac{1}{3}$	0	$\frac{1}{3}$	25	
		4	$1\frac{1}{3}$	0	$1\frac{1}{3}$	100	= O.F.
	S.C. =	0	$-\frac{1}{3}$	0	$-1\frac{1}{3}$		

As the simplex coefficients are zero or negative, Tableau 2 is an optimal tableau. The optimum is at $x_1 = 25, x_2 = 0, x_3 = 75, x_4 = 0$. The non-zero slack variable $x_3 = 75$ indicates that the constraint $x_1 + 2x_2 \leqslant 100$ has 75 units of spare capacity. The solution corresponds to the point A of Fig. 1.9.

Checking Procedures

To achieve numerical accuracy it is suggested that the following checking procedures be adopted in hand calculations using the simplex method.

(a) Mark the pivot element (it should always be positive).

(b) Indicate the row operations near the tableau.

(c) Verify that in all tableaux the columns under the basis elements are base vectors of the form

Basis	$x_1 \ldots x_r \ldots x_{n+k}$	B.F.S.
x_r	$\begin{matrix} 0 \\ \vdots \\ 0 \\ 1 \\ 0 \\ \vdots \\ 0 \end{matrix}$	

(d) Verify that all elements in the B.F.S. column are positive.

(e) It is convenient to introduce a checking column to confirm the accuracy of each row manipulation. Add the elements in each row and put the total in the check column. In each new tableau perform the row operations on the check column also. The elements in the check column should be the sum of the row elements.

It is suggested that the reader work through the following problem and sketch the feasible region to follow the path to the optimum.

EXAMPLE 3   Maximize $10x_1 + 20x_2 + 5x_3$

subject to
$$5x_1 + 5x_2 + 10x_3 + x_4 \qquad\qquad = 10,$$
$$10x_1 + 8x_2 + 5x_3 \qquad + x_5 \qquad = 20,$$
$$10x_1 + 5x_2 \qquad\qquad\qquad + x_6 = 5,$$

where x_4, x_5, x_6 are slack variables and $x_1, \ldots, x_6 \geqslant 0$.

		10	20	5	0	0	0		
C_B	Basis	x_1	x_2	x_3	x_4	x_5	x_6	B.F.S.	Check
0	x_4	5	5	10	1	0	0	10	31	$R_1 - R_3$
0	x_5	10	8	5	0	1	0	20	44	$R_2 - \frac{8}{5}R_3$
0	x_6	10	⑤	0	0	0	1	5	21	$R_3/5$
		0	0	0	0	0	0	0	= O.F.
	S.C. =	10	20	5	0	0	0		

		10	20	5	0	0	0		
C_B	Basis	x_1	x_2	x_3	x_4	x_5	x_6	B.F.S.	Check
0	x_4	−5	0	⑩	1	0	−1	5	10	$R_1/10$
0	x_5	−6	0	5	0	1	−1.6	12	10.4	$R_2 - \frac{1}{2}R_1$
20	x_2	2	1	0	0	0	0.2	1	4.2	$R_3 - 0R_1$
		40	20	0	0	0	4	20	= O.F.
	S.C. =	−30	0	5	0	0	−4		

C_B	Basis	x_1	x_2	x_3	x_4	x_5	x_6	B.F.S.	Check
		10	20	5	0	0	0		
5	x_3	−0.5	0	1	0.1	0	−0.1	0.5	1
0	x_5	−3.5	0	0	−0.5	1	−1.1	9.5	5.4
20	x_2	2	1	0	0	0	0.2	1	4.2
		37.5	20	5	0.5	0	3.5	22.5	= O.F.
	S.C. =	−27.5	0	0	−0.5	0	−3.5		

The optimum solution is $x_1 = 0, x_2 = 1, x_3 = 0.5, x_4 = 0, x_5 = 9.5, x_6 = 0$. At the optimum the first and third constraints are active and the second constraint is slack.

Artificial Variables

So far the simplex method has been applied to linear programming problems of the type

maximize $\quad c_1 x_1 + \ldots + c_n x_n$

subject to $\quad \mathbf{AX} \leqslant \mathbf{B}, \ \mathbf{X} \geqslant \mathbf{0}$.

Here and subsequently the matrix inequality $\mathbf{X} \geqslant \mathbf{0}$ will imply that all elements of $\mathbf{X}$ are non-negative, and we employ the more concise matrix notation for the constraints. In addition we have assumed $\mathbf{B} \geqslant \mathbf{0}$ so that the very convenient slack variable solution may be used to form the initial tableau. However, more general types of linear programming problems occur and all can be solved by this method.

First, the problem may be a minimizing problem: for example, minimize $3x_1 - 4x_2$ subject to linear constraints. This has the same optimum point as the maximum of $-3x_1 + 4x_2$ subject to the same constraints, so that all L.P. problems can be written as maximizing (or minimizing) problems.

Second, some constraints may be equality constraints and others 'greater than or equal to' constraints. These have been excluded from the discussion thus far. In general an L.P. problem will contain constraints of the types

linear form $1 \leqslant b_1$,

linear form $2 \geqslant b_2$, $\qquad\qquad\qquad\qquad\qquad$ (34)

linear form $3 = b_3$,

where a linear form in $x_1, \ldots, x_n$ is any sum $a_{11}x_1 + \ldots + a_{1n}x_n$ in which the a_{1i} are known constants. It may be assumed without loss of generality that b_1, b_2, b_3 are positive. (If, for example, $b_1 = -1$, the first constraint could be written as $-(\text{linear form } 1) \geqslant 1$, which is a constraint of the second type.) The first constraint is augmented by the addition of a slack variable s_1 to give

(linear form 1) $+ s_1 = b_1$, $\quad s_1 \geqslant 0$.

The second constraint may be made an equality by the subtraction of a positive slack variable s_2 so that

$$\text{(linear form 2)} - s_2 = b_2, \quad s_2 \geqslant 0 .$$

The third constraint is already an equality, and therefore has no slack variable associated with it. The most convenient method of starting the simplex procedure is to use the slack variable solution. In this case, setting all variables except the slack variables equal to zero gives the solution $s_1 = b_1, s_2 = -b_2$ (which is not feasible), and in addition the third constraint is not satisfied. Hence a new method of forming an initial tableau is required when a problem contains greater than and/or equality conditions. A simple basic feasible solution can be found if non-negative artificial variables a_2, a_3 are introduced into the greater than condition and the equality condition, so that the constraints become

$$
\begin{aligned}
&\text{(linear form 1)} + s_1 && = b_1, && s_1 \geqslant 0, \\
&\text{(linear form 2)} - s_2 + a_2 && = b_2, && s_2 \geqslant 0, && \text{(35)} \\
&\text{(linear form 3)} && + a_3 = b_3.
\end{aligned}
$$

Now a simple solution is $s_1 = b_1, s_2 = 0, a_2 = b_2, a_3 = b_3$ with all other variables zero and this may be used to form an initial tableau for the simplex method. However the presence of the non-zero artificial variables a_2 and a_3 in the equalities (35) means that the original constraints (34) are not satisfied and the solution of the augmented problem will bear no relation to that of the original problem. We therefore restrict the artificial variables to be greater than or equal to zero and introduce them into the objective function with large negative weightings so that in the maximizing operations of the simplex method they will be reduced to zero automatically and the constraints (34) satisfied. The procedure is illustrated in the following example.

EXAMPLE 4 $\quad$ Maximize $\quad x_1 + 2x_2$

$$
\begin{aligned}
\text{subject to} \quad & 4x_1 + x_2 \leqslant 2, \\
& x_1 + x_2 \geqslant 1, \\
& x_2 \geqslant \tfrac{3}{4}, \\
& x_1, x_2 \geqslant 0.
\end{aligned}
$$

The feasible region is shown on Fig. 1.10 as $BCDE$. On introducing slack variables x_3, x_4, x_5, the augmented constraints become

$$
\begin{aligned}
4x_1 + x_2 + x_3 \quad\quad &= 2, \\
x_1 + x_2 \quad - x_4 \quad &= 1, \\
x_2 \quad\quad - x_5 &= \tfrac{3}{4}.
\end{aligned}
$$

The slack variable solution is $X = (0, 0, 2, -1, -\tfrac{3}{4})^T$ and is not feasible. We therefore introduce artificial variables x_6, x_7 into the second and third constraints to give

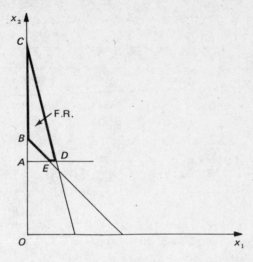

Fig. 1.10

$$4x_1 + x_2 + x_3 \qquad\qquad = 2 ,$$
$$x_1 + x_2 \qquad - x_4 \qquad + x_6 \qquad = 1 , \tag{36}$$
$$x_2 \qquad\quad - x_5 \quad\; + x_7 = \tfrac{3}{4} ,$$
$$x_1, \dots , x_7 \geqslant 0 .$$

The basic solution $(0, 0, 2, 0, 0, 1, \tfrac{3}{4})^T$ is feasible but contains non-zero artificial variables. To eliminate the (non-negative) artificial variables x_6, x_7 from the solution, introduce them into the objective function with large negative weightings M and N. The problem becomes:

$$\text{maximize} \quad x_1 + 2x_2 - Mx_6 - Nx_7 ,$$

subject to the constraints (36). The initial tableau is Tableau 1.

TABLEAU 1

		1	2	0	0	0	$-M$	$-N$	
C_B	Basis	x_1	x_2	x_3	x_4	x_5	x_6	x_7	B.F.S.
0	x_3	4	1	1	0	0	0	0	2
$-M$	x_6	1	1	0	-1	0	1	0	1
$-N$	x_7	0	①	0	0	-1	0	1	$\tfrac{3}{4}$
		$-M$	$-M-N$	0	M	N	$-M$	$-N$	$-M-\tfrac{3}{4}N$ = O.F.
	S.C. =	$1+M$	$2+M+N$	0	$-M$	$-N$	0	0	

Tableau 1 indicates that we must introduce x_2 and eliminate the artificial variable x_7 to produce the second tableau.

TABLEAU 2

		1	2	0	0	0	$-M$	$-N$	
C_B	Basis	x_1	x_2	x_3	x_4	x_5	x_6	x_7	B.F.S.
0	x_3	4	0	1	0	1	0	-1	$1\frac{1}{4}$
$-M$	x_6	1	0	0	-1	①	1	-1	$\frac{1}{4}$
2	x_2	0	1	0	0	-1	0	1	$\frac{3}{4}$
	S.C. =	$-M$	2	0	M	$-M-2$	$-M$	$M+2$	$-\frac{1}{4}M+\frac{3}{2}$ = O.F.
		$1+M$	0	0	$-M$	$M+2$	0	$-N-M-2$	

Tableau 2 indicates that we must introduce x_5 and eliminate x_6. Both artificial variables have now been eliminated and do not appear in Tableau 3.

TABLEAU 3

		1	2	0	0	0	$-M$	$-N$	
C_B	Basis	x_1	x_2	x_3	x_4	x_5	x_6	x_7	B.F.S.
0	x_3	3	0	1	①	0	-1	0	1
0	x_5	1	0	0	-1	1	1	-1	$\frac{1}{4}$
2	x_2	1	1	0	-1	0	1	0	1
	S.C. =	2	2	0	-2	0	2	0	2 = O.F.
		-1	0	0	2	0	$-M-2$	$-N$	

In Tableau 3 we must introduce x_4. As two of the possible pivots are negative, we eliminate x_3.

TABLEAU 4

		1	2	0	0	0	$-M$	$-N$	
C_B	Basis	x_1	x_2	x_3	x_4	x_5	x_6	x_7	B.F.S.
0	x_4	3	0	1	1	0	-1	0	1
0	x_5	4	0	1	0	1	0	-1	$1\frac{1}{4}$
2	x_2	4	1	1	0	0	0	0	2
	S.C. =	8	2	2	0	0	0	0	4 = O.F.
		-7	0	-2	0	0	$-M$	$-N$	

The optimal solution is $x_1 = 0, x_2 = 2, x_3 = 0, x_4 = 1, x_5 = 1\frac{1}{4}, x_6 = x_7 = 0$. Note that the path to the optimum on Fig. 1.10 is $O \to A \to B \to C$.

It should be remarked that if an artificial variable remains non-zero in the optimal solution, then the original constraints are not satisfied. This indicates that either a slip has been made or the constraints are inconsistent and the feasible region does not exist.

In a hand calculation it is easy to keep the large negative weightings of the artificial variables as $-M$, $-N$ etc. If a computer is used, care has to be taken to make the numerical equivalents of M, N sufficiently large so that the artificial variables are reduced to zero, but not too large so that 'round-off errors' dominate the objective function. In many commercial L.P. programs slack and artificial variables are inserted automatically by the program once each constraint is specified. In addition the artificial variables are eliminated systematically by the L.P. routine.

In large L.P. problems both computational time and storage must be reduced to a minimum. The simplex method as formulated here is not in its most efficient form and a variant of the method referred to as the *revised simplex method* is used in most commercial L.P. routines. The main differences are that the new tableau is generated by matrix multiplication routines and only essential information is computed and recorded at each stage.

A final worked example illustrating the simplex method is given below.

EXAMPLE 5   Minimize $x_1 - 4x_3$
  subject to $5x_1 + 5x_2 + 10x_3 \leqslant 10$,
    $10x_1 + 5x_2 \qquad \geqslant 5$,
    $x_2 + \ x_3 = \frac{1}{2}$,
  $x_1, x_2, x_3 \geqslant 0$.

The augmented problem is to maximize $-x_1 + 4x_3 - Mx_6 - Nx_7$
  subject to $5x_1 + 5x_2 + 10x_3 + x_4 \qquad = 10$,
    $10x_1 + 5x_2 \qquad\qquad - x_5 + x_6 \qquad = 5$,
    $x_2 + \ x_3 \qquad\qquad + x_7 = \frac{1}{2}$,
  $x_1, \ldots, x_7 \geqslant 0$.

Take $M = N = 100$.

		-1	0	4	0	0	-100	-100			
C_B	Basis	x_1	x_2	x_3	x_4	x_5	x_6	x_7	B.F.S.	Check	
0	x_4	5	5	10	1	0	0	0	10	31	$R_1 - \frac{1}{2}R_2$
-100	x_6	$\boxed{10}$	5	0	0	-1	1	0	5	20	$\frac{1}{10}R_2$
-100	x_7	0	1	1	0	0	0	1	0.5	3.5	$R_3 - 0R_2$
		-1000	-600	-100	0	100	-100	-100	-550	$=$O.F.	
	S.C. $=$	999	600	104	0	-100	0	0			

									B.F.S.	Check	
0	x_4	0	2.5	10	1	0.5	-0.5	0	7.5	21	$R_1 - 10R_3$
-1	x_1	1	0.5	0	0	-0.1	0.1	0	0.5	2	$R_2 - 0R_3$
-100	x_7	0	1	$\boxed{1}$	0	0	0	1	0.5	3.5	R_3
		-1	-100.5	-100	0	0.1	-0.1	-100	-50.5	$=$O.F.	
	S.C. $=$	0	100.5	104	0	-0.1	-99.9	0			

		-1	0	4	0	0	-100	-100		
C_B	Basis	x_1	x_2	x_3	x_4	x_5	x_6	x_7	B.F.S.	Check
0	x_4	0	-7.5	0	1	0.5	-0.5	-10	2.5	-14
-1	x_1	1	0.5	0	0	-0.1	0.1	0	0.5	2
4	x_3	0	1	1	0	0	0	1	0.5	3.5
		-1	3.5	4	0	0.1	-0.1	4	1.5	$=$ O.F.
	S.C. $=$	0	-3.5	0	0	-0.1	-99.9	-96		

The optimum solution is $x_1 = 0.5, x_2 = 0, x_3 = 0.5, x_4 = 2.5, x_5 = 0 = x_6 = x_7$.

Exercises

1. Maximize $10x_1 + 20x_2 + 5x_3$
subject to $3x_1 + 2.5x_2 + 1.5x_3 \leqslant 900$,
$\qquad x_1 + \quad x_2 \qquad \leqslant 300$,
$\qquad x_1, x_2, x_3 \geqslant 0$.

2. Maximize the function $3x_1 + x_2$ subject to the constraints

$\qquad x_1 + x_2 \leqslant 10$,
$\qquad -x_1 + x_2 \leqslant 5$,
$\qquad 4x_1 + x_2 \leqslant 24$,
$\qquad x_1, x_2 \geqslant 0$,

by (a) geometrical methods and (b) the simplex method.

3. Minimize the function x_2 subject to the constraints

$\qquad x_1 - x_2 \leqslant 5$,
$\qquad x_2 \leqslant 8$,
$\qquad x_1 + x_2 \geqslant 10$,
$\qquad x_1, x_2 \geqslant 0$,

by (a) geometrical methods and (b) the simplex method.

4. Use the simplex method to solve examples 1 and 3 of §1.1.
Further exercises are given in the problems at the end of the chapter.

1.6 PARAMETRIC ANALYSIS

The basic linear programming problem of maximizing a linear function of n structural variables subject to k constraints and n non-negativity conditions has been extended in the last section by the addition of k slack variables and as many artificial variables as required, say $m - n - k$, to formulate the augmented linear programming problem:

$$\text{Maximize} \quad c_1 x_1 + \ldots + c_m x_m = \mathbf{CX}$$
$$\text{subject to} \quad \mathbf{AX} = \mathbf{B}, \quad \mathbf{X} \geqslant 0, \quad \mathbf{B} \geqslant 0 , \tag{37}$$

where the constraints $\mathbf{AX} = \mathbf{B}$ are k equality conditions in the m variables (n structural variables, k slack variables, and $m - n - k$ artificial variables) and $\mathbf{B}$ may be taken to be positive. The matrix $\mathbf{A}$ in equation (37) is the matrix of the original constraints augmented by $m - n$ (negative and positive) base vector columns corresponding to the slack and artificial variables.

It is obviously prudent to examine how sensitive the optimum point and the maximum value of the objective function are to changes in the constants occurring in the problem. In a practical problem the constants $a_{11}, a_{12}, \ldots, a_{kn}, b_1, b_2, \ldots, b_k$, occurring in the constraints may change due to breakdowns, strikes, availability of supplies etc, or they may be measured constants and subject to experimental error. If the objective function is profit, then it clearly depends on varying resource costs, wages, selling prices and the 'state of the market' so that in this case $\mathbf{C} = (c_1, \ldots, c_m)$ will vary. Before examining this problem analytically, let us consider the effect of variations in the standard geometrical example.

EXAMPLE 1   Maximize $x_1 + x_2$
subject to $x_1 + 2x_2 \leqslant 100$,
$3x_1 + x_2 \leqslant 75$,
$x_1 \geqslant 0, x_2 \geqslant 0$.

The optimum occurs at corner B of Fig. 1.11. Variations may occur in

$$\mathbf{A} = \begin{pmatrix} 1 & 2 \\ 3 & 1 \end{pmatrix}, \quad \mathbf{B} = \begin{pmatrix} 100 \\ 75 \end{pmatrix} \quad \text{and} \quad \mathbf{C} = (1, 1).$$

Variations in $\mathbf{C}$ In this case the feasible region remains unchanged with corners at $OABC$. As $\mathbf{C}$ varies the slope of the contours of the objective function will change. Consider the objective function $(1 + \delta)x_1 + x_2$. As δ increases from zero the contours of the objective function will steepen but the optimum will remain at B until $\delta = 2$. Then the contour is parallel to AB so that the optimum can occur at any point on AB.

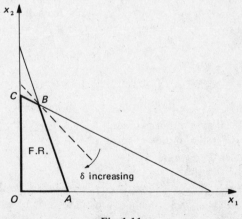

Fig. 1.11

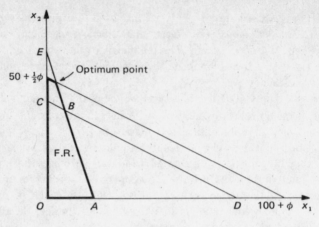

Fig. 1.12

For $\delta > 2$ the optimum point has moved along BA to A. It will be seen that for any *small* changes in C the optimum point remains fixed at B. For greater changes the optimum point may jump to a neighbouring corner point of the original feasible region.

Variations in B   In this case the boundaries of the feasible region move parallel to themselves. Hence the corner points of the feasible region move but, as the gradient of the objective function remains unchanged, the optimum remains at the same (moving) corner, until the geometrical changes are such that two corners coincide. For example, consider the constraints

$$x_1 + 2x_2 \leqslant 100 + \phi ,$$
$$3x_1 + x_2 \leqslant 75, \quad x_1 \geqslant 0 , \quad x_2 \geqslant 0 .$$

As ϕ increases from zero, the optimum point moves along BE in Fig. 1.12, until, for $\phi > 50$, it reaches and remains at E.

Variations in A   In this case the slopes of the boundaries of the feasible region change and hence the corner points move. For small changes in slope the optimum will remain attached to the same corner point but, as the configuration changes, it will move to another corner. Consider

$$(1 + \psi)x_1 + 2x_2 \leqslant 100 ,$$
$$3x_1 + x_2 \leqslant 75, \quad x_1 \geqslant 0, \quad x_2 \geqslant 0 .$$

As ψ increases from zero the optimum point moves along BA from B towards A in Fig. 1.13. When $\psi = 1$ the optimum has reached the point $(12.5, 37.5)$. At this value of ψ the constraint is parallel to the objective function. For $\psi > 1$, the optimum jumps to C and remains there.

The properties of these simple geometrical solutions are reproduced in the algebraic analysis of the general linear programming problem when subjected to variations in C, B or A. This analysis requires certain results associated with the simplex tableau.

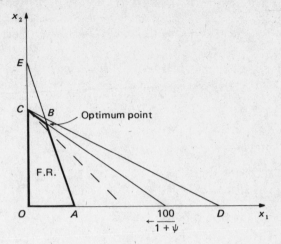

Fig. 1.13

Properties of the Simplex Tableau

In vector form the augmented constraint conditions are

$$x_1 \mathbf{A}_1 + x_2 \mathbf{A}_2 + \ldots + x_n \mathbf{A}_n + \ldots + x_m \mathbf{A}_m = \mathbf{B} . \tag{38}$$

Suppose the basis consists of the k linearly independent vectors $\mathbf{A}_{j_1}, \mathbf{A}_{j_2}, \ldots, \mathbf{A}_{j_k}$ with the corresponding basic feasible solution

$$\mathbf{X} = (0, \ldots, 0, x_{j_1}, 0, \ldots, 0, x_{j_2}, 0, \quad \ldots \quad 0, x_{j_k}, 0, \ldots, 0)^T .$$

On separating out the basis vectors, the constraint equations may be written in the form

$$x_{j_1} \mathbf{A}_{j_1} + x_{j_2} \mathbf{A}_{j_2} + \ldots + x_{j_k} \mathbf{A}_{j_k} + (\text{rest of } x_i \mathbf{A}_i) = \mathbf{B} ,$$

or, in matrix form, as

$$\mathbf{E} \mathbf{X}_B + \mathbf{R} \mathbf{X}_R = \mathbf{B} , \tag{39}$$

where $\mathbf{E} =$ matrix of the basis columns $= (\mathbf{A}_{j_1}, \mathbf{A}_{j_2}, \ldots, \mathbf{A}_{j_k})$,
  $\mathbf{X}_B =$ column vector of the basis variables $= (x_{j_1}, x_{j_2}, \ldots, x_{j_k})^T$,
  $\mathbf{R} =$ remainder of the columns $\mathbf{A}_i$ taken in order,
  $\mathbf{X}_R =$ column vector of the remainder of the variables x_i taken in order.

As $\mathbf{E}$ is a non-singular $k \times k$ matrix we can solve equation (39) to determine $\mathbf{X}_B$ in terms of $\mathbf{B}$ and $\mathbf{X}_R$ by multiplying by $\mathbf{E}^{-1}$, giving

$$\mathbf{X}_B + (\mathbf{E}^{-1}\mathbf{R})\mathbf{X}_R = \mathbf{E}^{-1}\mathbf{B} .$$

The basic feasible solution is given by putting $\mathbf{X}_R = \mathbf{0}$ and we find $\mathbf{X}_B = \mathbf{E}^{-1}\mathbf{B}$. This is exactly the operation that is performed in the simplex tableau. The principal result is given in the following theorem.

THEOREM   The simplex tableau consists of the columns of $\mathbf{E}^{-1}\mathbf{A}$ and $\mathbf{E}^{-1}\mathbf{B}$ taken in order, where $\mathbf{E}$ is the matrix whose columns are the current basis vectors.

Proof: In the construction of the tableau the column under x_r contains the coefficients $t_{j_1 r}, \ldots, t_{j_k r}$ which express $\mathbf{A}_r$ in terms of the current basis, namely

$$\mathbf{A}_r = t_{j_1 r}\mathbf{A}_{j_1} + \ldots + t_{j_k r}\mathbf{A}_{j_k},$$
$$= \mathbf{E}(t_{j_1 r}, \ldots, t_{j_k r})^T.$$

Hence the column under x_r is

$$(t_{j_1 r}, \ldots, t_{j_k r})^T = \mathbf{E}^{-1}\mathbf{A}_r .$$

Thus the simplex tableau consists of the columns

$$\mathbf{E}^{-1}\mathbf{A}_1, \mathbf{E}^{-1}\mathbf{A}_2, \ldots, \mathbf{E}^{-1}\mathbf{A}_m$$

where $\mathbf{E}^{-1}$ is the inverse of the matrix $\mathbf{E}$ of the current basis vectors. The basic feasible solution column contains the solution $\mathbf{E}^{-1}\mathbf{B}$.

As an exercise the reader should confirm that the column of a tableau under a non-zero variable in the basic feasible solution is a base vector.

This theorem enables us to identify the matrix $\mathbf{E}^{-1}$ within a tableau by the following rule.

The matrix $\mathbf{E}^{-1}$ The columns of the tableau which contain the matrix $\mathbf{E}^{-1}$ correspond to the columns containing the unit matrix $\mathbf{I}$ in the augmented constraints (38).

To prove this suppose that the vector $\mathbf{A}_p$ in the constraints (38) is of the form $\mathbf{A}_p = (0, \ldots, 0, 1, 0, \ldots, 0)^T = \mathbf{e}_s$ where the 1 occurs in the sth row, and $\mathbf{e}_s$ is the sth base vector of the space V_k. Then in this tableau the column under x_p is $\mathbf{E}^{-1}\mathbf{e}_s = \mathbf{E}^{-1}(0, \ldots, 1, \ldots, 0)^T$ which is the sth column of $\mathbf{E}^{-1}$. Hence by identifying the variables in the augmented constraints which multiply the columns $\mathbf{e}_1, \mathbf{e}_2, \ldots, \mathbf{e}_k$, the columns of $\mathbf{E}^{-1}$ can be found in their correct order.

If there are no artificial variables in an augmented problem, the slack variables multiply the base vectors in the constraint equations. Hence $\mathbf{E}^{-1}$ may be found under the slack variable columns of the tableau. However, if artificial variables are present, some of these slack variables multiply negative base vectors in the constraints and care has to be exercised in identifying $\mathbf{E}^{-1}$.

EXAMPLE 2   Determine $\mathbf{E}^{-1}$ for the optimum basis of example 3 of §1.5. The augmented problem is

$$\begin{aligned}
\text{maximize} \quad & 10x_1 + 20x_2 + 5x_3 \\
\text{subject to} \quad & 5x_1 + 5x_2 + 10x_3 + x_4 && = 10, \\
& 10x_1 + 8x_2 + 5x_3 && + x_5 && = 20, \\
& 10x_1 + 5x_2 && + x_6 = 5, \\
& x_1, \ldots, x_6 \geqslant 0,
\end{aligned}$$

and the optimal tableau is given below and will be referred to as Tableau 1.

TABLEAU 1

C_B	Basis	x_1	x_2	x_3	x_4	x_5	x_6	B.F.S.
5	x_3	−0.5	0	1	0.1	0	−0.1	0.5
0	x_5	−3.5	0	0	−0.5	1	−1.1	9.5
20	x_2	2	1	0	0	0	0.2	1

This optimal tableau corresponds to the basis A_3, A_5, A_2 (taken in this order) so that

$$E = (A_3, A_5, A_2) = \begin{pmatrix} 10 & 0 & 5 \\ 5 & 1 & 8 \\ 0 & 0 & 5 \end{pmatrix}.$$

From the above theory, E^{-1} occurs in the tableau under the variables x_4, x_5, x_6 (in order) so that

$$E^{-1} = \begin{pmatrix} 0.1 & 0 & −0.1 \\ −0.5 & 1 & −1.1 \\ 0 & 0 & 0.2 \end{pmatrix}.$$

To become convinced that this matrix is indeed E^{-1} it is suggested that the reader evaluates $EE^{-1} = I$ and $E^{-1}B = E^{-1}(10, 20, 5)^T = (0.5, 9.5, 1)^T$ which is the B.F.S. column of the tableau. This illustration has been based on the optimal tableau for the given problem. However, it could be based on any tableau and the corresponding matrices E and E^{-1} identified.

Parametric Analysis

Since the data in many linear programming problems are either not known accurately or are subject to fluctuations, it is desirable to determine the sensitivity of the solution to changes in the data. If the augmented problem is written as equations (37), then changes may occur in C, B or A.

Variations in C

Suppose the objective function coefficient of the variable x_r changes from c_r to $c_r + \delta_r$, the other coefficients remaining fixed. Let us examine how this affects the optimal tableau for increasing values of δ_r. The behaviour depends on whether x_r is positive or zero in the optimum basic feasible solution.

Case 1: If A_r is not in the optimal basis, so that $x_r = 0$ in the optimal solution, the optimal tableau remains the same except that the simplex coefficient for the x_r column changes to $\delta_r + SC_r$, where we use the notation SC_r to denote the simplex coefficient corresponding to the variable x_r in the optimal tableau. Now SC_r is negative. Hence for small values of δ_r, the optimum value of the objective function is unchanged. When δ_r has increased until $\delta_r + SC_r$ becomes positive, this particular corner ceases to be optimal. In this case we follow the simplex method and introduce x_r into the basic feasible solution, so that the optimum changes to another corner of the feasible region.

Case 2: If $\mathbf{A}_r$ is in the optimal basis so that x_r is (almost always) non-zero in the optimal solution, the new optimal tableau contains

$\mathbf{C_B}$	Basis	$x_1 \ldots x_r \ldots x_m$	B.F.S.
$c_r + \delta_r$	x_r	0 $\vdots$ 1 $\vdots$ 0	$\bar{x}_r$
	S.C. =	0	

The change in the objective function coefficients causes the optimal value to increase by the amount $\delta_r \bar{x}_r$. Except for the x_r term, the new simplex coefficient row becomes the old simplex coefficient row minus the x_r row of the tableau multiplied by δ_r. For small δ_r this will remain less than or equal to zero, but as δ_r increases some simplex coefficients will become positive, indicating that the optimum point should move to a different corner. This type of analysis is easily performed and programmed.

EXAMPLE 3   The standard example in augmented form is:

maximize $x_1 + x_2$

subject to $x_1 + 2x_2 + x_3 \qquad = 100$,

$\qquad 3x_1 + x_2 \qquad + x_4 = 75$,

$\qquad x_1, \ldots, x_4 \geqslant 0$.

The optimal tableau is

$\mathbf{C_B}$	Basis	1 x_1	1 x_2	0 x_3	0 x_4	B.F.S.	
1	x_2	0	1	0.6	−0.2	45	
1	x_1	1	0	−0.2	0.4	10	
		1	1	0.4	0.2	55	= O.F.
	S.C. =	0	0	−0.4	−0.2		

Case 1: Consider the objective function $x_1 + x_2 + \delta x_3$. The only tableau changes are in the simplex coefficient row which becomes

$$0, 0, \delta - 0.4, -0.2$$

These are not positive for $\delta \leqslant 0.4$. Hence the optimum for $\delta \leqslant 0.4$ is at $(10, 45, 0, 0)^T$.

For $\delta > 0.4$ we must introduce x_3 and eliminate x_2 which causes the optimum to move to $(25, 0, 75, 0)^T$. This process may be continued; for $\delta > 1$, the optimum is at $(0, 0, 100, 75)^T$.

Case 2: Consider the objective function $(1 + \delta)x_1 + x_2$. The optimal tableau for small δ is

C_B	Basis	$1 + \delta$ x_1	1 x_2	0 x_3	0 x_4	B.F.S.
1	x_2	0	1	0.6	−0.2	45
$1 + \delta$	x_1	1	0	−0.2	0.4	10
		$1 + \delta$	1	$0.4 - 0.2\delta$	$0.2 + 0.4\delta$	$55 + 10\delta$ = O.F.
	S.C. =	0	0	$0.2\delta - 0.4$	$-0.2 - 0.4\delta$	

This is the optimum for $\delta \leqslant 2$. For $\delta > 2$, we must introduce x_3 and eliminate x_2 causing the optimum to move to $(25, 0, 75, 0)$. It will be seen that increasing δ steepens the contours of the objective function and for $\delta = 2$ they are parallel to the second constraint. This has been illustrated on Fig. 1.11 on p. 41.

Variations in B

Consider changes in **B**, the column vector of the constraints. Let us suppose the change in **B** is of the form

$$\mathbf{B} \to \mathbf{B} + \phi\mathbf{V} \tag{41}$$

where ϕ is a positive parameter and **V** is a fixed vector. This is not the most general change in **B**.

EXAMPLES (a) For a change in b_1 only,

$$\mathbf{B} = (b_1, \ldots, b_k)^T \to (b_1 \pm \phi, b_2, \ldots, b_k)^T.$$

Take $\mathbf{V} = (\pm 1, 0, \ldots, 0)^T$.

(b) Suppose an increase of 2 units in b_2 accompanies a decrease of 5 units in b_3; then

$$\mathbf{B} = (b_1, b_2, b_3, \ldots, b_k)^T \to (b_1, b_2 + 2\phi, b_3 - 5\phi, \ldots, b_k)^T.$$

Take $\mathbf{V} = (0, 2, -5, 0, \ldots, 0)^T$.

We examine the effect on the optimal solution of the change (41) in **B** as the parameter ϕ increases from zero. At the optimum the constraints of the augmented problem have the form

$$EX_B + RX_R = B \tag{42}$$

where E, X_B, R, X_R have the same significance as in equation (39). The optimum solution is obtained by multiplying by E^{-1},

$$X_B + (E^{-1}R)X_R = E^{-1}B ,$$

and it will be remembered that these matrices occur in the optimal tableau. The optimum solution is given by

$$X_R = 0, \quad X_B = E^{-1}B . \tag{43}$$

The new problem is

$$EX_B + RX_R = B + \phi V \tag{44}$$

which has the basic solution

$$X_R = 0, \quad X_B = E^{-1}B + \phi E^{-1}V . \tag{45}$$

As the original optimum solution (43) was feasible, this solution is feasible for small values of ϕ. It is also the optimum solution. This is obvious geometrically for small ϕ. It is not so apparent mathematically until it is pointed out that the simplex coefficients are calculated from and depend only on the values of the elements of the matrices A and C. Thus the simplex coefficients are independent of B and therefore of any change in B. Hence the simplex coefficients corresponding to the solution (45) are identical with those of the solution (43) and are negative or zero.

The solution (45) will remain the optimum until one of the x_i in X_B just becomes negative, in which case this variable must be removed from the optimum solution (for larger values of ϕ) and another variable introduced. In equation (45) let us put $E^{-1}B = (\bar{x}_1, \ldots , \bar{x}_k)^T, E^{-1}V = (d_1, \ldots , d_k)^T$; then the ith non-zero element of the basic feasible solution has the form

$$\bar{x}_i + \phi d_i \quad \text{where} \quad \bar{x}_i > 0 .$$

If $d_i > 0$ for each $i = 1, 2, \ldots , k$, this solution will always be feasible and hence it remains the optimum solution. If d_i is negative $\bar{x}_i + \phi d_i$ will decrease for increasing ϕ and reach zero when

$$\phi = -\bar{x}_i/d_i .$$

Clearly several of the constants d_i may be negative. Hence the solution (45) is the optimum until ϕ reaches the value

$$\phi_{min} = \underset{\text{all } d_i < 0}{\text{minimum}} (-\bar{x}_i/d_i) \tag{46}$$

where the minimum is taken over those ratios in which d_i is negative. Since the optimum point must be feasible for values of $\phi > \phi_{min}$, the negative coordinate must be replaced. The process of replacement is best illustrated by an example.

EXAMPLE 4   Consider the augmented problem of example 3 of §1.5 which is to

$$\text{maximize} \quad 10\,x_1 + 20x_2 + 5x_3$$

$$\begin{aligned}
\text{subject to} \quad & 5x_1 + 5x_2 + 10x_3 + x_4 && = 10, \\
& 10x_1 + 8x_2 + 5x_3 && + x_5 && = 20, \\
& 10x_1 + 5x_2 && && + x_6 = 5, \\
& && x_1, \ldots, x_6 \geqslant 0.
\end{aligned}$$

The optimal tableau is Tableau 1.

TABLEAU 1

		10	20	5	0	0	0		
C_B	Basis	x_1	x_2	x_3	x_4	x_5	x_6	B.F.S.	
5	x_3	−0.5	0	1	0.1	0	−0.1	0.5	
0	x_5	−3.5	0	0	−0.5	1	−1.1	9.5	(47)
20	x_2	2	1	0	0	0	0.2	1	
		37.5	2	5	0.5	0	3.5	22.5	= O.F.
	S.C. =	−27.5	0	0	−0.5	0	−3.5		

Let us consider the effect of a decrease of the first two constraints in the ratio 1:2. Then

$$\mathbf{B} \to (10, 20, 5)^T - \phi(1, 2, 0)^T$$

so that $\mathbf{V} = -(1, 2, 0)^T$.

It has been shown in example 2 that for this optimum solution

$$\mathbf{E}^{-1} = \begin{pmatrix} 0.1 & 0 & -0.1 \\ -0.5 & 1 & -1.1 \\ 0 & 0 & 0.2 \end{pmatrix}.$$

Hence from equation (45), as $\mathbf{E}^{-1}\mathbf{V} = (-0.1, -1.5, 0)^T$, the new optimum solution is

$$x_3 = 0.5 - 0.1\phi, \quad x_5 = 9.5 - 1.5\phi, \quad x_2 = 1.$$

This solution is feasible provided that

$$0.5 - 0.1\phi \geqslant 0, \quad 9.5 - 1.5\phi \geqslant 0$$

that is, if ϕ remains less than 5. Hence the optimal tableau for $\phi \leqslant 5$ is simply the optimal tableau above with the modified B.F.S. and is given in Tableau 2.

TABLEAU 2

C_B	Basis	10 x_1	20 x_2	5 x_3	0 x_4	0 x_5	0 x_6	B.F.S.
5	x_3	−0.5	0	1	0.1	0	−0.1	$0.5 − 0.1\phi$
0	x_5	−3.5	1	0	−0.5	1	−1.1	$9.5 − 1.5\phi$
20	x_2	2	1	0	0	0	0.2	1
		37.5	20	5	0.5	0	3.5	$22.5 − 0.5\phi$ = O.F.
	S.C. =	−27.5	0	0	−0.5	0	−3.5	

For $\phi > 5$, as x_3 is the first variable to become negative it must be eliminated from the basic feasible solution. The only candidates for introduction into the basic feasible solution are x_1, x_4 and x_6. The corresponding pivot elements from the x_3 row of the tableau are −0.5, 0.1, −0.1. If a positive pivot element is chosen, the new variable introduced into the basic feasible solution will remain negative and hence give a non-feasible solution. Thus a negative pivot element must be used to generate a feasible solution. In this case there are two possible pivots corresponding to x_1 and x_6. In order to minimize labour, we select the pivot which enables us to remain at an optimum solution for $\phi > 5$. At present all simplex coefficients are zero or negative. If the new basic feasible solution is to be an optimum, the new simplex coefficients must also be negative or zero. For the pth column of the tableau, if the old simplex coefficient is SC_p and x_r is introduced into the basic feasible solution and x_j eliminated from it, then it may be shown that the new simplex coefficient for the pth column is

$$SC_p - \frac{t_{jp}}{t_{jr}} SC_r.$$

For the new basic feasible solution to be an optimum this must be negative or zero for all values of p. Note that in this case $SC_p \leqslant 0$, $SC_r \leqslant 0$ and the pivot element t_{jr} must be negative to generate a feasible solution for $\phi > 5$. Hence if t_{jp} is positive then the new simplex coefficient is negative or zero. Normally several t_{jp} are negative so that for variables corresponding to a negative t_{jp}

$$SC_p - \frac{t_{jp}}{t_{jr}} SC_r \leqslant 0,$$

which implies

$$\frac{SC_r}{t_{jr}} \leqslant \frac{SC_p}{t_{jp}}$$

for all possible p. Thus from all possible variables for introduction into the basic feasible solution (those for which $t_{jp} < 0$) we introduce the one for which

$$SC_p/t_{jp} \tag{48}$$

is a minimum.

In Tableau 2 we are eliminating x_3 and can introduce either x_1 with pivot -0.5 or x_6 with pivot -0.1. For x_1, the ratio (48) is $-27.5/-0.5$ and for x_6, $-3.5/-0.1$. Hence to remain at an optimum point we introduce x_6 with pivot -0.1.

The optimum solution for $\phi > 5$ is given in Tableau 3.

TABLEAU 3

		10	20	5	0	0	0		
C_B	Basis	x_1	x_2	x_3	x_4	x_5	x_6	B.F.S.	
0	x_6	5	0	-10	-1	0	1	$\phi - 5$	
0	x_5	2	1	-11	-1.6	1	0	$4 - 0.4\phi$	
20	x_2	1	1	2	0.2	0	0	$2 - 0.2\phi$	
		20	20	40	4	0	0	$40 - 4\phi$	= O.F.
	S.C. =	-10	0	-35	-4	0	0		

Note that the objective function is continuous at $\phi = 5$. For $0 \leqslant \phi \leqslant 5$, the objective function is $22.5 - 0.5\phi$, and for $5 \leqslant \phi \leqslant 10$, the objective function is $40 - 4\phi$.

It will be observed that the solution in Tableau 3 breaks down at $\phi = 10$, when both x_5 and x_2 become zero simultaneously. If only x_5 became negative for $\phi > 10$ it would be possible to eliminate x_5 and to introduce x_3 or x_4 (as these have negative pivots) to produce a new basic feasible solution. However x_2 also becomes negative for $\phi > 10$. In this case there are no negative pivots along the x_2 row of the tableau, so that it is not possible to find a basic feasible solution for $\phi > 10$. This result is to be expected since the constraints are

$$5x_1 + 5x_2 + 10x_3 \leqslant 10 - \phi,$$
$$10x_1 + 8x_2 + 5x_3 \leqslant 20 - 2\phi,$$
$$10x_1 + 5x_2 \qquad \leqslant 5.$$

For $\phi > 10$, these contradict $x_1, x_2, x_3 \geqslant 0$ and consequently the feasible region has been reduced to zero.

Sensitivity Analysis

We can now examine how sensitive the optimum solution is to changes in the vector **B**. Let us examine the effect of a change in the rth constraint and put

$$\mathbf{B} \to \mathbf{B} + \phi\mathbf{V}, \quad \text{where} \quad \mathbf{V} = (0, \ldots, 0, 1, 0, \ldots, 0)^T = \mathbf{e}_r.$$

Then, for small ϕ, the new optimum solution is

$$\mathbf{X}_B = \mathbf{E}^{-1}\mathbf{B} + \phi\mathbf{E}^{-1}\mathbf{V}$$
$$= \mathbf{E}^{-1}\mathbf{B} + \phi\mathbf{E}_r^{-1} \tag{49}$$

where E_r^{-1} is the rth column of E^{-1}. By 'small' we mean all values of ϕ for which this new optimum is feasible. Similarly the optimum value of the objective function changes to

$$C_B^T(E^{-1}B + \phi E_r^{-1})$$

where C_B is the first column of the optimum tableau. The change in optimum value due to a (small) increase ϕ in b_r is $\phi C_B^T E_r^{-1}$. We have shown that E^{-1} lies in the optimum simplex tableau and the column E_r^{-1} lies under the variable which multiplies the rth base vector $e_r = (0, \ldots, 0, 1, 0, \ldots, 0)^T$ in the constraint equation (38). This quantity $C_B^T E_r^{-1}$ is simply the product of the C_B column and a column of the tableau and is evaluated in calculating the simplex coefficient. It is found in the objective function row of the tableau under the appropriate column and is referred to as the rth *shadow price*.

To illustrate this, consider example 4 of §1.6. The shadow prices may be found from the objective function row of the optimal tableau (47). The shadow price corresponding to the first constraint lies in the x_4 column of Tableau (47) and is $y_1 = 0.5$. Note that x_4 is the slack variable for that constraint. Similarly the shadow prices for the second and third constraints are $y_2 = 0, y_3 = 3.5$. Hence a small change of

ϕ_1 in the first constraint gives $0.5\phi_1$ change in the optimum value of the objective function,

ϕ_2 in the second constraint gives 0 change in the optimum value of the objective function,

ϕ_3 in third constraint gives $3.5\phi_3$ change in the optimum value of the objective function.

Note that the optimum solution (47) has $x_5 \neq 0$ so that the second constraint has spare capacity. Hence no improvement in the objective function is to be expected from a small change in this constraint, and this is borne out by the result $y_2 = 0$. The ranges of validity of these changes correspond to the ranges for which the basic feasible solution (49) is feasible. For example, for a change ϕ_1 in the first constraint

$$X_B = E^{-1}B + \phi_1 E_1^{-1} = (0.5, 9.5, 1)^T + \phi_1(0.1, -0.5, 0)^T.$$

This is feasible provided that $0.5 + 0.1\phi_1 \geqslant 0$ and $9.5 - 0.5\phi_1 \geqslant 0$, which imply that ϕ_1 lies in the range $-5 \leqslant \phi_1 \leqslant 19$. For values of ϕ_1 outside this range the method of parametric analysis should be used. Similar ranges can be determined for changes in the second and third constraints. This process is sometimes called right-hand side ranging.

A knowledge of the set of shadow prices is of use in indicating regions for future investment. In the above example, suppose the constraint vector B represents the amounts of different raw materials bought for processing during the planning period. Then the return per unit change in the first constraint is 0.5, and per unit change in the third constraint is 3.5. If the costs of a unit increase in the first and third constraints are about equal it will pay to invest in the third constraint. However, if a unit increase in the third constraint costs more than seven times the cost of a unit increase in the first constraint, obviously more of the first material should be purchased.

The definition given above of the shadow price of a constraint may yield a shadow price with a negative value. Consider the constraints

$$4x_1 + x_2 \leqslant 7 ,$$
$$x_1 + x_2 \geqslant 4 , \qquad\qquad (50)$$
$$x_1 \geqslant 0, \quad x_2 \geqslant 0 .$$

To determine the shadow price y_1 of the first constraint, we increase the quantity 7 by ϕ units. This increases the area of the feasible region. Hence the increase in profit, $y_1\phi$, must be positive (or zero), and consequently y_1 is positive (or zero).

The shadow price y_2 of the second constraint is found by increasing the quantity 4 by ϕ units. This decreases the area of the feasible region. Consequently the profit will either decrease or remain unchanged so that y_2 must be negative or zero. The reader will easily confirm that if x_1 is maximized subject to the constraints (50), the shadow prices are $y_1 = \frac{1}{3}, y_2 = -\frac{1}{3}$.

The sign of a shadow price forms a useful check on the nature of the associated constraint. However, some computer programs arrange the sensitivity analysis in such a way that the feasible region is never decreased and consequently the shadow prices are always non-negative. Analytically this is achieved by expressing *all* constraints as 'less than or equal to' constraints and then performing the sensitivity analysis.

In the above example the constraints are

$$\begin{pmatrix} 4 & 1 \\ -1 & -1 \end{pmatrix} \begin{pmatrix} x_1 \\ x_2 \end{pmatrix} \leqslant \begin{pmatrix} 7 \\ -4 \end{pmatrix} . \qquad\qquad (51)$$

The sensitivity analysis changes the second constraint to

$$-x_1 - x_2 \leqslant -4 + \phi$$

which increases the area of the feasible region and consequently leads to a non-negative shadow price $y_2 = \frac{1}{3}$. The magnitude of a shadow price is the same whether the sensitivity analysis is performed on constraints expressed in the form of equation (50) or (51).

Changes in A

If more than one element of **A** is changed it is very difficult to evaluate the consequent changes in the optimum solution by a perturbation technique. It is necessary to solve the linear programming problem again with the new matrix **A**. If only one element of **A** is changed then it is possible to determine the new solution algebraically in terms of the old solution (see Dantzig [2], Ch 12). However the formulae are rather complicated and in most cases it is easier to re-run the linear programming problem.

To complete this section on parametric analysis a brief mention should be made of the dual linear programming problem.

Duality

Consider the standard linear programming problem:

    maximize   **CX**
    subject to $\mathbf{AX} \leqslant \mathbf{B}, \quad \mathbf{X} \geqslant \mathbf{0} .$

We refer to this as the *Primal problem*. Let us associate with the first constraint a shadow price y_1, with the second constraint a shadow price y_2, etc. It may be shown that the set of shadow prices $y_1, \ldots, y_k$ (which have already been defined in the sensitivity analysis of the problem) satisfy a linear programming problem. This linear programming problem is referred to as the *dual problem* and is

minimize $\mathbf{B}^T \mathbf{Y}$
subject to $\mathbf{A}^T \mathbf{Y} \geqslant \mathbf{C}^T, \quad \mathbf{Y} \geqslant 0$,

where $\mathbf{Y} = (y_1, \ldots, y_k)^T$.

The shadow prices defined this way are identical with those defined via the parametric analysis of the primal problem. Note that the primal problem has n variables and k constraints, but the dual problem has k variables and n constraints. The following results can be proved.

(a) The dual of the dual is the primal.

(b) (Primal) If any resource is not fully utilized in the optimum solution of the primal problem, e.g. $\sum_{r=1}^{n} a_{ir} x_r < b_i$, the shadow price corresponding to that resource is zero, i.e., $y_i = 0$.

(c) (Dual) If any commodity is strictly unprofitable in terms of shadow prices, e.g. $\sum_{r=1}^{k} a_{ri} y_r > c_i$ in the optimum solution of the dual, that commodity will not be produced $(x_i = 0)$ in the optimum solution of the primal.

(d) The optimum solutions of the primal and dual occur together and have identical values.

The principal reasons for interest in the dual problem are as follows. First, it may be interpreted using concepts from business economics. Second, in using the revised simplex method the computing time largely depends upon the number of constraints. In the primal problem we have n variables and k constraints. If n is less than k it may be more efficient numerically to solve the dual problem rather than the primal. Note from (a) that the shadow prices of the constraints of the dual are the variables of the primal problem, and can be found in the optimum tableau of the dual.

The dual problem is used in some commercial linear programming routines for parametric analysis calculations. Since variations in the constraint vector $\mathbf{B}$ of the primal problem correspond to changes in the objective function coefficients of the dual problem, it is often more efficient to use the dual problem for right-hand side ranging. Finally, computing algorithms which iterate between the primal and dual problems have been constructed and found to be more efficient than the simplex method (see Zionts [4], Ch. 6).

Exercises

The following exercises all relate to example 2 of §1.6.

1. Consider the effect of attaching a penalty of $-\delta$ to the slack variable x_5 of the second constraint so that the objective function becomes

$$10x_1 + 20x_2 + 5x_3 - \delta x_5.$$

2. Consider the effect of attaching a profit δ to the slack variable x_5.

Show that the solution $(0, 1, 0.5, 0, 9.5, 0)^T$ is the optimum for $0 \leqslant \delta \leqslant 1$ but for $1 \leqslant \delta \leqslant 2.5$ the optimum solution becomes $(0, 1, 0, 5, 12, 0)^T$.

3. Consider the effect of increasing the third constraint by ϕ units. Show that the optimum solution for $\phi \leqslant 5$ is

$$(0, 1 + 0.2\phi, 0.5 - 0.1\phi, 0, 9.5 - 1.1\phi, 0)^T$$

and for $\phi > 5$ the optimum solution is

$$(0, 2, 0, 0, 4, \phi - 5)^T.$$

PROBLEMS

1. A small car-producing firm is capable of manufacturing three models, model A being composed of engine E_1 and body B_1, model B having engine E_1 and body B_2, model C with engine E_2 and body B_2. The number of hours taken in manufacture or assembly for each unit of output are given in the following table, the last column giving the total capacity in hours per week of each division of the firm.

	E_1	E_2	B_1	B_2	A	B	C	Capacity
Engine Division	9	6						9000
Body Division			3	6				5000
Assembly Division					3	6	9	6000

Determine the rate of production of each model which will maximize the total profits, given that the estimated profits per car are £20, £30, and £40 respectively. Which division is not utilized to its maximum capacity?

2. A firm has two plants A and B for converting bauxite into aluminium. Plant A has available 20,000 tonnes of bauxite per annum and for every 10 tonnes of bauxite processed produces 1 tonne of aluminium at a cost of £100. Plant B has available 40,000 tonnes of bauxite per annum and for every 5 tonnes of bauxite processed produces 1 tonne of aluminium at a cost of £300. The aluminium is shipped from plants A and B to two markets M and N with transportation costs per tonne of aluminium given in the table:

	Market M	Market N
Plant A	£100	£300
Plant B	£200	£400

The sales requirements in markets M and N are that at least 4000 tonnes should be shipped to M and 3000 tonnes to N per annum. Determine the production plan for the firm which minimizes the sum of production and transportation costs. Indicate which shipping routes are not used (if any), and the amounts of bauxite required at each plant. Is your answer unique or can another production plan yield the same minimum cost?

3. A paint manufacturer produces a new paint by blending three existing paints with the following properties:

Paint	A	B	C
Colour Density	1	3	2
Viscosity	2	3	1
Drying Time	5	1	2

It is found experimentally that the blending process combines the paints in such a way that the above properties of the blend are given as a linear combination of the measured properties with the volume fractions x_A, x_B and x_C of the paints A, B and C so that, for example, the colour density of the blend is $x_A + 3x_B + 2x_C$, where $x_A + x_B + x_C = 1$. The blend is required to have a colour density in the range 2.4 to 2.6, a viscosity of less than 2.1 and a drying time of less than 4. If the profit on the blend is estimated at $3x_A + 2x_B + x_C$, use the simplex method to determine the optimum volume fractions in order that the profit may be maximized.

4. Use the simplex method to solve example 2 of §1.1.

5. A power station is supplied with coal from three collieries, the cost of a delivered tonne, the thermal units produced per tonne and the amounts available for transportation per day being given in the following table.

Colliery	A	B	C
Cost/tonne	4	5	2
Thermal units/tonne	3	2	1
Tonnes available/day	600	2000	600

If the handling capacity of coal at the power station is limited to 1800 tonnes per day and its heat requirements are at least 2700 thermal units per day, determine its purchasing policy so that it may operate at minimum cost.

If the thermal requirements of the power station increase, use the methods of parametric analysis to determine the new optimum purchasing policies. Show that no solution is possible when the thermal requirements exceed 4200 units per day.

6. In problem 1,
(a) consider the effect of increasing the production of car engines;
(b) suppose some capacity can be switched from car body production to assembly so that if the body division reduces its capacity by 2ϕ units the assembly division increases by ϕ units. Find the effect of increasing ϕ.

7. A canning factory produces three products: cans containing 16 sausages, cans containing 8 oz of beans and cans of sausages and beans comprising 8 sausages and

4 oz of beans. The cans are identical and the sterilizing, capping and labelling department can handle a *total* of 300 cans per hour. The availability of raw materials limits the number of sausages to 1600 per hour and the amount of beans to 800 oz per hour. The factory is required to produce at least 40 cans of sausages per hour. It is estimated that the number of cans of beans and the number of cans of sausages and beans together should total at least 150 cans per hour to meet sales targets. If it is estimated that the profit on each can of sausages is 3p, on each can of sausages and beans is 4p, and there is zero profit on a can of beans, what are the optimum production rates of the three products?

What are the shadow prices of the constraints? Explain why certain shadow prices are zero. Indicate what steps should be taken to improve profitability.

8. A steel works produces sheet steel of uniform thickness which is cut and then bent and welded into pipes. It manufactures pipes with diameters of 0.1 m, 0.2 m and 0.4 m in standard 10 m lengths. The capacity of the sheet steel plant is limited and the number of pipes produced per week depends on the total surface area of the pipes, since cutting losses are negligible. If all of the sheet steel were to be cut for 0.1 m diameter pipes, there would be enough steel for 1700 pipes per week. The 0.1 m diameter pipes are produced on one set of bending and welding machines which have a capacity of 800 0.1 m pipes per week. A second set of bending and welding machines is used to produce *both* the 0.2 m and 0.4 m pipes. The weekly capacity of this second set is such that it may produce up to 300 0.2 m pipes (if no 0.4 m pipes are made), it may produce up to 600 0.4 m pipes (if no 0.2 m pipes are made), or a linear combination of both types of pipe in these proportions may be produced.

The works are required to produce at least 150 0.4 m pipes per week to meet existing contracts. If it is estimated that the profit is $x_1 + 3x_2 + 2x_3$ money units per week where x_1, x_2 and x_3 are the numbers of 0.1 m, 0.2 m and 0.4 m pipes produced per week, what is the optimum production plan?

What are the shadow prices of these constraints? Explain the occurrence of zero and negative shadow prices. What is the range of validity of the shadow price corresponding to the 0.2 m/0.4 m bending constraint? If the sheet steel production decreases by the equivalent of 100 0.1 m diameter pipes per week and the sales requirement is increased by 50 0.4 m pipes per week, determine the new optimum solution and profit.

9. A firm manufactures three products A, B and C, each of which can be produced on either one of two machines 1 and 2, but must be finished off on a third machine 3. The time (in hours) required to produce one item of each product on machine 1 and on machine 2, and the finishing time required for each item on machine 3 is as given in the table:

Product	Machine			Profit (£)
	1	2	3	
A	3	$2\frac{1}{2}$	1	5
B	5	$4\frac{1}{2}$	$\frac{3}{4}$	7
C	2	$1\frac{1}{2}$	$\frac{3}{4}$	2
Time available	42	40	32	

The profit on the sale of each item is shown in the last column of the table and the time available per week on each machine is shown in the last row. Use the simplex method to determine the number of each product the firm should produce weekly in order to maximize its profit.

The firm proposes to buy a second machine of type 2 (40 hours weekly capacity) returning machine 1 to the manufacturers in part exchange. Find the optimum weekly production policy the firm should adopt if machine 1 is so replaced.

If, by doing this, the firm involves itself in additional costs which represent a loss of £2 weekly, determine whether or not this step is economic.

BIBLIOGRAPHY

[1]   Carr, C. R. and C. W. Howe, *Quantitative Decision Procedures in Management and Economics*, McGraw-Hill, New York (1964).
[2]   Dantzig, G. B., *Linear Programming and Extensions*, Princeton University Press, Princeton, N.J. (1963).
[3]   Driebeek, N. J., *Applied Linear Programming*, Addison-Wesley, Reading, Mass. (1969).
[4]   Zionts, S., *Linear and Integer Programming*, Prentice-Hall, Englewood Cliffs, N.J. (1974).

CHAPTER 2

Non-linear and Dynamic Programming

2.1 INTRODUCTION

In its most general form, the problem under consideration in this chapter is

$$\text{maximize } f(x_1, x_2, \ldots, x_n),$$

subject to the constraints

$$g_1(x_1, x_2, \ldots, x_n) \leqslant 0,$$
$$g_2(x_1, x_2, \ldots, x_n) \leqslant 0,$$
$$\ldots \ldots \ldots \ldots \ldots \ldots$$
$$g_k(x_1, x_2, \ldots, x_n) \leqslant 0.$$

Here the *objective function* $f(x_1, x_2, \ldots, x_n)$ and the k *constraint functions* $g_1(x_1, x_2, \ldots, x_n), g_2(x_1, x_2, \ldots, x_n), \ldots, g_k(x_1, x_2, \ldots, x_n)$ are in general non-linear functions of the n independent variables $x_1, x_2, \ldots, x_n$. This problem is known as the *non-linear programming problem*.

The equation

$$g_1(x_1, x_2, \ldots, x_n) = 0$$

represents a surface in n-dimensional space, and a point $(x_1, x_2, \ldots, x_n)$ satisfying the inequality

$$g_1(x_1, x_2, \ldots, x_n) \leqslant 0$$

lies on or entirely to one side of this surface. The set of inequalities

$$g_1(x_1, x_2, \ldots, x_n) \leqslant 0,$$
$$g_2(x_1, x_2, \ldots, x_n) \leqslant 0,$$
$$\ldots \ldots \ldots \ldots \ldots \ldots$$
$$g_k(x_1, x_2, \ldots, x_n) \leqslant 0$$

defines a region of space termed the *feasible region*. Any point satisfying these inequalities is termed a *feasible point*. The number k of inequalities may be less than, equal to, or greater than n. In order to solve the non-linear programming problem it is necessary to determine the feasible point at which the objective function $f(x_1, x_2, \ldots, x_n)$ has its greatest value. The objective function may achieve its

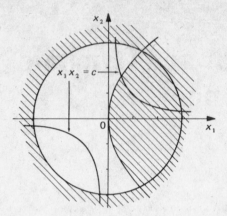

Fig. 2.1   The feasible region of example 1 is the area between the circle and the parabola which is not hatched.

maximum on the boundary of the feasible region or at an interior point of the feasible region, as the following examples illustrate.

EXAMPLE 1   Maximize $f(x_1, x_2) = x_1 x_2$,

subject to the constraints

$$g_1(x_1, x_2) \equiv x_1^2 + x_2^2 - 9 \leqslant 0 ,$$
$$g_2(x_1, x_2) \equiv 4x_1 - x_2^2 \leqslant 0 .$$

In this example, points satisfying the first constraint lie within or on the circle with centre at the origin and radius 3. Points satisfying the second constraint lie on or to the left of the parabola $x_2^2 = 4x_1$, and the feasible region is illustrated in Fig. 2.1.

The problem may be solved graphically. The equation

$$f(x_1, x_2) \equiv x_1 x_2 = c ,$$

where c is a constant, represents a family of rectangular hyperbolae one of which is illustrated in Fig. 2.1. It is readily seen that $f(x_1, x_2)$ has its maximum in the feasible region on the hyperbola with the greatest value of c. This is the hyperbola which touches the boundary of the feasible region at the point $x_1 = x_2 = -3/\sqrt{2}$, and for which $c = 9/2$.

EXAMPLE 2   Maximize $f(x_1, x_2) = 1 - (x_1 + 1)^2 - (x_2 - 1)^2$,

subject to the constraints

$$g_1(x_1, x_2) \equiv x_1^2 + x_2^2 - 9 \leqslant 0 ,$$
$$g_2(x_1, x_2) \equiv 4x_1 - x_2^2 \leqslant 0 .$$

Here the feasible region is the same as in example 1 and $f(x_1, x_2)$ clearly has its maximum value of 1 at $x_1 = -1, x_2 = 1$, which is a point inside the feasible region.

Non-linear programming problems arise in a variety of engineering and industrial situations of which the following are two simple examples.

EXAMPLE 3   A small firm generates its own power, the amount P (kilowatts) being related to the speed of rotation of the generator ω (revolutions per minute), by the expression

$$P = 3.7 \times 10^{-4}\omega^2 .$$

The hourly cost of fuel C (pence) is given by

$$C = 0.085\omega(1 + 0.0002\omega) .$$

The firm requires 550 kilowatts for its own use and can sell any amount of surplus power to a neighbouring firm at a price of 0.90p per kilowatt hour. For safety reasons, the speed of rotation of the generator must not exceed 1800 rev/min. It is required to determine the speed of rotation which minimizes the cost of power to the firm.

The objective function $\bar{F}(\omega)$ is given by

$$\bar{F}(\omega) = C - 0.90(P - 550)$$
$$= 0.085\omega(1 + 0.0002\omega) - 0.90(3.7 \times 10^{-4}\omega^2 - 550)$$
$$= 495 + 0.085\omega - 3.16 \times 10^{-4}\omega^2 .$$

This expression gives the hourly cost of the firm's power which consists of the hourly cost of fuel C minus the hourly return from the sale of excess power. The objective function is to be *minimized* subject to the constraints that the power P must be not less than 550 kilowatts and that the speed of rotation ω must not exceed 1800 rev./min. The problem may be written in the following form:

$$\text{minimize } \bar{F}(\omega) = 495 + 0.085\omega - 3.16 \times 10^{-4}\omega^2 ,$$

subject to the constraints

$$G_1(\omega) \equiv 550 - P = 550 - 3.7 \times 10^{-4}\omega^2 \leqslant 0 ,$$
$$G_2(\omega) \equiv \omega - 1800 \leqslant 0 .$$

This problem may be put in the standard form of maximizing the function $F(\omega) = -\bar{F}(\omega)$, subject to the same constraints. For purposes of computation it is convenient to make a change of variable and to define new functions as follows:

$$x = 10^{-3}\omega, \quad f(x) = 10^{-1}F(10^3 x), \quad g_1(x) = 10^{-2}G_1(10^3 x), \quad g_2(x) = 10^{-3}G_2(10^3 x).$$

In terms of the new functions of the variable x the problem becomes

$$\text{maximize } f(x) = 31.6x^2 - 8.5x - 49.5 ,$$

$$\text{subject to the constraints } g_1(x) \equiv 5.5 - 3.7x^2 \leqslant 0 ,$$
$$g_2(x) \equiv x - 1.8 \leqslant 0 .$$

It is a straightforward matter to solve this problem and the solution is given in example 1 of §2.2.

EXAMPLE 4   The rate of fuel consumption R of an aircraft varies with the cruising
height h (feet) and cruising speed u (mile/h) according to the relation

$$R = 3.28 + \frac{19240}{3020 + h} + 0.039u - 3.12 \times 10^{-5}u^2 \ .$$

The aircraft has a maximum speed of 680 mile/h and a stalling speed of 150 mile/h
and it is restricted to cruising at an altitude between 20,000 ft and 29,000 ft.
Determine the speed and altitude which will minimize its fuel consumption over a
cruising distance of 5000 miles.

The objective function in this problem is the total fuel consumed $\bar{F}$, and is obtained
by multiplying the rate of consumption R by the time of travel which is $5000/u$. The
problem is then to

$$\text{minimize } \bar{F}(h, u) = \frac{16400}{u} + \frac{962 \times 10^5}{u(3020 + h)} + 195 - 0.156u \ ,$$

subject to the constraints

$$150 \leqslant u \leqslant 680 \ ,$$

$$20,000 \leqslant h \leqslant 29,000 \ .$$

It is convenient to scale the independent variables and the objective function according
to the following relations

$$x_1 = 10^{-2}u, \quad x_2 = 10^{-4}h, \quad \bar{f} = 10^{-1}\bar{F}.$$

With the use of the function $f(x_1, x_2) = -\bar{f}(x_1, x_2)$ the problem may be put in the
standard form as follows:

$$\text{maximize } f(x_1, x_2) = 1.56x_1 - 19.5 - \frac{9.62}{x_1(0.302 + x_2)} - \frac{16.4}{x_1} \ ,$$

subject to the constraints,

$$1.5 - x_1 \leqslant 0 \ ,$$

$$x_1 - 6.8 \leqslant 0 \ ,$$

$$2.0 - x_2 \leqslant 0 \ ,$$

$$x_2 - 2.9 \leqslant 0 \ .$$

This problem is solved as example 4 in §2.3.

The problem posed in example 3 involves functions of a single variable only, and
some of the techniques for the solution of single variable problems are outlined in
§2.2. Section 2.3 deals with some of the basic techniques for the solution of multi-
variable problems, such as the problem posed in example 4. Many of the techniques in
§§2.2 and 2.3 are iterative in nature (see §9.4 of Volume 1) and do not locate the
exact maximum in a finite number of operations. In practice it is necessary only to
locate the maximum to within some specified accuracy and the procedures are

terminated after a finite number of iterations when this accuracy is attained. In general the techniques of §§2.2 and 2.3 lead to a *local maximum* of the objective function which may not be the overall or *global maximum*. A function having only one local maximum within or on the boundary of some feasible region is said to be *unimodal* in that region and for such functions the local maximum is also the global maximum. For functions which are not known to be unimodal it is virtually impossible to determine whether or not the global maximum has been obtained.

Many industrial processes consist of a sequence of operations or stages, at each of which it is necessary to choose the values of the operating parameters in such a way as to optimize the overall performance. Examples of such processes arise frequently in the production engineering and chemical process industries. The *method of dynamic programming* which is described in §2.4 is particularly applicable to the problem of optimizing these multi-stage processes.

2.2 FUNCTIONS OF A SINGLE VARIABLE

Method of the Calculus

The simplest non-linear programming problem is that of finding the maximum of a function of a single variable subject to constraints. This problem may arise naturally as in example 1 of §2.1, or may form part of the search procedure for the multi-variable problem as will be shown in §2.3. In order to conform with the notation of §2.3 it is convenient to take s as the independent variable throughout this section. The effect of one or more equations of constraint will be to limit s to values lying within some interval $a \leqslant s \leqslant b$ say, (the feasible region), and the problem is to find the maximum of $f(s)$ in this interval. If the objective function $f(s)$ is differentiable, the stationary points are given by

$$f'(s) = 0 . \tag{1}$$

For some objective functions, the first derivative $f'(s)$ fails to exist at isolated points, corresponding to discontinuities in $f(s)$ itself or in the slope of its tangent, and there is the possibility of the maximum occurring at such a point (see Fig. 2.2). Alternatively, when the feasible region is bounded the maximum may occur at one or other of the end points as shown in Fig. 2.3. The simplest way to find the maximum is to evaluate the function at each of the end points, at every point within the feasible region at which $f'(s)$ does not exist and at every root of equation (1) within the feasible region. The greatest value of $f(s)$ may then be determined by inspection.

EXAMPLE 1   Solve example 3, §2.1, namely,

maximize $f(s) = 31.6s^2 - 8.5s - 49.5$,

subject to

$$g_1(s) \equiv 5.5 - 3.7s^2 \leqslant 0 ,$$
$$g_2(s) \equiv s - 1.80 \leqslant 0 .$$

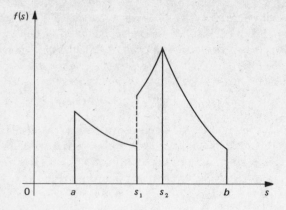

Fig. 2.2   Discontinuity of $f(s)$ at $s = s_1$ and of $f'(s)$ at $s = s_2$, with the maximum of $f(s)$ at $s = s_2$.

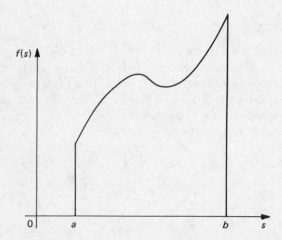

Fig. 2.3   Maximum at the end point $s = b$.

Together the constraints restrict the positive quantity s to the interval $1.22 \leqslant s \leqslant 1.80$. The stationary point of the objective function is given by

$$f'(s) = 63.2s - 8.5 = 0 \, ,$$

which is satisfied by $s = 0.13$. This point lies outside the feasible region and thus need not be examined. Since $f'(s)$ exists for all values of s, there are no discontinuities and therefore no interior points of the feasible region at which the maximum can occur. Accordingly it is necessary to examine the values of $f(s)$ at the end points only. These are $f(1.22) = -12.84$ and $f(1.80) = 37.58$, and the latter gives the required maximum.

In general, equation (1) is a non-linear equation whose roots must be determined numerically using one of the iteration methods of §9.4 of Volume 1. An appropriate method, making use of values of $f'(s)$ only, is the variable secant iteration method which gives

$$s_{n+1} = s_n - \frac{(s_n - s_{n-1})}{f'(s_n) - f'(s_{n-1})}\, f'(s_n)\,.$$

Alternatively, if the second derivative $f''(s)$ is available, equation (1) may be solved using the Newton–Raphson method which gives the iteration scheme

$$s_{n+1} = s_n - \frac{f'(s_n)}{f''(s_n)}\,.$$

Both schemes require an initial estimate s_1 of the location of the stationary point.

Polynomial Approximations

In many problems of practical interest the objective function $f(s)$ is given by a table of values, at discrete points, $s_1, s_2, \ldots, s_n$, rather than by a mathematical formula. If the function is known to be continuous in the region of the maximum then it may be approximated by a polynomial $P_m(s)$ of degree m, which can be made to have the same values as $f(s)$ at $m + 1$ of these points (see §11.3 of Volume 1). The maximum value of $P_m(s)$ can then be taken as an approximation to the maximum of $f(s)$.

The simplest polynomial which possesses a turning point is a quadratic $P_2(s)$ which can be made to take the same values as $f(s)$ at any three points s_{r-1}, s_r, s_{r+1}, say. It is convenient to write $P_2(s)$ in the forward difference form (§11.3, Volume 1)

$$P_2(s) = a_0 + a_1(s - s_{r-1}) + a_2(s - s_{r-1})(s - s_r)\,. \tag{2}$$

The coefficients a_0, a_1, a_2 are determined by putting

$$P_2(s_{r-1}) = f(s_{r-1}) \equiv f_{r-1}, \quad P_2(s_r) = f(s_r) \equiv f_r, \quad P_2(s_{r+1}) = f(s_{r+1}) \equiv f_{r+1}\,.$$

This leads to a triangular system of equations which are readily solved to give

$$a_0 = f_{r-1}, \quad a_1 = \frac{f_r - f_{r-1}}{s_r - s_{r-1}}\,,$$

$$a_2 = \frac{1}{s_{r+1} - s_r}\left\{\frac{(f_{r+1} - f_{r-1})}{(s_{r+1} - s_{r-1})} - \frac{(f_r - f_{r-1})}{(s_r - s_{r-1})}\right\}\,. \tag{3}$$

The turning point of the quadratic is given by

$$s = \tfrac{1}{2}(s_{r-1} + s_r - a_1/a_2) \tag{4}$$

and this corresponds to a maximum if $a_2 < 0$. If the points are arranged such that $s_{r-1} < s_r < s_{r+1}$ and if the function values satisfy the inequalities $f_{r-1} < f_r$ and $f_{r+1} < f_r$, there is a maximum of $f(s)$ within the interval (s_{r-1}, s_{r+1}). The same conditions ensure that $a_2 < 0$, and the turning point of the quadratic gives the approximate location of this maximum.

EXAMPLE 2   Estimate the maximum value of the function $f(s)$ given by the following table, in the region $0 \leqslant s \leqslant 1$.

s	0	0.1	0.2	0.3	0.4	0.5
$f(s)$	0.8414	0.8912	0.9320	0.9636	0.9854	0.9975

s	0.6	0.7	0.8	0.9	1.0
$f(s)$	0.9996	0.9917	0.9738	0.9463	0.9093

It is clear from the table that there is a local maximum in the interval $(0.5, 0.7)$ and the quadratic is therefore made to pass through $s_{r-1} = 0.5$, $s_r = 0.6$ and $s_{r+1} = 0.7$. Using the tabulated function values at these points in equations (3) gives the coefficients as

$$a_0 = 0.9975, \quad a_1 = 0.021, \quad a_2 = -0.500 .$$

The turning point as given by equation (4) is at $s = 0.571$ at which $P_2(s) = 1.0000$. The tabulated function is $\sin(1 + s)$ which has a maximum value of 1.0000 at $s = 0.571$. The agreement here is fortuitous.

Search Methods

It has already been remarked that a mathematical expression for the objective function $f(s)$ is not always available. Thus, if $f(s)$ denotes the output from some system for a given level s of input it is possible to determine by experiment the numerical value of $f(s)$ for a given value of s without having available a mathematical expression for $f(s)$. In such a situation it is not possible to apply the calculus in order to locate the maximum since $f'(s)$ is not known. Even when this is not the case, and an expression for $f'(s)$ is available, the process of determining all the turning points is often time-consuming and is inefficient in that all the turning points must be found when only one of them furnishes the required maximum. As a consequence, direct methods of searching for a maximum have been developed. These *search methods* consist of evaluating the objective function at a sequence of points $s_1, s_2, \ldots$ The points are chosen according to some strategy designed so as to reduce the size of the interval in which the maximum is known to lie.

A simple example of a search method consists of moving from some initial point s_1 in the direction of increase of $f(s)$ in a series of steps of constant length δ until a decrease in the function value occurs. Thus if $s_2 = s_1 + \delta$ and if $f(s_2) \geqslant f(s_1)$ the function is evaluated successively at the points $s_3 = s_2 + \delta$, $s_4 = s_3 + \delta, \ldots$, provided $f(s_3) \geqslant f(s_2), f(s_4) \geqslant f(s_3)$, etc. The procedure is terminated at the first point s_{r+1} for which $f(s_{r+1}) < f(s_r)$, and since $f(s_r) \geqslant f(s_{r-1})$, there will be a maximum of $f(s)$ in the region (s_{r-1}, s_{r+1}) of length 2δ. The method may then be repeated starting from the point s_{r-1} and using a smaller step-length.

EXAMPLE 3   Find the maximum correct to four decimal places of

$$f(s) = 2.1419 + 0.7939s - 0.3745s^2 - 0.3333s^3 .$$

in the interval $0 \leqslant s \leqslant 2$.

The first aim is to estimate the location of the maximum in order to obtain the starting point s_1. The first two derivatives of $f(s)$ are

$$f'(s) = 0.7939 - 0.7490s - 1.0000s^2 ,$$

$$f''(s) = -0.7490 - 2.0000s .$$

The second derivative is negative for all $s > 0$ showing that $f'(s)$ decreases steadily as s increases. At $s = 0, f'(s) = 0.7939$, and at $s = 1, f'(s) = -0.9551$, so that a very rough estimate for the maximum point (at which $f'(s) = 0$) is $s_1 = 0.5$. Taking $\delta = 0.05$ gives the set of values

s	0.50	0.55	0.60	0.65
$f(s)$	2.4036	2.4098	2.4114	2.4082

These values indicate a maximum in the interval $(0.55, 0.65)$. The process is repeated from the point $s = 0.55$ using a step-length $\delta = 0.01$. This gives the set of values

s	0.55	0.56	0.57	0.58	0.59	0.60
$f(s)$	2.4098	2.4105	2.4110	2.4113	2.4115	2.4114

and the maximum of $f(s)$ is 2.4115 at $s = 0.59$.

Another Method

Once the bracketing of the maximum has been achieved it is possible to obtain the approximate location by fitting a quadratic through the three points s_{r-1}, s_r, s_{r+1}, and using equations (3) and (4) to locate the maximum of this quadratic. Let this be at the point $\bar{s}$. Then the function $f(s)$ is evaluated at $\bar{s}$ and another quadratic is fitted, using the point $\bar{s}$ and two of the original three points. The point to be discarded is that which gives the smallest value of $f(s)$ unless in doing this the bracketing of the maximum is lost. This new quadratic is then used to predict a further point at which $f(s)$ is to be evaluated and the process is continued until the required accuracy is achieved.

EXAMPLE 4   Determine, correct to two decimal places, the value of s which gives the maximum of

$$f(s) = 4e^{-s} \log(1 + 2s) - s ,$$

in the interval, $0 \leqslant s \leqslant 1$.

The procedure is started at the end point $s_1 = 0$ using a step-length $\delta = 0.2$ to give the results

s	0	0.2	0.4	0.6
$f(s)$	0	0.9019	1.1760	1.1309

There is clearly a maximum in the interval $(0.2, 0.6)$ and the quadratic through the points $s = 0.2, s = 0.4, s = 0.6$ has its maximum at $s = 0.472$. This gives the four points

s	0.2	0.4	0.6	0.472
$f(s)$	0.9019	1.1760	1.1309	1.1866

The point to be discarded from this set is $s = 0.2$ which gives the lowest value of $f(s)$. Note that the remaining three points give a bracketing of the maximum. Fitting a second quadratic through $s = 0.4$, $s = 0.472$, $s = 0.6$ leads to a predicted maximum at $s = 0.461$ and the set of values

s	0.4	0.472	0.6	0.461
$f(s)$	1.1760	1.1866	1.1309	1.1872

Here the point to be discarded is $s = 0.6$. The quadratic through the remaining three points has its maximum at $s = 0.458$, the corresponding value of $f(s)$ being 1.1872. The last two points agree to two decimal places and the maximum is 1.1872 at $s = 0.46$.

Optimal Search Methods

In attempting to maximize $f(s)$ for $a \leqslant s \leqslant b$, using a search method, it is natural to seek the method which is most efficient for the problem. For an arbitrary objective function $f(s)$ it is not possible to designate the best or *optimal search method*. Indeed, an arbitrary $f(s)$ may have more than one local maximum in the feasible region and there is no guarantee that any search method will find the global maximum. If the objective function is unimodal, however, it is possible to determine the search method which is optimal in the following sense. Let L_N be the length of the interval in which the maximum is known to lie after N function evaluations. The optimal search method is that which gives the lowest value of $L_N/(b - a)$ for a given N.

Let $f(s)$ be unimodal for $a \leqslant s \leqslant b$, then it will have a unique maximum at $s = c$ say, where $a \leqslant c \leqslant b$. If $f(s)$ is differentiable for all s in the feasible region then its derivative $f'(s)$ is positive for $a \leqslant s < c$ and negative for $c < s \leqslant b$. At a specified point s_1 in (a, b) it follows that one of the following situations holds

(a) $f'(s_1) > 0$ and $s_1 < c \leqslant b$,

(b) $f'(s_1) < 0$ and $a \leqslant c < s_1$,

(c) $f'(s_1) = 0$ and $c = s_1$.

Thus by evaluating $f'(s)$ at one point it is possible to reduce the length of the interval containing the maximum from one of length $(b - a)$ to one of length $(b - s_1)$ or $(s_1 - a)$. Clearly the best choice for the position of s_1 is at the mid-point $s_1 = \frac{1}{2}(b + a)$ so that the interval length is halved. The optimal strategy for N evaluations of $f'(s)$ is to repeat this process thus halving the interval length at each step and resulting in a final interval of length $(b - a)/2^N$. The technique is known as *Bolzano's method* and is highly efficient, giving an interval of length less than 1% the original length for $N = 7$ and an interval of approximately 0.1% of the original length for $N = 10$.

EXAMPLE 5   Use Bolzano's method with $N = 10$ to find the maximum of

$$f(s) = s \cos s \quad \text{for } 0 \leqslant s \leqslant 1.$$

Here the derivative is given by $f'(s) = \cos s - s \sin s$. The various steps in the

TABLE 2.1

Step	Interval	s_1	$f'(s_1)$
1	(0, 1)	0.5	0.64
2	(0.5, 1)	0.75	0.22
3	(0.75, 1)	0.875	−0.03
4	(0.75, 0.875)	0.8125	0.10
5	(0.8125, 0.875)	0.8438	0.034
6	(0.8438, 0.8750)	0.8594	0.002
7	(0.8594, 0.8750)	0.8672	−0.014
8	(0.8594, 0.8672)	0.8633	−0.006
9	(0.8594, 0.8633)	0.8614	−0.002
10	(0.8594, 0.8614)	0.8604	−0.0001

solution are shown in Table 2.1. It may be seen that the maximum lies in the interval $(0.8594, 0.8614)$. The value of $f(s)$ at each end point of this interval is 0.5611.

The Fibonacci Search Method

In order to construct the optimal search strategy which does not involve the use of the derivative of $f(s)$ it is necessary to make use of the following property of unimodal functions. If s_1 and s_2 are two points satisfying the inequalities $a < s_1 < s_2 < b$, one of the following situations must hold

(a) $f(s_1) > f(s_2)$ and $a \leqslant c < s_2$,

(b) $f(s_1) < f(s_2)$ and $s_1 < c \leqslant b$,

(c) $f(s_1) = f(s_2)$ and $s_1 < c < s_2$.

These three possibilities are illustrated in Fig. 2.4. It follows that by evaluating $f(s)$ at s_1 and s_2 it is possible to reduce the length of the interval containing the maximum to one of the three values $(s_2 - a), (b - s_1), (s_2 - s_1)$. Let L_2 denote the greatest of these

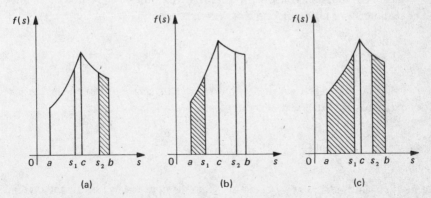

(a) (b) (c)

Fig. 2.4 Property of unimodal functions. The maximum cannot occur in the hatched regions.

three lengths, then the best choice of the positions s_1 and s_2 is that which makes L_2 a minimum, $\bar{L}_2$ say. Then

$$\bar{L}_2 = \underset{s_1, s_2}{\text{minimum}}\ L_2 = \underset{s_1, s_2}{\text{minimum}}\ [\max\{(s_2 - a), (b - s_1), (s_2 - s_1)\}]$$

Let ϵ be the smallest number such that the values of $f(s)$ and $f(s + \epsilon)$ can be distinguished numerically for $a \leqslant s \leqslant b$. Then the choice $s_1 = \frac{1}{2}(a + b - \epsilon)$, $s_2 = \frac{1}{2}(a + b + \epsilon)$ gives the required minimum of L_2 as $\bar{L}_2 = \frac{1}{2}(b - a + \epsilon)$. This choice of position for s_1 and s_2 is termed *minimax* and constitutes the best search strategy involving only two function evaluations. The strategy consists of placing the points a distance $\frac{1}{2}\epsilon$ on either side of the mid-point of the interval.

For $N(> 2)$ function evaluations, the greatest reduction in interval length is given by the *Fibonacci search method* which involves the Fibonacci numbers F_n defined by $F_0 = F_1 = 1$ and $F_n = F_{n-1} + F_{n-2}$ for $n \geqslant 2$. Let $L_1 = (b - a)$ be the length of the interval to be searched then the method proceeds as follows.

Evaluate the function at two points a distance d_1 from each of the two end points where

$$d_1 = \frac{F_{N-2}}{F_N} L_1 .$$

This allows the elimination of one region of length d_1 and reduces the interval to length L_2 where

$$L_2 = L_1 - d_1 = L_1 - \frac{F_{N-2}}{F_N} L_1 = \frac{F_{N-1}}{F_N} L_1 .$$

The remaining point is a distance d_1 from one end of the new interval and a distance $d_2 = L_2 - d_1$ from the other end where

$$d_2 = L_2 - d_1 = L_1 \left(\frac{F_{N-1}}{F_N} - \frac{F_{N-2}}{F_N} \right) = \frac{F_{N-3}}{F_N} L_1 = \frac{F_{N-3}}{F_{N-1}} L_2 .$$

Now evaluate the function at the point distant d_2 from the opposite end of the interval L_2 and eliminate one region of length d_2 leaving a new interval of length

$$L_3 = L_2 - d_2 = L_2 - \frac{F_{N-3}}{F_{N-1}} L_2 = \frac{F_{N-2}}{F_{N-1}} L_2 = \frac{F_{N-2}}{F_N} L_1 .$$

The remaining point will lie within the interval at a distance d_2 from one end and a distance d_3 from the other end, where

$$d_3 = L_3 - d_2 = L_3 \left(1 - \frac{F_{N-3}}{F_{N-2}} \right) = \frac{F_{N-4}}{F_{N-2}} L_3 = \frac{F_{N-4}}{F_N} L_1 .$$

The fourth point is placed at a distance d_3 from the opposite end of the interval L_3 etc. After $(N - 1)$ function evaluations, there results an interval of length

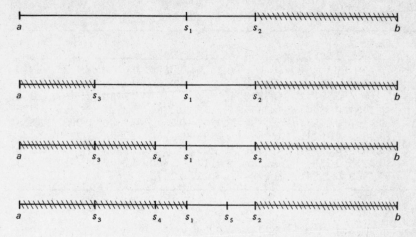

Fig. 2.5 The Fibonacci search strategy.

$$L_{N-1} = \frac{F_2}{F_N} L_1$$

containing a point distant d_{N-2} from one end point where

$$d_{N-2} = \frac{F_1}{F_3} L_{N-2} = \frac{F_1}{F_2} L_{N-1} = \tfrac{1}{2} L_{N-1},$$

i.e., the point is at the middle of the interval. The final point is then placed a small distance $\epsilon \ll 1$ from this, allowing the interval to be reduced to a length not greater than

$$\frac{L_{N-1}}{2} + \epsilon = \frac{F_1}{F_N} L_1 + \epsilon.$$

The process is illustrated graphically in Fig. 2.5.

It may be proved that, for a given number N of function evaluations, the Fibonacci search strategy results in a smaller final interval length than any other search strategy that uses the function values only. In this sense the Fibonacci search is the best or optimal strategy for unimodal functions. The number N of function evaluations must be chosen at the start of the process and it is the value of N which controls the final interval length. Thus a value of $N = 7$ results in a final interval of length 5% of the original length, for $N = 10$ the final interval length is 1.1% of the original, etc.

EXAMPLE 6   Use the Fibonacci search method to locate the maximum of the function $f(s)$ defined below to within an interval of length approximately 0.01:

$$f(s) = \begin{cases} 2 + s, & 0 \leqslant s \leqslant 0.25, \\ 0.5625/s, & 0.25 < s \leqslant 1. \end{cases}$$

TABLE 2.2

Step	Interval	L	d	s_1	s_2	$f(s_1)$	$f(s_2)$
1	(0, 1)	1	0.3820	0.3820	0.6180	1.4725	0.9102
2	(0, 0.6180)	0.6180	0.2360	0.2360	0.3820	2.2360	1.4725
3	(0, 0.3820)	0.3820	0.1461	0.1461	0.2360	2.1461	2.2360
4	(0.1461, 0.3820)	0.2359	0.0899	0.2360	0.2921	2.2360	1.9257
5	(0.1461, 0.2921)	0.1460	0.0562	0.2023	0.2360	2.2023	2.2360
6	(0.2023, 0.2921)	0.0898	0.0337	0.2360	0.2584	2.2360	2.1769
7	(0.2023, 0.2584)	0.0561	0.0225	0.2248	0.2360	2.2248	2.2360
8	(0.2248, 0.2584)	0.0336	0.0112	0.2360	0.2472	2.2360	2.2472
9	(0.2360, 0.2584)	0.0224	0.0112	0.2472		2.2472	

The specified final interval length corresponds to the choice of $N = 10$ and the various steps in the solution are set out in Table 2.2. The last step shown in the table is incomplete since it is necessary to determine ϵ so as to put $s_2 = s_1 + \epsilon$. A value of $\epsilon = 0.0002$ gives $| f(s + \epsilon) - f(s) | \geqslant 0.0001$ for all s such that $0 \leqslant s \leqslant 1$. Then $s_2 = 0.2474$ and $f(s_2) = 2.2474$ giving the final interval as (0.2472, 0.2584).

Exercises

1. Use the calculus method to determine the maximum of each of the following functions subject to the given constraints:

(a) $f(s) = s^3 + 4s^2 - 11s - 30$ for $-8 \leqslant s \leqslant 0.5$,

(b) $f(s) = e^s \sin s$ for $s^2 + 2s - 3 \leqslant 0$,

(c) $f(s) = \begin{cases} \sqrt{s}, & 0 \leqslant s \leqslant 1, \\ s \sin \dfrac{\pi s}{2}, & 1 \leqslant s \leqslant 3/2. \end{cases}$

2. Use quadratic interpolation to estimate the maximum of the function $f(s)$ tabulated below, in the region $0 \leqslant s \leqslant 1$.

s	0	0.1	0.2	0.3	0.4	0.5	0.6	0.7	0.8	0.9	1.0
f(s)	1.50	8.90	8.78	6.78	8.34	9.56	10.44	10.95	11.12	10.95	10.44

3. Use the fixed step search method to find the maximum of the function

$$f(s) = \sin \frac{\pi s}{2} - s^2$$

in the interval $0 \leqslant s \leqslant 1$, correct to two places of decimals.

4. Show that the function $f(s) = 2 + 12s - 12s^2 - s^4$ is unimodal for $0 \leqslant s \leqslant 1$, and use the Fibonacci search method to locate its maximum to within an interval of length 0.03.

5. Solve exercise 4 using Bolzano's method.

2.3 FUNCTIONS OF MORE THAN ONE VARIABLE

Search Methods

In the type of search method considered here the problem is reduced to a sequence of single variable searches, for each of which the methods of §2.2 are available. The procedure starts at some point $x^{(1)} = (x_1^{(1)}, x_2^{(1)}, \ldots, x_n^{(1)})$ and a search is carried out along a line through this point in the direction of the unit vector $1^{(1)} = (l_1^{(1)}, l_2^{(1)}, \ldots, l_n^{(1)})$. The coordinates x_i of a general point on the line are given by $x_i = x_i^{(1)} + l_i^{(1)}s$ ($i = 1, 2, \ldots, n$), where s is the distance from the initial point. Along the line the objective function becomes a function $F_1(s)$ of the single variable s only, where

$$F_1(s) = f(x_1^{(1)} + l_1^{(1)}s, x_2^{(1)} + l_2^{(1)}s, \ldots, x_n^{(1)} + l_n^{(1)}s).$$

A single variable search gives the maximum of this function at $s = s_1$, say, corresponding to the point $x^{(2)} = x^{(1)} + 1^{(1)}s_1$. At this point a new direction of search is chosen specified by the unit vector $1^{(2)} = (l_1^{(2)}, l_2^{(2)}, \ldots, l_n^{(2)})$, and a search is carried out along the line through $x^{(2)}$ in the direction $1^{(2)}$. The objective function again reduces to a function $F_2(s)$ of the single variable s which measures distance along the line from $x^{(2)}$, where

$$F_2(s) = f(x_1^{(2)} + l_1^{(2)}s, x_2^{(2)} + l_2^{(2)}s, \ldots, x_n^{(2)} + l_n^{(2)}s).$$

The value s_2 for which this function is a maximum leads to another point $x^{(3)} = x^{(2)} + 1^{(2)}s_2$ and the process continues in this way until terminated by an appropriate criterion. The differences between methods of this type lie in the strategy adopted for choosing the directions of search $1^{(1)}, 1^{(2)}, 1^{(3)} \ldots$. A simple strategy is to choose these search directions to be parallel to each of the coordinate axes in turn. Thus $1^{(1)} = (1, 0, 0, \ldots, 0), 1^{(2)} = (0, 1, 0, \ldots, 0), \ldots, 1^{(n)} = (0, 0, 0, \ldots, 1)$. After n steps the cycle of directions is complete and the process proceeds with further repetitions of the cycle so that $1^{(n+1)} = 1^{(1)}, 1^{(n+2)} = 1^{(2)}$ etc. If, at the point $x^{(r)}$, no increase in the function results after searching all n possible directions at the point, then the function is taken to have reached its maximum. More usually in practice the procedure is terminated either when the distance moved in one complete cycle of n searches is less than some specified value Δ, that is when $| x^{(r+n)} - x^{(r)} | < \Delta$, or after a specified number of cycles.

EXAMPLE 1   Use the method of search along the coordinate axes to maximize

$$f(x_1, x_2) = 3 - x_1 + 2x_2 - 4x_1^2 + 3x_1x_2 - x_2^2.$$

A convenient starting point is the origin, $x^{(1)} = (0, 0)$. Along the direction $1^{(1)} = (1, 0)$ though this point we have $x_1 = s, x_2 = 0$ and

$$F_1(s) = f(s, 0) = 3 - s - 4s^2.$$

This has a maximum at $s = -0.125$, giving $x^{(2)} = (-0.125, 0)$. Along the new search

TABLE 2.3

$x^{(2)} = (-0.125, 0)$	$x^{(3)} = (-0.125, 0.8125)$
$x^{(4)} = (0.1796, 0.8125)$	$x^{(5)} = (0.1797, 1.2695)$
$x^{(6)} = (0.3511, 1.2695)$	$x^{(7)} = (0.3511, 1.5266)$
$x^{(8)} = (0.4475, 1.5266)$	$x^{(9)} = (0.4475, 1.6712)$
$x^{(10)} = (0.5017, 1.6712)$	$x^{(11)} = (0.5017, 1.7526)$
$x^{(12)} = (0.5322, 1.7526)$	$x^{(13)} = (0.5322, 1.7983)$
$x^{(14)} = (0.5494, 1.7983)$	$x^{(15)} = (0.5494, 1.8241)$
$x^{(16)} = (0.5590, 1.8241)$	$x^{(17)} = (0.5590, 1.8385)$
$x^{(18)} = (0.5644, 1.8385)$	$x^{(19)} = (0.5644, 1.8466)$
$x^{(20)} = (0.5675, 1.8466)$	$x^{(21)} = (0.5675, 1.8512)$

direction $l^{(2)} = (0, 1)$ the general point is given by $x_1 = -0.125$, $x_2 = s$. The objective function is

$$F_2(s) = f(-0.125, s) = 3.0625 + 1.625s - s^2 .$$

This has a maximum at $s = 0.8125$ leading to $x^{(3)} = (-0.125, 0.8125)$. This completes one cycle of the procedure and the next search direction $l^{(3)}$ is thus $l^{(3)} = (1, 0)$ with the general point being $x_1 = -0.125 + s$, $x_2 = 0.8125$. Proceeding in this fashion gives the results shown in Table 2.3. Here the process has been terminated after 10 complete cycles and the point $x^{(21)} = (0.5675, 1.8512)$ is taken as the approximate location of the maximum. At this point $f(x_1, x_2) = 4.5715$. The problem is readily solved by the methods of §4.4 of Volume 1 and the maximum of the function is 4.5715 at the point $(0.5714, 1.8571)$. The contours $f(x_1, x_2) = $ constant, form a family of concentric ellipses, some of which are plotted in part in Fig. 2.6. The figure also shows the path followed by the search procedure up to the end of the fifth cycle. It may be seen that

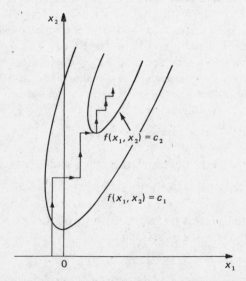

Fig. 2.6   Search along coordinate axes directions.

the step-lengths decrease as the maximum point is approached and the steps beyond the fifth cycle become too small to be distinguished on this scale.

The search strategy outlined here is by no means the most efficient. For accounts of other strategies the reader is referred to Adby and Dempster [1] and Box *et al.* [2]. A detailed comparison of different search methods is given by Himmelblau [3].

Method of Steepest Ascent

This method makes use of the derivatives of the objective function in order to select the direction of search at each point. Thus, let l be a unit vector and consider the line in the direction l through the point with position vector $\bar{x}$. Along this line, the objective function becomes a function of the single variable s, given by $F(s) = f(\bar{x}_1 + l_1 s, \bar{x}_2 + l_2 s, \ldots, \bar{x}_n + l_n s)$, where s is the distance from $\bar{x}$. The rate of change of the objective function in the direction l at the point $(\bar{x}_1, \bar{x}_2, \ldots, \bar{x}_n)$ is then (see §4.3 of Volume 1)

$$\left(\frac{\mathrm{d}F}{\mathrm{d}s}\right)_{s=0} = \left(\frac{\partial f}{\partial x_1}\right)_{s=0} \frac{\mathrm{d}x_1}{\mathrm{d}s} + \left(\frac{\partial f}{\partial x_2}\right)_{s=0} \frac{\mathrm{d}x_2}{\mathrm{d}s} + \ldots + \left(\frac{\partial f}{\partial x_n}\right)_{s=0} \frac{\mathrm{d}x_n}{\mathrm{d}s}$$

$$= l_1 g_1 + l_2 g_2 + \ldots + l_n g_n. \tag{5}$$

Here $g_i = \left(\dfrac{\partial f}{\partial x_i}\right)_{s=0}$ are the components of the n-dimensional vector grad f at the

point $\bar{x}$. Expression (5) is a maximum subject to the constraint $l_1^2 + l_2^2 + \ldots + l_n^2 = 1$, when the vector l is parallel to grad f. This direction is termed the direction of *steepest ascent* and the strategy of this method is to choose the vector $l^{(r)}$ at the point $x^{(r)}$ to be in the direction of steepest ascent.

EXAMPLE 2   Use the method of steepest ascent to find the maximum of

$$f(x_1, x_2) = 3 - x_1 + 2x_2 - 4x_1^2 + 3x_1 x_2 - x_2^2 .$$

This is the same objective function as in example 1 and the process will again be started from the origin, $x^{(1)} = (0, 0)$. The derivatives of the objective function are given by

$$\frac{\partial f}{\partial x_1} = -1 - 8x_1 + 3x_2, \qquad \frac{\partial f}{\partial x_2} = 2 + 3x_1 - 2x_2 .$$

At the point $x^{(1)}$ these give $\dfrac{\partial f^{(1)}}{\partial x_1} = -1$, $\dfrac{\partial f^{(1)}}{\partial x_2} = 2$ leading to $l^{(1)} = (-0.4472, 0.8944)$.
Along the line $x = x^{(1)} + l^{(1)}s$ the objective function is

$$F_1(s) = f(-0.4472s, 0.8944s) = 3 + 2.236s - 2.800s^2 .$$

This has a maximum at the value $s = 0.3993$ giving the next point as $x^{(2)} = (-0.1786, 0.3571)$. At $x^{(2)}$ the derivatives are $\partial f^{(2)}/\partial x_1 = 1.50$, $\partial f^{(2)}/\partial x_2 = 0.75$, leading to

TABLE 2.4

n	$x^{(n)}$	$l^{(n)}$
1	(0, 0)	(−0.4472, 0.8944)
2	(−0.1786, 0.3571)	(0.8944, 0.4472)
3	(0.1623, 0.5275)	(−0.4472, 0.8944)
4	(0.0350, 0.7831)	(0.8944, 0.4472)
5	(0.2790, 0.9051)	(−0.4472, 0.8944)
6	(0.1875, 1.0881)	(0.8944, 0.4472)
7	(0.3616, 1.1751)	(−0.4472, 0.8944)
8	(0.2960, 1.3063)	(0.8944, 0.4472)
9	(0.4212, 1.3689)	(−0.4472, 0.8944)
10	(0.3742, 1.4629)	(0.8944, 0.4472)
11	(0.4639, 1.5077)	(−0.4472, 0.8944)
12	(0.4302, 1.5751)	(0.8944, 0.4472)
13	(0.4945, 1.6073)	(−0.4472, 0.8944)
14	(0.4704, 1.6555)	(0.8944, 0.4472)
15	(0.5165, 1.6786)	(−0.4472, 0.8944)
16	(0.4994, 1.7128)	(0.8944, 0.4472)
17	(0.5320, 1.7291)	(−0.4472, 0.8944)
18	(0.5197, 1.7537)	(0.8944, 0.4472)
19	(0.5432, 1.7655)	(−0.4472, 0.8944)
20	(0.5344, 1.7831)	(0.8944, 0.4472)

$l^{(2)} = (0.8944, 0.4472)$. Along the line $x = x^{(2)} + l^{(2)}s$ the objective function is

$$F_2(s) = f(-0.1786 + 0.8944s, 0.3571 + 0.4472s)$$
$$= 3.7016 + 1.6773s - 2.200s^2 .$$

This has a maximum at $s = 0.3812$ and the corresponding point is $x^{(3)} = (0.1623, 0.5275)$. Proceeding in this way leads to the values shown in Table 2.4. The iterations have been discontinued after the 20th step but it may be seen that the method is converging slowly to the maximum point at (0.5714, 1.8571).

The path followed by this method is shown in Fig. 2.7. From this it may be seen that in this example successive search directions are orthogonal to each other. It is easy to show that this is the case for all objective functions and any number of dimensions. Thus the direction of steepest ascent at $x^{(r)}$ is normal to the contour of the objective function through $x^{(r)}$ (see §4.3 of Volume 1). Along this line the function has a maximum at $x^{(r+1)}$ where the line is tangent to the contour through $x^{(r+1)}$. Since the direction of steepest ascent at $x^{(r+1)}$ is orthogonal to the contour through $x^{(r+1)}$ it must also be orthogonal to the previous direction of steepest ascent.

In both the steepest ascent and the coordinate axes search methods the step-length decreases as the maximum is approached. This means that the rates of convergence become low, and alternative methods for locating the maximum are desirable. One possible alternative is to use a fixed step-length along each search direction provided that doing so results in an increase in the value of the objective function, and to halve

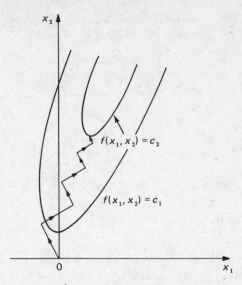

Fig. 2.7   Steepest ascent search.

the step whenever a drop in value occurs. Thus starting at $x^{(1)}$ with a fixed step δ the procedure moves to $x^{(2)} = x^{(1)} + l^{(1)}\delta$. Provided $f(x^{(2)}) \geqslant f(x^{(1)})$ the next point is taken as $x^{(3)} = x^{(2)} + l^{(2)}\delta$, etc. If at a step from $x^{(r)}$ to $x^{(r+1)} = x^{(r)} + l^{(r)}\delta$ it turns out that $f(x^{(r+1)}) < f(x^{(r)})$ the step δ is replaced by $\frac{1}{2}\delta$ and the process restarted from $x^{(r)}$.

Another possible approach is to approximate the objective function in the region of the maximum by a quadratic function of the n variables $x_1, x_2, \ldots, x_n$, and to determine the location of the maximum of this quadratic by some appropriate method. Since a quadratic in n variables has $\frac{1}{2}(n + 1)(n + 2)$ coefficients, it is necessary to evaluate the objective function at this number of distinct points in order to determine the approximating quadratic. For low values of n such an approach may be feasible but the number of function evaluations increases rapidly with n, and for large values of n the work involved becomes prohibitive. In this case, yet another alternative is to make use of Newton's method or methods derived from it.

Newton's Method

To derive the method for functions of n variables, let $(\bar{x}_1, \bar{x}_2, \ldots, \bar{x}_n)$ be the point at which the objective function has its maximum. Expanding the function about this point using Taylor's theorem (§4.2 of Volume 1) gives

$$f(x_1, x_2, \ldots, x_n) = f(\bar{x}_1, \bar{x}_2, \ldots, \bar{x}_n)$$

$$+ \sum_{i=1}^{n} (x_i - \bar{x}_i) \frac{\partial \bar{f}}{\partial x_i} + \frac{1}{2} \sum_{i=1}^{n} \sum_{j=1}^{n} (x_i - \bar{x}_i)(x_j - \bar{x}_j) \frac{\partial^2 \bar{f}}{\partial x_i \partial x_j} + \bar{R}_3 .$$

$$(6)$$

Here, $\partial \bar{f}/\partial x_i$, and $\partial^2 \bar{f}/\partial x_i \partial x_j$, denote the derivatives of f evaluated at the point $(\bar{x}_1, \bar{x}_2, \ldots, \bar{x}_n)$, and $\bar{R}_3$ is the remainder term defined in §4.2 of Volume 1. Since the point $(\bar{x}_1, \bar{x}_2, \ldots, \bar{x}_n)$ is a stationary point of the objective function it follows that

$$\frac{\partial \bar{f}}{\partial x_i} = 0 \quad \text{for } i = 1, 2, \ldots, n ,$$

and equation (6) reduces to

$$f(x_1, x_2, \ldots, x_n) = f(\bar{x}_1, \bar{x}_2, \ldots, \bar{x}_n) + \frac{1}{2} \sum_{i=1}^{n} \sum_{j=1}^{n} (x_i - \bar{x}_i)(x_j - \bar{x}_j) \frac{\partial^2 \bar{f}}{\partial x_i \partial x_j} + \bar{R}_3 .$$

Differentiating this equation with respect to x_k gives

$$\frac{\partial f}{\partial x_k} = \sum_{i=1}^{n} (x_i - \bar{x}_i) \frac{\partial^2 \bar{f}}{\partial x_i \partial x_k} + \frac{\partial \bar{R}_3}{\partial x_k}, \quad k = 1, 2, \ldots, n . \tag{7}$$

The last term in this equation is of order s^2 where s is the distance between the points $\mathbf{x}$ and $\bar{\mathbf{x}}$. Assuming $s \ll 1$ and neglecting the last term in equation (7) gives a system of linear simultaneous equations for $(x_i - \bar{x}_i)$ which may be written in matrix form as

$$\bar{\mathbf{H}}(\mathbf{x} - \bar{\mathbf{x}}) = \mathbf{g} . \tag{8}$$

Here $\bar{\mathbf{H}}$ is the Hessian matrix with elements $\bar{H}_{ij} = \partial^2 \bar{f}/\partial x_i \partial x_j$ and $\mathbf{x}$, $\bar{\mathbf{x}}$, $\mathbf{g}$ are column vectors with elements x_i, $\bar{x}_i$ and $g_i = \partial f/\partial x_i$, respectively. Equation (8) may be solved to give the approximate position of the maximum as

$$\bar{\mathbf{x}} = \mathbf{x} - \bar{\mathbf{H}}^{-1}\mathbf{g} . \tag{9}$$

Since, however, $\bar{\mathbf{H}}$ is not known it is replaced by the value of the Hessian at the point $\mathbf{x}$ and equation (9) then leads to an iteration method for locating $\bar{\mathbf{x}}$ according to the relation

$$\mathbf{x}_{r+1} = \mathbf{x}_r - \mathbf{H}_r^{-1}\mathbf{g}_r, \quad r = 0, 1, 2, \ldots$$

This is the extension of the single variable Newton's method (see Volume 1, §9.4) to n dimensions. In order to apply this iteration scheme it is necessary to evaluate the matrix of second derivatives $\mathbf{H}_r$ and its inverse $\mathbf{H}_r^{-1}$ at each step, and this process may be very time-consuming. An alternative approach is to evaluate these matrices at the first point $\mathbf{x}_0$ and to use these values for the first n steps. The matrices are then re-evaluated at $\mathbf{x}_n$ and kept at these constant values for the next n steps after which they are again re-evaluated, and so on. Variants of this method involve other techniques for updating the matrix $\mathbf{H}$.

EXAMPLE 3   Use Newton's method to maximize the objective function

$$f(x_1, x_2) = 3 - x_1 + 2x_2 - 4x_1^2 + 3x_1 x_2 - x_2^3$$

given the approximate location of the maximum as the point (0.25, 1.00).

The vector $\mathbf{g}$ and Hessian $\mathbf{H}$ are given by

$$g = \begin{pmatrix} \dfrac{\partial f}{\partial x_1} \\ \dfrac{\partial f}{\partial x_2} \end{pmatrix} = \begin{pmatrix} -1 - 8x_1 + 3x_2 \\ 2 + 3x_1 - 3x_2^2 \end{pmatrix}, \quad H = \begin{pmatrix} -8 & 3 \\ 3 & -6x_2 \end{pmatrix}.$$

The values of these and the inverse H^{-1} at the point $x_0 = (0.25, 1.00)^T$ are

$$g_0 = \begin{pmatrix} 0 \\ -0.25 \end{pmatrix}, \quad H_0 = \begin{pmatrix} -8 & 3 \\ 3 & -6 \end{pmatrix}, \quad H_0^{-1} = \frac{1}{39} \begin{pmatrix} -6 & -3 \\ -3 & -8 \end{pmatrix},$$

and the iteration formula gives

$$x_1 = \begin{pmatrix} 0.25 \\ 1.00 \end{pmatrix} - \frac{1}{39} \begin{pmatrix} -6 & -3 \\ -3 & -8 \end{pmatrix} \begin{pmatrix} 0 \\ -0.25 \end{pmatrix} = \begin{pmatrix} 0.25 \\ 1.00 \end{pmatrix} - \begin{pmatrix} 0.019 \\ 0.051 \end{pmatrix} = \begin{pmatrix} 0.231 \\ 0.949 \end{pmatrix}.$$

Evaluating g, H and H^{-1} at x_1 gives

$$g_1 = \begin{pmatrix} -0.001 \\ -0.009 \end{pmatrix}, \quad H_1 = \begin{pmatrix} -8 & 3 \\ 3 & -5.694 \end{pmatrix}, \quad H_1^{-1} = \frac{1}{36.552} \begin{pmatrix} -5.694 & -3 \\ -3 & -8 \end{pmatrix},$$

and the application of the iteration formula leads to

$$x_2 = \begin{pmatrix} 0.231 \\ 0.949 \end{pmatrix} - \begin{pmatrix} 0.001 \\ 0.002 \end{pmatrix} = \begin{pmatrix} 0.230 \\ 0.947 \end{pmatrix}.$$

At this point $g = 0$ to three decimal places, showing that $f(x_1, x_2)$ has a maximum at the point x_2 where its value is 4.257.

The methods considered here serve to illustrate some of the possible approaches to the unconstrained problem. Further details of these and other methods, including a discussion of the effectiveness of the methods are contained in Adby and Dempster [1], Box *et al.* [2], and Himmelblau [3].

Effect of Constraints

In some problems of maximizing an objective function subject to constraints, it may be possible to make a change of variable which leads to the elimination of the constraints. For example the constraint $x \geqslant a$ is eliminated by the introduction of a new variable y defined by $x = a + y^2$ or by introducing a new variable z defined by $x = a + e^z$. In the same way the constraint $a \leqslant x \leqslant b$ may be eliminated by introducing a new variable y given by $x = a + (b - a)\sin^2 y$ or by introducing a new variable z defined by $x = \frac{1}{2}\{(b + a) + (b - a)\sin z\}$. When the constraints are entirely of these types, such substitutions lead to an unconstrained problem in the new variables which may be solved by using the techniques already developed in this section.

EXAMPLE 4   Reduce the problem in example 4 of §2.1 to an unconstrained problem and hence obtain its solution.

The basic problem is to

$$\text{maximize } f(x_1, x_2) = 1.56x_1 - 19.5 - \frac{9.62}{x_1(0.302 + x_2)} - \frac{16.4}{x_1},$$

subject to the constraints, $1.5 \leqslant x_1 \leqslant 6.8$, $2.0 \leqslant x_2 \leqslant 2.9$. The substitutions $x_1 = 4.15 + 2.65 \sin z_1, x_2 = 2.45 + 0.45 \sin z_2$ ensure that the constraints are satisfied and lead to the unconstrained problem,

$$\text{maximize } F(z_1, z_2) = 1.56(4.15 + 2.65 \sin z_1) - 19.5$$

$$- \frac{9.62}{(4.15 + 2.65 \sin z_1)(2.752 + 0.45 \sin z_2)}$$

$$- \frac{16.4}{(4.15 + 2.65 \sin z_1)}.$$

This problem may be solved by using the calculus to determine the stationary points. These are given by $\partial F/\partial z_1 = 0$ and $\partial F/\partial z_2 = 0$, for which the solutions are $z_1 = (n + \frac{1}{2})\pi$, $z_2 = (m + \frac{1}{2})\pi$, $n, m = 0, 1, 2, \ldots$. These give $\sin z = \pm 1$ and lead to the four points in the x_1, x_2 plane which give the possible maxima. Evaluating the objective function at each of these points gives the values shown below from which it is clear that the maximum is -11.75 at the point $x_1 = 6.8$, $x_2 = 2.9$

x_1	1.5	1.5	6.8	6.8
x_2	2.0	2.9	2.0	2.9
$f(x_1, x_2)$	-30.88	-30.09	-11.92	-11.75

For more general constraints it may still be possible to eliminate the constraint by the use of an appropriate substitution.

EXAMPLE 5   Replace the following constrained problem by an equivalent unconstrained problem:

$$\text{maximize } f(x_1, x_2, x_3) = x_1(x_2^2 + 3x_3),$$

$$\text{subject to } 0 \leqslant x_1 \leqslant 1, \quad 0 \leqslant x_2 \leqslant 2, \quad 2x_1 + x_2^2 + 3x_3 \leqslant 9, \quad x_3 \geqslant 0.$$

The substitutions $x_1 = \frac{1}{2}(1 + \sin z_1)$, $x_2 = (1 + \sin z_2)$ ensure that the first two constraints are always satisfied. The third constraint then becomes

$$3x_3 \leqslant 7 - \sin z_1 - 2 \sin z_2 - \sin^2 z_2$$

and this, together with the constraint $x_3 \geqslant 0$, is satisfied by the substitution

$$3x_3 = (7 - \sin z_1 - 2 \sin z_2 - \sin^2 z_2)\sin^2 z_3.$$

The problem is then reduced to finding the unconstrained maximum of

$$F(z_1, z_2, z_3) = \frac{1}{2}(1 + \sin z_1)\{(1 + \sin z_2)^2$$

$$+ (7 - \sin z_1 - 2 \sin z_2 - \sin^2 z_2)\sin^2 z_3\}$$

This is readily solved by the coordinate axes search method and is left as an exercise for the reader.

Another approach to the constrained problem is the *penalty function method*. Here the objective function is modified by the inclusion of penalty functions which become operative to reduce the value of the objective function as a constraint is approached. An example of the penalty function technique is the *created response surface* employed by Carroll. The objective function $f(x)$ is replaced by a sequence of functions $F(x, r)$ corresponding to decreasing values of the positive parameter r and such that $\lim_{r \to 0} F(x, r) = f(x)$. In terms of the notation of the standard non-linear programming problems the functions $F(x, r)$ are given by

$$F(\mathbf{x}, r) = f(\mathbf{x}) + r \sum_{s=1}^{k} \frac{1}{g_s(\mathbf{x})} \; .$$

For every point within the feasible region the function F has a value smaller than that of f since each of the g_s is negative. Moreover as the point $\mathbf{x} = (x_1, x_2, \ldots, x_n)$ approaches the boundary of the feasible region one or more of the g_s tends to zero and the function F becomes negatively infinite. Hence there will be a maximum value of F within the feasible region and as $r \to 0$ this point will tend to the point which gives the maximum of the original objective function f subject to the constraints. The method based on this result consists of maximizing the function F for a sequence of decreasing values of r. Thus, starting with some fixed value r_0 of r at some point $\mathbf{x}_0$ within the feasible region, the point giving the maximum of $F(\mathbf{x}, r_0)$ is determined using one of the methods appropriate to the unconstrained problem. This point becomes the starting point for a further maximization of the function $F(\mathbf{x}, r_1)$ where $r_1 < r_0$. The procedure is repeated for a sequence of decreasing values of r until the maxima for consecutive values of r coincide to within some specified accuracy. In determining the maximum of $F(\mathbf{x}, r)$ care must be taken to ensure that any search technique employed is modified so as to generate only points within the feasible region. This is because the penalty function becomes positively infinite as the boundary of the feasible region is approached from the outside, and a search from an exterior point will always terminate on the boundary. Alternative objective functions to those proposed by Carroll are either

$$F(\mathbf{x}, r) = f(\mathbf{x}) + r \sum_{s=1}^{k} \log[-g_s(\mathbf{x})]$$

or

$$F(\mathbf{x}, r) = f(\mathbf{x}) - r \sum_{s=1}^{k} \left(\frac{1}{g_s(\mathbf{x})} \right)^2 .$$

EXAMPLE 6   Maximize $f(x_1, x_2) = x_1^2 x_2$,

subject to the constraint

$$g(x_1, x_2) \equiv 3x_1 + 2x_2 - 8 \leq 0.$$

For this problem the created response function $F(x_1, x_2, r)$ is given by

$$F(x_1, x_2, r) = x_1^2 x_2 + \frac{r}{(3x_1 + 2x_2 - 8)}.$$

For any value of r the maximum of this function is readily determined by using the techniques of the calculus. Starting with $r = 0.1$ and using a sequence of decreasing values of r leads to the following table:

r	(x_1, x_2)	$F(x_1, x_2, r)$	$f(x_1, x_2)$
0.1	(1.7200, 1.2900)	2.1496	3.8163
0.001	(1.7722, 1.3292)	4.1346	4.1746
0.00001	(1.7772, 1.3329)	4.2061	4.2099
0.0000001	(1.7777, 1.3333)	4.2132	4.2135

From the table it may be seen that the solutions converge on to the point (1.7777, 1.3333) at which the objective function has the value 4.214.

In the penalty function method proposed by Rosenbrock, a small boundary region of width δ_r is associated with each boundary $g_r(x) = 0$. The functions ϕ_r are then defined by the relations

$$\phi_r = \begin{cases} 0 & \text{for} \quad g_r > 0 \\ 1 - \left(1 + \dfrac{g_r}{\delta_r}\right)^2 & \text{for} \quad -\delta_r < g_r < 0 \\ 1 & \text{for} \quad g_r < -\delta_r \end{cases}$$

and the objective function $f(x)$ is replaced by the function $F(x)$ defined by $F(x) = \phi_1 \phi_2 \ldots \phi_k f(x)$. This new objective function is identical with $f(x)$ at feasible points not within any boundary zone but drops off to zero as the boundary is approached. If the maximum of $F(x)$ occurs within the feasible region and not within a boundary zone then this is the maximum of $f(x)$. If the maximum of $F(x)$ occurs within the boundary zone of the constraint $g_r \leqslant 0$ then the value of δ_r is reduced and the problem is re-examined.

For further details of these and other methods for coping with constrained problems the reader is referred to Adby and Dempster [1] and Himmelblau [3].

Exercises

1. Use the coordinate axes search method starting from the origin to locate a maximum of the function

$$f(x_1, x_2) = (1.7 + 2.5x_1 - 0.3x_1^2)(1 + x_2)\exp(-x_2^2).$$

2. Apply the method of steepest ascent to obtain the maximum of

$$f(x_1, x_2) = 9 + 4x_1 + 2x_2 - x_1^2 + x_1 x_2 - x_2^2.$$

3. The function $f(x_1, x_2) = -x_1^3 - 2x_2^2 + 3x_1 x_2 + 3x_1 + 9$ has a local maximum close to the point $(1.5, 1)$. Apply Newton's method once to obtain an improved estimate of the maximum point and compare the result with that obtained by using the methods of the calculus (see §4.4 of Volume 1).

4. Use Carroll's method to obtain the maximum of $f(x_1, x_2) = 3x_1 x_2^2$ subject to $x_1 + 2x_2 - 4 \leqslant 0$.

5. Convert the problem of exercise 4 into an unconstrained problem by a suitable change of variable and hence obtain the solution.

2.4 DYNAMIC PROGRAMMING

Multi-stage Processes

Many processes of practical interest involve a series of steps or operations, at each of which some decision must be made. The processes considered here are such that the decision taken at any step influences the state at the start of the following step. A four-step process of this kind is illustrated in Fig. 2.8, the steps being numbered backwards so that the final step is referred to as *stage 1* and the initial step is *stage 4*. In this way the operation denoted by stage r takes place before that labelled as stage $(r - 1)$. The state at the start of stage r will be denoted by w_r and the decision taken at stage r by d_r. The effect of this decision is to determine the state w_{r-1} at the start of stage $(r - 1)$ according to some relation of the form

$$w_{r-1} = T_{r-1}(w_r, d_r). \tag{10}$$

In the problems under consideration there exists some overall objective function which depends on the initial state w_n and the decisions $d_n, d_{n-1}, \ldots, d_1$ taken at each stage. The object is to determine the set of decisions, termed the *optimal policy*, which optimizes this objective function for some given initial state w_n. The method of *dynamic programming* is to work backwards from the last stage in the following way. To begin with, stage 1 is regarded as a single-stage process and the optimal decision d_1 appropriate to any initial state w_1, is determined. Next, stages 2 and 1 are taken as a two stage process with the initial state w_2, and the optimal decisions d_2 and d_1 are determined. This involves using the optimal solution for the one stage process. The next move is to optimize the three-stage process consisting of stages 3, 2, and 1, using the results for the two-stage process. Proceeding in this way leads eventually to the solution of the given n-stage problem.

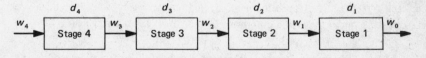

Fig. 2.8   A four-stage process.

The Basic Recurrence Relation

To express the dynamic programming method mathematically, let $P_1(w_1, d_1)$ denote the objective function for the one-stage process consisting of stage 1. Let $f_1(w_1)$ denote the optimum value of this function for any w_1, that is

$$f_1(w_1) = \underset{d_1}{\text{optimum}} \; [P_1(w_1, d_1)]. \tag{11}$$

Here the optimum (maximum or minimum) is determined with d_1 treated as the independent variable and w_1 as a fixed parameter. Let $P_2(w_2, d_2)$ denote the contribution of stage 2 to the objective function, such that the objective function for the two-stage process is $P_2(w_2, d_2) + P_1(w_1, d_1)$. Assume that the decision d_2 has been taken, then it is necessary to choose d_1 in such a way as to optimize the second term in the objective function. This latter problem has been solved already so that the objective function is given by the expression $P_2(w_2, d_2) + f_1(w_1)$. The choice of d_2 must be such as to optimize this expression. Since w_1 is determined in terms of w_2 and d_2 from equation (10) the optimum value $f_2(w_2)$ of this two-stage objective function is given by

$$f_2(w_2) = \underset{d_2}{\text{opt}} \; [P_2(w_2, d_2) + f_1\{T_1(w_2, d_2)\}] \; .$$

Proceeding in this way, let $f_{r-1}(w_{r-1})$ denote the optimum of the objective function for the $(r-1)$-stage process with initial state w_{r-1}. Consider the r-stage process obtained by placing stage r ahead of these and let the new initial state be w_r. The optimal decision d_r together with w_r will determine w_{r-1} by equation (10). The remaining decisions $d_{r-1}, d_{r-2}, \ldots, d_1$ must be the optimal policy for the $(r-1)$-stage process with initial state w_{r-1}. (If this were not the case then it would be possible to improve the value of the objective function by choosing the optimal $(r-1)$-stage policy.) Letting $P_r(w_r, d_r)$ denote the contribution to the objective function from stage r, the optimum $f_r(w_r)$ of the r-stage process is determined by the expression

$$f_r(w_r) = \underset{d_r}{\text{opt}} \; [P_r(w_r, d_r) + f_{r-1}\{T_{r-1}(w_r, d_r)\}] \; . \tag{12}$$

Equation (12) is the *basic recurrence relation* of dynamic programming.

The relation (12) embodies Bellman's *principle of optimality* which states that:

In an r-stage process with initial state w_r, the optimal policy is such that whatever the decision d_r, the remaining decisions $d_{r-1}, d_{r-2}, \ldots, d_1$ constitute the optimal policy for the $(r-1)$-stage process with initial state $w_{r-1} = T_{r-1}(w_r, d_r)$.

This principle is valid for multi-stage processes involving no feedback. In the case of feedback systems, the state at the beginning of any step can be influenced by decisions taken at subsequent steps and equations of the form (10) are not valid.

EXAMPLE 1   A manufacturer uses a machine to manufacture plastic cups in batches of 10,000. After each batch he has the option of replacing the machine by a new one or of retaining it to produce the next batch. The replacement cost of the machine is a function $C(s)$ of the number s of batches produced on that machine. The cost of production of the sth batch on the machine is $H(s)$. It is required to produce N batches starting with a new machine and ending with a new machine and to minimize the cost. Solve the problem for $N = 5$ when the replacement costs $C(s)$ and production costs $H(s)$ are as given below:

s	1	2	3	4	5
$C(s)$	230	280	310	340	360
$H(s)$	150	190	240	320	410

In this problem each batch constitutes a stage in the process. The state w_r at the start of stage r is the number s of batches already produced on the machine. The decision d_r is taken at the end of stage r and is either to replace the machine by a new one or to retain it. The transformation equation (10) is then

$$w_{r-1} = 0 \quad \text{if } d_r = \text{replace},$$

$$w_{r-1} = w_r + 1 \quad \text{if } d_r = \text{retain}.$$

Since the decision d_1 must always be to replace the machine there is no minimization involved in stage 1 and the cost consists of production cost plus replacement cost,

$$f_1(w_1) = H(w_1 + 1) + C(w_1 + 1).$$

For a two-stage process the cost of production at stage 2 is $H(w_2 + 1)$. There is the choice of replacing at a cost $C(w_2 + 1)$ and giving $w_1 = 0$, or of retaining with zero cost and giving $w_1 = w_2 + 1$. The choice is determined by the decision which gives the minimum total cost and

$$f_2(w_2) = \text{infimum}\,[\{H(w_2 + 1) + C(w_2 + 1) + H(1) + C(1)\},$$
$$\{H(w_2 + 1) + H(w_2 + 2) + C(w_2 + 2)\}].$$

Here the term infimum denotes the lower of the two quantities within the braces. For a process consisting of the first r stages the minimum cost is given by

$$f_r(w_r) = \text{infimum}\,[\{H(w_r + 1) + C(w_r + 1) + f_{r-1}(0)\},$$
$$\{H(w_r + 1) + f_{r-1}(w_r + 2)\}],$$

where $f_{r-1}(w_{r-1})$ is the minimum cost for the $(r - 1)$ stage process.

To solve the problem it is first necessary to evaluate $f_1(w_1)$ for $w_1 = 0, 1, 2, 3, 4$. This gives the table

w_1	0	1	2	3	4
$f_1(w_1)$	380	470	550	660	770

in which for example $f_1(2) = H(3) + C(3) = 240 + 310 = 550$. Since only three batches precede stage 2 the possible values of w_2 are $w_2 = 0, 1, 2, 3$ and the alternative decisions lead to the next table of values. The values shown underlined correspond to

$f_2(w_2)$ the optimum for each value of w_2

w_2	0	1	2	3
d_2 = replace	760	850	930	1040
d_2 = retain	620	740	900	1090

Proceeding in this way leads to the tables

w_3	0	1	2
d_3 = replace	1000	1090	1170
d_3 = retain	890	1090	1280

w_4	0	1
d_4 = replace	1270	1360
d_4 = retain	1240	1360

w_5	0
d_5 = replace	1620
d_5 = retain	1510

Note that for $w_3 = 1$ the two decisions give the same value of the objective function and both decisions are optimal. The same result holds for $w_4 = 1$. As an example of how these tables are constructed consider the entries for $w_3 = 2$. Here two batches have already been produced on the machine and the cost of producing the third batch $H(3)$ is 240. If the decision is to replace, then to this is added the replacement cost $C(3) = 310$ giving 550. This results in $w_2 = 0$ and the optimal cost for the two-stage process with this value of w_2 is 620 (underlined for $w_2 = 0$). Adding these two costs gives the value 1170. If on the other hand the decision is to retain the machine then $w_2 = 3$ and the minimum cost for this is shown underlined as 1040. Adding this to the production cost of 240 gives the value of 1280.

The optimal policy may now be read off from these tables. Thus the optimal decision at stage 5 is to retain the machine. This gives $w_4 = 1$ and either decision is optimal. The decision d_4 = replace, gives $w_3 = 0$ and d_3 = retain, whereas the decision d_4 = retain, gives $w_3 = 2$ and d_3 = replace. Proceeding in this way gives the following alternatives

$$
\begin{array}{ccccc}
d_5 & d_4 & d_3 & d_2 & d_1 \\
\end{array}
$$

retain $\begin{array}{l} \nearrow \text{replace} \rightarrow \text{retain} \rightarrow \text{retain} \rightarrow \text{replace} \\ \searrow \text{retain} \rightarrow \text{replace} \rightarrow \text{retain} \rightarrow \text{replace} \end{array}$

It will be seen that both policies involve the use of two machines. In the first policy two batches are produced on the first machine and three on the second, whereas in the second policy three batches are produced on the first machine and two on the second.

The example considered here is typical of the *replacement problem* in that the stages follow each other naturally in sequence. The dynamic programming approach is not restricted to such problems however, and may be applied in any situation in which it is possible to order a set of decisions, provided the principle of optimality holds. In particular the method may be applied to solve the *allocation problem*, in which it is required to allocate scarce resources between a number of operations or activities, each of which constitutes a stage. As an example of an allocation problem we consider the following:

EXAMPLE 2   A bulk grain carrier has the maximum capacity of 30,000 tonnes. Three different types of grain are to be transported in one voyage. The selling price of the grain varies with the amount delivered and the estimated profit P for the voyage is related to the weights x_1, x_2, x_3 (thousand tonnes) of each grain carried, by the expression

$$P = 3.2x_1 - 0.4x_1^2 + 8.9x_2 - 3x_2^2 + 2.7x_3.$$

Determine the quantities of each grain to be carried in order to maximize the profit.

To formulate this as a dynamic programming problem we regard the allocation of the amount of one type of grain to be carried as one stage in a three-stage process. The state w_r is the weight capacity (thousand tonnes) available at the start of stage r and the decision d_r is the weight x_r of grain r to be carried.

The one-stage problem is thus

$$f_1(w_1) = \max(3.2x_1 - 0.4x_1^2) \quad \text{subject to} \quad x_1 \leqslant w_1.$$

The solution to this problem is

$$f_1(w_1) = \begin{cases} 6.4 & \text{at} \quad x_1 = 4 & \text{if} \quad w_1 \geqslant 4, \\ 3.2w_1 - 0.4w_1^2 & \text{at} \quad x_1 = w_1 & \text{if} \quad 0 \leqslant w_1 < 4. \end{cases}$$

For the two-stage process we have

$$f_2(w_2) = \max\{(8.9x_2 - 3x_2^2) + f_1(w_2 - x_2)\} \quad \text{subject to} \quad x_2 \leqslant w_2$$

and two possibilities arise.
(a) If $w_2 - x_2 \geqslant 4$, then

$$f_2(w_2) = \max(8.9x_2 - 3x_2^2 + 6.4) \quad \text{subject to} \quad x_2 \leqslant w_2 - 4$$

and the solution is

$$f_2(w_2) = \begin{cases} 13.00 & \text{at} \quad x_2 = 1.483 & \text{if} \quad w_2 \geqslant 5.483, \\ -3w_2^2 + 32.9w_2 - 77.2 & \text{at} \quad x_2 = w_2 - 4 & \text{if} \quad 4 \leqslant w_2 < 5.483. \end{cases}$$

(b) If $0 \leqslant w_2 - x_2 < 4$, then

$$f_2(w_2) = \max\{8.9x_2 - 3x_2^2 + 3.2(w_2 - x_2) - 0.4(w_2 - x_2)^2\}$$
$$\text{subject to} \quad x_2 > w_2 - 4,$$

and the solution to this is

$$f_2(w_2) = \begin{cases} 2.3889 + 3.8703w_2 - 0.3529w_2^2 & \text{at} \quad x_2 = 0.8382 + 0.1176w_2 \\ & \text{if} \quad 0.9499 \leqslant w_2 < 5.483, \\ 8.9w_2 - 3w_2^2 & \text{at} \quad x_2 = w_2 \quad \text{for} \quad 0 \leqslant w_2 < 0.9499. \end{cases}$$

The solutions (a) and (b) give two different expressions for $f_2(w_2)$ in the region $4 \leqslant w_2 < 5.483$. It may be shown that in this region the expression given by (b) is the larger of the two and the complete result for the two-stage process is

$$f_2(w_2) = \begin{cases} 13.00 & \text{at} \quad x_2 = 1.483 \quad \text{if} \quad w_2 \geqslant 5.483, \\ 2.3889 + 3.8703w_2 - 0.3529w_2^2 & \text{at} \quad x_2 = 0.8382 + 0.1176w_2 \\ & \text{if} \quad 0.9499 \leqslant w_2 < 5.483, \\ 8.9w_2 - 3w_2^2 & \text{at} \quad x_2 = w_2 \quad \text{for} \quad 0 \leqslant w_2 < 0.9499. \end{cases}$$

In the complete three-stage process, we have $w_3 = 30$ and

$$f_3(w_3) = \max\{2.7x_3 + f_2(30 - x_3)\} \quad \text{for} \quad x_3 \leqslant 30.$$

There are now three cases to consider:

(a) $30 - x_3 \geqslant 5.483$ or $x_3 \leqslant 24.517$

$$f_3(w_3) = \max(2.7x_3 + 13.00) = 79.196 \quad \text{at} \quad x_3 = 24.517.$$

(b) $24.517 < x_3 \leqslant 29.050$

$$f_3(w_3) = \max\{2.7x_3 + 2.3889 + 3.8703(30 - x_3) - 0.3529(30 - x_3)^2\}$$
$$= 84.377 \quad \text{at} \quad x_3 = 28.34.$$

(c) $29.050 < x_3 \leqslant 30$

$$f_3(w_3) = \max\{2.7x_3 + 8.9(30 - x_3) - 3(30 - x_3)^2\} = 84.182 \quad \text{at} \quad x_3 = 29.05.$$

From these results it may be seen that the maximum profit is 84.377 corresponding to $x_3 = 28.34, x_2 = 1.034, x_1 = 0.626$.

Aside from the difference in formulation, the problems considered in example 1 and example 2 differ in the fact that the independent decision variables in example 1 take only discrete values (for or against replacement) whereas in example 2 they take on continuous values. Because of this, the actual determination of the optima $f_r(w_r)$ involve two different techniques. In example 1 the technique is a direct enumeration of the possibilities whereas in example 2 use is made of the analytical techniques for maximizing a function of a single continuous variable. These techniques are further illustrated in exercise 1 below.

Exercises

1. Maximize $f(x_1, x_2, x_3) = x_1^2 - 2x_2^2 - \dfrac{3}{x_3}$

    subject to $3x_1 + 2x_2 + 5x_3 \leqslant 9,$ $x_1, x_2, x_3 \geqslant 0,$
(a) for continuous values of x_1, x_2, x_3 and (b) for integer values of x_1, x_2, x_3.

2. Use the method of dynamic programming to maximize

$$f(x_1, x_2, x_3) = 3x_1 + 2(x_2 - 5)^2 - 2/(x_3 + 3),$$

subject to $x_1 + 3x_2 + 4x_3 \leqslant 9, \quad x_1, x_2, x_3 \geqslant 0.$

3. A firm engaged in buying and selling identical items operates from a warehouse which has a capacity of 100 items. Stock purchased by the firm during any month is available in the warehouse at the start of next month. The warehousing costs for each month is $2w$ where w is the stock at the start of the month. The firm has 25 items in stock on 1st January and must have a stock of 50 items on 1st April. Determine its buying and selling policy in order to maximize its profit over three months given the details below.

	Purchase Price	Selling Price
January	14	14
February	12	15
March	15	16

4. A student has available b hours to complete his revision for n examination papers. He estimates that his mark m_r on the rth paper will be a function of the time x_r spent on revising for that paper, given by $m_r = P_r(x_r)$ for $r = 1, 2, \ldots, n$. His objective is to allocate the time available in such a way as to maximize his total marks. Formulate the problem as a dynamic programming problem and obtain the basic recurrence relation. Solve for the case $n = 3$, $b = 30$ and

$$P_1(x_1) = \frac{100x_1 + 600}{x_1 + 30}, \quad P_2(x_2) = \frac{100x_2}{x_2 + 20}, \quad P_3(x_3) = \frac{100x_3 + 300}{x_3 + 10}.$$

PROBLEMS

1. Use the quadratic search method to find the maximum of

$$f(x) = -10(x - \tfrac{1}{2})^2 + e^{-x},$$

over the interval $0 \leqslant x \leqslant 1$.

2. Use the fixed step search method to locate the minimum of

$$f(x) = \frac{2}{x + 1} + \sin \frac{\pi x}{2}, \quad \text{for} \quad 0 \leqslant x \leqslant 1.$$

3. Devise a search strategy for approximately locating the maximum of any function $f(x)$ for $0 \leqslant x \leqslant 1$. Apply your method to find the maximum of

$$f(x) = (x + 1)^2 + 3 \cos \frac{\pi x}{2}, \quad \text{for} \quad 0 \leqslant x \leqslant 1.$$

4. The response $f(x)$ of a system to an input x is given over three different portions of the interval $0 \leqslant x \leqslant 1$ by the formulae,

$$f(x) = \begin{cases} (1 + x^2)^{\frac{1}{2}}, & 0 \leqslant x < 0.5, \\ 10(\sin 3x^2 - x), & 0.5 \leqslant x < 0.8, \\ 1.3965, & 0.8 \leqslant x \leqslant 1. \end{cases}$$

Given that $f(x)$ is unimodal, use the Fibonacci search technique with $n = 5$ to reduce the interval containing the maximum. Using the two end points and the interior point of this final interval, obtain a quadratic approximation for the function and hence determine the approximate maximum. (Use $\epsilon = 0.01$ in the Fibonacci search.)

5. Use the coordinate axes search method starting from the point $(1, 1)$ to find the maximum of

$$f(x_1, x_2) = (x_1 - x_1^2)(4x_2 - x_2^2)^{1/2}, \quad \text{in the region} \quad x_1 \geqslant 0, \quad 4 \geqslant x_2 \geqslant 0.$$

6. Apply the coordinate axes search method to minimize

$$f(x_1, x_2, x_3) = x_1^2 + 4x_2^2 - 4x_2 x_3 + 2x_3^2 - 8x_3 + 16.$$

7. The following table gives the values of a function $f(x_1, x_2)$ at the indicated points. By fitting a quadratic function through these points determine an approximate minimum of the function in this neighbourhood.

(x_1, x_2)	$(0, 0)$	$(1, 0)$	$(-1, 0)$	$(0, 1)$	$(0, -1)$	$(1, -1)$
$f(x_1, x_2)$	1.2214	1.3499	2.0138	1.8221	1.0000	1.1052

8. Determine the direction of steepest descent of the function

$$f(x_1, x_2) = \exp\{\tfrac{1}{10}(3x_1^2 + x_2^2 - 2x_1 + 3x_2 + 2)\}$$

at the point $(0, 0)$ and find the minimum value of the function along this direction.

9. Use an n-dimensional search method starting from $(0, 0, 0)$ to find the minimum of $(x_1 - 3)^2 + 2(x_2 - 3)^2 + (x_3 - 1)^2$ over the region defined by

$$x_1 + 2x_2 + 3x_3 \leqslant 6, \quad x_1 \geqslant 0, \quad x_2 \geqslant 0, \quad x_3 \geqslant 0.$$

10. Determine the turning value of the function

$$u = (1 + x_3^2)[1 + (x_1 - 1)^2 + (x_2 - x_1^2)^2]$$

and confirm that this is a local minimum by expanding the function in a Taylor series. Find the minimum value of the above function in the region defined by $0 \leqslant x_1 \leqslant \frac{1}{2}$, $0 \leqslant x_3 \leqslant 1$.

11. Use an n-dimensional search method starting from $(1, 1, 0)$ to find the maximum of $x_1 x_2 x_3$ over the region $0 \leqslant x_1 \leqslant 2, 0 \leqslant x_2 \leqslant 4, x_3 \geqslant 0, x_1 + x_2 + 2x_3 \leqslant 9$.

12. (a) Use the method of steepest descent starting from the point $(0, 1)$ to determine the minimum of the function $3(x_1 - 1)^2 + 5(x_2 - 2)^2$ in the region $x_2 \leqslant 2.1$, $x_1 + x_2 \leqslant 2.9$.
(b) By defining new variables (or otherwise) express the above problem as one of unconstrained minima. Hence determine its solution.

13. Use Newton's method to locate the maximum of

$$f(x_1, x_2) = 4 + 3x_1 - 5x_2 - 2x_1^2 + x_1 x_2 - 3x_2^2.$$

14. The function

$$f(x_1, x_2) = 2 - 2x_1 + 2x_1^2 + 3x_1 x_2^2 + 3x_2^3$$

has a maximum close to the point $(\frac{1}{2}, -\frac{1}{3})$. Use Newton's method to locate the maximum correct to two places of decimals.

15. Apply Carroll's technique to find the maximum of $f(x_1, x_2) = x_1 + x_2$ subject to $x_1^2 + 3x_2^2 - x_1 - 4x_2 - 9 \leqslant 0$.

16. By making a change of variable reduce the following problem to an unconstrained problem and find its solution:

Minimize $f(x_1, x_2) = x_1^2 + 2x_2^2 - 3x_1 - 5x_2$,
subject to $x_2 \leqslant 5$, $3x_1 + 2x_2 \leqslant 15$.

17. Use the substitution $x_1 = 3 \sin v \cos u$, $x_2 = 2 \sin v \sin u$ to transform the following problem to an unconstrained problem and hence find the solution:

Maximize $f(x_1, x_2) = x_1 x_2^2 + 3x_1^2$,
subject to $\dfrac{x_1^2}{9} + \dfrac{x_2^2}{4} \leqslant 1.$

18. A manufacturer uses a machine to produce n batches of a particular article. Due to wear on the machine the production cost per batch is a function $C(r)$ of the number r of batches previously produced on the machine since new or since overhaul. After each batch the machine may be retained or it may be replaced at a cost $H(r)$ or overhauled at a cost $S(r)$, both functions of the number r of batches produced since new or since overhaul. Assuming that a new machine is available initially and that an overhaul or replacement immediately after the n batches must be budgeted for, set up the recurrence relation of dynamic programming to determine the policy which minimizes the total cost.

The following table gives values of $C(r)$, $H(r)$ and $S(r)$ covering a production of $n = 5$ batches. Determine the optimal policy in this case.

r	0	1	2	3	4	5
$C(r)$	200	220	250	280	330	–
$H(r)$	–	200	300	380	450	530
$S(r)$	–	160	280	390	470	560

19. Determine the basic recurrence relation for the dynamic programming formulation of the problem

$$\text{maximize} \quad \sum_{1}^{N} g_r(x_r)$$

$$\text{subject to} \quad \sum_{1}^{N} a_r x_r \leqslant W, \quad x_r \geqslant 0 \quad (r = 1, \ldots, N).$$

Use dynamic programming to determine the maximum of $x_1^2 + 3x_2^2 + 10x_3^2$ subject to

$x_1 + 2x_2 + 3x_3 \leqslant 6.5$, $\quad x_1, x_2, x_3 \geqslant 0$ when

(a) x_1, x_2 and x_3 are continuous variables;

(b) x_1, x_2 and x_3 are integers.

If the restriction becomes $x_1 + 2x_2 + 3x_3 \leqslant 5.5$, what is the optimum value in case (b)?

20. A communications satellite may be fitted with four types of repeater equipment with the following specifications:

Type	Weight (kg)	Channels
A	20	72
B	18	60
C	14	40
D	12	35

If the design of the satellite allows for at most 50 kg of equipment use the method of dynamic programming to determine how many of each type should be fitted to maximize the number of channels available.

If type A is found to be unreliable and is scrapped, what should the new fitting policy be?

21. A manufacturer produces a perishable commodity which if not sold in the month of manufacture must be scrapped and which if out of stock incurs a loss of goodwill. It is estimated that in a given month if x units are produced and s units are sold the financial loss to the manufacturer due to either over- or under-production is $3(x - s)^2$. It is also estimated that the cost of changing the level of production of the commodity from x units in one month to y units in the succeeding month is $6(x - y)^2$. If the current month's production is 200 units and the estimated sales for the next three months are 250, 200, 300 units respectively, use dynamic programming to show that next month's production should be 222 units approximately.

BIBLIOGRAPHY

[1]   Adby, P. R. and M. A. A. Dempster, *Introduction to Optimization Methods*, Chapman and Hall, London (1974).

[2]   Box, M. J., D. Davies, and W. H. Swann, *Non-linear Optimization Techniques*, Oliver and Boyd, Edinburgh (1969).

[3]   Himmelblau, D. M. *Applied Non-linear Programming*, McGraw-Hill, New York (1972).

[4]   Wilde, D. J. and C. S. Beightler, *Foundations of Optimization*, Prentice-Hall, Englewood Cliffs, N.J. (1967).

[5]   Carr, C. R. and C. W. Howe, *Quantitative Decision Procedures in Management and Economics*, McGraw-Hill, New York (1964).

[6]   Bellman, R. E. and S. E. Dreyfus, *Applied Dynamic Programming*, Princeton University Press, Princeton (1972).

CHAPTER 3

Further Statistics — Estimation and Inference

3.1 INTRODUCTION

Whenever sampling is undertaken, the prime objectives are to make 'sensible' estimates and draw 'plausible' conclusions based on the evidence afforded by the data. As *statistical inference* is founded on the theory of probability, familiarity with the fundamental ideas and results of the latter, as outlined in Chapter 12 of Volume 1, will be assumed.

The types of question which it may be possible to consider are many and varied, for example

Is a particular coin biased?

Is there a significant difference between the numbers of faulty components produced by two machines?

Is a drug actually effective in combating a particular disease?

Does the evidence support a manufacturer's claim regarding 'average lifetime of the product'?

Do traffic-census figures follow a Poissonian distribution?

Do engineers receive above-average salaries?

Questions such as these can be very complex and to handle them some sophisticated techniques have been developed. In this chapter it will only be possible to consider the more simple types of problem.

Populations, Samples and Estimates

In §12.3 and §12.5 of Volume 1 attention was drawn to the difference between a *population* and a *sample*. A population consists of all possible members whereas a sample consists of a selection of these members. The relative frequency approach to probability, considered in §12.3 of Volume 1, by its very nature must be concerned with samples. A parent population may be finite or infinite in size, according to the class under investigation, whereas a sample is necessarily finite.

From any sample, quantities such as the sample mean $\bar{X}$ and sample variance S^2 may be calculated, but these *statistics* are only *estimates* of the fixed values μ and σ^2 which pertain to the population. As quantities like $\bar{X}$ and S^2 change in value from sample to sample *they are themselves random variables (r.v.'s)*. They have their own probability density functions, and these p.d.f.'s are known as *sampling distributions*. A particular value of the r.v. $\bar{X}$ will be denoted by $\bar{x}$, and s^2 will be used to denote a particular value of the estimator S^2. As far as common usage permits, population parameters will be denoted by Greek letters, and Roman letters will be associated with sample values.

In matters of inference the task is to use observations on *part* of a population in order to make statements about the *whole* population, and it is therefore necessary to take care that the sample to be studied is as representative as possible. To select names 'at random' from a list of private subscribers in a telephone directory will not produce a random sample of the community but merely a random sample of private telephone subscribers. Many sampling schemes exist, but in this chapter discussion will be limited to the *Simple Random Sample* which has the following properties:

(a) in each selection each member of the parent population is equally likely to be chosen,

(b) successive selections are independent,

(c) during the sampling of a quantity its distribution in the parent population remains invariant.

It will be realized that some of these conditions may be difficult to enforce. Criteria (b) and (c) require that the sampling be done 'with replacement', (see §12.4 in Volume 1), but this is often impracticable and becomes impossible if the sampled item is to be tested to destruction. Nevertheless, populations are usually sufficiently large that lack of replacement introduces little error into the analysis. In the remainder of this chapter it will be assumed that the conditions appropriate to a simple random sample have been met.

Given then such a sample, the first task is to establish how the parameters of the parent population may best be estimated. An *estimate* is a particular value of an *estimator* and for any parameter several alternative estimators may exist. An example occurs in the Poissonian distribution $Po(\lambda)$, described in §12.6 of Volume 1, in which $P\{X = x\} = e^{-\lambda}\lambda^x/x!$ for $x = 0, 1, \ldots, n, \ldots$ where any sample cumulant could be used to estimate the value of the population mean λ. (It can be shown that the sample mean $\bar{X}$, the first sample cumulant, is to be preferred.) In order to discuss the properties desirable in an estimator, consider Fig. 3.1 which shows the sampling distributions (which need not be symmetric) of four hypothetical estimators T_1, T_2, T_3, T_4 of a certain population parameter τ. Estimators T_1 and T_2 shown in (a) and (b) have the property that their means coincide with the actual value of τ, and they are therefore said to be *unbiased*. The second pair of estimators do not have this property and are therefore *biased*. On the other hand T_1 and T_3 have a sampling distribution with a small variance and are therefore said to be *efficient*, whereas the greater spread in (b) and (d) shows the right-hand estimators to be *inefficient*. The quest is usually for the most efficient unbiased estimator, though, as Fig. 3.1 shows, an efficient biased estimator such as T_3 can be preferable to an inefficient unbiased one like T_2 because it more frequently produces an estimate 'near' the true population value.

To illustrate these ideas we will show that the sample mean $\bar{X}$ is an unbiased estimator of the population mean μ and also that the sample variance S^2 is an unbiased estimator of the population variance σ^2.

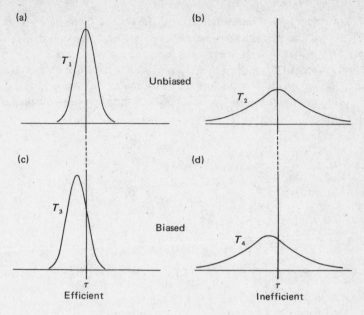

Fig. 3.1   The sampling distributions of four estimators of parameter τ.

Let X_i be the ith observation in a simple random sample of size n, so that

$$\bar{X} = \frac{1}{n} \sum_{i=1}^{n} X_i.$$

Then the expected value of the sample mean is given by

$$E\{\bar{X}\} = E\left\{\frac{1}{n}(X_1 + X_2 + \ldots + X_n)\right\} = \frac{1}{n}E\{X_1 + X_2 + \ldots + X_n\}$$

$$= \frac{1}{n}(E\{X_1\} + E\{X_2\} + \ldots + E\{X_n\}) = \frac{1}{n}(\mu + \mu + \ldots + \mu) = \frac{n\mu}{n} = \mu. \quad (1)$$

If successive independent samples were taken the individual sample means $\bar{X}$ could be calculated. If these were plotted along the x axis it would be observed that, although the position varied, the spread was very much less than that of the individual values of X obtained in sampling . Indeed, the variance $\sigma_{\bar{x}}^2$ of the sample mean is

$$\text{Var}(\bar{X}) = \text{Var}\left(\frac{X_1 + X_2 + \ldots + X_n}{n}\right) = \frac{1}{n^2}\text{Var}(X_1 + X_2 + \ldots + X_n)$$

$$= \frac{1}{n^2}\{\text{Var}(X_1) + \text{Var}(X_2) + \ldots + \text{Var}(X_n)\} = \frac{1}{n^2}(\sigma^2 + \sigma^2 + \ldots + \sigma^2)$$

$$= \frac{n\sigma^2}{n^2} = \frac{\sigma^2}{n}. \quad (2)$$

The *standard error* (*s.e.*) of a statistic is the square root of the variance of its sampling distribution, so that the standard error of the sample mean is $\sigma/\sqrt{n}$. The reciprocal of the standard error is often taken as a measure of the *precision* with which an observation can be made so that the precision of a sample mean varies as the square root of the number of observations on which the calculation is based.

Equation (10a) in Chapter 12 of Volume 1 gives as the expression for the sample variance

$$S^2 = \frac{1}{n-1} \sum_{i=1}^{n} (X_i - \bar{X})^2 \, ,$$

and this may be rewritten as

$$S^2 = \frac{1}{n-1} \sum_i \{(X_i - \mu) - (\bar{X} - \mu)\}^2$$

$$= \frac{1}{n-1} \left\{ \sum_i (X_i - \mu)^2 - 2(\bar{X} - \mu) \sum_i (X_i - \mu) + n(\bar{X} - \mu)^2 \right\}$$

$$= \frac{1}{n-1} \left\{ \sum_i (X_i - \mu)^2 - 2(\bar{X} - \mu)(n\bar{X} - n\mu) + n(\bar{X} - \mu)^2 \right\}$$

$$= \frac{1}{n-1} \left\{ \sum_i (X_i - \mu)^2 - n(\bar{X} - \mu)^2 \right\} \, .$$

Then

$$E\{S^2\} = \frac{1}{n-1} \; E \left\{ \sum_i (X_i - \mu)^2 - n(\bar{X} - \mu)^2 \right\}$$

$$= \frac{1}{n-1} \left\{ \sum_i E\{(X_i - \mu)^2\} - nE\{(\bar{X} - \mu)^2\} \right\}$$

$$= \frac{1}{n-1} \; (n\sigma^2 - n\sigma_{\bar{x}}^2) = \frac{1}{n-1} \left\{ n\sigma^2 - n\left(\frac{\sigma^2}{n}\right) \right\} = \sigma^2 \, . \tag{3}$$

The appearance of $(n-1)$ in the denominator stems from the fact that the value for $\bar{X}$ has itself been calculated from the n values which constitute the sample. In the expression for S^2 there are only $(n-1)$ independent relationships and therefore $(n-1)$ is referred to as the number of *degrees of freedom*, (*d.f.'s*).

It is customary to use the symbol ˆ to denote an estimator of a parameter, and to reserve the symbol ν for the number of degrees of freedom. Therefore $\hat{\mu} = \bar{X}$ and, for the variance, $\hat{\sigma}^2 = S^2$ and $\nu = n - 1$.

If n observations (X_i, Y_i) for $i = 1, 2, \ldots, n$ are taken from a bivariate distribution then the corresponding estimators of the covariance μ_{11} and correlation coefficient ρ are respectively

$$\frac{1}{n-1} \Sigma \{(X_i - \bar{X})(Y_i - \bar{Y})\} \quad \text{and} \quad \frac{\Sigma \{(X_i - \bar{X})(Y_i - \bar{Y})\}}{\{\Sigma(X_i - \bar{X})^2 \Sigma(Y_i - \bar{Y})^2\}^{\frac{1}{2}}}$$

where

$$\Sigma \equiv \sum_{i=1}^{n} .$$

The sample covariance is unbiased, but this is only true of the sample correlation coefficient when $\rho = 0$.

Furthermore, if T is an estimator of τ, then T is said to be *consistent* if, as the sample size n is increased indefinitely, $E\{T\} \to \tau$ and the standard error tends to zero. Equations (1) and (2) show $\bar{X}$ to be a consistent estimator of μ, and it may also be shown that S^2 is a consistent estimator of σ^2.

Exercises

1. Take forty-five digits $x_i, i = 1, 2, \ldots, 45$ each digit $0, 1, \ldots, 9$ having a probability of $\frac{1}{10}$ of occurring in any one selection, and calculate their mean $\bar{x} = \frac{1}{45} \Sigma_{i=1}^{45} x_i$. Now divide these forty five digits into nine successive groups of five. Calculate the means for each of these nine groups and denote the means by $y_j, j = 1, \ldots, 9$. Let $\bar{y} = \frac{1}{9} \Sigma_{j=1}^{9} y_j$. Verify that $\bar{x} = \bar{y} \simeq 4.5$ and investigate the extent to which the following approximations hold:

$$\frac{1}{45} \sum_i (x_i - 4.5)^2 \simeq \frac{1}{44} \sum_i (x_i - \bar{x})^2 \simeq 5 \left\{ \frac{1}{9} \sum_j (y_j - 4.5)^2 \right\} \simeq 5 \left\{ \frac{1}{8} \sum_j (y_j - \bar{y})^2 \right\}$$

$$\simeq 8.25 .$$

How would you account for any 'discrepancies' between the actual figures you have obtained and the above expressions?

2. From a Bernoulli population (see §12.6 of Volume 1), two independent simple random samples are taken of sizes n_1 and n_2 respectively, where $n_1 \neq n_2$. If in the first sample there are m_1 'successes' and in the second there are m_2 'successes' show that

$$p_1 = \left(\frac{m_1 + m_2}{n_1 + n_2} \right) \quad \text{and} \quad p_2 = \frac{1}{2} \left(\frac{m_1}{n_1} + \frac{m_2}{n_2} \right)$$

are each unbiased estimates of the true proportion of successes. Determine which of these expressions is the more efficient.

3.2 SIGNIFICANCE TESTING

Before specific tests of significance may be considered it is necessary to discuss the general concepts involved. As subsequent sections show, the calculations themselves are easy to perform but it is essential that they be carried out only when there is clear understanding of the implications.

Consider the first question posed at the start of this chapter: is a particular coin fair or is it biased? A record of the outcomes of successive tosses can *never* give a *conclusive* answer. The probability of 100 'heads' from 100 throws for an unbiased coin is $(\frac{1}{2})^{100}$. This probability, though small, is not zero and so the event is *possible*. In practice it is necessary to set bounds to credulity. If asked, most observers would indicate that they would be prepared to believe a coin to be unbiased if the number of heads recorded in a given number of tosses fell between certain limits – though the particular limits suggested by untutored laymen might show wide divergence. The purpose of the test of significance is to base a decision on the *quantitative* assessment of the evidence. As will now be shown the knowledge available in Chapter 12 of Volume 1 will permit a direct attack to be made on the matter of the unbiasedness of a coin, whilst in §3.3 the introduction of the Central Limit Theorem permits deeper consideration of this and allied problems.

Let p be the probability of a 'head' occurring in a single throw of a coin, and let $q \equiv 1 - p$. If X represents the number of 'heads' recorded in n throws then §12.6 of Volume 1 shows that X is the binomial variate $Bi(n, p)$ which, for large n, may be approximated by the normal distribution $N(np, npq)$ since $\mu_X = np$ and $\sigma_X^2 = npq$. Therefore we may take

$$Z \equiv \frac{X - np}{\sqrt{(npq)}} \tag{4}$$

to be distributed as the standardized normal variate, (s.n.v.), $N(0, 1)$, and

$$f(z) = \frac{1}{\sqrt{2\pi}} e^{-\frac{1}{2}z^2} \quad \text{for} \quad -\infty < z < \infty$$

where $f(z)$ is the probability density function, (p.d.f.), of Z. If the coin is unbiased $p = q = \frac{1}{2}$, so that when $n = 100$ we have $np = 50$ and $\sqrt{(npq)} = 5$. It is now a straightforward task to evaluate the probability that the number of heads lies between any particular pair of values. For example, following the method of example 5 of §12.6 in Volume 1, the probability that in 100 tosses of an unbiased coin, X lies between 40 and 60 inclusive, interpreted here as $39.5 < X < 60.5$, is given by $P\{|Z| < 2.1\}$ where Z is $N(0, 1)$, and this probability is 0.964, (see, for example, Table A2 of Volume 1, or interpolate from Table A1 in this text). It follows that if the coin *is* unbiased there is a probability of 0.964 that in 100 tosses the number of heads will lie in the inclusive range (40, 60). Other ranges would correspond to other values of the probability. In practice therefore the following approach is customarily adopted. A *null hypothesis* is made, and on the basis of the truth of this null hypothesis a *test statistic* is constructed. A numerical value for the test statistic is calculated from the supplied data and this value is compared with a *critical value*. This critical value, which is usually taken from prepared tables, is the number that the test statistic will exceed only with a *preselected probability* when the null hypothesis is true. The value of the pre-selected probability is called the *significance level* and is commonly denoted by α. If the calculated value of the test statistic exceeds the critical value the null hypothesis is *rejected* but otherwise it is *accepted* at the appropriate significance level α. These ideas will be amplified in the remainder of this section.

First observe that, however the question is framed initially, it is always a null hypothesis, commonly denoted by H_0, which is put to the test. If as a result of the significance test the data are held *not* to be consistent with the null hypothesis then the *alternative* hypothesis, labelled H_1, is accepted. Our null hypothesis is always specific, a typical example being that a coin is unbiased, i.e., $H_0 : p = \frac{1}{2}$. The alternative hypothesis is generally non-specific, here $H_1 : p \neq \frac{1}{2}$. This is a *two-tailed test*, because if the null hypothesis is *not true* values of p less than $\frac{1}{2}$ and greater than $\frac{1}{2}$ are considered to be equally plausible. On occasions the alternative hypothesis is *one-tailed*, a matter to which we will return in the next sub-section.

In engineering, tests of significance are usually performed in order to come to a conclusion on which further action may be based. It is therefore evident that the attendant penalties and benefits must have some bearing on the significance level to be chosen. Suppose that the '5% significance level' is selected, i.e. $\alpha = 0.05$. If the null hypothesis is *true* then, on average, for nineteen occasions in every twenty the value of the test statistic will be less than the critical value and on one occasion in twenty, again on average, the test statistic will exceed the critical value. The consequent rejection of the null hypothesis when it is in fact true is called a *Type I Error* or *Error of the First Kind*. The probability of making a Type I Error can obviously be reduced by choosing a smaller significance level, but this tactic increases the probability of a *Type II Error* or *Error of the Second Kind*, which occurs if the null hypothesis is accepted when it is actually false. The probability of a Type II Error is customarily denoted by β. Further considerations of the conflicting claims made by the two types of error follow later in this section. Suffice it now to note that in many instances it has been found appropriate to select a 5% significance level, and this will be the customary value for α in this chapter. Inspection of the values for the cumulative distribution of the s.n.v. Z given in Table A1 show that

$$P\{|Z| > 1.96\} = 0.05 \quad (P\{Z < -1.96\} = 0.025, P\{Z > 1.96\} = 0.025).$$

Thus when the test statistic is the standardized normal variate, and the alternative hypothesis is two-sided, the test statistic should yield a figure less in absolute value than 1.96 for the null hypothesis to be accepted at the 5% significance level, see Fig. 3.2(a). It is convenient to denote critical values by a subscript, this subscript indicating the significance level. Thus $z_{0.05} = 1.96$ and $z_{0.01} = 2.58$. Some texts adopt the usage that if the 5% critical value is exceeded then the result is 'significant' and if the 1% critical value is exceeded the result is 'highly significant'.

One- and Two-tailed Tests

Now let us return to the matter of one- and two-tailed tests. When a two-tailed test is adopted, the implication is that H_0, the null hypothesis of equality, is being tested against a hypothesis of inequality in which 'greater than' and 'less than' are considered an equally plausible pair of alternatives. This is reflected in the fact that the *rejection*

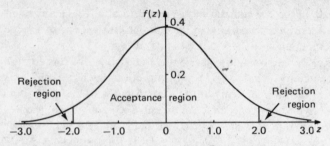

Fig. 3.2(a)   Acceptance and rejection (or critical) regions with the s.n.v. Z as test statistic for a two-tailed test and a significance level of 0.05. $z_{0.05} = 1.96$

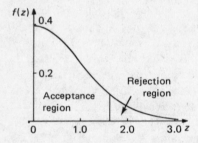

Fig. 3.2(b)   Corresponding situation with a one-tailed test, and the same significance level. $z_{0.05}^* = 1.645$.

or *critical region* consists of two parts, see for example Fig. 3.2(a). For a significance level of α each critical region in the diagram has an area $\alpha/2$. If then the value of the test statistic falls between the two critical values the null hypothesis is accepted, and if it falls outside we adopt the alternative 'greater than' or the alternative 'less than' as appropriate.

On occasions it is desirable to investigate whether or not the value of a parameter has changed *in a particular direction*, as might be the case when a new manufacturing process is introduced in an attempt to improve, say, the durability of a product. The formal hypothesis under test is still the appropriate null hypothesis but the alternative hypothesis H_1 is only one-sided, so that if the null hypothesis of equality is rejected then the move in the indicated direction is accepted.

Clearly it will be necessary to decide, *in advance of the calculation*, whether a given situation makes a one-tailed or two-tailed test appropriate. Four test statistics are discussed in this chapter, namely Z, t, χ^2 and F. The former pair assume both positive and negative values and the latter pair are never negative but all four may be involved in one-sided and two-sided situations. If ξ is the test statistic, ξ_α^* will be used to denote the value of ξ such that $P\{\xi > \xi_\alpha^*\} = \alpha$. This means that if in a one-sided test the critical region is to the right, as in Fig. 3.2(b), then the null hypothesis will be accepted at a significance level α if $\xi < \xi_\alpha^*$, whilst for a two-sided test acceptance demands $\xi_{(1-\frac{1}{2}\alpha)}^* < \xi < \xi_{\frac{1}{2}\alpha}^*$. Since Z and t are symmetrically distributed about zero, for this pair of statistics the latter requirement is equivalent to $|\xi| < \xi_\alpha$ where $\xi_\alpha = \xi_{\frac{1}{2}\alpha}^*$. Thus absence of the asterisk implies the critical value which corresponds to a two-sided test, agreeing with the usage on p. 99.

It should be noted that some other books adopt different conventions in the presentation of tables of critical values, and the student should always be well aware of the format adopted in a particular instance.

Confidence Intervals

Equation (4) may be rewritten as

$$Z = \frac{\hat{p} - p}{\sqrt{\left(\dfrac{pq}{n}\right)}}, \tag{5}$$

where $\hat{p} \equiv X/n$ is an unbiased estimator of p, the population proportion. Since Z is approximately $N(0, 1)$ it will be true that if many repeated samples of size n are taken, about 95% of all observed values of $\hat{p}$ will lie in the range

$$\left\{ p - 1.96\left(\frac{pq}{n}\right)^{\frac{1}{2}}, p + 1.96\left(\frac{pq}{n}\right)^{\frac{1}{2}} \right\}.$$

This interval is illustrated by the top line in Fig. 3.3. It is clear that if a particular value of $\hat{p}$ *does* lie in this interval then p will itself be within the interval of equal length centred on this value of $\hat{p}$. The remaining lines in Fig. 3.3 illustrate the intervals

$$\left\{ \hat{p} - 1.96\left(\frac{\hat{p}\hat{q}}{n}\right)^{\frac{1}{2}}, \hat{p} + 1.96\left(\frac{\hat{p}\hat{q}}{n}\right)^{\frac{1}{2}} \right\}$$

for 20 successive samples of equal size, and all but one of these intervals 'cover' p. It will be noted that since p is unknown it has been necessary to use the estimated standard error $\{\hat{p}(1 - \hat{p})/n\}^{\frac{1}{2}}$ in the expression. Such a range of values is spoken of as a

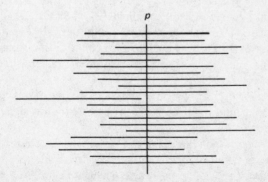

Fig. 3.3 The interval $(p - 1.96\,(pq/n)^{\frac{1}{2}}, p + 1.96\,(pq/n)^{\frac{1}{2}})$ for the indicated value of p together with twenty 95% confidence intervals based on $\hat{p}$ and a constant value of n.

95% *central confidence interval* for the true proportion p. The smaller value is referred to as the *lower confidence limit* and the greater as the *upper confidence limit* for the *confidence coefficient* in question, which here is 0.95. Further, more general, examples of confidence intervals will be given in the following sections.

Power Considerations

A further important aspect of hypothesis-testing now deserves attention. Suppose, for example, that it has been suggested that in a population the proportion having a certain attribute is one-third, and a sample of size 80 is available. Then the null hypothesis $p = \frac{1}{3}$ will *not* be rejected at the 5% significance level if the number observed to possess the attribute lies within the 95% confidence interval, which is here given by

$$\{(80 \times \tfrac{1}{3}) - 1.96(80 \times \tfrac{1}{3} \times \tfrac{2}{3})^{\frac{1}{2}}, (80 \times \tfrac{1}{3}) + 1.96(80 \times \tfrac{1}{3} \times \tfrac{2}{3})^{\frac{1}{2}}\},$$

namely (18.4, 34.9). Suppose however that in the sample the number which possesses the attribute is found to lie between 19 and 34 inclusive, even though $p \neq \frac{1}{3}$. In this case a Type II Error will have been made, namely the acceptance of the null hypothesis when it is false. If, for example, the true value of p is 0.45, then the probability that a sample of size 80 will have, formally, between 18.4 and 34.9 possessing the attribute is given by

$$F\left\{\frac{\dfrac{34.9 - 0.45 \times 80}{80}}{\left(\dfrac{0.45 \times 0.55}{80}\right)^{\frac{1}{2}}}\right\} - F\left\{\frac{\dfrac{18.4 - 0.45 \times 80}{80}}{\left(\dfrac{0.45 \times 0.55}{80}\right)^{\frac{1}{2}}}\right\} = F(-0.247) - F(-3.96)$$

where F is the cumulative distribution function of the s.n.v. Z. Here the evaluation requires greater information than is provided by Table A1 of the Appendix, and reference may therefore be made to Table A2 in the Appendix to Volume 1. From such a table, $F(-0.247) \simeq 0.402$ and $F(-3.96) \simeq 0.000$. It therefore follows that β, the probability of making a Type II Error by accepting the hypothesis $p = \frac{1}{3}$ when in fact $p = 0.45$ is, for this size of sample, approximately 0.4. Similar calculations can be made for other specific figures for the true value of p. In this way a graph of β versus p can be established and this is known as the *operating characteristic curve*. It is commonly referred to as the *o.c. curve* and for the problem under discussion is shown in Fig. 3.4.

Note that the o.c. curve peaks where the hypothesized value of p is equal to its actual value, and this maximum value of β is $(1 - \alpha)$ where α is the significance level adopted for the test.

Figure 3.5 shows the corresponding graph of $(1 - \beta)$ versus p. This latter is called the *power curve* of the test, indicating as it does the ability of a test to reject hypotheses that are false. To illustrate the effects which the choices of sample size and significance level have on the power and o.c. curves, Fig. 3.5 also contains the power curves for the cases $n = 160$, $\alpha = 0.05$ and $n = 160$, $\alpha = 0.10$. It is also possible

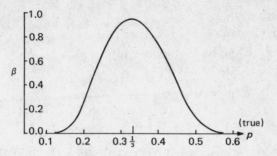

Fig. 3.4 The *operating characteristic curve* for $H_0 : p = \frac{1}{3}, H_1 : p \neq \frac{1}{3}$. β vs true value of p when sample size $n = 80$, significance level $\alpha = 0.05$.

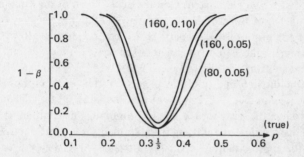

Fig. 3.5 The *power curves* for values of (n, α) as indicated, for null hypothesis $p = \frac{1}{3}$ with two-sided alternative.

to determine minimum sample sizes and corresponding *decision rules* when the Type I and Type II Errors are to be within specified limits, and an example of the procedure is given in the next section.

Ideally a significance test should have an operating characteristic curve in which the peak is well defined and the sides fall away rapidly so that the ability to make an Error of the Second Kind is as small as possible. Although it will not be proved here, it can be shown that for a sample of given size the power curves of the tests to be discussed in §3.3 and §3.4 lie above the power curves of any other test. Such tests are therefore termed the *most powerful* under the conditions appropriate.

Exercises

1. Show that if a die is tossed 60 times and the numbers 1 and 6 occur a total of 24 times then a 95% confidence interval for the probability of throwing one of these pair of numbers is (0.276, 0.524).

2. Calculate the values of β which complete the following table. [Use Table A2 of Volume 1, or an equivalent, of $F(z)$ for the standardized normal variate.]

Sample size n	$H_0:$ $p =$	True p value	α	β
80	$\frac{1}{3}$	0.45	0.05	0.402
80	$\frac{1}{3}$	0.45	0.10	
100	$\frac{1}{3}$	0.45	0.05	
100	0.40	0.45	0.05	

3.3 TESTS OF SIGNIFICANCE BASED ON THE NORMAL DISTRIBUTION

The preceding approach can be extended to more general problems of inference when appeal is made to a most important result, the *Central Limit Theorem*. This states that if the variate X has mean μ and standard deviation σ, and successive independent samples of size n are taken, then the distribution of the sample mean $\bar{X}$ tends, in general, to that of the normal variate $N(\mu, \sigma^2/n)$ as n increases.

As any attempt at a proof of this theorem would be inappropriate in a book of this nature we merely remark that although variates exist to which the theorem cannot be applied, no such case will arise in the following work.

By virtue of the additive property of independent normal distributions (see §12.6 of Volume 1), it will be immediately apparent that the Central Limit Theorem is true for *any* value of n when the basic variate X is itself normally distributed. It is also true that the more the distribution of X differs from normality the greater must be the value of n before the approximation becomes reasonable. Nevertheless even when the variate X is quite skew, the variate Z defined by

$$Z \equiv \frac{\bar{X} - \mu}{\sigma/\sqrt{n}} \tag{6}$$

is approximately $N(0, 1)$ when n is as large as 50.

In this section we shall therefore be discussing 'large' samples with n never less than about 30. Attention will be directed to small samples in §3.4.

Comparison of an Observed Proportion in a Large Sample with a Hypothesized Value

Whereas in the preceding section the normal approximation to the binomial distribution was used to produce equation (5), application of the Central Limit Theorem leads *directly* to this expression when X represents the proportion of successes. Although the following example is therefore of the same type as the problem discussed in §3.2, this presentation is more in line with the remaining examples in this section.

EXAMPLE 1   An interviewer was asked to obtain a simple random sample of opinion among adult men in a certain locality, and of whom it was known that one-sixth was retired. It was subsequently discovered that 39 of the 150 men interviewed were retired. Is it reasonable to conclude that the sampling was random? Use a significance level of 5%.

Let p be the probability that, with the sampling scheme adopted by the interviewer, a retired man is selected. By the Central Limit Theorem, if

$$Z = \frac{p - \hat{p}}{\sqrt{(pq/n)}} \tag{7}$$

then Z is approximately distributed as $N(0, 1)$.

Now make the null hypothesis $H_0 : p = \frac{1}{6}$. The alternative hypothesis is $H_1 : p \neq \frac{1}{6}$, i.e. the alternative is two-tailed.

The estimate of p is given by $\hat{p} = \frac{39}{150}$ so

$$\frac{|p - \hat{p}|}{\sqrt{(pq/n)}} = \frac{|\frac{1}{6} - \frac{39}{150}|}{(\frac{1}{6} \times \frac{5}{6}/150)^{1/2}} = \frac{0.0933}{0.0304} = 3.07 > 1.96 = z_{0.05} .$$

Since the critical value of the s.n.v. for a significance level of 0.05 is exceeded we conclude that the sampling was biased and that the selection contained too many retired men. The cumulative probabilities listed in Table A1 show that only on about one occasion in a thousand could as many retired men as this be found in an unbiased sample of this size.

No *reason* for the apparent bias is ever revealed by a significance test, but with care it is possible to avoid mis-sampling by the use of selections based on random numbers, discussed in Chapter 12 of Volume 1.

The Comparison of a Sample Mean with a Population Mean

Suppose that a large sample, of size n, is taken and the value of $\bar{X}$ is computed. Does this value support the contention that the population mean μ has the value μ_0?

When the hypothesis that $\mu = \mu_0$ is true, and

$$Z = \frac{\bar{X} - \mu_0}{\sigma/\sqrt{n}} \tag{8}$$

then, by the Central Limit Theorem, Z is distributed approximately as $N(0, 1)$. It is necessary to estimate σ by $(\frac{1}{n}\sum(x_i - \bar{x})^2)^{1/2}$. If the alternative hypothesis is two-tailed, the null hypothesis is rejected at (say) the 5% significance level when $z > 1.96$.

EXAMPLE 2   Fifty electrical devices were found to have a mean resistance of 14.86Ω. The sum of the squares of the deviations from this mean value was $8.30\Omega^2$. Is it reasonable to suppose that for the whole population of such devices the mean resistance is 15Ω? Obtain a 95% confidence interval for the mean resistance.

Make the null hypothesis $H_0 : \mu = 15 \; \Omega$, with the two-tailed alternative hypothesis $H_1 : \mu \neq 15 \; \Omega$. If H_0 is true, then by the Central Limit Theorem the values of $\frac{\bar{X} - 15}{\sigma/\sqrt{n}}$ are distributed approximately as $N(0, 1)$. Here $\bar{x} = 14.86$, $n = 50$ and the estimate for σ^2 is 8.30/50 so $\sigma/\sqrt{n} = 0.0576$. Then

$$\frac{|14.86 - 15.00|}{0.0576} = 2.43 > 1.96 = z_{0.05} .$$

The null hypothesis is therefore rejected at the 5% significance level.

A 95% confidence interval for the population mean is given by

$\{(14.86 - 1.96 \times 0.0576)\Omega, \ (14.86 + 1.96 \times 0.0576)\Omega\}$, i.e. $(14.75\Omega, 14.97\Omega)$.

The Comparison of Proportions from Two Large Samples

Suppose that in a simple random sample from population A a proportion p'_A was found to possess a certain attribute. An independent simple random sample from population B contained a proportion p'_B with the attribute. The respective sample sizes, n_A and n_B were large. Is it reasonable to infer that the parent populations possess identical proportions of this attribute?

Let the proportion with this attribute in population A be p_A and in population B let it be p_B. Then, since n_A is large, with repeated sampling the distribution of the recorded values of p'_A will be normal, with mean p_A and variance $p_A q_A / n_A$. Similarly p'_B will be normally distributed with mean p_B and variance $p_B q_B / n_B$, and hence

$p'_A - p'_B$ is normally distributed with mean $p_A - p_B$ and variance $\dfrac{p_A q_A}{n_A} + \dfrac{p_B q_B}{n_B}$ so that if

$$Z = \frac{(p'_A - p'_B) - (p_A - p_B)}{\left(\dfrac{p_A q_A}{n_A} + \dfrac{p_B q_B}{n_B}\right)^{\frac{1}{2}}} \tag{9}$$

then Z is approximately $N(0, 1)$.

The null hypothesis is $H_0 : p_A = p_B$, and when it is true expression (9) reduces to

$$Z = \frac{p'_A - p'_B}{\left(\dfrac{pq}{n_A} + \dfrac{pq}{n_B}\right)^{\frac{1}{2}}} , \tag{10}$$

where p denotes this common value of p_A, p_B. As the values of p and q which appear in the denominator are unknown, it is necessary to use estimates. The preferred estimator of p is the unbiased estimator with minimum variance and this is

$$\hat{p} = \frac{n_A p'_A + n_B p'_B}{n_A + n_B} \quad \text{with } \hat{q} = 1 - \hat{p} . \tag{11a, b}$$

For a two-tailed alternative hypothesis the null hypothesis is rejected at the 5% significance level if, with p and q estimated as indicated

$$\frac{|p'_A - p'_B|}{(\hat{p}\hat{q})^{\frac{1}{2}} \left(\dfrac{1}{n_A} + \dfrac{1}{n_B}\right)^{\frac{1}{2}}} > 1.96 = z_{0.05} .$$

EXAMPLE 3   One hundred and thirty pieces of timber were randomly divided into two batches. The first batch, which consisted of 50 pieces, was stored at a certain location and the remaining pieces were stored elsewhere. After a given period each batch was examined. If 18 of the first batch and 20 of the second batch were found to have deteriorated, is it reasonable to conclude that there was no essential difference in the storage quality of the two locations?

Make the null hypothesis H_0: there is no difference between the storage quality of these locations, with alternative hypothesis H_1: the data do suggest a difference. The test is therefore two-tailed.

Adopting the obvious notation, we write

$$n_A = 50, \quad n_B = 80, \quad p'_A = \tfrac{18}{50}, \quad p'_B = \tfrac{20}{80}.$$

Under the null hypothesis, $p_A = p_B = p$ and the common probability p is estimated by $\hat{p} = \tfrac{18+20}{50+80} = \tfrac{38}{130}$, so that $\hat{q} = \tfrac{92}{130}$. Then

$$|z| = \frac{|\tfrac{18}{50} - \tfrac{20}{80}|}{(\tfrac{38}{130} \times \tfrac{92}{130})^{\frac{1}{2}} (\tfrac{1}{50} + \tfrac{1}{80})^{\frac{1}{2}}} = \frac{0.110}{0.4548 \times 0.1803} = 1.34 < 1.96 = z_{0.05}.$$

It is therefore reasonable to accept the null hypothesis that there is no difference between the respective storage qualities of these two locations.

The Comparison of Means from Two Large Samples

From population A, which has unknown mean μ_A, a simple random sample $\{x_{A1}, x_{A2}, \ldots, x_{An_A}\}$ of size n_A was taken. An independent sample $\{x_{B1}, x_{B2}, \ldots, x_{Bn_B}\}$ of size n_B was taken from population B, which has an unknown mean μ_B. On the basis of these samples is it reasonable to suppose that the population means are equal?

Let the sample means be $\bar{X}_A, \bar{X}_B$. Then, since n_A and n_B are large, with repeated sampling

$\bar{X}_A$ is normally distributed with mean μ_A and variance σ_A^2/n_A,

$\bar{X}_B$ is normally distributed with mean μ_B and variance σ_B^2/n_B,

and hence

$\bar{X}_A - \bar{X}_B$ is normally distributed with mean $\mu_A - \mu_B$ and variance $\left(\dfrac{\sigma_A^2}{n_A} + \dfrac{\sigma_B^2}{n_B}\right)$,

so that if

$$Z = \frac{(\bar{X}_A - \bar{X}_B) - (\mu_A - \mu_B)}{\left(\dfrac{\sigma_A^2}{n_A} + \dfrac{\sigma_B^2}{n_B}\right)^{\frac{1}{2}}} \tag{12}$$

then Z is approximately $N(0, 1)$.

The null hypothesis is $H_0 : \mu_A = \mu_B$. When this is true, expression (12) reduces to

$$Z = \frac{\bar{X}_A - \bar{X}_B}{\left(\dfrac{\sigma_A^2}{n_A} + \dfrac{\sigma_B^2}{n_B}\right)^{1/2}}. \tag{13}$$

The sample means are respectively given by $\dfrac{1}{n_A} \displaystyle\sum_{i=1}^{n_A} x_{Ai}$ and $\dfrac{1}{n_B} \displaystyle\sum_{j=1}^{n_B} x_{Bj}$. We estimate

σ_A^2 by $\dfrac{1}{n_A} \displaystyle\sum_{i=1}^{n_A} (x_{Ai} - \bar{x}_A)^2$, and σ_B^2 by $\dfrac{1}{n_B} \displaystyle\sum_{j=1}^{n_B} (x_{Bj} - \bar{x}_B)^2$.

For a two-tailed alternative the null hypothesis is rejected at the 5% significance level if

$$\frac{|\bar{x}_A - \bar{x}_B|}{\left(\dfrac{\sigma_A^2}{n_A} + \dfrac{\sigma_B^2}{n_B}\right)^{1/2}} > 1.96 = z_{0.05}.$$

A 95 % confidence interval for the value of $\mu_A - \mu_B$ is given by

$$\left\{ (\bar{x}_A - \bar{x}_B) - 1.96 \left(\frac{\sigma_A^2}{n_A} + \frac{\sigma_B^2}{n_B}\right)^{1/2}, (\bar{x}_A - \bar{x}_B) + 1.96 \left(\frac{\sigma_A^2}{n_A} + \frac{\sigma_B^2}{n_B}\right)^{1/2} \right\}.$$

EXAMPLE 4   Eighty electrical components of a certain brand A had a mean operational life of 1240 hours and a standard deviation of 136 hours. Sixty components of another brand B had a mean operational life of 1198 hours and a standard deviation of 94 hours. Do these data suggest that the mean lives of these two brands are equal?

Make the null hypothesis $H_0 : \mu_A = \mu_B$, with alternative hypothesis $H_1 : \mu_A \neq \mu_B$.

The estimated standard error for the difference in means is $\left(\dfrac{136^2}{80} + \dfrac{94^2}{60}\right)^{1/2} = 19.45$ so that

$$\frac{|\bar{x}_A - \bar{x}_B|}{\left(\dfrac{\sigma_A^2}{n_A} + \dfrac{\sigma_B^2}{n_B}\right)^{1/2}} = \frac{|1240 - 1198|}{19.45} = 2.16 > 1.96 = z_{0.05}.$$

At the 5% significance level the hypothesis of equal lives is therefore rejected in favour of the view that population A has the greater mean operational life.

Decision Rules

The concept of *power* enables *minimum sample sizes* and *decision rules* to be established for given values of α and β. The following example illustrates the technique.

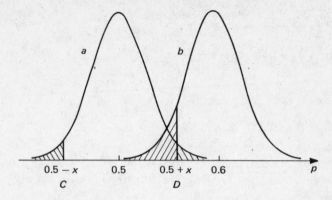

Fig. 3.6 Normal variates with means of 0.5 and 0.6. Their variances are functions of sample sizes, to be determined (see example 5).

EXAMPLE 5 Determine the minimum sample size necessary, and the corresponding decision rule, to investigate the hypothesis $p = \frac{1}{2}$ in a sequence of Bernoulli trials under the constraints that

1. the probability of rejecting the hypothesis when it is in fact true is not more than $\frac{1}{20}$, and
2. the probability of accepting this hypothesis when $|p - \frac{1}{2}| \geqslant \frac{1}{10}$ is also not more than $\frac{1}{20}$.

Under the stated conditions, the values of the true probability p which are most likely to produce a Type II Error are $p = 0.4$ and $p = 0.6$. Because of the symmetry present the calculation can effectively be limited to the one for the case $p = 0.6$. Refer now to Fig. 3.6 which shows normal variates corresponding to $p = 0.5$ and $p = 0.6$. The *locations* of these curves are fixed because their means are known but their *spreads* are a function of sample size which has still to be determined.

To satisfy the condition $\alpha = 0.05$, the location of point C must be such that the area to the left of C and below curve a must be 0.025, and similarly the area to the right of D and below curve a must also be 0.025. In this instance, by symmetry, the values of C and D may be written $(0.5 - x)$ and $(0.5 + x)$ respectively. Remembering that $p = q = 0.5$ for curve a, the position of D must be such that, by Table A1,

$$\frac{(0.5 + x) - 0.5}{\left(\dfrac{0.5 \times 0.5}{n}\right)^{\frac{1}{2}}} = 1.96 = z_{0.025}^{*} \ .$$

This simplifies immediately to

$$x = 0.98 n^{-\frac{1}{2}} \tag{14}$$

To satisfy the condition $\beta = 0.05$, the locations of C and D must be such that the area under curve b between the ordinates at C and D must be 0.05. On the assumption that the area under curve b to the left of C is very small indeed, it follows from the

Normal Table that, since $p = 0.6$ here,

$$\frac{(0.5 + x) - 0.6}{\left(\dfrac{0.6 \times 0.4}{n}\right)^{\frac{1}{2}}} = -1.645 = z_{0.95}^{*}.$$

This may be rewritten as

$$x - 0.1 = -0.806 n^{-\frac{1}{2}}. \tag{15}$$

The formal solutions of the simultaneous linear equations (14) and (15) are $x = 0.055$ and $n^{-\frac{1}{2}} = 17.86^{-1}$. Since it is necessary to take n and $n(0.5 + x)$ as integers n becomes 319 and, to the nearest integer below, $n(0.5 + x)$ is 176. Similarly we take $n(0.5 - x)$ to be 143.

We therefore conclude that for a sample to be acceptable the size must be at least 319 and the *decision rule* associated with the minimum size is to accept the null hypothesis if the number of successes is found to lie in the range (143, 176) and to reject it otherwise.

Quality Control

The preceding analysis in this section permits the consideration of *quality control*. This arises in production runs in which it is necessary to keep a specified parameter within certain limits. For example, a machine may have to dispense a quantity of yeast extract to a proprietary food or a (different) machine produce axles for heavy goods vehicles, within certain tolerances. The procedure is as follows.

The appropriate characteristics of the process in question are first established by carrying out a sufficiently large number of trials with the machine acting 'satisfactorily', so that the mean and variance of the parameter in these runs can be taken as true representatives of the population values μ and σ^2. From a production run a sample, of size n, is taken. When the machine is working to the initially established values of μ and σ^2 it is evident from Table A1 that we expect the value of the sample mean $\bar{X}$ to fall between the values $\mu - k\sigma/\sqrt{n}$ and $\mu + k\sigma/\sqrt{n}$ in about 68%, 95% and 99.8% of the cases for $k = 1, 2$ and 3 respectively.

This concept can be displayed graphically by plotting the sample values as ordinates and using time (or sample number) as horizontal axis. An example of such a graph, known as a *Quality Control Chart*, is shown in Fig. 3.7. If the sampling is correctly performed and yet a point is found to lie an appreciable distance from the mean μ then either a rare event has happened or a process parameter has changed. Again the conflicting claims of a Type I Error and a Type II Error (which in this context are often known respectively as *producer's risk* and *consumer's risk*), must be balanced. Clearly it is desirable neither to have the process go awry nor to needlessly inhibit production and, legal requirements apart, the relative economics of these situations dictate the precise width of the acceptable *control band*. It is customary to have *'warning' lines* at a certain distance from the mean μ with *'action' lines* at a greater distance, as shown. For a point to lie just beyond such a warning line

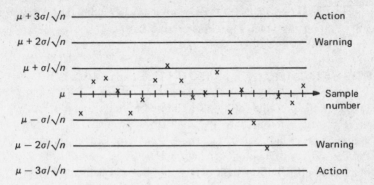

Fig. 3.7 Typical *Quality Control Chart*. In this example the process appears to be under control.

may be merely a signal for closer attention to be paid to the next batch of results or it may necessitate an increase in the rate of sampling. To exceed an action line may indicate that the machine must be inspected at the end of the shift. Some automated procedures are programmed so that when *'danger' lines* are exceeded production is halted forthwith.

The sampling should be carried out at random intervals, for otherwise the effects of some regular or quasi-regular fluctuations, e.g. voltage drops at peak load times, may be overlooked. Even though a significant *increase* in (say) a proportion of acceptable items appears to be to the advantage of the manufacturer, it requires investigation to establish the cause.

Because these charts, known as *Shewhart Control Charts*, produce a visual display which is capable of ready comprehension they have proved of considerable use in practical situations. Nevertheless an alteration in machine behaviour may sometimes produce undetected changes in the values of the mean or the variance or both, without such changes being obvious from the chart because the sample points continue to lie within the control band. To overcome this hazard several more sophisticated designs of chart have been produced in recent years, in particular the *Cumulative Sum (Cusum) Control Chart*. For a discussion of these, more specialized books on production inspection and control should be consulted.

Exercises

1. Show that a 95% confidence interval for the difference in mean operational life of the two brands of electrical components, which are described in example 4, is (3.9, 80.1) hours.

2. Show that the estimate of p provided by equation (11a) is (a) unbiased, (b) the most efficient.

3. Confirm that in example 5 the area under curve b to the left of the ordinate at C is negligible. Also write down the analogue of the expressions which lead to equation (15) when $p = 0.4$, rather than $p = 0.6$, is chosen as the situation most likely to produce a Type II Error.

4. Discuss how to set up a Quality Control Chart for checking the *proportion* of acceptable components which a machine produces.

3.4 TESTS OF SIGNIFICANCE BASED ON THE *t* DISTRIBUTION

Discussion in the preceding section was limited to 'large' samples, but on many occasions it is possible to obtain only a small set of observations. What modifications to the approach prove necessary in such cases? The problem hinges on the fact that use of the Central Limit Theorem demands a knowledge — in principle — of the standard deviation (s.d.) of the basic variate and this is usually unknown. Inspection of the examples considered in §3.3 confirms that it is generally necessary to use an *estimated* value which is based on the data supplied. When the sample is small it can be shown that such an estimate is not, in general, a good one, with the result that the distribution of the statistic $(\bar{X} - \mu)/(S/\sqrt{n})$ differs appreciably from that of a standardized normal variate. Fortunately, when the parent variate X is *normal* the distribution of this statistic is known. The discovery was due to W. S. Gosset who wrote under the pen name of 'Student' and as the statistic is customarily denoted by t, significance tests which employ it are commonly called *Student t-tests*. More precisely, if

$$t_{[n-1]} \equiv \frac{\bar{X} - \mu}{S/\sqrt{n}} \tag{16}$$

where $\bar{X}$ and S refer to a sample of size n, then we have a t *distribution on* $(n-1)$ *degrees of freedom*. As the title implies, the precise form of the distribution depends upon the number of degrees of freedom, ν. Because $s^2 \to \sigma^2$ (and $s/\sqrt{n} \to \sigma/\sqrt{n}$) as n becomes large it is clear that, as $\nu \to \infty$, $t_{[\nu]} \to Z$ where Z is $N(0, 1)$. Each t variate is symmetric about $t = 0$ so that Fig. 3.8 presents half-graphs of two typical t distributions, namely $t_{[2]}$ and $t_{[10]}$, for comparison with the standardized normal variate. Although the differences may appear to be slight, for small ν the flatter

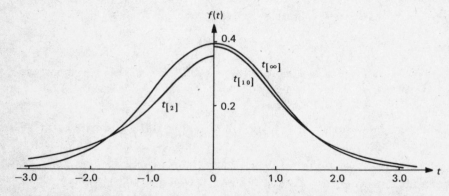

Fig. 3.8   Comparison of (half-graphs of) the probability density functions for $t_{[2]}$ and $t_{[10]}$ with s.n.v. $Z \,(\equiv t_{[\infty]})$.

shape of the t distribution implies, for example, that when $\alpha = 0.05$ the critical value $t_{[\nu]0.05}$ is somewhat greater than 1.96, the corresponding figure for a s.n.v. This may be seen from Table A2 in the Appendix, where critical t values are given for $\alpha = 0.025$ and 0.05. The corresponding values for degrees of freedom other than those quoted may be found by interpolation. Thirty is confirmed as a suitable boundary between the size of samples considered to be 'small' and 'large' since above this value the distributions of $t_{[\nu]}$ and Z are virtually indistinguishable.

Because of their general similarity to the corresponding large sample situations most of the following small sample investigations call for little comment. Even the formal requirement that the distribution in the parent population be normal is not a major handicap, for it can be shown that these t tests are not particularly sensitive to the manner in which the basic variate is distributed. The t tests are therefore said to be *robust*.

The Comparison of a Sample Mean with a Population Mean

A small sample of size n, taken from a normal population, has a sample mean $\bar{x}$ and sample variance s^2. Is the result consistent with a hypothesized value of μ_0 for the population mean μ?

The argument adopted is similar to that for the corresponding 'large' sample situation on p. 105. The null hypothesis is $\mu = \mu_0$. If this is true, then for repeated sampling

$$t \equiv \frac{\bar{X} - \mu_0}{S/\sqrt{n}} \tag{17}$$

has a t distribution on $(n-1)$ degrees of freedom. If the alternative hypothesis is two-sided, the null hypothesis is accepted at a significance level α if $\dfrac{|\bar{x} - \mu_0|}{s/\sqrt{n}} < t_{[n-1]\alpha}$ where $P\{|t_{[n-1]}| > t_{[n-1]\alpha}\} = \alpha$. When the alternative hypothesis is one-sided the customary modifications are made.

EXAMPLE 1   Written on the exteriors of a certain type of matchbox were the words 'Average contents not less than 35'. A 'spot check' of six boxes, taken at random, revealed counts of 35, 33, 36, 32, 33, 35. The number of matches in a box may be assumed to be normally distributed. Do these data provide evidence that the manufacturer's claim is not being met?

That the manufacturer's claim is being met we make into the specific null hypothesis $H_0 : \mu = 35$.

The alternative hypothesis, that the claim is not being met, is $H_1 : \mu < 35$. The test is therefore one-sided.

From the data,

$$\bar{x} = \tfrac{1}{6}(35 + 33 + 36 + 32 + 33 + 35) = 34.0$$

$$s^2 = \tfrac{1}{5}(1 + 1 + 4 + 4 + 1 + 1) = 2.4 .$$

Then

$$\frac{\bar{x} - \mu_0}{s/\sqrt{n}} = \frac{34 - 35}{\sqrt{(2.4/6)}} = -1.58 \ .$$

For this one tailed test, $t_{[5]0.05}^* = -2.02$ from Table A2, and therefore there is insufficient evidence to refute the manufacturer's claim.

Comparison of Means in Two Small Samples from Normal Populations with Equal Variances

Suppose now that two small independent random samples $\{x_{A1}, x_{A2}, \ldots\}$ and $\{x_{B1}, x_{B2}, \ldots\}$ of sizes n_A and n_B respectively are drawn from two normal populations A and B, which have an assumed common but unknown variance σ^2. The hypothesis to be tested, against a suitable alternative, is that the population means are equal.

Let

$$\bar{x}_A = \frac{1}{n_A} \sum_{i=1}^{n_A} x_{Ai}, \quad s_A^2 = \frac{1}{n_A - 1} \sum_{i=1}^{n_A} (x_{Ai} - \bar{x}_A)^2 \ ,$$

with similar expressions for $\bar{x}_B$ and s_B^2.

S_A^2 and S_B^2 are each unbiased estimators of the (unknown) population variance, and it can be shown that the unbiased estimator with smallest variance is given by

$$S^2 = \frac{(n_A - 1)S_A^2 + (n_B - 1)S_B^2}{n_A + n_B - 2} \tag{18}$$

Now, by following an argument similar to that used for the comparison of means of large samples, see p. 107, it is found that when μ_A and μ_B are equal then the quantity t defined by

$$t \equiv \frac{\bar{X}_A - \bar{X}_B}{S\left(\dfrac{1}{n_A} + \dfrac{1}{n_B}\right)^{\frac{1}{2}}} \tag{19}$$

is distributed like a t variate on $(n_A + n_B - 2)$ degrees of freedom.

EXAMPLE 2   A blood bank has to supply blood to hospitals in a given region. The route to a particular hospital is mainly along a motorway, but there are two possible exits from the motorway to the hospital. In order to see which route might be preferable, routes and journey times were noted with the following results:

	Number of journeys	Mean time taken	Sum of squares of deviations from these sample means
Route A	10	34 min	154 min^2
Route B	12	30 min	104 min^2

Provided that the journey times may be assumed to be normally distributed, do these data indicate a significant difference between the routes?

From the data

$$\bar{x}_A = 34, \quad \bar{x}_B = 30,$$

and

$$s^2 = \frac{154 + 104}{9 + 11} = \frac{258}{20} = 12.9.$$

Make the null hypothesis $\mu_A = \mu_B$. The alternative hypothesis is two-sided. Then

$$\frac{|\bar{x}_A - \bar{x}_B|}{s\left(\frac{1}{n_A} + \frac{1}{n_B}\right)^{\frac{1}{2}}} = \frac{|34 - 30|}{(12.9)^{\frac{1}{2}}(\frac{1}{10} + \frac{1}{12})^{\frac{1}{2}}} = \frac{4.0}{\sqrt{2.365}} = 2.60.$$

This value is greater than $2.09 = t_{[20]0.05}$, from Table A2. The data therefore indicate that the difference *is* significant and that route B is faster than route A.

Two points to note are as follows:
1. It has been assumed that the underlying population variances are equal. In principle it is therefore necessary to investigate whether or not the values of the sample variances differ significantly. This requires a test based on the F distribution which is discussed in §3.6. In particular, exercise 4 at the end of that section shows this condition to be satisfied.
2. The calculation of s^2 involves the sums of squares of deviations from the *respective* means, *not* from the *pooled* mean.

The t Test for Paired Samples

When additional factors are present it is usually desirable to modify the preceding method for investigating the difference between the means of two small samples. It is readily apparent, for example, that the yield-producing capacities of two types of seed designed for similar soils can scarcely be compared if one type is planted in a region essentially more fertile than the other. A common technique for lessening the effects of extraneous factors is to take 'paired samples'. In the above case this could be accomplished by taking (say) ten plots of land, dividing each into two and then allocating the seed randomly, one type to each half. A similar situation which often demands a paired sample test occurs when 'before and after' investigations are carried out on a set of individuals. The technique is readily appreciated by considering an example.

EXAMPLE 3   In order to reduce the consumer demand for a certain luxury item, the tax is increased. Sales returns from each of ten large stores distributed throughout the country show the number of these items sold in the three-month period immediately following the tax change and this figure is compared with the sales in the corresponding

TABLE 3.1

| Number of items sold | Store | | | | | | | | | |
	A	*B*	*C*	*D*	*E*	*F*	*G*	*H*	*I*	*J*
Earlier quarter	62	48	69	70	64	63	50	44	49	53
Later quarter	57	50	60	67	59	63	47	40	44	56

three-month period of the previous year. If these figures are derived from normal populations, do they indicate a significant drop in sales?

There is clearly appreciable variation in the figures from one store to another and a paired t test is appropriate. The contention that there is no decrease in the overall sales of the items is tested against the alternative that a decrease has occurred.

Let X_k denote the fall in sales, between these quarters, for the kth store, so that

$$x_i = 5 \;\; -2 \;\; 9 \;\; 3 \;\; 5 \;\; 0 \;\; 3 \;\; 4 \;\; 5 \;\; -3 \quad \text{for} \quad i = 1, 2, \ldots, 10 \, .$$

Therefore

$$\sum_{i=1}^{10} x_i = 29, \quad \text{so that} \quad \bar{x} = 2.9 \, ,$$

and

$$\sum_{i=1}^{10} x_i^2 = 203, \quad \text{so that} \quad s^2 = \tfrac{1}{9} \{203.0 - 10 \times 2.9^2\} = 13.21 \, .$$

The null hypothesis is $H_0 : \mu = 0$, and if this is true then

$$\frac{\bar{x} - \mu}{s/\sqrt{n}} = \frac{2.9 - 0}{\sqrt{(13.21/10)}} = \frac{2.9}{1.149} = 2.52 \, .$$

For a significance level of 0.05 the appropriate critical value is $t_{[9]0.05}^{*} = 1.83$ since the test is one-sided. The conclusion is therefore that in the population at large the sales of these items have decreased.

Note that, notwithstanding the fact that the test is one-sided, a central 95% confidence interval for the average quarterly reduction is still given by

$(\bar{x} \pm t_{[9]0.05} \frac{s}{\sqrt{n}})$, which here is $(2.9 \pm 26 \times 1.149)$, i.e. $(0.3, 5.5)$.

Exercises

1. Discuss how you would establish the power curve for a t test on a given number of degrees of freedom.

2. Prove that S^2, defined by equation (18), is an unbiased estimator of the common population variance σ^2.

3. If α is a typical significance level, (say $\leqslant 10\%$), write down the inequalities which connect $t_{[\nu]\alpha}^*, t_{[\nu]\frac{1}{2}\alpha}^*, z_\alpha^*$. Estimate $t_{[40]0.05}^*, t_{[\infty]0.02}^*$. [The true values, correct to 2 d.p., are given in the Answers section at the back of the book.]

3.5 TESTS OF SIGNIFICANCE BASED ON THE χ^2 DISTRIBUTION

Goodness of Fit

The third distribution to be considered is the χ^2 (*chi-squared* or *chi-square*) variate. This is particularly associated with 'goodness of fit' problems, so called because the task is to determine whether or not a set of observed frequencies is compatible with a set of 'theoretical' frequencies which have been computed according to some hypothesis. A typical example is 'do given data on the breaking strengths of cables follow a normal distribution?'

Whether the variate associated with the observed frequencies is discrete or continuous it is necessary in goodness of fit problems to divide the range into a finite number of classes. Suppose that there are k such classes and let p_i be the probability that the random variable falls in the ith class, according to the theory proposed. In a simple random sample of size n the expected number in the ith class is therefore np_i. If the actual number observed in the ith class is f_i there is an associated 'disparity' of $|np_i - f_i|$. Although the mathematical derivation is beyond the scope of this chapter it transpires that the appropriate measure of the total disparity is

$$\sum_{i=1}^k \frac{(f_i - np_i)^2}{np_i} \quad \text{which may conveniently be written} \quad \sum_{i=1}^k \frac{(O_i - E_i)^2}{E_i},$$

where O_i is the 'observed' number in the ith class, E_i is the corresponding 'expected' number, and there are k classes to be considered. If the sample size is sufficiently large and the null hypothesis is true it may be shown that

$$u \equiv \sum_{i=1}^k \frac{(O_i - E_i)^2}{E_i} \tag{20}$$

is approximately distributed as a $\chi^2_{[\nu]}$ variate, where ν, the number of degrees of freedom, is at most $(k - 1)$. The number of constraints imposed in the calculation of the expected values affects the number of degrees of freedom and the value of ν is further reduced by 1 for each parameter it has been necessary to estimate *from the data*. The third factor affecting ν is that the formal derivation of the result precludes situations where the *expected* number in a class is particularly small and a commonly quoted criterion is that any E_i should not be less than about 5. This stipulation can legitimately be met by pooling some of the classes with the proviso that wherever m classes are combined into a single class the number of degrees of freedom is reduced by $(m - 1)$. All of these points are illustrated in the examples which follow.

The easily-established graphs of the distributions of $\chi^2_{[3]}$ and $\chi^2_{[6]}$ are shown, by way

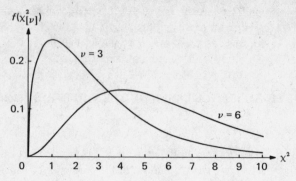

Fig. 3.9   The probability density functions for $\chi^2_{[3]}$ and $\chi^2_{[6]}$.

of example, in Fig. 3.9. All that is necessary in a goodness of fit test is to compare the

computed value of $\sum_i \dfrac{(O_i - E_i)^2}{E_i}$ with the critical value of $\chi^2_{[\nu]}$ at the desired

significance level α. If $\chi^2_{[\nu]\alpha}{}^{*}$ is exceeded then it is argued that the observed data are not consistent with the theory proposed. With $\alpha = 0.01$ and $\alpha = 0.05$ critical values of χ^2 appear as Table A3 in the Appendix. It should be noted that goodness of fit tests are customarily one-tailed as the smaller is the calculated value of χ^2 the better is the agreement between 'observed' and 'theoretical' values.

Comparison of an Observed Frequency Distribution with a Theoretical One

In Chapter 12 of Volume 1 it was shown how to fit certain theoretical distributions to observed sets of data. We will now investigate in particular instances whether or not the measure of agreement may be considered satisfactory.

EXAMPLE 1   An hour-long traffic census at a particular location recorded the number O_i of time intervals of one minute in which i vehicles passed. Use the data to fit a Poissonian distribution and test for goodness of fit.

The census data are supplied as the first two lines of Table 3.2. The expected

TABLE 3.2

Number of vehicles i	0	1	2	3	4	5	6 or more
Observed frequency O_i	6	11	15	12	10	6	0
Expected frequency E_i	5.2	12.7	15.5	12.7	7.8	3.8	2.3
$O_i - E_i$	0.8	−1.7	−0.5	−0.7	2.2		−0.1
$(O_i - E_i)^2$	0.64	2.89	0.25	0.49	4.84		0.01
$(O_i - E_i)^2/E_i$	0.12	0.23	0.02	0.04	0.62		0.00

frequencies, the set of E_i values, are given on the third line. They have been computed on the basis of a Poissonian distribution, the parameter λ having been estimated by the sample mean $\bar{x}$, found to be 2.45. (These are values used in Table 12.1, p. 440, and Table 12.4, p. 478 of Volume 1.) The remainder of Table 3.2 is devoted to the computation of χ^2 on the hypothesis that the supplied data is consistent with a $Po(2.45)$ distribution.

The seven classes originally present have the basic constraint $\sum_i O_i = \sum_i E_i$, one para-meter, namely the mean λ, had to be estimated from these data in order to compute the expected values, and to produce an *expected* value of sufficient size it has proved necessary to combine the results for $i = 5$ and $i \geqslant 6$. The net number of degrees of freedom is therefore $7 - 1 - 1 - 1 = 4$, and from Table A3, $\chi^2_{[4]0.05} = 9.49$. The computed value of $\displaystyle\sum_i \frac{(O_i - E_i)^2}{E_i}$ is 1.03, which is much less than the critical value. The hypothesis that the parent distribution is Poissonian is therefore accepted.

EXAMPLE 2   Two hundred and fifty-six lengths of cable were chosen at random from a production run and the load x (in tons) necessary to break each of these cables was determined. The results were grouped and then published as the first two lines in Table 3.3. Fit a normal distribution to this data and test for goodness of fit.

From the data $\bar{x}$ and s^2 are computed to be 10.07 ton and 0.165 ton^2. Using these as respective estimates of μ and σ^2, the expected values E_i corresponding to the distribution $N(10.07, 0.165)$ are displayed in the third line of Table 3.3, (see also Table 12.2, p. 441, and Table 12.5, p. 482, of Volume 1), and the remainder of Table 3.3 completes the calculation of χ^2 under the appropriate hypothesis.

It will be noted that the expected values at each end of the range have been grouped to provide numbers of adequate size so that there are now 9 classes. As the two parameters μ and σ had to be estimated from the data the appropriate number of degrees of freedom is $9 - 1 - 2 = 6$. From Table A3, $\chi^2_{[6]0.05} = 12.59$ which is greater than the calculated value 7.48, and the null hypothesis is accepted.

Independence-testing in a Two-way Contingency Table

In a two-way frequency contingency table, introduced in §12.7 of Volume 1, the sampled items have precisely two categories, e.g. diameter and weight, by which they are classified. Let one category be denoted by G and contain r classes and let the other category be denoted by H and contain s classes. If f_{ij} is the number observed to belong simultaneously to the ith G class and jth H class, then Table 3.4 illustrates the corresponding frequency contingency table. Associated with each (i, j) cell is a probability p_{ij} that an observation taken at random will belong to that cell, so that the expected number in a sample of size n is np_{ij}. Suppose that it is desired to test whether or not there is some degree of association between the two categories G and H. If the two categories are independent then $p_{ij} = p_{i.} \times p_{.j}$ for all i, j where $p_{i.}$ and $p_{.j}$ are the marginal probabilities described in §12.7 of Volume 1. The appropriate estimates for

TABLE 3.3

Applied load (mid-interval) x_i	8.9	9.1	9.3	9.5	9.7	9.9	10.1	10.3	10.5	10.7	10.9	11.1	11.3
Observed frequency O_i	0	1	8	26	35	40	54	37	26	19	8	2	0
Expected frequency E_i	1.0	3.1	8.7	18.7	33.0	46.1	49.4	42.5	29.2	15.1	6.4	2.0	0.8
$O_i - E_i$		−3.8		7.3	2.0	−6.1	4.6	−5.5	−3.2	3.9		0.8	
$(O_i - E_i)^2$		14.4		53.3	4.0	37.2	21.2	30.3	10.2	15.2		0.6	
$(O_i - E_i)^2/E_i$		1.13		2.85	0.12	0.81	0.43	0.71	0.35	1.01		0.07	

$$\sum_i \frac{(O_i - E_i)^2}{E_i} = 7.48 \ .$$

TABLE 3.4

	H_1	$H_2 \ldots$	H_s	Total
G_1	f_{11}	$f_{12} \ldots$	f_{1s}	$f_{1\cdot}$
G_2	f_{21}			
$\vdots$	$\vdots$			
G_r	f_{r1}		f_{rs}	$f_{r\cdot}$
Total	$f_{\cdot1}$		$f_{\cdot s}$	n

$p_{i\cdot}$ and $p_{\cdot j}$ are respectively $f_{i\cdot}/n$ and $f_{\cdot j}/n$, so that, with independence, the expected value np_{ij} is estimated by $(f_{i\cdot} \times f_{\cdot j})/n$. If u is defined by

$$u \equiv \sum_{i=1}^{r} \sum_{j=1}^{s} \left\{ \frac{(O_{ij} - E_{ij})^2}{E_{ij}} \right\} = \sum_{i=1}^{r} \sum_{j=1}^{s} \left\{ \frac{\{f_{ij} - (f_{i\cdot} \times f_{\cdot j})/n\}^2}{(f_{i\cdot} \times f_{\cdot j})/n} \right\}, \quad (21)$$

then, when the categories are independent, u has approximately a χ^2 distribution on $(r-1) \times (s-1)$ degrees of freedom. The number of degrees of freedom follows from the fact that a knowledge of the row and column totals, together with all but one value in each row and each column enables the full table to be constructed. The analysis can readily be extended to three-way (or more) contingency tables.

EXAMPLE 3   In a cake-baking competition open to wives of professional engineers, the cakes were rated 'excellent', 'very good' and 'good' in the two categories for which they were judged, namely appearance and taste, and Table 3.5 shows the decisions on the 213 cakes submitted. Determine whether or not these data suggest that the two categories were independent.

TABLE 3.5: The 'O_{ij}' values

Cake	Appearance			
Taste	Excellent	Very good	Good	Total
Excellent	10	26	8	44
Very good	17	86	24	127
Good	12	15	15	42
Total	39	127	47	213

On the hypothesis that the categories were independent, the following may be obtained:

$$E_{ij}$$

8.1	26.2	9.7
23.3	75.7	28.0
7.7	25.0	9.3

$$(O_{ij} - E_{ij})$$

1.9	−0.2	−1.7
−6.3	10.3	−4.0
4.3	−10.0	5.7

$$(O_{ij} - E_{ij})^2$$

3.6	0.0	2.9
39.7	106.1	16.0
18.5	100.0	32.5

$$(O_{ij} - E_{ij})^2 / E_{ij}$$

0.45	0.00	0.30
1.70	1.40	0.57
2.40	4.00	3.49

The calculated value of $\sum\limits_{i=1}^{3} \sum\limits_{j=1}^{3} \dfrac{(O_{ij} - E_{ij})^2}{E_{ij}}$ is 14.31. The number of degrees of

freedom is $(3-1) \times (3-1) = 4$, and $\chi^{2*}_{[4]0.05} = 9.49$. Therefore the categories do not appear to be independent.

Testing the Homogeneity of Populations

A similar situation arises when a sample is drawn from each of s populations, each population being divided into r categories and the problem is to determine whether the populations may be regarded as homogeneous, in the light of the evidence which this sample affords.

Let p_{ij} be the probability that a sample member falls in the ith class when drawn from the jth population. If the populations *are* homogeneous then p_{ij} must be independent of j and therefore can conveniently be designated by p_i. The estimate of p_i is then obtained by pooling the s samples as $\dfrac{1}{n} \sum\limits_{j} f_{ij}$, which, in the usual notation is $\dfrac{f_{i.}}{n}$.

On the basis of homogeneity the expected number in the ith class of the jth sample is $f_{.j} \times f_{i.}/n$ whereas the observed number is f_{ij}. When

$$u \equiv \sum_{i=1}^{r} \sum_{j=1}^{s} \left\{ \frac{\{f_{ij} - (f_{i.} \times f_{.j})/n\}^2}{(f_{i.} \times f_{.j})/n} \right\} \tag{22}$$

and the populations are homogeneous then u has approximately a χ^2 distribution on $(r-1) \times (s-1)$ degrees of freedom. It will be appreciated that although the function to be evaluated is mathematically identical with the one encountered in the preceding case, equation (21), there are essential distinctions in the questions posed and the ensuing arguments.

EXAMPLE 4   From samples of householders in four different parts of the country the numbers who possessed central heating systems of each of the three types were established as in Table 3.6. Are the data in Table 3.6 consistent with the hypothesis that the choice of central heating is independent of the location?

TABLE 3.6

House with	Location			
	A	*B*	*C*	*D*
Solid fuel	32	26	17	12
Gas	14	29	17	13
Oil	7	12	11	15

With the hypothesis that the populations are homogeneous with respect to the choice of central heating we obtain

E_{ij}				$(O_{ij} - E_{ij})^2 / E_{ij}$			
22.5	28.4	19.1	17.0	4.01	0.20	0.23	1.47
18.9	23.9	16.0	14.2	1.27	1.09	0.06	0.10
11.6	14.7	9.9	8.8	1.82	0.50	0.12	4.36

The calculated value of $\displaystyle\sum_{i=1}^{3} \sum_{j=1}^{4} \frac{(O_{ij} - E_{ij})^2}{E_{ij}}$ is therefore 15.23. The number of degrees of freedom is $(3-1) \times (4-1) = 6$ and $\chi^2_{[6]0.05} = 12.59$. Since the critical value of χ^2 at the 5% significance level is exceeded we reject the hypothesis of homogeneous populations in favour of the hypothesis that location of the house does have some bearing on the type of central heating installed. In particular, inspection of the above figures reveals that location *A* has proportionally more solid fuel installations and location *D* proportionally more oil-fired systems.

Further Remarks

1. In a 2 x 2 contingency table the observed frequencies can be written in the form

TABLE 3.7

	A	$\bar{A}$	Σ
B	α	β	$\alpha + \beta$
$\bar{B}$	γ	δ	$\gamma + \delta$
Σ	$\alpha + \gamma$	$\beta + \delta$	$\alpha + \beta + \gamma + \delta$

and the associated number of degrees of freedom is 1. It is also apparent that certain large sample situations discussed in § 3.3 can also be written like this. For example the data in example 5 of that section, which concerns defective pieces of timber, may be written as

TABLE 3.8

Site	Sound	Deteriorated	
		Condition	
A	32	18	50
B	60	20	80
	92	38	130

The implication is that when investigating the difference in proportions recorded in two large samples a choice of techniques is available. It can be shown that if X is $N(0, 1)$ then X^2 possesses the $\chi^2_{[1]}$ distribution, and the two procedures are equivalent.

2. It is evident from Fig. 3.8 that χ^2 has a continuous distribution whereas the values of $\sum_i \frac{(O_i - E_i)^2}{E_i}$ must be discrete. A revised formula to take some account of this is

$$\chi^2 = \sum_i \frac{\{|O_i - E_i| - \frac{1}{2}\}^2}{E_i}. \tag{23}$$

The general effect of this, which is known as *Yates's Correction*, is to reduce the calculated value of the test statistic, and a decision to make the adjustment is usually made only when $\nu = 1$.

3. If there are k mutually-exclusive classes, the probability that a particular sample of n items has n_1 outcomes in the first class, n_2 items in the second class, $\ldots$, n_k items in the kth class, is

$$\frac{n!}{n_1! n_2! \ldots n_k!} p_1^{n_1} p_2^{n_2} \ldots p_k^{n_k} \quad \text{where} \quad \sum_{i=1}^{k} n_i = n, \quad \sum_{i=1}^{k} p_i = 1 \tag{24}$$

and p_i is the probability that a single observation will belong to the ith class (see Volume 1, p. 483). For a proposed set of values for the $\{p_i\}$, it is only with very small values of n and k that it is feasible to evaluate these multinomial probabilities and then perform an *exact* goodness of fit test. For larger samples, as discussed in this section, the χ^2 distribution serves as an approximation to the test statistic in 'goodness-of-fit' problems. Other situations exist where the truth of the null hypothesis leads to the exact χ^2 variate, irrespective of sample size, but these will not be considered here.

4. The χ^2 distribution has an additive property. If X_1 is distributed like a χ^2 variate on ν_1 degrees of freedom and X_2 is distributed like a χ^2 variate on ν_2 degrees of freedom and X_1, X_2 are independent, then it can be shown that $X_1 + X_2$ is distributed like a χ^2 variate on $\nu_1 + \nu_2$ degrees of freedom.

EXAMPLE 5　　An experiment to investigate a null hypothesis in a certain goodness of fit problem yielded a calculated value of 10.5 for $\chi^2_{[6]}$. A similar but independent experiment gave $\chi^2_{[8]} = 13.3$. Confirm that neither result is significant at the 5% level, but when considered together these two outcomes produce a figure which *is* significant at this level.

From Table A3, $\chi^2_{[6]0.05}^* = 12.59$, $\chi^2_{[8]0.05}^* = 15.51$. Therefore neither result is significant at the 5% level. Consultation of more extensive tables will confirm that neither is significant even at the 10% level. Nevertheless the *independent* results may be combined to give a value of 23.8 for $\chi^2_{[14]}$ whereas the corresponding 5% critical value is 23.68.

Exercises

1. Show that

$$\sum_i \frac{(O_i - E_i)^2}{E_i} = \sum_i \frac{O_i^2}{E_i} - n \tag{25}$$

where $\sum_i O_i = \sum_i E_i = n$.

2. Show, by simple algebra, that in a 2 x 2 contingency table,

$$\chi^2_{[1]} = \frac{(\alpha\delta - \beta\gamma)^2(\alpha + \beta + \gamma + \delta)}{(\alpha + \beta)(\gamma + \delta)(\alpha + \gamma)(\beta + \delta)} \tag{26}$$

where $\alpha, \beta, \gamma, \delta$ are identified in Table 3.7.
[More complicated formulae exist for larger contingency tables.]

3. Apply a χ^2 test to the timber data, expressed in Table 3.8. What do you observe concerning the calculated value of the test statistic?

3.6 TESTS OF SIGNIFICANCE BASED ON THE *F* DISTRIBUTION

Comparison of Sample Variances from Two Normal Populations

Suppose that from a normal population A a sample $\{x_{Ai}\}$ for $i = 1, 2, \ldots, n_A$ is taken. Similarly $\{x_{Bj}\}$, a sample of size n_B, is obtained from a normal population B. Let

$$\bar{x}_A = \frac{1}{n_A} \sum_{i=1}^{n_A} x_{Ai}, \quad s_A^2 = \frac{1}{n_A - 1} \sum_{i=1}^{n_A} (x_{Ai} - \bar{x}_A)^2,$$

with similar expressions for $\bar{x}_B$ and s_B^2. Now consider the statistic F defined by the quotient

$$F \equiv \frac{S_A^2}{\sigma_A^2} \bigg/ \frac{S_B^2}{\sigma_B^2}. \tag{27}$$

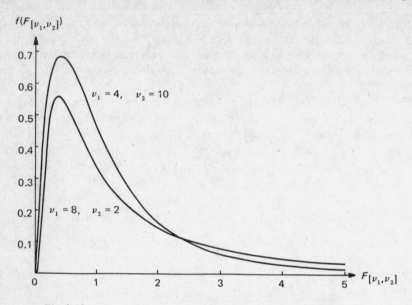

Fig. 3.10   The probability density functions for $F_{[8,2]}$ and $F_{[4,10]}$.

In the particular case $\sigma_A^2 = \sigma_B^2$ the right-hand expression reduces to S_A^2/S_B^2 and this result provides a statistical method for testing the equality of the variances of two normal populations.

This new distribution is known as the *variance ratio* and is denoted by F in honour of Sir Ronald Fisher, a pioneer in the modern theory of statistical inference. As is apparent from its derivation the F statistic has two independent degrees of freedom associated with it, one due to the numerator and one to the denominator. If these are respectively denoted by ν_1 and ν_2 then the appropriate distribution is signified by $F_{[\nu_1, \nu_2]}$. In general no simple relation connects $F_{[\nu_1, \nu_2]}$ and $F_{[\nu_2, \nu_1]}$. The graphs for the distributions of $F_{[4,10]}$ and $F_{[8,2]}$ are shown in Fig. 3.10.

According to the problem under consideration the null hypothesis $H_0 : \sigma_A^2 = \sigma_B^2$ may be tested against a one-tailed or two-tailed alternative. Consider first the situation when the alternative hypothesis is $H_1 : \sigma_A^2 > \sigma_B^2$. We calculate s_A^2/s_B^2 and then the null hypothesis is accepted or is rejected in favour of the one-tailed alternative according to whether or not this ratio is less than $F_{[\nu_A, \nu_B]\overset{*}{\alpha}}$, where $P\{F_{[\nu_A, \nu_B]} > F_{[\nu_A, \nu_B]\overset{*}{\alpha}}\} = \alpha$ and α is the chosen significance level.

More commonly the alternative hypothesis is $H_1 : \sigma_A^2 \neq \sigma_B^2$ and the test is two-tailed. Acceptance of the null hypothesis at a significance level α then requires that

$$F_{[\nu_A, \nu_B](1-\overset{*}{\tfrac{1}{2}\alpha})} < \frac{s_A^2}{s_B^2} < F_{[\nu_A, \nu_B]\overset{*}{\tfrac{1}{2}\alpha}} \quad \text{where} \quad \begin{cases} P\{F_{[\nu_A, \nu_B]} < F_{[\nu_A, \nu_B](1-\overset{*}{\tfrac{1}{2}\alpha})}\} = \tfrac{1}{2}\alpha \\ P\{F_{[\nu_A, \nu_B]} > F_{[\nu_A, \nu_B]\overset{*}{\tfrac{1}{2}\alpha}}\} = \tfrac{1}{2}\alpha. \end{cases}$$

Now if $s_A^2/s_B^2 < c$, where c is any positive number, then $s_B^2/s_A^2 > c^{-1}$, and it follows that $F_{[\nu_A, \nu_B](1-\overset{*}{\tfrac{1}{2}\alpha})}$ is the reciprocal of $F_{[\nu_B, \nu_A]\overset{*}{\tfrac{1}{2}\alpha}}$. A consequence is that separate tabulation of the lower critical values $F_{(1-\frac{1}{2}\alpha)}$ can be obviated by the introduction of a new variate G where G is the larger estimate of the variance divided by the smaller. Clearly G cannot have a value less than 1 and is not an F variate as such, but if d is any number greater than unity then

$$\left. \begin{array}{ll} \text{either} & s_A^2/s_B^2 > d \\ \text{or} & s_B^2/s_A^2 > d \end{array} \right\} \text{ is equivalent to } G > d.$$

This means that when a two-tailed test is being considered, the null hypothesis is accepted *at a significance level* α if

$$G \equiv \frac{\text{larger sample variance, on } \nu_n \text{ degrees of freedom}}{\text{smaller sample variance, on } \nu_d \text{ degrees of freedom}} < F_{[\nu_n, \nu_d]\frac{1}{2}\alpha}^{*}$$

where

$$P\{F_{[\nu_n, \nu_d]} > F_{[\nu_n, \nu_d]\frac{1}{2}\alpha}^{*}\} = \tfrac{1}{2}\alpha.$$

Table A4 in the Appendix contains the upper critical values of the F distribution for selected values of ν_n and ν_d when $\alpha = 0.025$ and $\alpha = 0.05$.

EXAMPLE 1   The sample variance for the diameters of 23 nominally identical ball bearings was 1.93 mm^2. For a simple random sample of size 17 taken from a second normally distributed population the corresponding figure was 4.06 mm^2. Would one be justified in assuming that the two populations have diameters with the same variability?

Make the null hypothesis H_0: the population variances are equal, with alternative H_1: the difference in these sample variances is significant. The test is therefore two-tailed.

If we divide the larger sample variance by the smaller, we obtain

$$G = \frac{4.06}{1.93} = 2.10 .$$

For the numerator and denominator the respective number of degrees of freedom are $\nu_n = 17 - 1 = 16$ and $\nu_d = 23 - 1 = 22$. If the significance level is chosen to be 0.05 it is necessary to estimate $F_{[16,22]0.025}^{*}$, and from Table A4 this must be approximately 2.49. As this critical value is not exceeded, we accept the null hypothesis.

Comparison of a Sample Variance with a Hypothesized Value

As $\nu_B \to \infty$, we have $s_B^2 \to \sigma_B^2$ so that in the limit

$$F_{[\nu, \infty]} = \frac{S^2}{\sigma^2} \tag{28}$$

for normal distributions, a result which may be used to make a statistical comparison of a sample variance with a population variance. An example follows.

EXAMPLE 2   Using a 10% significance level, investigate whether the data in §3.4, example 1, supports the contention that the standard deviation of the normal population is two matches.

The null hypothesis is $H_0 : \sigma^2 = 4$. The alternative hypothesis is two-sided. From the data, p. 113, $s^2 = 2.4$ so that if the null hypothesis is true $\dfrac{s^2}{\sigma^2} = \dfrac{2.4}{4.0} = 0.60$. By Table A4, $F_{[5, \infty]0.05}^* = 2.21$ and $F_{[5, \infty]0.95}^* = \dfrac{1}{F_{[\infty, 5]0.05}^*} = \dfrac{1}{4.36} = 0.23$. The value of the test statistic lies between these two critical values, and hence the null hypothesis is accepted at the 10% significance level.

It can be shown that the χ^2, t and Z variates are all equivalent to special limiting forms of the F distribution. This F statistic is therefore of fundamental importance being especially useful in 'analysis of variance'. This latter technique is associated with the design of experiments in which it is wished to test whether, say, the difference between one treatment and another is greater than the difference within the treatments themselves. It is not possible to give further consideration to such problems here.

Exercises

1. If α is a typical significance level, (say $\leqslant 10\%$), what inequalities connect $F_{[\nu_1, \nu_2]\alpha}^*$, $F_{[\nu_1, \nu_2]\frac{1}{2}\alpha}^*$, $F_{[\nu_1, \nu_2+1]\alpha}^*$?

2. Use Table A4 to estimate $F_{[7,15]0.05}^*$, $F_{[15,7]0.05}^*$ and $F_{[10,10]0.025}^*$. [The true values, correct to 2 d.p., are given in the Answers section at the back of the book.]

3. What are the critical values appropriate to example 2 above when a significance level of 5% is chosen?

4. Show that in example 2 of §3.4 the value of the larger sample variance divided by the smaller is 1.81, and deduce that this figure is not significant for $\alpha = 0.05$.

3.7 LEAST SQUARES TECHNIQUES, CURVE FITTING AND REGRESSION

Further consideration will now be given to the topic of estimation, which was introduced at the start of this chapter, and to allied matters, in particular the fitting of curves to experimental data. The present discussion differs from the contribution to curve fitting contained in Chapter 11 of Volume 1 in that the data values, which constitute the points, will be regarded as subject to random 'errors' (not 'mistakes') so that with each value a probability distribution is associated.

Estimators with Minimum Variance

Suppose that $X_1, X_2, \ldots, X_r$ are unbiased, independent estimators of a parameter, η say, and the respective variances $\sigma_1^2, \sigma_2^2, \ldots, \sigma_r^2$ for these distributions are known. What linear combination of these X_i is unbiased and possesses the minimum variance?

Let

$$Y = a_1 X_1 + a_2 X_2 + \ldots + a_r X_r . \tag{29}$$

Then if Y is to be unbiased,

$$\eta = E\{Y\} = E\{a_1 X_1 + a_2 X_2 + \ldots + a_r X_r\} = \sum_{i=1}^{r} a_i E\{X_i\} = \sum_{i=1}^{r} a_i \eta ,$$

so that

$$\sum_{i=1}^{r} a_i = 1 . \tag{30}$$

Furthermore,

$$\text{Var}(Y) = a_1^2 \text{Var}(X_1) + a_2^2 \text{Var}(X_2) + \ldots + a_r^2 \text{Var}(X_r) . \tag{31}$$

The problem is therefore to find the set of values for $a_1, a_2, \ldots, a_r$ which minimizes $\sum_{i=1}^{r} a_i^2 \sigma_i^2$ subject to the constraint $\sum_{i=1}^{r} a_i = 1$. This problem may be treated as an exercise in the application of Lagrange multipliers, see problem 7 of Chapter 4 in Volume 1. The solution is

$$a_j = \frac{1}{\sigma_j^2} \bigg/ \left(\sum_{i=1}^{r} \frac{1}{\sigma_i^2} \right) \quad \text{for } j = 1, 2, \ldots, r . \tag{32}$$

In particular, when all the variances are equal, $a_j = r^{-1}$ and for this case

$$Y = \frac{1}{r} \sum_{i=1}^{r} X_i . \tag{33}$$

Least Squares Estimators

Other estimation techniques are available and a popular choice is the *method of least squares*. This approach, referred to in §4.5 of Volume 1, is one with which Gauss and Legendre have their names associated, and it is particularly suitable when the object is to 'fit' a curve to a set of observed results. Before this particular aspect is considered an example of the general technique will be given.

Suppose that n independent measurements have been taken, with values $x_1, x_2, \ldots, x_n$, and from these values it is wished to estimate the population mean μ.

It is here assumed that each x_i satisfies the equation

$$x_i = \mu + e_i ,\tag{34}$$

where e_i is a random 'error' and $E\{e_i\} = 0$.

The problem undertaken is to minimize the sum of the squares of these errors, namely $\sum\limits_{i=1}^{n} e_i^2$. We therefore set to zero $\dfrac{d}{d\mu}\left\{ \sum\limits_{i=1}^{n} (x_i - \mu)^2 \right\}$. This gives

$-2 \sum\limits_{i=1}^{n} (x_i - \mu) = 0$ so that $\sum\limits_{i=1}^{n} x_i - n\mu = 0$. It follows that the sample mean $\bar{X}$ is also *the least squares estimator* of μ.

Under the simple conditions that

(a)   the $\{e_i\}$ are independent
(b) $\text{Var}(e_1) = \text{Var}(e_2) = \ldots = \text{Var}(e_n)$

the least squares estimators and the minimum variance estimators already discussed in this section may be shown to be identical. This result is known as the *Gauss–Markov theorem* and confirms the importance of least squares estimators.

'Best' Straight Lines

The simplest task in curve fitting is to put a straight line 'through' a set of values. Consider the situation in which there are n pairs of measured values (x_i, y_i), $i = 1, 2, \ldots, n$, of the variables X and Y and, either on theoretical grounds or merely from the lie of the points when plotted, it is wished to express the relationship between X and Y in the form

$$y = ax + b.\tag{35}$$

This is called *linear regression* and the problem is to determine the constants a, *the regression coefficient*, and b so that the line may be considered, in the appropriate sense, a 'best fit'.

Assume for the moment that all the 'errors' are in the measurements of Y, the X values being considered 'exact'. The assumption that X is *controlled* may be quite reasonable for many experiments where it is possible to select the values of the independent variable X conveniently and then measure the corresponding Y value. For example X might be the load applied to a beam and Y the resulting deflection. On this basis

$$y_i = (ax_i + b) + e_i, \quad \text{where } e_i \text{ is the 'error', } \quad \text{for } i = 1, 2, \ldots, n.\tag{36}$$

The method of least squares requires that $\sum\limits_{i=1}^{n} e_i^2$ be minimized, see Fig. 3.11. It is convenient to adopt the notation $\Sigma \equiv \sum\limits_{i=1}^{n}$, (so that, for example, $\Sigma 1 = n$), and to let

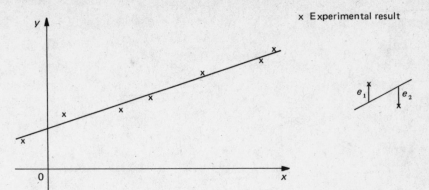

Fig. 3.11   Linear regression.

$$\theta(a, b) \equiv \Sigma\{y_i - (ax_i + b)\}^2 , \tag{37}$$

giving

$$\frac{\partial \theta}{\partial b} = -2 \Sigma\{y_i - (ax_i + b)\}, \quad \frac{\partial \theta}{\partial a} = -2\Sigma x_i\{y_i - (ax_i + b)\} . \tag{38a, b}$$

For an extremum of θ these partial derivatives are set to zero, and after slight simplification we therefore obtain the pair of simultaneous linear equations

$$bn + a\Sigma x_i = \Sigma y_i , \tag{39a}$$

$$b\Sigma x_i + a\Sigma x_i^2 = \Sigma x_i y_i . \tag{39b}$$

The solutions of these *normal equations* are

$$a = \frac{n\Sigma x_i y_i - \Sigma x_i \Sigma y_i}{n\Sigma x_i^2 - (\Sigma x_i)^2} \tag{40}$$

and

$$b = \frac{\Sigma y_i - a\Sigma x_i}{n} \tag{41}$$

where a is given by equation (40). It is easy to verify that these expressions for a and b correspond to the *minimum* value of this non-negative function θ, see exercise 1.

There are several useful alternative ways of writing these formulae, the most common being

$$a = \frac{\Sigma\{(x_i - \bar{x})(y_i - \bar{y})\}}{\Sigma(x_i - \bar{x})^2}, \quad b = \bar{y} - a\bar{x} . \tag{42), (43}$$

The first of this pair of results shows that a may be expressed as the sample covariance divided by the sample variance in x, and the second equation shows that this line of Y *regressing on* X passes through the centroid of the observations.

When X *regresses on* Y the roles of X and Y are interchanged so that the Y variate is

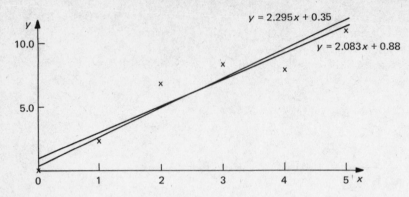

Fig. 3.12   Linear regression of Y on X and of X on Y. Data and lines correspond to values in example 1.

regarded as controlled and all the 'errors' are held to be in the X measurements. If the corresponding equation of linear regression is written as

$$y = \alpha x + \beta \tag{44}$$

then α and β are obtained by minimization of

$$\phi(\alpha, \beta) \equiv \Sigma \left\{ x_i - \left(\frac{y_i - \beta}{\alpha} \right) \right\}^2 = \Sigma \{ y_i' - (a'x_i' + b') \}^2 \tag{45}$$

where $x' = y, y' = x, a' = 1/\alpha$ and $b' = -\beta/\alpha$. Comparison with equation (37) and use of equations (40) and (41) then show that α and β are given by

$$\alpha = \frac{n\Sigma y_i^2 - (\Sigma y_i)^2}{n\Sigma x_i y_i - \Sigma x_i \Sigma y_i}, \quad \beta = \frac{\Sigma y_i - \alpha\Sigma x_i}{n}. \tag{46, 47}$$

Alternative methods of writing the expressions for α, β may be found preferable for a particular situation. As before, $(\bar{x}, \bar{y})$ lies on the regression line, so the two regression lines must intersect in the centroid, Fig. 3.12. The more closely the data express a linear relationship, the closer these lines become.

These 'best straight lines in the least squares sense' have a more fundamental role to play than their method of derivation suggests. Recall that initially it was assumed that the x values were exact and the y values subject to error, and this was followed by the reverse situation. A graph of height of fathers (the x variable) plotted against height of paternal grandfathers (the y values) might reveal a sensibly linear relationship but it would be improper to regard one height as 'exact' and the other as 'due to experimental error'. Rather, given that the height of a (hypothetical) man is x_A the line of Y regressing on X may be used to determine the least squares estimate y_A of the height of his father, and given the height y_B of a man the line of X regressing on Y may be used to establish the corresponding least squares estimate x_B of a (fully-grown) son.

EXAMPLE 1   The production of a paint factory in each of six successive years was

100.0   102.4   106.9   108.3   107.9   111.0

Fit the best straight line, in the least squares sense, to this *time series* data when the output regresses on the year of production. Use this *trend line* to estimate the outputs for the next two years.

Find the line of regression when the year regresses on production and estimate the year in which the output will reach 121.

Measure X, the year number from the year for which the first output is reported, and let Y be the percentage increase, based on the initial output. Then Table 3.9 may be constructed to read

TABLE 3.9

x_i	0	1	2	3	4	5	$\Sigma x_i = 15.0$
y_i	0.0	2.4	6.9	8.3	7.9	11.0	$\Sigma y_i = 36.5$
x_i^2	0.0	1.0	4.0	9.0	16.0	25.0	$\Sigma x_i^2 = 55.0$
y_i^2	0.0	5.8	47.6	68.9	62.4	121.0	$\Sigma y_i^2 = 305.7$
$x_i y_i$	0.0	2.4	13.8	24.9	31.6	55.0	$\Sigma x_i y_i = 127.7$

Thus, successive use of equation (40) and equation (41) gives

$$a = \frac{6 \times 127.7 - 15.0 \times 36.5}{6 \times 55.0 - (15.0)^2} = \frac{218.7}{105.0} = 2.083 ,$$

$$b = \frac{36.5 - 2.083 \times 15}{6} = \frac{5.26}{6} = 0.877 .$$

The equation for the line of Y regressing on X is therefore

$$y = 2.083x + 0.88.$$

In particular,

when $\quad x = 6, \qquad y = (2.083 \times 6) + 0.88 = 12.50 + 0.88 = 13.38,$

and when $\quad x = 7, \qquad y = (2.083 \times 7) + 0.88 = 14.58 + 0.88 = 15.46.$

The outputs in the next two years are therefore estimated to be 113.4 and 115.5.

To estimate the year in which the output will reach 121.0, the regression of X on Y is required. If this line is written $y = \alpha x + \beta$, then by equations (46) and (47),

$$\alpha = \frac{6 \times 305.7 - (36.5)^2}{218.7} = \frac{501.9}{218.7} = 2.295 ,$$

$$\beta = \frac{36.5 - 2.295 \times 15.0}{6} = \frac{2.08}{6} = 0.35 .$$

The equation for the line of X regressing on Y is therefore

$$y = 2.295x + 0.35 .$$

When $y = 21$,

$$x = \frac{21.0 - 0.35}{2.295} = 9.00.$$

Therefore the output is estimated to reach 121 in the tenth year of production.

Multiple Linear Regression

Suppose now that the variable Y is regarded as a linear function of k random variables $X_1, X_2, \ldots, X_k$, i.e.,

$$Y = a_0 + a_1 X_1 + a_2 X_2 + \ldots + a_k X_k, \tag{48}$$

where the a_i are to be determined. In the situation we have just considered k had the value 1. A linear equation of the above form may be taken to represent the equation of a plane in $(k + 1)$ dimensions, and the task is to minimize the sums of the squares of the distances, measured in the y-direction, of the sample points from this hyperplane.

If n sets of values $(x_{1i}, x_{2i}, \ldots, x_{ki}, y_i)$ are available, where $i = 1, \ldots, n$ and $n > k + 1$, and $\theta \equiv \sum_{i=1}^{n} \{y_i - (a_0 + a_1 x_{1i} + \ldots + a_k x_{ki})\}^2$, the $(k + 1)$ normal equations

are given by $\dfrac{\partial \theta}{\partial a_0} = \dfrac{\partial \theta}{\partial a_1} = \ldots = \dfrac{\partial \theta}{\partial a_k} = 0$. After simplification these may be written

$$
\begin{aligned}
a_0 n \quad + a_1 \Sigma x_{1i} \quad + a_2 \Sigma x_{2i} \quad + \ldots + a_k \Sigma x_{ki} &= \Sigma y_i, \\
a_0 \Sigma x_{1i} + a_1 \Sigma x_{1i}^2 \quad + a_2 \Sigma x_{1i} x_{2i} + \ldots + a_k \Sigma x_{1i} x_{ki} &= \Sigma x_{1i} y_i, \\
&\;\;\vdots \\
a_0 \Sigma x_{ki} + a_1 \Sigma x_{ki} x_{1i} + a_2 \Sigma x_{ki} x_{2i} + \ldots + a_k \Sigma x_{ki}^2 &= \Sigma x_{ki} y_i,
\end{aligned}
\tag{49}
$$

where again $\Sigma \equiv \sum_{i=1}^{n}$.

These $(k + 1)$ linear equations must now be solved for the $(k + 1)$ unknowns $a_0, a_1, \ldots, a_k$. Suitable methods have already been discussed in Chapters 8 and 10 of Volume 1.

Non-linear Regression

Although in the case of two variables the most simple choice of regression curve is the straight line, other more sophisticated equations may be needed, either on theoretical grounds or merely from the lie of the points. The curve to be fitted is often a polynomial and due to its flexibility this is a popular choice for an empirical curve. The general polynomial of degree k has equation

$$Y = a_0 + a_1 X + a_2 X^2 + \ldots + a_k X^k. \tag{50}$$

The associated normal equations follow from the preceding work, since the discussion of multiple linear regression merely requires that the $\{X_i\}$ be *linearly* independent. Setting $X_r = X^r$ for $r = 1, 2, \ldots, k$ in equation (48), we obtain from equations (49)

$$a_0 n \quad + a_1 \Sigma x_i \quad + a_2 \Sigma x_i^2 \quad + \ldots + a_k \Sigma x_i^k \quad = \Sigma y_i,$$

$$a_0 \Sigma x_i + a_1 \Sigma x_i^2 \quad + a_2 \Sigma x_i^3 \quad + \ldots + a_k \Sigma x_i^{k+1} = \Sigma x_i y_i, \tag{51}$$

$$\vdots$$

$$a_0 \Sigma x_i^k + a_1 \Sigma x_i^{k+1} + a_2 \Sigma x_i^{k+2} + \ldots + a_k \Sigma x_i^{2k} = \Sigma x_i^k y_i,$$

so that again there are $(k + 1)$ simultaneous linear equations to be solved for $a_0, a_1, \ldots, a_k$.

In many instances the curve to be fitted is such that the corresponding normal equations are non-linear. Since their solution may give rise to computational difficulties, it may be considered preferable to rewrite, if possible, the relationship in an alternative linear form and *then* apply the method of least squares.

Suppose, for example, that the desired curve is of the form

$$y = b e^{ax}. \tag{52}$$

Then $\log y = ax + \log b$, which is of the form $y' = ax + b'$ where $y' \equiv \log y$ and $b' \equiv \log b$. Determination of a and b' (and hence b) by the least squares method will now give values different from those obtained by solving the normal equations appropriate to the given relationship, equation (52), and which are:

$$b \Sigma e^{2ax_i} = \Sigma y_i e^{ax_i} \quad \text{and} \quad b \Sigma x_i e^{2ax_i} = \Sigma x_i y_i e^{ax_i}. \tag{53a, b}$$

However, the differences may be quite small and in any case the values may not necessarily be inferior for the purpose in hand.

EXAMPLE 2   In an experiment associated with certain sedimentation investigations grains of sand were violently agitated in a bath of fluid and then allowed to settle. The thickness of the deposited layer was measured at successive time intervals after the agitation ceased and this depth was then expressed as a proportion of the total particle content. The results are shown in Table 3.10. On the assumption that the proportion deposited Y and the time T are related by an equation of the form $y = 1 - e^{-at}$, determine the value of a which minimizes the sum of the squares of the Y deviations from the curve.

TABLE 3.10

Time (min), t_i	$\frac{1}{2}$	1	$1\frac{1}{2}$	2	$2\frac{1}{2}$
Proportion of the particles deposited, y_i	0.552	0.798	0.910	0.960	0.981

It is convenient to introduce new variables v and w defined by

$$v = 1 - y \quad \text{and} \quad w = \log v.$$

The basic relationship may then be rewritten as $v = e^{-at}$, so that $w = -at$. The corresponding normal equation for this linear expression may readily be found as $a\Sigma t_i^2 + \Sigma t_i w_i = 0$. We therefore have

TABLE 3.11

t_i	$\frac{1}{2}$	1	$1\frac{1}{2}$	2	$2\frac{1}{2}$	
$v_i = 1 - y_i$	0.448	0.202	0.090	0.040	0.019	
$w_i = \log v_i$	−0.803	−1.599	−2.408	−3.219	−3.963	
$t_i w_i$	−0.401	−1.599	−3.612	−6.438	−9.908	$\Sigma t_i w_i = -21.958$
t_i^2	0.25	1	2.25	4	6.25	$\Sigma t_i^2 = 13.75$

Hence $a = -\dfrac{\Sigma t_i w_i}{\Sigma t_i^2} = \dfrac{21.958}{13.75} = 1.597$.

If return is made to the exponential form of the relation, the corresponding normal equation may be written

$$\Sigma v_i t_i e^{-ati} = \Sigma t_i e^{-2ati}.$$

An iterative method of solution for this equation gives the value of a as 1.603 so that in this example the linear approximation certainly yields a value which is close to the exact solution.

Significance Tests for Linear Regression

Based as they are on *sample* data, the values of a and b computed according to equations (40) and (41) are only *estimates* of the corresponding population values a_0 and b_0. Appropriate tests of significance follow from the fact that if

$$\epsilon^2 = \frac{\Sigma\{Y_i - (aX_i + b)\}^2}{n - 2} \quad \text{and} \quad \Sigma \equiv \sum_{i=1}^{n},$$

then

$$\frac{(a - a_0)\{\Sigma(X_i - \bar{X})^2\}^{\frac{1}{2}}}{\epsilon} \quad \text{and} \quad \frac{(b - b_0)}{\epsilon}\left\{\frac{\Sigma(X_i - \bar{X})^2}{\Sigma X_i^2/n}\right\}^{\frac{1}{2}}$$

are each t variates on $(n - 2)$ degrees of freedom.

Interest often centres on whether or not the quantities X and Y are correlated. If $\rho = 0$ and the estimator $\hat{\rho}$ of the correlation coefficient is calculated according to the expression on p. 97, then

$$\hat{\rho}\left(\frac{n - 2}{1 - \hat{\rho}^2}\right)^{\frac{1}{2}}$$

is also distributed like a t variate on $(n - 2)$ d.f.'s. (The significance test for a non-zero population correlation coefficient is more complicated.) It should also be remembered that the correlation coefficient is essentially a measure of the extent to which the values assumed by two random variables may be represented by a *linear* relationship. Thus a high value for $|\rho|$ may merely be an expression of the fact that each variable is strongly related, in linear manner, to a third, possibly causal, variable. On the other hand a low value of $|\rho|$ may merely be indicative that the relationship between the variables is non-linear.

Rank Correlation

To conclude the discussion on correlation, consider the situation when $\{(x_i, y_i)\}$, for $i = 1, 2, \ldots, n$ consist of paired *ranked* values so that the values of the $\{x_i\}$ are the numbers $1, 2, \ldots, n$ in some order, as also are the $\{y_i\}$ values. Ranking (which has been mentioned in §12.3 of Volume 1) can be introduced whenever there is no precise numerical scale for the measurement of the parameter. Alternatively, it is possible to suppress actual numerical values and replace them with their rank values. Then

$$\sum x_i = \sum y_i = \sum_{i=1}^{n} i = \tfrac{1}{2}n(n + 1), \quad \bar{x} = \bar{y} = \tfrac{1}{2}(n + 1) \tag{54}$$

and

$$\sum x_i^2 = \sum y_i^2 = \sum_{i=1}^{n} i^2 = \tfrac{1}{6}n(n + 1)(2n + 1) \tag{55}$$

so

$$\sum x_i^2 - n\bar{x}^2 = \sum y_i^2 - n\bar{y}^2 = \tfrac{1}{6}n(n + 1)(2n + 1) - \tfrac{1}{4}n(n + 1)^2 = \tfrac{1}{12}n(n^2 - 1). \tag{56}$$

Furthermore, if $d = x - y$ then $xy = \tfrac{1}{2}\{x^2 + y^2 - (x - y)^2\} = \tfrac{1}{2}(x^2 + y^2 - d^2)$ so

$$\sum x_i y_i = \tfrac{1}{2}\{\sum x_i^2 + \sum y_i^2 - \sum d_i^2\} = \tfrac{1}{6}n(n + 1)(2n + 1) - \tfrac{1}{2}\sum d_i^2. \tag{57}$$

The expression on p. 97 for the estimator of the correlation coefficient may be written as

$$\frac{\Sigma X_i Y_i - n\bar{X}\bar{Y}}{\{(\Sigma X_i^2 - n\bar{X}^2)(\Sigma Y_i^2 - n\bar{Y}^2)\}^{\frac{1}{2}}}$$

It is therefore necessary, using equations (54), (56) and (57), to compute

$$\frac{\tfrac{1}{6}n(n + 1)(2n + 1) - \tfrac{1}{2}\Sigma d_i^2 - n\{\tfrac{1}{2}(n + 1)\}^2}{\tfrac{1}{12}n(n^2 - 1)} = \frac{\tfrac{1}{12}n(n^2 - 1) - \tfrac{1}{2}\Sigma d_i^2}{\tfrac{1}{12}n(n^2 - 1)}$$

$$= 1 - \frac{6\Sigma d_i^2}{n(n^2 - 1)}. \tag{58}$$

This expression must usually produce a numerical value different from the *product moment* formula for ρ employed with general values of the x's and y's. This *coefficient of rank correlation*, devised by Spearman, is denoted by R to distinguish it from ρ. Whilst not as 'sensitive' as the usual expression, discussed in Chapter 12 of Volume 1, R has many analogous characteristics, in particular $|R| \leqslant 1$.

EXAMPLE 3   Evaluate the coefficient of rank correlation for the following set of results, Table 3.12.

TABLE 3.12

x-ranking	5	9	2	1	3	4	7	10	8	6
y-ranking	5	7	3	1	4	2	8	10	9	6
Difference	0	+2	−1	0	−1	+2	−1	0	−1	0

Here $\Sigma d_i^2 = 2\times4 + 4\times1 = 12$ and $n = 10$ so that

$$R = 1 - \frac{6 \times 12}{10 \times 99} = 1 - \frac{72}{990} = 0.927 .$$

It is clearly immaterial whether the order of ranking is from the 'largest' or 'most preferred', or from the 'smallest' or 'least preferred' provided that the same procedure is adopted for both variables. Also it is customary, when ranking introduces 'ties', to give each of the tied members a rank equal to the average value of the ranks which would have been awarded had no tie been present, for instance

the values	1.3	1.7	1.7	1.7	1.7	1.9	2.0	2.0	2.0	2.1
may be ranked	1	$3\frac{1}{2}$	$3\frac{1}{2}$	$3\frac{1}{2}$	$3\frac{1}{2}$	6	8	8	8	10.

Exercises

1. Show that $\dfrac{\partial^2 \theta}{\partial b^2} > 0$ and $\left(\dfrac{\partial^2 \theta}{\partial a^2}\right) \left(\dfrac{\partial^2 \theta}{\partial b^2}\right) > \left(\dfrac{\partial^2 \theta}{\partial a \partial b}\right)^2$, where $\theta(a, b)$ is defined by equation (37), so that sufficiency conditions are satisfied for equations (40) and (41) to correspond to a minimum of θ, (see §4.4 of Volume 1).

2. Start from equations (44) and (45) and use first principles to obtain equations (46) and (47).

3. Prove from equations (40) and (46) that $a = \hat\rho^2 \alpha$ and deduce that, of the two lines of linear regression, the line of Y regressing on X is the less steep. Also verify that in example 1 the sample correlation coefficient is 0.953.

4. Combine the approaches to multiple and curvilinear regression to obtain the normal equations for a_0, a_1, a_2 when $Y = a_0 + a_1 X_1 + a_2 X_1 X_2$.

5. Show that the product moment correlation coefficient for the data in Table 3.1 is 0.923 and test whether this sample value supports the hypothesis that the sets of 'before' and 'after' results are uncorrelated. Also verify that, when ranked, the sales results in Table 3.1 provide the values given in Table 3.12.

3.8 DISTRIBUTION-FREE TESTS OF SIGNIFICANCE

The preceding calculation of rank correlation makes no use of the actual distibutions of the variates involved, and serves to introduce the concept of *distribution-free* investigations.

It will be recalled that the t tests, and the F test on equality of variances, essentially require that the parent populations be normally distributed. Although, in engineering, normality of the population may be an entirely reasonable assumption or may even have been tested on an earlier occasion there are times when, even allowing for the robustness of the t test, the assumption of normality may be inappropriate. In such a situation it may be possible to employ a distribution-free test of significance and much work in recent years has attended this aspect of inference. Just one such test will now be considered, the *Sign Test*. The ideas are well illustrated by an example.

EXAMPLE 1   Use a distribution-free test to investigate whether or not the 'after' results of Table 3.1 are significantly lower than the 'before' results.

From Table 3.1, the *signs* of the differences, ('before' minus 'after'), are noted as

$$+ - + + + 0 + + + -$$

We disregard the single zero, and in the 9 results which remain there are 7 'pluses' and 2 'minuses'. On the basis of no overall change, about as many positives as negatives would be anticipated, the probability of either in any single observation being $\frac{1}{2}$. The probability of getting 7 or more positives out of nine is then

$$^9C_0(\tfrac{1}{2})^9(\tfrac{1}{2})^0 + {}^9C_1(\tfrac{1}{2})^8(\tfrac{1}{2}) + {}^9C_2(\tfrac{1}{2})^7(\tfrac{1}{2})^2 = (1 + 9 + 36)(\tfrac{1}{2})^9 = 46(\tfrac{1}{2})^9 = \frac{23}{256} > \frac{1}{20}.$$

Using the test, therefore, the result is not significant at the 5% level.

It may appear a little surprising to arrive at a result contrary to that obtained in example 3 of §3.4, where the paired t test was used. However, as the tests are not *identical* it is not possible for them to give the same result in *every* instance. As has already been stated, tests based on the normal and t distributions are always the most powerful, and therefore to be preferred, provided that all pertinent conditions concerning the distributions of the parent populations are satisfied.

Exercise

1. Let there be r positive values and s negative values recorded in n observations where $r + s = n$, (i.e., there are no zeros). The null hypothesis is that the probability p of a positive value is $\frac{1}{2}$, the significance level is 5% and the sign test is to be used. Establish the smallest value of n which is capable of producing a significant result when

(a) the alternative hypothesis is $p < \frac{1}{2}$,

(b) the alternative hypothesis is $p \neq \frac{1}{2}$.

Tabulate those values of r which correspond to a significant result, up to $n = 9$.

If $n \geqslant 10$, form an approximate standardized normal variate and deduce that for a two-sided test a 'rule of thumb' indication that the result is significant is $|r - s| > 2\sqrt{n}$.

PROBLEMS

1. Explain why, as a general rule, computational rounding errors are of little importance in tests of significance.

2. A machine makes bolts. Independent of other items, the probability of any bolt being defective is 0.1. It is required that a random sample has a probability of only 0.01 that the proportion of defectives exceeds 12%. By using a normal approximation determine the minimum size of such a sample.

3. As a result of pre-installation tests on wires it was concluded that not more than about 4% would fail when in service for a year. Of the 1200 wires subsequently used, 62 failed in that period. Does this suggest that the conclusions drawn from the initial tests were too optimistic?

4. After the conclusion of an advertising campaign 31 out of 120 people questioned in a sample survey said they bought 'Feat'. In an independent sample of the same size, questioned before the campaign began, 28 said they bought 'Feat'. On this evidence ought the advertisers to feel that their campaign has had any impact?

5. The design of a tyre was slightly changed. The mean life of the tyre with the original design was 10,400 miles. One hundred of the new design were tested and it was found that the mean life was 10,150 miles and the associated standard deviation was 1050 miles. Do these figures suggest that the change in design produced a real alteration in life of a tyre? If so, construct a 95% confidence interval for the new mean life.

6. As a result of a proposal to build a reservoir it was necessary to obtain accurate measurements of the rainfall in two valleys. The 80 gauges installed in the first valley indicated a mean annual rainfall of 1183 mm with an associated standard deviation of 125 mm and the corresponding figures for the 68 gauges in the second valley were respectively 1238 mm and 186 mm. Is there any significant difference in the mean rainfall for the two valleys?

7. A machine produced an average of 190 components per shift. After a routine overhaul its output of components for the first six shifts was

172, 190, 188, 184, 192, 181.

Do these figures provide any evidence that the machine had not been restored to its customary working capacity?

8. Two alternative methods of sealing were adopted for containers used for keeping a particularly volatile liquid. Identical quantities of the fluid were placed in each container before sealing and the vessels were stored under nominally identical conditions. After a certain time random samples of these containers were reweighed and, due to seepage, the following weight losses (in grams) were reported.

Type of Sealing	Weight loss									
A	1.239	1.054	1.315	0.760	0.883	1.295	1.106	1.004	0.811	0.911
B	1.062	1.423	0.742	1.631	1.112	1.295	1.489	1.228	0.983	1.602

Under the assumption that the losses, both for Type A and Type B sealing, are normally distributed in the parent populations, show that the sample variances do not differ at the 5% significance level and investigate whether or not there is a significant difference in the mean losses recorded for the two types of sealing.

9. The amounts of a certain metal in eight ore samples of equal weight were determined by method G. Method H was then used to repeat the determination using the same eight samples and the following differences in the amounts were noted:

Sample number	1	2	3	4	5	6	7	8
Method G – Method H	0.2	0.6	1.2	−0.8	−0.2	1.3	0.1	0.2

Employ suitable tests to determine whether or not a significant difference between the two methods exists when
(a) the parent populations are assumed to be normally distributed,
(b) no such assumption is made.

10. Each of 100 new houses was inspected to determine the number of faulty tiles which had been laid, with the following results:

Number of faulty tiles/house	0	1	2	3	4	5	6 or more
Number of houses	20	31	23	16	5	5	0

Fit a Poissonian distribution to these data using the sample mean as estimate of the parameter, and verify that on this basis about 9.2% of houses can be expected to have more than three faulty tiles. Investigate the goodness of fit.

11. In an experiment to compare two different heat treatments twenty-eight ingots were assigned to treatment γ and thirty to treatment δ. Do the results given below indicate a real difference between the two treatments?

Treatment	γ	δ
Number of accepted ingots	22	21
Number of rejected ingots	6	9

12. A sample survey was made of the attitudes of residents who lived near each end of

a proposed link road. The result was as follows:

	Construction of the link road		
	In favour	Neutral	Against
End M	134	43	83
End N	71	43	51

Do these figures suggest any difference in the attitudes at the two ends?

13. To test babies' hearing an instrument was designed in the form of a rattle. Using one type of granular material the standard deviation was found to be 2 decibels. With a new type of material tests on six prototype rattles gave dbA levels of 62, 64, 65, 65, 61 and 67.

Do these data indicate that the new material will give more consistent noise levels?

14. The following data give measured values of Young's modulus E of a fibre-reinforced composite material for various fibre concentrations c. It is assumed that there are no errors in the value of c.

E (10^{10} N/m^2)	18.2	25.6	34.3	41.9
c	0.20	0.40	0.60	0.80

It is believed that E and c satisfy a relation of the form $E = cE_1 + (1 - c)E_2$, where E_1 and E_2 are moduli for the fibre and the matrix. Find the values of E_1 and E_2 which give the best fit, in the least squares sense, to the above data.

15. Samples of soil were taken at nine different depths (x) and the percentages of sand (y) recorded were

x (mm)	0	400	800	1200	1600	2000	2400	2800	3200
y (%)		70.2	52.9	54.2	52.4	47.4	49.1	30.7	36.8	37.4

Calculate the equation of the line (a) of Y regressing linearly on X, and (b) of X regressing linearly on Y.

Plot the data and regression lines on suitable graph paper and estimate (1) the depth at which sand will constitute 25% of the soil, and (2) the percentage of sand at a depth of 600 mm.

16. The following fuel consumption figures (y) were obtained from a vehicle driven at the indicated speeds (x). Use this information to estimate the consumption for a speed of 125 km/h, using a relationship $Y = a_0 + a_1 X + a_2 X^2$ where a_0, a_1, a_2 are determined from the least squares condition. Also obtain the corresponding estimate when a linear relationship is assumed.

x (km/h)	50	65	80	95	110
y (km/l)	15.2	14.4	13.1	11.4	9.6

Draw a graph to show the experimental points and the regression lines. Which of your estimates do you consider to be the better?

17. Sometimes, when a particularly small value of the test statistic χ^2 is computed in a goodness of fit test, the agreement is referred to as 'too good'. Why? Discuss also the implications of small values of the test statistics $|z|$, $|t|$.

BIBLIOGRAPHY

[1] Spiegel, M. R., *Probability and Statistics*, McGraw-Hill, New York (1975).
[2] Neville, A. M., and J. B. Kennedy, *Basic Statistical Methods for Engineers and Scientists*, International Textbook Co., Scranton, Pa (1964).
[3] Chatfield, C., *Statistics for Technology*, Chapman & Hall, London (1975).
[4] Belz, M. H., *Statistical Methods in the Process Industries*, Macmillan, London (1973).

CHAPTER 4

Complex Variables

4.1 INTRODUCTION

Complex numbers arose from the study of algebraic equations, and the theory which subsequently developed, called the theory of complex variables, has found wide application in theoretical studies in many branches of engineering and science. For example, complex impedances are used in electrical engineering, complex potentials are used in fluid mechanics and elasticity, and a complex time dependence is used extensively whenever vibration and wave problems are studied. The introduction of complex quantities into a problem will obviously cause initial conceptual difficulties, but the resulting mathematical problems are often more easily solved than the corresponding problem in real variable analysis.

4.2 COMPLEX NUMBERS

In this section the main features of complex numbers will be discussed.

> DEFINITION   A complex number is a number of the form $a + ib$, where a and b are real numbers and i is such that $i^2 = -1$.

If $z = a + ib$, then the number a is said to be the *real part of z* written Re z, and the number b is said to be the *imaginary part of z* written Im z. It is sometimes convenient to represent the number $a + ib$ as (a, b), an *ordered pair* of numbers, for example $2 + 3i$ can be written $(2, 3)$ and $3 + 2i$ can be written $(3, 2)$. The number $0 + ib$ or equivalently $(0, b)$ is called an *imaginary number* and the number $a + i0 \equiv (a, 0)$ is a *real number*. Hence a real number is a particular kind of complex number, or alternatively the complex number system is a generalization of the real number system. The complex number zero is the number $0 + i0 \equiv (0, 0)$, that is, the real and imaginary parts are both zero. The number $a - ib$ is said to be the *complex conjugate* of $z = a + ib$ and is denoted by $\bar{z}$.

The Algebra of Complex Numbers

If the complex numbers z, z_1 and z_2 are defined to be $z = a + ib, z_1 = a_1 + ib_1$ and $z_2 = a_2 + ib_2$, then the following laws hold

$$z_1 = z_2 \quad \text{if and only if} \quad a_1 = a_2 \quad \text{and} \quad b_1 = b_2 , \tag{1}$$

$$z_1 \pm z_2 = a_1 \pm a_2 + \mathrm{i}(b_1 \pm b_2) ,$$

$$z_1 z_2 = a_1 a_2 - b_1 b_2 + \mathrm{i}(a_1 b_2 + a_2 b_1) ,$$

$$z\bar{z} = a^2 + b^2, \tag{2a}$$

$$z + \bar{z} = 2a = 2 \operatorname{Re} z, \tag{2b}$$

$$z - \bar{z} = 2\mathrm{i}b = 2\mathrm{i} \operatorname{Im} z, \tag{2c}$$

$$\frac{z_1}{z_2} = \frac{z_1 \bar{z}_2}{z_2 \bar{z}_2} = \frac{a_1 a_2 + b_1 b_2}{a_2^2 + b_2^2} + \mathrm{i}\left(\frac{b_1 a_2 - a_1 b_2}{a_2^2 + b_2^2} \right) .$$

It follows from equation (1) that in any equation involving complex numbers, the real parts of both sides of the equation are equal, as are the imaginary parts of both sides of the equation.

Geometrical Representation of Complex Numbers

The complex number $z = (a, b)$ can be represented geometrically by a point P on a plane called the *z plane* or the *Argand diagram*. In Fig. 4.1, Re z is measured along the horizontal axis and Im z is measured along the vertical axis. A point on a plane can also be described in terms of polar coordinates (r, θ) (see Fig. 4.1) so that

$$z = a + \mathrm{i}b = r \cos \theta + \mathrm{i}r \sin \theta = r(\cos \theta + \mathrm{i} \sin \theta) , \tag{3}$$

where

$$r = |OP| = \sqrt{(a^2 + b^2)} \quad \text{and} \quad \theta = \tan^{-1}(b/a) .$$

The quadrant in which θ lies is determined from the equations

$$a = r \cos \theta \quad \text{and} \quad b = r \sin \theta .$$

The quantity $r = \sqrt{(a^2 + b^2)}$ is called the *modulus of z*, denoted by $|z|$, and therefore

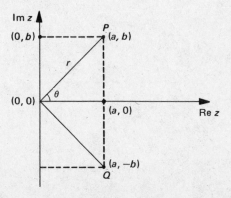

Fig. 4.1   The numbers z and $\bar{z}$ on the Argand diagram.

equation (2a) can be expressed concisely as

$$z\bar{z} = |z|^2.$$

The quantity θ is called the *argument of z*, denoted by $\arg z$, and the value of $\arg z$ lying in $0 \leqslant \theta < 2\pi$ is known as the *principal value* of $\arg z$. On the Argand diagram (Fig. 4.1) the point Q, which represents the number $\bar{z}$, is the mirror image in the real axis of the point P which represents the number z. Clearly $|\bar{z}| = |z|$ and $\arg \bar{z} = -\arg z$.

EXAMPLE 1   Show that

(a) $|z_1 z_2| = |z_1||z_2|$,

(b) $\arg(z_1 z_2) = \arg z_1 + \arg z_2$,

(c) $|z_1 + z_2| \leqslant |z_1| + |z_2|$,

(d) $|z_1 - z_2| \leqslant |z_1| + |z_2|$,

(e) $\big||z_1| - |z_2|\big| \leqslant |z_1 - z_2|$.

(a) (b) Let $z_1 = r_1(\cos\theta_1 + i\sin\theta_1)$ and $z_2 = r_2(\cos\theta_2 + i\sin\theta_2)$, then

$$z_1 z_2 = r_1 r_2\{(\cos\theta_1\cos\theta_2 - \sin\theta_1\sin\theta_2) + i(\sin\theta_1\cos\theta_2 + \cos\theta_1\sin\theta_2)\}$$

$$= r_1 r_2\{\cos(\theta_1 + \theta_2) + i\sin(\theta_1 + \theta_2)\}.$$

Hence $|z_1 z_2| = r_1 r_2$ and $\arg(z_1 z_2) = \theta_1 + \theta_2 = \arg z_1 + \arg z_2$.

(c) The laws of addition and subtraction give the result

$$z_1 \pm z_2 = (r_1\cos\theta_1 \pm r_2\cos\theta_2) + i(r_1\sin\theta_1 \pm r_2\sin\theta_2).$$

On the Argand diagram, Fig. 4.2, the numbers $z_1, z_2, z_1 + z_2$ and $z_1 - z_2$ are represented by the points P, Q, S and T, respectively. The required inequality follows immediately from the geometrical result that the sum of the sides of a triangle must be less than or

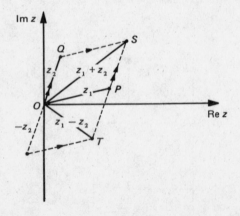

Fig. 4.2   Addition and subtraction on the Argand diagram.

equal to the length of the third side, that is

$$OS \leqslant OP + PS,$$

where $OS = |z_1 + z_2|$, $OP = |z_1|$ and $PS = OQ = |z_2|$.

(d) It can be seen from Fig. 4.2 that $PQ = OT$ and therefore $|z_1 - z_2|$ is the length PQ. The required result may now be deduced from the geometrical result $PQ \leqslant OP + OQ$.

(e) If $|z_1| > |z_2|$ then

$$|z_2| + |z_1 - z_2| \geqslant |z_2 + (z_1 - z_2)| = |z_1|,$$

which on rearrangement gives the result

$$|z_1| - |z_2| \leqslant |z_1 - z_2|.$$

Similarly, if $|z_2| > |z_1|$ then

$$|z_2| - |z_1| \leqslant |z_1 - z_2|,$$

and hence

$$\big||z_1| - |z_2|\big| \leqslant |z_1 - z_2|.$$

The results (c), (d) and (e), which are very important, are known as the *triangle inequalities*.

The General Polar Form of a Complex Number

Equation (3) expresses the complex number z in terms of its modulus r and argument θ. This expression is often called the *polar form* of a complex number. The functions $\cos \theta$ and $\sin \theta$ are periodic with period 2π, and so a complex number z can be expressed as

$$r[\cos(\theta + 2k\pi) + i\sin(\theta + 2k\pi)] \quad \text{for} \quad k = 0, \pm1, \pm2, \dots . \tag{4}$$

The expression (4) is called the *general polar form* of a complex number and it is important to reiterate that *all* integer values of k specify the *same* complex number. The argument of the complex number is thus $\theta + 2k\pi$ for $k = 0, \pm1, \pm2, \dots$, where θ is the principal value of the argument (see example 2).

EXAMPLE 2   Express the complex number $z = i$ in polar form.

If $z = i$, then $|z| = 1$ and $\arg z = \frac{1}{2}\pi + 2k\pi$ for $k = 0, \pm1, \pm2, \dots$. Therefore $z = i$ can be written as $\cos\frac{1}{2}\pi + i\sin\frac{1}{2}\pi$, and $\cos\frac{5}{2}\pi + i\sin\frac{5}{2}\pi$, etc.

Euler's Formula

If θ is real, then it can be shown that

$$e^{i\theta} = \cos\theta + i\sin\theta.$$

The derivation of this result, which is known as *Euler's formula*, may be found in Lennox and Chadwick [1] (see also exercise 4 of this section).

It follows from Euler's formula that $e^{i\theta}$ is periodic with period 2π. It is interesting to note also that the irrational numbers e and π and the imaginary number i are related through the equation

$$e^{i\pi} = -1.$$

It is easy to show that

$$\cos\theta - i\sin\theta = e^{-i\theta} = \overline{e^{i\theta}},$$

and the index law for exponentials with imaginary indices can be quickly verified. The polar form of a complex number z can therefore be written concisely as

$$z = re^{i\theta},$$

and the general polar form of z as

$$z = re^{i(\theta + 2k\pi)} \quad \text{for} \quad k = 0, \pm 1, \pm 2, \ldots .$$

De Moivre's Theorem

If n is a positive or negative integer or rational fraction, that is, a number p/q where p and q are integers and $q \neq 0$, then

$$(e^{i\theta})^n = e^{in(\theta + 2k\pi)}$$

where $k = 0, \pm 1, \pm 2, \ldots$. When n is an integer, all the values of k give the same result and when $n = p/q$, distinct values of the right-hand side are obtained for $k = 0, 1, 2, \ldots, q - 1$. The proof of this theorem follows from the index properties of exponentials and may be found in Lennox and Chadwick [1].

EXAMPLE 3   Find the square roots of $\sqrt{3} + i$.

Let $z = \sqrt{3} + i$, then $|z| = 2$ and

$$z = 2\left(\frac{\sqrt{3}}{2} + \frac{1}{2}i\right) = 2(\cos\tfrac{1}{6}\pi + i\sin\tfrac{1}{6}\pi) = 2e^{i\pi/6}.$$

De Moivre's theorem gives

$$\sqrt{z} = \sqrt{2}\exp\{i\tfrac{1}{2}(\tfrac{1}{6}\pi + 2k\pi)\}$$

with distinct values for $k = 0$ and 1. The square roots of $\sqrt{3} + i$ are therefore

$$\sqrt{2}\exp\{i\tfrac{1}{12}\pi\} = \sqrt{2}(\cos\tfrac{1}{12}\pi + i\sin\tfrac{1}{12}\pi),$$

$$\sqrt{2}\exp\{i\tfrac{13}{12}\pi\} = \sqrt{2}(\cos\tfrac{13}{12}\pi + i\sin\tfrac{13}{12}\pi) = -\sqrt{2}\exp\{i\tfrac{1}{12}\pi\}.$$

Curves and Regions on the Argand Diagram

If x and y are real variables, then $z = x + iy$ is a *complex variable* and for an arbitrary pair of values x and y, z can be represented by a point P on the Argand diagram. As x and y vary, z will vary, and P will trace out a locus in the z plane. For example, if z varies so that

$$|z - z_0| = c,$$ (5a)

where $z_0 = x_0 + iy_0$ is a fixed complex number and c is real, then equation (5a) can be written as

$$|(x + iy) - (x_0 + iy_0)| = c,$$

or alternatively as

$$(x - x_0)^2 + (y - y_0)^2 = c^2.$$ (5b)

Equation (5b) is the equation of a circle and therefore when z varies so that equation (5a) is satisfied, P moves on a circle with centre z_0 and radius c. This result may be deduced geometrically by noting that equation (5a) states that the distance in the Argand diagram between the points representing z and z_0 is a constant c (example 1(d)). Another important example is the locus defined by the equation

$$\arg z = \alpha.$$

This locus is the ray or half-line from the origin at angle α to the Re z axis.

If z can take any value subject only to the restriction that

$$|z - z_0| < c,$$

then the point P, which represents z, can be any point *inside* the circle specified by equation (5a). This inequality therefore specifies a *region* of the z plane, namely the interior of the circle with centre z_0 and radius c, shown in Fig. 4.3 as the stippled area. The inequality

$$|z - z_0| > c$$

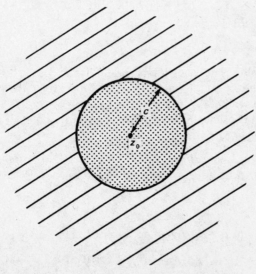

Fig. 4.3   The exterior and interior of a circle.

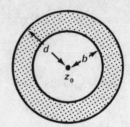

Fig. 4.4   An annulus in the z plane.

specifies the region which consists of all points outside the circle, shown in Fig. 4.3 as the lined region. If $b < d$, then the inequality

$$b < |z - z_0| < d \qquad (6)$$

specifies the annulus which consists of all points between the two circles with centre z_0 and with radii b and d respectively, shown as the stippled region in Fig. 4.4.

EXAMPLE 4   (a) Determine the locus in the z plane represented by the equation

$$|z + 2| = |z + 3|.$$

(b) Determine the region in the z plane represented by the inequality

$$-\pi < \operatorname{Im} z < \pi.$$

   Let $z = x + iy$ then

(a) $| (x + iy) + 2 | = | (x + iy) + 3 |,$

or alternatively

$$\{(x + 2)^2 + y^2 \}^{\frac{1}{2}} = \{(x + 3)^2 + y^2 \}^{\frac{1}{2}},$$

which may be simplified to give the equation

$$x = \operatorname{Re} z = -\tfrac{5}{2}.$$

   The result can also be obtained geometrically. Let P, Q and R represent z, $(-2, 0)$ and $(-3, 0)$ respectively on the Argand diagram. Then $|z + 2| = PQ$ and $|z + 3| = PR$, therefore the equation $|z + 2| = |z + 3|$ can be written $PQ = PR$. If P moves so that $PQ = PR$ then P moves along the perpendicular bisector of the line QR, that is along the line $x = -\tfrac{5}{2}$ (see Fig. 4.5).

(b) The inequality can be written $-\pi < y < \pi$ and therefore represents a strip of width 2π in the z plane, shown in Fig. 4.5 as the stippled region.

Exercises

1. If $z_1 = a_1 + ib_1$ and $z_2 = a_2 + ib_2$, find the real and imaginary parts of

     (a) $z_1^2 + 3z_2 + 1$,   (b) $z_1 \bar{z}_2 + z_2 \bar{z}_1$,   (c) $(z_1 + \bar{z}_2)^3$,   (d) $(z_1 + 1)/(z_2 - 1)$.

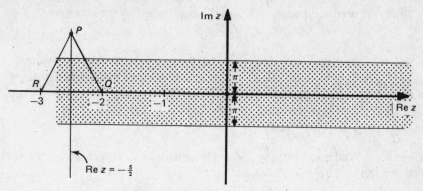

Fig. 4.5 The strip $-\pi < \text{Im } z < \pi$.

2. If $z_1 = R_1 + i\omega L$ and $z_2 = R_2 - i/(\omega C)$ and z is defined by

$$\frac{1}{z} = \frac{1}{z_1} + \frac{1}{z_2},$$

find the values of ω for which z is real.

3. Express the following numbers in general polar form:

    (a) $1 + \sqrt{3}i$,   (b) $1 - \sqrt{3}i$,   (c) $(3 + i)/(2i - 1)$,

    (d) $(1 + i)^4$,   (e) $(\sqrt{2} + i)^{4/3}$.

4. Substitute $x = i\theta$ in the power series for e^x, where θ is real, and hence show that

    $e^{i\theta} = \cos \theta + i \sin \theta$.

5. Describe the curves in the z plane specified by

    (a) $\arg\left(\dfrac{z - 3}{z - i}\right) = \dfrac{\pi}{6}$,   (b) $|z + 2i| + |z - 2i| = 5$,   (c) $|z - 2| - |z + 2| = 3$.

6. Determine the regions in the z plane specified by

    (a) $1 < |z + 2| < 2$,   (b) $0 < |z - i| < 1$,   (c) $|z + 2| + |z - 2| < 5$,

    (d) $\text{Re}(z^2) > 2$.

4.3 FUNCTIONS OF A COMPLEX VARIABLE

Consider two complex variables z and w and suppose that to each value of z in some region of the z plane there corresponds at least one value of w. Then w is said to be a function of z, that is, a *function of a complex variable*, written

    $w = f(z)$.   (7)

Equation (7) is the rule for calculating the w which corresponds to a particular z. For example, the w corresponding to z could be determined by the equation

$$w = z^2. \tag{8a}$$

In this example there is only one value of w for each value of z, and in this case $f(z) = z^2$ is said to be *single-valued*. But in examples where there is more than one value of w for each z, $f(z)$ is said to be *multiple-valued*.

If z is replaced by $x + iy$, then equation (7) can be written as

$$w = u(x, y) + iv(x, y),$$

where $u(x, y)$ and $v(x, y)$ are the real and imaginary parts respectively of $f(x + iy)$. In equation (8a), for example,

$$w = z^2 = (x + iy)^2 = x^2 - y^2 + i2xy,$$

so that

$$u = x^2 - y^2 \quad \text{and} \quad v = 2xy. \tag{8b}$$

Equations (8b) define u and v for all x and y and therefore equation (8a) defines w for all z.

As in the theory of real variables, it is often convenient to exhibit the properties of a function of a complex variable geometrically by plotting on a diagram the points $f(z)$ as z varies. However, w and z are each specified by two coordinates and must each be plotted on a plane. To plot the function $w = f(z)$ we therefore use two planes, the z plane and the w plane. It is not difficult to see that if z moves along some curve C in the z plane, then w will move along some curve C' in the w plane, and as z varies throughout a specified region R in the z plane, w will vary throughout some region R' in the w plane. The function $w = f(z)$ thus sets the curve C' and the region R' of the w plane in correspondence with the curve C and region R respectively of the z plane. We say that C and R are *mapped* by the function $w = f(z)$ into C' and R' respectively. For example, if w and z are related by equation (8a) with $z = re^{i\theta}$, then $w = r^2 e^{2i\theta}$ and it can be seen that

$$|w| = r^2 = |z|^2 \quad \text{and} \quad \arg w = 2\theta = 2 \arg z.$$

If R is the first quadrant of the z plane, then

$$0 \leqslant r < \infty \quad \text{and} \quad 0 \leqslant \theta \leqslant \pi/2,$$

and its *image* R' in the w plane is given by

$$0 \leqslant |w| < \infty \quad \text{and} \quad 0 \leqslant \arg w \leqslant \pi,$$

which is the upper half of the w plane (see Fig. 4.6).

It can be shown similarly that under the mapping $w = z^2$, the second quadrant of the z plane, labelled S in Fig. 4.6, corresponds to the lower half of the w plane, labelled S'. Hence the upper half of the z plane is mapped into the whole of the w plane by the function $w = z^2$.

If C is the curve $y = a$ in the z plane, where a is a real constant, then C', the image of C in the w plane under the mapping $w = z^2$, is given by equations (8b) with $y = a$.

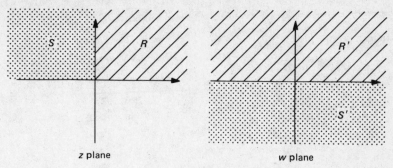

Fig. 4.6 Illustration of the mapping $w = z^2$.

Hence

$$u = \left(\frac{v}{2a}\right)^2 - a^2 \quad \text{or alternatively} \quad v^2 = 4a^2(u + a^2),$$

which is the equation of a parabola in the w plane, shown in Fig. 4.7. If a is put equal to zero in the above theory, it can be seen that the x axis is mapped to the positive u axis. Therefore all points in the *infinite strip* between the x axis and C in the z plane are mapped into points to the right of C' in the w plane (see Fig. 4.7). If Γ is the line $x = b$ in the z plane where b is a constant, then it can be shown similarly that its image Γ' under the mapping $w = z^2$ is the parabola

$$v^2 = 4b^2(b^2 - u),$$

which is also shown in Fig. 4.7. The points between the y axis and Γ are mapped into points to the left of Γ' and hence the points inside $OQSP$ in the z plane are mapped into the points inside $O'Q'S'P'$ in the w plane.

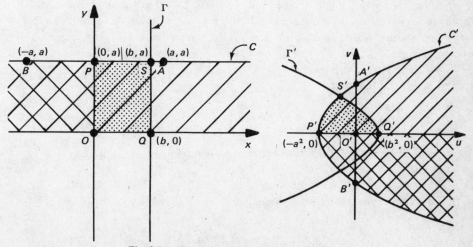

Fig. 4.7 Illustration of the mapping $w = z^2$.

(a) *Polynomials*

A function of the form

$$P(z) = a_n z^n + a_{n-1} z^{n-1} + \ldots + a_{n-r} z^{n-r} + \ldots + a_0,$$

where $a_n, a_{n-1}, \ldots, a_{n-r}, \ldots, a_0$ are complex constants, $a_n \neq 0$ and n is a positive integer, is called a polynomial of degree n. In complex variable theory, a polynomial equation $P(z) = 0$, where $P(z)$ is of degree n, has exactly n roots, though they may not all be distinct. If the coefficients of $P(z)$ are real and $z = a + ib$ is a root of $P(z) = 0$, then $z = a - ib$ is a root also (see Lennox and Chadwick [1]).

(b) *Rational Functions*

A function of the form

$$\frac{P(z)}{Q(z)},$$

where $P(z)$ and $Q(z)$ are polynomials, is called a *rational function*. It is defined at points where $Q(z) \neq 0$. For example, a simple rational function is

$$w = f(z) = \frac{1}{z},$$

which may be written as

$$f(z) = \frac{1}{re^{i\theta}} = \frac{1}{r} e^{-i\theta}.$$

If r and θ vary so that $0 \leqslant r < \infty$ and $0 \leqslant \theta \leqslant \pi$, then w varies so that $0 \leqslant |w| < \infty$ and $-\pi \leqslant \arg w \leqslant 0$. Therefore the upper half of the z plane is mapped by $w = 1/z$ into the lower half of the w plane. It can be shown similarly that the lower half of the z plane is mapped by $w = 1/z$ into the upper half of the w plane. If now r and θ vary so that $1 < r < \infty$ and $0 \leqslant \theta < 2\pi$, then w varies so that $0 \leqslant |w| < 1$ and $-2\pi < \arg w \leqslant 0$. In other words, the region exterior to the circle $|z| = 1$ maps to the interior of the circle $|w| = 1$ and vice versa.

The rational function

$$w = \frac{az + b}{cz + d},$$

known as the *bilinear function*, will be discussed in §4.6.

(c) *The Exponential Function $w = e^z$*

If $z = x + iy$ then

$$e^z = e^{x+iy} = e^x e^{iy},$$

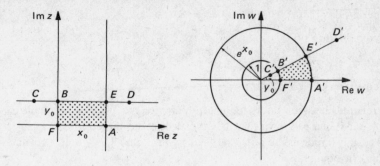

Fig. 4.8 Illustration of the mapping $w = e^z$.

and using Euler's formula for e^{iy}, e^z can be expressed as

$$e^z = e^x(\cos y + i \sin y).$$

If w is expressed in polar form as $w = \rho e^{i\phi}$, then

$$w = \rho e^{i\phi} = e^x e^{iy},$$

that is

$$\rho = e^x \quad \text{and} \quad \phi = y + 2k\pi \quad \text{for} \quad k = 0, \pm 1, \pm 2, \dots .$$

A line $x = x_0$ in the z plane, where x_0 is a constant, is mapped by the function $w = e^z$ into the circle $\rho = e^{x_0}$ in the w plane. A line $y = y_0$ in the z plane, where y_0 is constant, is mapped into the radial line, or half-line, $\phi = y_0 + 2k\pi$ in the w plane (see Fig. 4.8). The interior of the rectangle $AEBF$ in the z plane is mapped into the interior of the curve $A'E'B'F'$ in the w plane. If y_0 takes the value π then the line $B'E'$ in Fig. 4.8 lies on the negative real axis. If now $x_0 \to +\infty$, then the arc $E'A'$ extends to a semi-circle at infinity. Further, if x_0 is negative the radius of the arc $E'A'$ is less than unity and if $x_0 \to -\infty$ the arc $E'A'$ shrinks to the origin. Thus it can be shown that the strip defined by $0 \leqslant y \leqslant \pi$ and $-\infty < x < \infty$ in the z plane is mapped by the function $w = e^z$ into the upper half of the w plane. This mapping will be used in §4.6.

(d) *Trigonometric Functions*

If z in equations (2b) and (2c) is replaced by $z = e^{i\theta}$, where θ is real, then the results

$$\cos \theta = \tfrac{1}{2}(e^{i\theta} + e^{-i\theta}) \quad \text{and} \quad \sin \theta = \frac{1}{2i}(e^{i\theta} - e^{-i\theta}) \tag{9}$$

are obtained. We now *define* $\cos z$ and $\sin z$, where z is complex, to be

$$\cos z = \tfrac{1}{2}(e^{iz} + e^{-iz}) \quad \text{and} \quad \sin z = \frac{1}{2i}(e^{iz} - e^{-iz}),$$

and the other trigonometric functions are defined similarly. It is easily shown from these definitions that

$$\cos^2 z + \sin^2 z = 1$$

and that

$$\cos(z_1 + z_2) = \cos z_1 \cos z_2 - \sin z_1 \sin z_2.$$

Other relations between the trigonometric functions of a complex variable can also be derived, and it can be shown that they are identical to those for real variables. However, it is important to note that $|\cos z|$ and $|\sin z|$ may both exceed one. For example, the equation

$$\cos z = 2$$

can be written as

$$e^{iz} + e^{-iz} = 4,$$

which is equivalent to

$$e^{2iz} - 4e^{iz} + 1 = 0,$$

a quadratic in e^{iz}, and which has solutions

$$z = -i \log(2 \pm \sqrt{3}).$$

(e) *The Hyperbolic Functions*

The definitions of $\sinh \theta$ and $\cosh \theta$, where θ is real, are

$$\cosh \theta = \tfrac{1}{2}(e^\theta + e^{-\theta}) \quad \text{and} \quad \sinh \theta = \tfrac{1}{2}(e^\theta - e^{-\theta}).$$

If z is a complex variable the functions $\cosh z$ and $\sinh z$ are *defined* by replacing θ by z in the above definitions, and so are given by

$$\cosh z = \tfrac{1}{2}(e^z + e^{-z}) \quad \text{and} \quad \sinh z = \tfrac{1}{2}(e^z - e^{-z}).$$

With these definitions of $\cosh z$ and $\sinh z$, it is a simple matter to show that

$$\sin iz = i \sinh z, \qquad \cos iz = \cosh z, \qquad \tan iz = i \tanh z,$$

$$\sinh iz = i \sin z, \qquad \cosh iz = \cos z, \qquad \tanh iz = i \tan z.$$

Multiple-valued Functions

The functions (a) to (e) discussed above are all single-valued functions. There are, however, several commonly occurring multiple-valued functions, for example $f(z) = z^{1/2}$.

The general polar form of z is

$$z = r \exp\{i(\theta + 2k\pi)\} \quad \text{for} \quad k = 0, \pm 1, \pm 2, \dots$$

where $0 \leqslant \theta < 2\pi$. If $w = z^{1/2}$, the polar form of w is expressed as

$$w = r^{1/2} \exp\{i(\tfrac{1}{2}\theta + k\pi)\} \quad \text{for} \quad k = 0, \pm 1, \pm 2, \dots,$$

(see example 3 of §4.2) and as the function $e^{ik\pi}$ takes the values

$$e^{ik\pi} = \begin{cases} 1 & \text{for} \quad k = 0, \pm 2, \pm 4, \ldots \\ -1 & \text{for} \quad k = \pm 1, \pm 3, \pm 5, \ldots, \end{cases}$$

there are two values of w for each value of z, namely

$$w = \pm r^{\frac{1}{2}} \exp(\tfrac{1}{2}i\theta)$$

where $0 \leqslant \theta < 2\pi$. The function $w = z^{\frac{1}{2}}$ is therefore a 'two-valued' function. For example, the number $z = i$ expressed in general polar form (see example 2 of §4.2) is

$$i = \exp\left\{i\left(\frac{1}{2}\pi + 2k\pi\right)\right\} \quad \text{for} \quad k = 0, \pm 1, \pm 2, \ldots$$

and therefore $i^{\frac{1}{2}}$ is given by

$$i^{\frac{1}{2}} = \exp\left\{i\left(\frac{1}{4}\pi + k\pi\right)\right\} = \pm \exp(i\pi/4) = \pm(1 + i)/\sqrt{2}.$$

The 'two-valuedness' of $w = z^{\frac{1}{2}}$ can be illustrated geometrically in the following way. If Γ is the circle $|z| = c$ and P is a point on Γ, initially at $\theta = \arg z = 0$, then Q, the image of P in the w plane, is specified by $|w| = \sqrt{c}$ and $\arg w = 0$. If P moves from $\theta = 0$ to $\theta = 2\pi$ on Γ then its image Q moves from $\arg w = 0$ to $\arg w = \pi$ on the curve Γ', which is the circle $|w| = \sqrt{c}$. In other words, if P moves round Γ and returns to its starting point, Q moves along Γ' but does not make a complete circuit (solid line in Fig. 4.9). If P now continues to move on Γ, travelling from $\theta = 2\pi$ to $\theta = 4\pi$, then Q moves on Γ' from $\arg w = \pi$ to $\arg w = 2\pi$. Thus Q makes a complete circuit of Γ' when P completes two circuits of Γ (broken line in Fig. 4.9).

The curve Γ was chosen to be a circle for the sake of convenience but there is no reason why Γ should not be any closed curve enclosing the origin. This is because the z plane specified by $0 \leqslant \arg z < 2\pi$ is mapped by the function $w = z^{\frac{1}{2}}$ into the upper half of the w plane, and the z plane specified by $2\pi \leqslant \arg z < 4\pi$ is mapped by $w = z^{\frac{1}{2}}$ into the lower half of the w plane (see Fig. 4.10). It is interesting to note that the mapping $w = z^{\frac{1}{2}}$ is the inverse of $z = w^2$, the properties of which can be deduced from the earlier part of this section.

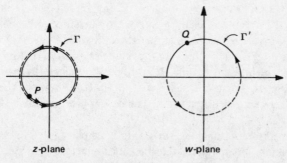

z-plane   w-plane

Fig. 4.9 Illustration of the mapping $w = z^{\frac{1}{2}}$.

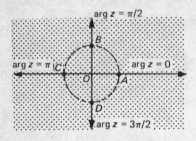
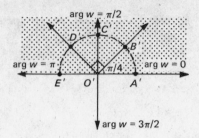
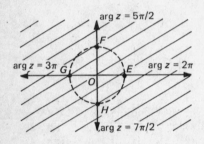
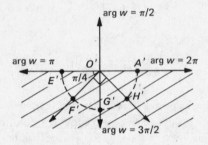

Fig. 4.10   Illustration of the mapping $w = z^{1/2}$.

It is clear from Fig. 4.10 that the *two-valued* function $f(z) = z^{1/2}$ can be separated into two single-valued functions by defining points on the z plane as

(a) $|z| = r$ and $\arg z = \theta$, where $0 \leqslant \theta < 2\pi$
   and w is then given by $w = r^{1/2}e^{i\theta/2}$, or as

(b) $|z| = r$ and $\arg z = \theta + 2\pi$, where $0 \leqslant \theta < 2\pi$
   and w is then given by $w = -r^{1/2}e^{i\theta/2}$.

The two functions into which $f(z) = z^{1/2}$ is separated are called *branches* of the function. For example, on branch (a), $z = i$ is specified by $r = 1$ and $\theta = \frac{1}{2}\pi$, which leads to the result $i^{1/2} = e^{i\pi/4}$. On branch (b), however, $z = i$ is specified by $r = 1$ and $\arg z = 2\pi + \frac{1}{2}\pi$, which leads to the result $i^{1/2} = -e^{i\pi/4}$.

The first circuit of Γ in Fig. 4.9 was on branch (*a*) of $f(z) = z^{1/2}$ and the second circuit was on branch (b). The change of branch occurred on the line $\arg z = 2\pi$ and the second value of $f(z) = z^{1/2}$ must be considered when the line $\arg z = 2\pi$ is crossed. In order to isolate the branches, we imagine that there exists an impenetrable *barrier* or, alternatively, that the z plane is *cut* along the line $\arg z = 2\pi$, so that it becomes impossible for a path which begins on branch (a) to pass to branch (b) and vice versa. A point P in the z plane can be described either by (a) or (b) above, and the two branches of $f(z) = z^{1/2}$ are kept clearly distinct. The barrier just described is called a *branch line* or *branch cut*.

If the point P moves from A along the curve Π in the z plane (see Fig. 4.11), and returns to A after making a complete circuit, then $\arg z$ increases from zero to $\frac{1}{2}\pi$ and then returns to zero. It is not difficult to see that as P moves from A around any

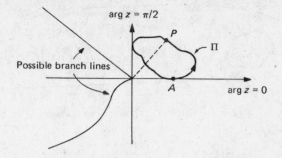

Fig. 4.11 The circuit Π which does not enclose the origin in the z plane and possible branch lines of the function $f(z) = z^{\frac{1}{2}}$.

closed curve, arg z returns to zero provided the curve does not enclose the origin. If P moves from A around any curve which *does* enclose the origin, then arg z increases from zero to 2π and P then passes on to another branch of $f(z) = z^{\frac{1}{2}}$. The branch cut therefore prevents P from following a path which completely encloses $z = 0$. Clearly any non-intersecting curve from $z = 0$ to infinity would do this and therefore the branch line is not unique (see Fig. 4.11). The point $z = 0$ is thus seen to be a special point of the function $f(z) = z^{\frac{1}{2}}$ and is called a *branch point* of the function.

EXAMPLE 1   Show that the branch point of the function

$$w = (z - a)^{\frac{1}{2}}$$

is $z = a$.

Let $z - a = t$, then $w = t^{\frac{1}{2}}$ and the point $t = 0$ is a branch point of the function $w = t^{\frac{1}{2}}$. The point $z = a$ is therefore a branch point of $w = (z - a)^{\frac{1}{2}}$.

EXAMPLE 2   Show that the branch points of the function

$$w = (z^2 - a^2)^{\frac{1}{2}}$$

are $z = \pm a$, and determine possible branch lines.

Let $\Delta \text{arg } z$ represent the increase in the argument of z as the point P moves on the z plane, and consider the corresponding increase $\Delta \text{arg } w$ in arg w. The argument of w is given by

$$\text{arg } w = \tfrac{1}{2} \text{arg}(z^2 - a^2) = \tfrac{1}{2}\{\text{arg}(z + a) + \text{arg}(z - a)\},$$

and therefore

$$\Delta \text{arg } w = \tfrac{1}{2}\{\Delta \text{arg}(z + a) + \Delta \text{arg}(z - a)\}.$$

Let C_1 be a closed curve which encloses $z = a$ but not $z = -a$, C_2 be a closed curve which encloses $z = -a$ but not $z = a$, and C_3 be a closed curve which encloses both $z = a$ and

Fig. 4.12   The circuits C_1, C_2 and C_3 of example 2.

$z = -a$ (see Fig. 4.12). If P makes a complete circuit of C_1, then

$$\Delta \arg(z + a) = 0 \quad \text{and} \quad \Delta \arg(z - a) = 2\pi \, ,$$

therefore

$$\Delta \arg w = \tfrac{1}{2}(0 + 2\pi) = \pi \, .$$

Hence P', the image of P in the w plane, does not return to its starting point when P returns to its starting point after one circuit of C_1, but only after P has completed *two* circuits of C_1 (that is $\Delta \arg w = 2\pi$). The point $z = a$ is therefore a branch point of the function. It can be shown in a similar way that if P makes a complete circuit of C_2 then

$$\Delta \arg(z + a) = 2\pi \quad \text{and} \quad \Delta \arg(z - a) = 0 \, ,$$

and therefore

$$\Delta \arg w = \tfrac{1}{2}(2\pi + 0) = \pi \, .$$

The point $z = -a$ is thus also a branch point of the function. If P makes a complete circuit of C_3, however, then

$$\Delta \arg(z + a) = 2\pi \quad \text{and} \quad \Delta \arg(z - a) = 2\pi \, ,$$

which leads to

$$\Delta \arg w = 2\pi \, .$$

Hence P' returns to its starting point in the w plane if P makes a complete circuit enclosing both branch points. The branch lines must therefore prevent complete circuits of $z = a$ and of $z = -a$, but need not prevent complete circuits of both $z = a$ and $z = -a$ together. Possible branch lines, or cuts, are shown in Fig. 4.13.

Fig. 4.13   Possible branch lines of the function $f(z) = (z^2 - a^2)^{\frac{1}{2}}$.

Logarithm

If z and w are complex variables and $z = e^w$, then the expression for w as a function of z is written as $w = \log z$. The function $\log z$ is thus defined to be the inverse of the function e^z. The general polar form of z is

$$z = re^{i(\theta + 2k\pi)} \quad \text{for} \quad k = 0, \pm1, \pm2, \ldots$$

where $0 \leqslant \theta < 2\pi$, and, if $w = u + iv$, then $z = e^w$ can be written as

$$re^{i(\theta + 2k\pi)} = e^u e^{iv},$$

from which it can be seen that

$$v = \theta + 2k\pi \quad \text{and} \quad r = e^u .$$

Hence $u = \log r$ and

$$w = \log z = \log r + i(\theta + 2k\pi) \quad \text{for} \quad k = 0, \pm1, \pm2, \ldots . \tag{10}$$

This expression has distinct values for each value of k and therefore $\log z$ is a multiple-valued function.

For example, the number $z = 1 + i$ expressed in general polar form is $z = \sqrt{2} \exp\{i(\tfrac{1}{4}\pi + 2k\pi)\}$ for $k = 0, \pm1, \pm2, \ldots$. Although each value of k specifies the same number $z = 1 + i$, the expression

$$\log(1 + i) = \log\sqrt{2} + i\tfrac{1}{4}\pi + i2k\pi \quad \text{for} \quad k = 0, \pm1, \pm2, \ldots$$

has infinitely many values.

The value of $\log z$ such that $0 \leqslant \operatorname{Im} \log z < 2\pi$ is called the *principal value of* $\log z$, written $\operatorname{Log} z$. If the z plane is cut from the origin to infinity along any line, then $\log z$ will be rendered single-valued. The origin is therefore a branch point and any radial line is a branch line. If points on the z plane are specified by

(a) $\quad |z| = r \quad$ and $\quad \arg z = \theta \quad$ with $\quad 0 \leqslant \theta < 2\pi$,

then $\log z$ takes its principal value $\operatorname{Log} z$, that is

$$\log z = \operatorname{Log} z = \log r + i\theta .$$

However, if points on the z plane are specified by

(b) $\quad |z| = r \quad$ and $\quad \arg z = \phi \quad$ with $\quad 2\pi \leqslant \phi < 4\pi$,

then $\log z$ is defined to be

$$\log z = \log r + i\phi = \operatorname{Log} z + i2\pi .$$

The function $\log z$ is sometimes written $\log_e z$ or $\ln z$.

Complex Exponents

The real number a can be expressed as

$$a = e^q \quad \text{where} \quad q = \log a ,$$

that is

$$a = \exp(\log a).$$

Hence if $z = x + iy$ is any complex number where x and y are real then the function a^z can be expressed as

$$a^z = \{\exp(\log a)\}^z = \exp(z \log a)$$

$$= \exp(x \log a) \exp(iy \log a)$$

$$= a^x \exp(iy \log a).$$

If w is also complex then w^z can be expressed as

$$w^z = \{\exp(\log w)\}^z = \exp(z \log w) = e^s,$$

where $s = z \log w$ and generally is multiple-valued.

EXAMPLE 3   Evaluate (a) i^{-2i}, (b) i^2.

(a) $i^{-2i} = \exp(-2i \log i) = \exp\{-2i(\tfrac{1}{2}i\pi + i2k\pi)\} = \exp\{(4k + 1)\pi\}$,

    for $k = 0, \pm1, \pm2, \ldots$.

(b) $i^2 = \exp(2 \log i) = \exp\{2(\tfrac{1}{2}i\pi + i2k\pi)\} = \exp\{i(4k + 1)\pi\}$,

    for $k = 0, \pm1, \pm2, \ldots$.

However, $\exp(i\pi) = -1$ and $\exp(i4k\pi) = 1$ for $k = 0, \pm1, \pm2, \ldots$, hence $i^2 = -1$, a result which shows that the theory is so far consistent.

Exercises

1. Separate into real and imaginary parts

(a) e^{3iz},   (b) $z \cos z$,   (c) $\sin 2z$,   (d) $z^2 e^{2z}$,   (e) $\sinh 2z$.

2. Prove that, if z is complex, then

(a) $1 + \tan^2 z = \sec^2 z$,   (b) $\overline{\sin z} = \sin \bar{z}$,

(c) $\exp(i\bar{z}) \neq \overline{\exp iz}$ unless $z = \pm n\pi, n = 0, 1, 2, \ldots$.

3. Show that

$$\sinh(z + \pi i) = -\sinh z,$$

$$\cosh(z + \pi i) = -\cosh z.$$

4. If u_0 and v_0 are real constants, find the curves in the z plane that transform under the mapping $w = z^2$ into the straight lines $u = u_0$, $v = v_0$ in the w plane, where $w = u + iv$.

5. Show that under the mapping $w = \sin z$ the lines Re $z = c \neq 0$, Im $z = d \neq 0$ in the z plane are mapped into a hyperbola and an ellipse respectively in the w plane.

6. If $z = re^{i\theta}$ and $z_0 = \rho e^{i\psi}$, show that

$$\log(z - z_0) = \tfrac{1}{2} \log\{r^2 - 2r\rho \cos(\theta - \psi) + \rho^2\} + i(\phi + 2k\pi)$$

for $k = 0, \pm 1, \pm 2, \ldots$, where

$$\tan \phi = \frac{r \sin \theta - \rho \sin \psi}{r \cos \theta - \rho \cos \psi}.$$

7. Find all the values of $(-i)^i$.

8. Find the branch points of (a) $(z^2 - 9)^{1/3}$, (b) $\log(z^2 - 4)$. Construct appropriate branch lines.

4.4 ANALYTIC FUNCTIONS

In order to extend the analysis of functions of a complex variable it is necessary to discuss the concepts of limit, continuity and differentiability.

Limit

If, as z approaches some complex number z_0, the value of a function $w = f(z)$ tends to some value w_0, then w_0 is the limit of $f(z)$ as $z \to z_0$, written

$$\lim_{z \to z_0} f(z) = w_0 \qquad \text{or} \qquad f(z) \to w_0 \quad \text{as} \quad z \to z_0.$$

It is important to note that w_0 need not equal $f(z_0)$ even if $f(z_0)$ exists.

> DEFINITION   A function $f(z)$ of a complex variable z has the limit w_0 as $z \to z_0$, that is
>
> $$\lim_{z \to z_0} f(z) = w_0 ,$$
>
> if, given any small positive number ϵ, there exists a number δ depending on ϵ such that
>
> $$|f(z) - w_0| < \epsilon \quad \text{when} \quad |z - z_0| < \delta.$$

Geometrically, this definition implies that $f(z) \to w_0$ if $f(z)$ lies within a circle with centre w_0 and of arbitrarily small radius ϵ whenever z lies within a circle with centre z_0 and of radius δ, as indicated in Fig. 4.14.

The above definition of limit should be compared with the definitions of limit in real analysis given in §4.1 of Volume 1. As in the definition of limit in the theory of functions of two real variables, the direction in which z approaches z_0 in the above definition is completely arbitrary. Therefore w_0 is the limit of $f(z)$ as $z \to z_0$ if and only if $f(z) \to w_0$ as $z \to z_0$ along every path inside the disc $|z - z_0| < \delta$.

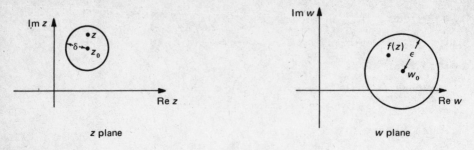

Fig. 4.14   The definition of a limit.

THEOREM 1   If $z = x + iy$ and $z_0 = x_0 + iy_0$, where x_0 and y_0 are real numbers and $f(z) = u(x, y) + iv(x, y)$, then

$$f(z) \to u_0 + iv_0 \quad \text{as} \quad z \to z_0$$

if and only if

$$u(x, y) \to u_0 \quad \text{and} \quad v(x, y) \to v_0 \quad \text{as} \quad x \to x_0 \quad \text{and} \quad y \to y_0$$

where the limits may be taken in either order.

The proof of this theorem will be omitted and may be found in Churchill, Brown and Verhey [2].

Theorem 1 shows the connection between the limit of a function of a complex variable and the theory of limits of functions of two variables in real analysis. With this connection firmly established, it is easy to prove the following theorem on limits and therefore the proof will be omitted.

THEOREM 2   If $f(z) \to A$ and $g(z) \to B$ as $z \to z_0$ where A and B are complex, then as $z \to z_0$

$$f(z) \pm g(z) \to A \pm B, \quad f(z)g(z) \to AB, \quad f(z)/g(z) \to A/B \quad \text{(provided } B \neq 0).$$

Continuity

A function $f(z)$ may tend to a limit w_0 as $z \to z_0$, even though the function is not defined at $z = z_0$. If, however, the function is defined at $z = z_0$ and $f(z_0)$ equals w_0, then the function is said to be *continuous at* $z = z_0$.

DEFINITION   A function $f(z)$ is continuous at $z = z_0$ if and only if $f(z_0)$ exists and

$$f(z) \to f(z_0) \quad \text{as} \quad z \to z_0.$$

DEFINITION   A function is continuous in a region if it is continuous at every point of the region.

If $f(z) = u + iv$, it follows from Theorem 1 that $f(z)$ is continuous if and only if u and v are continuous. Hence the theorems on the continuity of functions of a complex variable, stated in Theorem 3, may be deduced from the theorems of continuity in real analysis and the proof will be omitted.

THEOREM 3   (a) If $f(z)$ is continuous within and on a closed curve, then $f(z)$ is bounded within and on the curve, that is there exists a number M such that

$$|f(z)| < M$$

within and on the curve.

(b) If $f(z)$ and $g(z)$ are continuous functions in some region, then $f \pm g$, fg, and f/g (at points where $g \neq 0$) are continuous.

It can now be shown that all the functions of a complex variable which were discussed in §4.3 are continuous in some region of the z plane.

Differentiation

The definition of the derivative of a function of a complex variable is similar to the definition of the derivative in real analysis.

DEFINITION   If $f(z)$ is single-valued, the derivative of $f(z)$ is defined to be

$$f'(z) = \frac{df}{dz} = \lim_{\delta z \to 0} \frac{f(z + \delta z) - f(z)}{\delta z}$$

provided that the limit exists.

It is important to remember that this limit exists only if it takes the same value whatever the manner in which $\delta z \to 0$. Therefore, although derivatives may be found by using the above definition and the theorems on limits, great care must be taken when evaluating the limit. The theorems on derivatives which are familiar in real analysis still hold, however, and will be stated without proof.

THEOREM 4   If $f(z)$ and $g(z)$ are differentiable with derivatives $f'(z)$ and $g'(z)$ then

(a) $\dfrac{d}{dz}(f \pm g) = f' \pm g'$,

(b) $\dfrac{d}{dz}(cf) = cf'$,   where c is a complex constant,

(c) $\dfrac{d}{dz}(fg) = fg' + gf'$,

(d) $\dfrac{d}{dz}\left(\dfrac{f}{g}\right) = \dfrac{gf' - fg'}{g^2}$ provided $g(z) \neq 0$,

(e) if $z = z(\zeta)$ is a function of the complex variable ζ then

$$\frac{\mathrm{d}}{\mathrm{d}\zeta}[f(z)] = \frac{\mathrm{d}f}{\mathrm{d}z}\frac{\mathrm{d}z}{\mathrm{d}\zeta}.$$

Inspection of the definition of $f'(z)$ shows that the limit can exist only if $f(z + \delta z) \to f(z)$ as $\delta z \to 0$. Hence if $f'(z)$ exists at a point then $f(z)$ is continuous at that point. However, the converse is not always true; a continuous function is not necessarily differentiable.

EXAMPLE 1   The function $|z|^2$ is continuous. Show that it is differentiable only at $z = 0$.

The limit occurring in the definition of the derivative is

$$\lim_{\delta z \to 0}\left\{\frac{|z + \delta z|^2 - |z|^2}{\delta z}\right\} = \lim_{\delta z \to 0}\left\{\frac{(z + \delta z)(\bar{z} + \overline{\delta z}) - z\bar{z}}{\delta z}\right\}$$

$$= \lim_{\delta z \to 0}\left\{\bar{z} + \overline{\delta z} + z\frac{\overline{\delta z}}{\delta z}\right\}.$$

If δz is written as $\delta z = e^{i\theta}\delta r$, then $\overline{\delta z} = e^{-i\theta}\delta r$, so that $\overline{\delta z} \to 0$ as $\delta z \to 0$ and the limit may be expressed as

$$\lim_{\delta z \to 0}\{\bar{z} + \overline{\delta z} + ze^{-2i\theta}\} = \bar{z} + z\lim_{\delta z \to 0}e^{-2i\theta}.$$

For $z \neq 0$, this limit clearly depends on the angle θ at which the path approaches the point z and therefore $f'(z)$ does not exist. For $z = 0$, $\bar{z} = 0$ and $f'(z) = 0$ and therefore $f(z) = |z|^2$ is differentiable at $z = 0$.

A function which is differentiable at every point of a region R is said to be *analytic in the region* R. The terms *holomorphic* and *regular* are sometimes used. A function is said to be *analytic at a point* $z = z_0$ if it is differentiable at $z = z_0$ and also at every point of a small region surrounding $z = z_0$. Although the function $|z|^2$ is differentiable at $z = 0$, is not analytic at $z = 0$ because it is impossible to find any region enclosing $z = 0$ in which $|z|^2$ is differentiable at every point.

THEOREM 5   A necessary condition for $f(z) = u + iv$ to be analytic in a region R is that

$$\frac{\partial u}{\partial x} = \frac{\partial v}{\partial y} \quad \text{and} \quad \frac{\partial u}{\partial y} = -\frac{\partial v}{\partial x}. \qquad\qquad \text{(11a), (11b)}$$

These equations are called the *Cauchy–Riemann equations* and if $u(x, y)$ and $v(x, y)$ satisfy these equations, they are said to be *conjugate functions*.

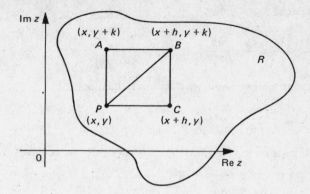

Fig. 4.15 Illustration of the paths in the derivation of the Cauchy–Riemann equations.

Proof If $f(z)$ is analytic in a region R then

$$f'(z) = \lim_{\delta z \to 0} \left[\frac{f(z + \delta z) - f(z)}{\delta z} \right]$$

exists at each point z of R and is independent of the way in which $\delta z \to 0$. That is, if P represents the number z and Q represents the number $z + \delta z \equiv z_Q$ in the z plane, then

$$f'(z) = \lim_{Q \to P} \frac{f(z_Q) - f(z)}{z_Q - z}$$

as $Q \to P$ along any path.

In particular, if Q is initially at B in Fig. 4.15, the limit as $Q \to P$ along the path BAP must be the same as the limit as $Q \to P$ along the path BCP. Now

$$\frac{f(z_Q) - f(z)}{z_Q - z} = \frac{u(x + \delta x, y + \delta y) + iv(x + \delta x, y + \delta y) - u(x,y) - iv(x,y)}{\delta x + i\delta y}$$

and if $Q \to P$ along the path BAP, then $\delta x \to 0$ followed by $\delta y \to 0$, so that

$$\lim_{Q \to P} \frac{f(z_Q) - f(z)}{z_Q - z} = \lim_{\delta y \to 0} \left[\frac{u(x, y + \delta y) + iv(x, y + \delta y) - u(x,y) - iv(x,y)}{i\delta y} \right].$$

The limit may be evaluated to give the result

$$\lim_{Q \to P} \frac{f(z_Q) - f(z)}{z_Q - z} = -i \frac{\partial u}{\partial y} + \frac{\partial v}{\partial y}.$$

If $Q \to P$ along the path BCP, then $\delta y \to 0$ followed by $\delta x \to 0$, so that

$$\lim_{Q \to P} \frac{f(z_Q) - f(z)}{z_Q - z} = \lim_{\delta x \to 0} \left[\frac{u(x + \delta x, y) + iv(x + \delta x, y) - u(x,y) - iv(x,y)}{\delta x} \right],$$

and the result

$$\lim_{Q \to P} \frac{f(z_Q) - f(z)}{z_Q - z} = \frac{\partial u}{\partial x} + i \frac{\partial v}{\partial x}$$

follows. On equating the two limits we obtain the equation

$$\frac{\partial u}{\partial x} + i \frac{\partial v}{\partial x} = -i \frac{\partial u}{\partial y} + \frac{\partial v}{\partial y}$$

which, if the real parts are equated and the imaginary parts are equated, gives the result

$$\frac{\partial u}{\partial x} = \frac{\partial v}{\partial y} \quad \text{and} \quad \frac{\partial v}{\partial x} = -\frac{\partial u}{\partial y}.$$

Let $\Phi(x, y)$ be defined as

$$\Phi(x, y) = u + iv$$

where $u(x, y)$ and $v(x, y)$ are any two functions defined in R with u, v, x and y real and $z = x + iy$. Then, from equations (2b) and (2c)

$$x = \tfrac{1}{2}(z + \bar{z}) \quad \text{and} \quad y = -\frac{1}{2i}(z - \bar{z})$$

and therefore, with these substitutions for x and y, $\Phi(x, y)$ can be written in terms of z and $\bar{z}$. It can be shown, though the proof will be omitted (see Milne–Thompson [3])
that
    (a) if $u, v, \partial u/\partial x, \partial u/\partial y, \partial v/\partial x$ and $\partial v/\partial y$ are continuous in R, and
    (b) if u and v satisfy the Cauchy–Riemann equations (11) in R,
then $\bar{z}$ does not appear in the expression $\Phi\{x(z, \bar{z}), y(z, \bar{z})\}$. That is $\Phi(x, y)$ can be written as $f(z)$ and further, $f(z)$ is analytic in R. Conditions (a) and (b) above are *sufficient conditions* for $u + iv$ to be analytic in R.

If the second partial derivatives of u and v also exist in R, then the Cauchy–Riemann equations may be differentiated to show that

$$\frac{\partial^2 u}{\partial x^2} = \frac{\partial^2 v}{\partial x \partial y} \quad \text{and} \quad \frac{\partial^2 u}{\partial y^2} = -\frac{\partial^2 v}{\partial y \partial x}.$$

If the second partial derivatives are continuous, then

$$\frac{\partial^2 v}{\partial x \partial y} = \frac{\partial^2 v}{\partial y \partial x}$$

and therefore

$$\frac{\partial^2 u}{\partial x^2} + \frac{\partial^2 u}{\partial y^2} = 0. \tag{12a}$$

It can be shown similarly that

$$\frac{\partial^2 v}{\partial x^2} + \frac{\partial^2 v}{\partial y^2} = 0. \tag{12b}$$

The functions $u(x, y)$ and $v(x, y)$ therefore satisfy Laplace's equation (see §7.6 of Volume 1), that is each is a *harmonic function*.

The level curves (see §4.3 of Volume 1) of u and v are orthogonal at points where $f'(z) \neq 0$. To prove this result consider the two curves

$$u(x, y) = u_0 \quad \text{and} \quad v(x, y) = v_0$$

where u_0 and v_0 are real constants. We see from equation (23) of §4.3 in Volume 1 that the slopes of these level curves are

$$\left(\frac{dy}{dx}\right)_u = -\frac{u_x}{u_y} \quad \text{and} \quad \left(\frac{dy}{dx}\right)_v = -\frac{v_x}{v_y}$$

respectively, provided that $f'(z) \neq 0$. The functions u and v are conjugate functions and therefore satisfy the Cauchy–Riemann equations, hence

$$\left(\frac{dy}{dx}\right)_u \left(\frac{dy}{dx}\right)_v = \frac{u_x v_x}{u_y v_y} = -1,$$

and the curves are thus orthogonal.

EXAMPLE 2   Show that $u(x, y) = x(1 - y)$ is harmonic for all x and y and find the conjugate function $v(x, y)$. Find the function $f(z) = u + iv$ and write it in terms of z.

If $u = x(1 - y)$ then

$$\frac{\partial u}{\partial x} = 1 - y, \quad \frac{\partial^2 u}{\partial x^2} = 0, \quad \frac{\partial u}{\partial y} = -x \quad \text{and} \quad \frac{\partial^2 u}{\partial y^2} = 0.$$

The function $u(x, y)$ thus satisfies Laplace's equation and is therefore a harmonic function. The Cauchy–Riemann equation (11a) may be used to show that

$$\frac{\partial v}{\partial y} = \frac{\partial u}{\partial x} = 1 - y,$$

which may be integrated to give $v = y - \frac{1}{2}y^2 + g(x)$. If $v = y - \frac{1}{2}y^2 + g(x)$ is differentiated with respect to x the equation

$$\frac{\partial v}{\partial x} = \frac{dg}{dx}$$

is obtained which, together with the Cauchy–Riemann equation (11b) gives

$$\frac{dg}{dx} = x,$$

and therefore $g(x) = \frac{1}{2}x^2 + \text{const.}$ The conjugate function $v(x, y)$ is therefore given by

$$v = y - \frac{1}{2}y^2 + \frac{1}{2}x^2 + C.$$

If $f(z) = u + iv$ then $f(z)$ is

$$f(z) = x - xy + i(y - \tfrac{1}{2}y^2 + \tfrac{1}{2}x^2) + iC$$
$$= z + \tfrac{1}{2}iz^2 + K,$$

where K is an imaginary constant.

Singular points

A point where $f(z)$ is not analytic is called a *singular point* or a *singularity of* $f(z)$. It is easy to see that $f(z) = 1/z$ is not analytic at $z = 0$ and therefore $z = 0$ is a singularity of the function $1/z$. The point $z = a$ is a singularity of the function $(z - a)^{-1}$ and also of $(z - a)^{-n}$ where n takes the values $1, 2, 3, \ldots$. In these examples $z = a$ is said to be a *pole* of the function.

DEFINITION   A function $f(z)$, which fails to be analytic at $z = a$, has a pole of order n at a if

$$\lim_{z \to a} (z - a)^n f(z) = A,$$

where n is a positive integer and A is finite and non-zero.

When $n = 1$, $z = a$ is a *simple pole* and when $n = 2$, $z = a$ is a *double pole*.

A *branch point* of a multiple-valued function is a singularity. For example $z = 0$ is a singularity of the function $z^{1/2}$ and $z = a$ is a singularity of the function $\log(z - a)$. If a function $f(z)$ is undefined at a point $z = z_0$, then it is not analytic at $z = z_0$. However, if $f(z)$ is defined at every point of $|z - z_0| < \epsilon$ except $z = z_0$, but the limit of $f(z)$ as $z \to z_0$ exists, then $f(z)$ is said to have a *removable singularity* at $z = z_0$. For example, if

$$f(z) = \frac{\sin z}{z},$$

then $f(0)$ is not defined but

$$\lim_{z \to 0} \frac{\sin z}{z} = 1.$$

Hence $f(z)$ has a removable singularity and it is possible to define a function $F(z)$ by

$$F(z) = \begin{cases} \dfrac{\sin z}{z} & \text{for} \quad z \neq 0, \\ 1 & \text{for} \quad z = 0, \end{cases}$$

which is analytic at $z = z_0$.

If the point $z = z_0$ is a singularity of the function $f(z)$ and there exists a circle $|z - z_0| = \delta$, where $\delta > 0$, which encloses no other singularity, then $z = z_0$ is said to be an *isolated singularity*. Poles are therefore always isolated singularities.

EXAMPLE 3   (a) $f(z) = \dfrac{3z + 2}{(z - i)(z + 2)^2}$

has a simple pole at $z = i$ and a double pole at $z = -2$. A circle of radius δ where $\delta < \sqrt{5}$ can be drawn with $z = i$ as centre and this circle will enclose no other ·singularity, therefore $z = i$ is an isolated singularity. Similarly $z = -2$ is an isolated singularity.

(b) $f(z) = \dfrac{z^{\frac{1}{2}}(5z - 2)}{(z - a)^{\frac{1}{2}}(z + 10)^5}$

has branch points at $z = 0$ and $z = a$ and a pole of order 5 at $z = -10$. The pole at $z = -10$ is an isolated singularity of each branch.

(c) $f(z) = \operatorname{cosec}\left(\dfrac{1}{z}\right)$

has singularities at $z = 1/n\pi$ for $n = \pm 1, \pm 2, \pm 3, \ldots$. The point $z = 0$ is therefore the limit of a sequence of singularities and is *non-isolated*.

Complex Integrals

If $f(t) = u(t) + iv(t)$, where t is real and such that $a \leqslant t \leqslant b$, then

$$\int_a^b f(t)\,dt = \int_a^b u(t)\,dt + i\int_a^b v(t)\,dt ,$$

provided that $u(t)$ and $v(t)$ are integrable. Hence the properties of $\int f(t)\,dt$ can be obtained from the properties of $\int u(t)\,dt$ and $\int v(t)\,dt$. The integral of $f(z)$ between z_0 and z_1, where $f(z) = u(x, y) + iv(x, y)$ and $z = x + iy$, is a *line integral* (see §5.4 of Volume 1), that is, the value may depend on the path of integration as well as on the end points z_0 and z_1. It is therefore necessary to consider

$$\int_L f(z)\,dz ,$$

where L is a specified curve in the z plane. In terms of real line integrals

$$\int_L f(z)\,dz = \int_L (u + iv)(dx + i\,dy) = \int_L (u\,dx - v\,dy) + i\int_L (v\,dx + u\,dy) . \tag{13}$$

EXAMPLE 4   Evaluate $\displaystyle\int_L \bar{z}\,dz$ when L is the path

(a) $L_a = L_1 + L_2$, where L_1 is the line from $(-1, -1)$ to $(1, -1)$ and L_2 is the line from $(1, -1)$ to $(1, 1)$;
(b) $L_b = L_3 + L_4$, where L_3 is the line from $(-1, -1)$ to $(-1, 1)$ and L_4 is the line from $(-1, 1)$ to $(1, 1)$.

In this example $f(z) = \bar{z}$ so that $u(x, y) = \operatorname{Re} f(z) = x$ and $v(x, y) = \operatorname{Im} f(z) = -y$.
From equation (13)

$$I_a = \int_{L_a} \bar{z} \, dz = \int_{L_a} x \, dx + \int_{L_a} y \, dy + i \int_{L_a} x \, dy - i \int_{L_a} y \, dx ,$$

and

$$I_b = \int_{L_b} \bar{z} \, dz = \int_{L_b} x \, dx + \int_{L_b} y \, dy + i \int_{L_b} x \, dy - i \int_{L_b} y \, dx .$$

(a) Along $L_1, y = -1$ and $dy = 0$, and along $L_2, x = 1$ and $dx = 0$, therefore

$$I_a = \int_{-1}^{1} x \, dx + i \int_{-1}^{1} dx + \int_{-1}^{1} y \, dy + i \int_{-1}^{1} dy$$

$$= [\tfrac{1}{2}x^2 + ix + \tfrac{1}{2}y^2 + iy]_{-1}^{1} = 4i .$$

(b) Along $L_3, x = -1$ and $dx = 0$, and along $L_4, y = 1$ and $dy = 0$, therefore

$$I_b = \int_{-1}^{1} y \, dy - i \int_{-1}^{1} dy + \int_{-1}^{1} x \, dx - i \int_{-1}^{1} dx$$

$$= [\tfrac{1}{2}y^2 - iy + \tfrac{1}{2}x^2 - ix]_{-1}^{1} = -4i .$$

Hence

$$\int_{L_a} \bar{z} \, dz \neq \int_{L_b} \bar{z} \, dz .$$

EXAMPLE 5   Evaluate $\int_{L} z^{-1} \, dz$ when L is the curve

(a) from $r = a, \theta = \pi$ to $r = a, \theta = 0$ along the semicircle L_a with radius a and centre at the origin, drawn in the upper half-plane,
(b) from $r = a, \theta = \pi$ to $r = a, \theta = 2\pi$ along the semicircle L_b with radius a and centre at the origin, drawn in the lower half-plane.

The paths L_a and L_b are shown in Fig. 4.16. On the circle $|z| = a, z = a e^{i\theta}$ and $dz = i a e^{i\theta} \, d\theta$, therefore

(a)   on L_a, $I_a = \int_{L_a} \dfrac{dz}{z} = \int_{\pi}^{0} \dfrac{i a e^{i\theta} \, d\theta}{a e^{i\theta}} = i \int_{\pi}^{0} d\theta = -\pi i ,$

(b)   on L_b, $I_b = \int_{L_b} \dfrac{dz}{z} = \int_{\pi}^{2\pi} \dfrac{i a e^{i\theta} \, d\theta}{a e^{i\theta}} = i \int_{\pi}^{2\pi} d\theta = \pi i .$

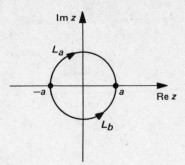

Fig. 4.16   Contours for example 5.

Hence

$$\int_{L_a} \frac{dz}{z} \neq \int_{L_b} \frac{dz}{z} \, .$$

DEFINITION   A *contour* is a continuous non-intersecting chain of a finite number of smooth arcs.

In the above examples L_a and L_b are contours and the integrals are said to be *contour integrals*. If the points z_0 and z_1 are joined by a contour C, a function $f(z)$ may be integrated along C from z_0 to z_1 or from z_1 to z_0. It is clear therefore that in addition to specifying C, it is necessary to specify the direction along C in which the function is to be integrated. If the path from z_0 to z_1 along C is chosen as the positive direction of C, the path from z_1 to z_0 along C would be described as the path $-C$. The contour C from z_0 to z_1 may consist of the contour C_1 from z_0 to z' followed by the contour C_2 from z' to z_1. The contour C is then written $C = C_1 + C_2$. A contour which begins at a point z_0, say, and ends at the same point z_0 is said to be a *closed contour*, the positive sense of which is, by convention, fixed to be the direction in which an observer travelling along the curve has the enclosed region on his left-hand side.

A closed contour is often specified as the boundary of a given simply-connected region R and *the positive sense of the contour is always chosen to be counter-clockwise* (see Fig. 4.17). The integral around a closed contour is written

$$\oint_C f(z) \, dz \, .$$

The following properties of contour integrals can easily be deduced.

(a) $\displaystyle\int_C f(z) \, dz = - \int_{-C} f(z) \, dz \, ,$ (14a)

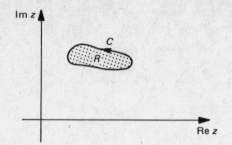

Fig. 4.17   The positive sense of a closed contour.

(b)   if k is a complex constant,

$$\int_C kf(z)\, \mathrm{d}z = k \int_C f(z)\, \mathrm{d}z \, , \tag{14b}$$

(c) $\displaystyle\int_C \{f(z) + g(z)\}\, \mathrm{d}z = \int_C f(z)\, \mathrm{d}z + \int_C g(z)\, \mathrm{d}z \, , \tag{14c}$

(d)   if $C = C_1 + C_2$ where C_1 and C_2 are possibly disjoint, then

$$\int_C f(z)\, \mathrm{d}z = \int_{C_1} f(z)\, \mathrm{d}z + \int_{C_2} f(z)\, \mathrm{d}z \, , \tag{14d}$$

(e)   if $|f(z)| \leqslant M$ when z lies on C, where M is constant, then

$$\left| \int_C f(z)\, \mathrm{d}z \right| \leqslant \int_C |f(z)|\,|\, \mathrm{d}z\,| \leqslant ML \, , \tag{14e}$$

where L is the length of C.

The Cauchy–Goursat Theorem

CAUCHY'S THEOREM   If $f(z)$ is analytic and $f'(z)$ is continuous at all points within and on a closed contour C, then

$$\oint_C f(z)\, \mathrm{d}z = 0 \, .$$

Proof   If $f(z) = u + \mathrm{i}v$, then the integral of $f(z)$ around C is given by equation (13), that is

$$\oint_C f(z)\, \mathrm{d}z = \oint_C (u\, \mathrm{d}x - v\, \mathrm{d}y) + \mathrm{i} \oint_C (v\, \mathrm{d}x + u\, \mathrm{d}y) \, .$$

If Green's theorem in the plane (see §5.4 of Volume 1) is applied to each integral on the right-hand side of this equation, then the equations

$$\oint_C (u \, dx - v \, dy) = \iint_R \left(-\frac{\partial v}{\partial x} - \frac{\partial u}{\partial y} \right) dx \, dy \tag{15a}$$

and

$$\oint_C (v \, dx + u \, dy) = \iint_R \left(\frac{\partial u}{\partial x} - \frac{\partial v}{\partial y} \right) dx \, dy \tag{15b}$$

are obtained, where C is the boundary of the region R. If $f(z)$ is analytic in R, then u and v satisfy the Cauchy–Riemann equations (11) and the right-hand sides of equations (15a) and (15b) are seen to be zero. Hence the theorem is proved.

The continuity condition on $f'(z)$ can be removed from Cauchy's theorem, which then becomes more widely applicable. The theorem without the condition on $f'(z)$ is called the Cauchy–Goursat theorem and may be stated as follows.

THE CAUCHY–GOURSAT THEOREM   If $f(z)$ is analytic at all points within and on a closed contour C, then

$$\oint_C f(z) \, dz = 0. \tag{16}$$

The proof is omitted, but may be found in Churchill *et al.* [2].

The theorem has many remarkable consequences, some of which are discussed in the remainder of this section.

EXAMPLE 6   The functions $f(z) = 1, f(z) = z$ and $f(z) = z^2$ are analytic everywhere throughout the z plane, therefore from the Cauchy–Goursat theorem (16)

$$\oint_C dz = 0, \quad \oint_C z \, dz = 0, \quad \text{and} \quad \oint_C z^2 \, dz = 0$$

for all closed contours C.

EXAMPLE 7   Integrate $f(z) = z^{-2}(z^2 + 9)^{-1}$ around the boundary of the annulus $1 \leqslant z \leqslant 2$.

The function $f(z) = z^{-2}(z^2 + 9)^{-1}$ has poles at $z = 0$ and $z = \pm 3i$, which are outside the annulus. The function $f(z)$ is therefore analytic within the annulus. If C_1 is the closed contour specified by the outer boundary of the annulus and C_2 is the closed contour specified by the inner boundary of the annulus, then the positive senses of C_1 and of C_2 are shown in Fig. 4.18. Let L be any contour from C_1 to C_2, also shown in Fig. 4.18, then

$$C_1 + L + C_2 - L$$

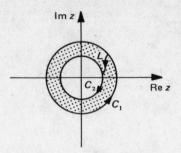

Fig. 4.18   Contours for example 7.

is the boundary of a simply-connected region shown as the stippled region in Fig. 4.18. From the Cauchy–Goursat theorem (16)

$$\oint_{C_1} f(z)\,dz + \int_L f(z)\,dz + \oint_{C_2} f(z)\,dz + \int_{-L} f(z)\,dz = 0 \ .$$

However, result (14a) gives

$$\int_L f(z)\,dz + \int_{-L} f(z)\,dz = 0 \ ,$$

and therefore

$$\oint_{C_1} f(z)\,dz + \oint_{C_2} f(z)\,dz = 0 \ .$$

If C represents the boundary of the annulus, we may write $C = C_1 + C_2$ and then

$$\oint_C f(z)\,dz = 0 \ ,$$

even though C consists of two portions C_1 and C_2 which are disjoint.

Example 7 is a particular example of the generalization of the Cauchy–Goursat theorem (16) to the boundary C of a multiply-connected region R which consists of several disjoint closed contours as in Fig. 4.19.

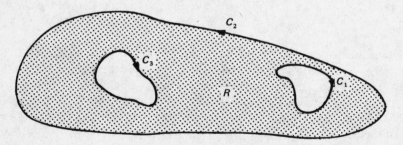

Fig. 4.19   Disjoint contours.

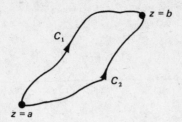

Fig. 4.20   Contours from $z = a$ to $z = b$.

In this case, the boundary C of R may be written as $C = C_1 + C_2 + C_3$ and the Cauchy–Goursat theorem states that if $f(z)$ is analytic within C, then

$$\oint_C f(z)\,dz = \oint_{C_1} f(z)\,dz + \oint_{C_2} f(z)\,dz + \oint_{C_3} f(z)\,dz = 0.$$

Therefore, in the statement of the Cauchy–Goursat theorem (16), $\dot{C}$ may be taken as the boundary of any region R (either simply- or multiply-connected).

Several important results concerning analytic functions follow immediately from the Cauchy–Goursat theorem (16). If C_1 and C_2 are different contours from $z = a$ to $z = b$ (see Fig. 4.20), and C is defined to be $C = C_2 - C_1$, then C is a closed contour. If $f(z)$ is analytic within and on C, then

$$\oint_C f(z)\,dz = 0,$$

by the Cauchy–Goursat theorem. However,

$$\oint_C f(z)\,dz = \oint_{C_2 - C_1} f(z)\,dz = \int_{C_2} f(z)\,dz - \int_{C_1} f(z)\,dz = 0,$$

therefore, provided $f(z)$ has no singularities between or on the contours C_1 and C_2,

$$\int_{C_1} f(z)\,dz = \int_{C_2} f(z)\,dz. \tag{17}$$

If Γ is a closed contour which completely encloses the closed contour γ, as shown in Fig. 4.21, and $f(z)$ is analytic in the region between Γ and γ, then $C = \Gamma - \gamma$ encloses a region in which $f(z)$ is analytic.

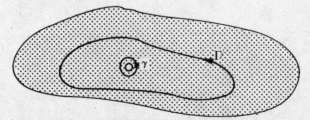

Fig. 4.21   The contour Γ may be deformed into the contour γ through the region (shown stippled) in which $f(z)$ is analytic.

The Cauchy–Goursat theorem gives

$$\oint_C f(z)\,dz = \oint_{\Gamma-\gamma} f(z)\,dz = \oint_\Gamma f(z)\,dz - \oint_\gamma f(z)\,dz = 0,$$

and therefore

$$\oint_\Gamma f(z)\,dz = \oint_\gamma f(z)\,dz. \tag{18}$$

Hence the integral of $f(z)$ around Γ can be replaced by the integral of $f(z)$ around γ, provided that $f(z)$ has no singularities between or on the contours. The results (17) and (18) imply that contours can be *deformed* without changing the value of the integral, provided that no singularities are crossed as the contour is deformed.

EXAMPLE 8   Evaluate $\oint_C (z - z_0)^{-1}\,dz$ where C is a contour which

(a) does not enclose $z = z_0$,
(b) encloses $z = z_0$.

(a) If C does not enclose $z = z_0$, then $(z - z_0)^{-1}$ is analytic within C and therefore

$$\oint_C \frac{dz}{z - z_0} = 0.$$

(b) If C encloses $z = z_0$, let Γ be a circle with centre at $z = z_0$ and radius ϵ. The function $(z - z_0)^{-1}$ is analytic between the two contours, hence

$$\oint_C \frac{dz}{z - z_0} = \oint_\Gamma \frac{dz}{z - z_0}.$$

The equation of Γ is $|z - z_0| = \epsilon$ and therefore $z = z_0 + \epsilon e^{i\theta}$ from which we obtain $dz = i\epsilon e^{i\theta}\,d\theta$ for $0 \leqslant \theta < 2\pi$. Hence

$$\oint_\Gamma \frac{dz}{z - z_0} = \int_0^{2\pi} \frac{i\epsilon e^{i\theta}\,d\theta}{\epsilon e^{i\theta}} = i\int_0^{2\pi} d\theta = 2\pi i,$$

thus, when C encloses $z = z_0$,

$$\oint_C \frac{dz}{z - z_0} = 2\pi i. \tag{19}$$

If C is the circle $|z| = a$ and $z_0 = 0$, the result (19) reduces to

$$\oint_C \frac{dz}{z} = 2\pi i.$$

If C is written as $C = L_b - L_a$, where L_a and L_b are defined in example 5 of this section, then

$$\int_{L_b} \frac{dz}{z} = \int_{L_a} \frac{dz}{z} + 2\pi i,$$

a result which verifies the calculations in that example.

EXAMPLE 9   Evaluate $\oint_C (z - a)^{-n} dz$ where n is a positive integer and C encloses the point $z = a$.

The function $(z - a)^{-n}$ is analytic everywhere in the z plane except at $z = a$. Therefore the contour C can be deformed to the contour Γ defined in example 8 above, and

$$\oint_\Gamma \frac{dz}{(z - a)^n} = \int_0^{2\pi} \frac{i\epsilon e^{i\theta} d\theta}{\epsilon^n e^{in\theta}} = \frac{i}{\epsilon^{n-1}} \int_0^{2\pi} \exp\{(1 - n)i\theta\} d\theta$$

$$= \frac{1}{\epsilon^{n-1}} \left[\frac{\exp\{(1 - n)i\theta\}}{1 - n} \right]_0^{2\pi} = 0 \quad \text{for } n \neq 1.$$

The results of examples 8 and 9 can be summarized as follows. If $f(z) = (z - a)^{-n}$ where n is a positive integer, then

(a) $\oint_C f(z)\, dz = 0$ for all n if C does not enclose $z = a$, and

(b) $\oint_C f(z)\, dz = \begin{cases} 2\pi i & \text{when } n = 1 \\ 0 & \text{when } n = 2, 3, 4, \ldots, \end{cases}$ if C encloses $z = a$.

These results underlie the *theory of residues* which is discussed in §4.5.

Exercises

1. Evaluate the following limits:

   (a) $\lim_{z \to 2i} (z^2 + 3z + 1)$,   (b) $\lim_{z \to \exp(i\pi/4)} \left(\dfrac{z}{z^4 + z + 1} \right)$,

   (c) $\lim_{z \to \exp(i\pi/3)} \left(\dfrac{\{z - \exp(i\pi/3)\}z^2}{z^3 + 1} \right)$.

2. Find the points where the following functions are discontinuous:

   (a) $\dfrac{3z^2 + 2}{z^5 + 25}$,   (b) $\dfrac{1}{z} - \sec z$,   (c) $\dfrac{\tanh z}{z^2 + 2}$.

3. Show, by using the definition of the derivative of a function that $1/z$ is not differentiable at $z = 0$.

4. Show that the function $u = xe^x \cos y - ye^x \sin y$ is harmonic for all x and y and find the conjugate function v. Express $u + iv$ in the form $f(z)$ where $z = x + iy$.

5. Locate and name the singularities of the following functions:

(a) $\dfrac{2z^2 + 1}{z^4 - 1}$,   (b) $\dfrac{\log(z + 2i)}{z^2}$,

(c) $z^{1/3}(z^2 + a)^{1/2}$,   (d) $\dfrac{z^{p-1}}{1 + z}$,   for $0 < p < 1$,

(e) $\dfrac{e^{az}}{\cosh z}$,   (f) $\dfrac{\cot z \coth z}{z}$,   (g) $\dfrac{z - \sin z}{z^3}$.

6. If $f(z) = z + 1$ and C is the curve $y = x^2 + 2x + 1$ from $z = i$ to $z = 1 + 4i$, evaluate
$\displaystyle\int_C f(z)\,dz$.

4.5 THE RESIDUE THEOREM

Consider a function $F(z)$ defined as

$$F(z) = a_0 + a_1(z - z_0) + a_2(z - z_0)^2 + \frac{b_1}{(z - z_0)} + \frac{b_2}{(z - z_0)^2},$$

where z is a complex variable and z_0 is a complex number. The integral of $F(z)$ around a closed contour can, in view of equation (14c), be written

$$\oint_C F(z)\,dz = \oint_C a_0\,dz + \oint_C a_1(z - z_0)\,dz + \oint_C a_2(z - z_0)^2\,dz$$

$$+ \oint_C \frac{b_1\,dz}{z - z_0} + \oint_C \frac{b_2\,dz}{(z - z_0)^2},$$

the right-hand side of which can be evaluated as in example 9 of §4.4 to give

$$\oint_C F(z)\,dz = \begin{cases} 2\pi i b_1 & \text{if } C \text{ has counterclockwise sense and encloses } z = z_0 \\ 0 & \text{if } C \text{ does not enclose } z = z_0. \end{cases}$$

The above procedure can be used to show that if $F(z)$ is a series of the form

$$F(z) = \sum_{n=0}^{N} a_n(z - z_0)^n + \sum_{n=1}^{M} b_n(z - z_0)^{-n},$$

and C is a closed contour, then

$$\oint_C F(z)\,dz = \begin{cases} 2\pi i b_1 & \text{if } C \text{ has counterclockwise sense and encloses } z = z_0 \\ 0 & \text{if } C \text{ does not enclose } z = z_0. \end{cases}$$

In view of this result, it seems reasonable to investigate the possibility of representing an arbitrary function of z as a series in $(z - z_0)$ and $(z - z_0)^{-1}$ for any constant z_0.

In the theory of real variables, many functions can be expanded in a power series by the use of Taylor's theorem and it is not surprising that a similar theorem exists in complex analysis. The Taylor series for a function of a complex variable takes the same form as that for a function of a real variable, and the theorem will be stated without proof (see Churchill *et al.* [2]).

TAYLOR'S THEOREM   If $f(z)$ is analytic within a circle C with centre at z_0, then at each point z inside C

$$f(z) = f(z_0) + f'(z_0)(z - z_0) + \frac{f''(z_0)}{2!}(z - z_0)^2 + \ldots + \frac{f^{(n)}(z_0)}{n!}(z - z_0)^n + \ldots .$$

(20)

The series (20) is called the Taylor series for $f(z)$ about $z = z_0$ and will in general be an infinite series. The region of convergence of an infinite series in ascending powers of $(z - z_0)$ is the interior of a circle, called the *circle of convergence*, with centre at $z = z_0$. The radius R of the circle of convergence is called the *radius of convergence* and the region of convergence can be written as $|z - z_0| < R$. Taylor's theorem therefore implies that the circle of convergence of the Taylor series for $f(z)$ about $z = z_0$ is the largest circle C with centre at $z = z_0$ in which $f(z)$ is analytic. The magnitude of R will obviously depend on the position of the singularities of $f(z)$. For example, if $f(z)$ is analytic at $z = z_0$ and the nearest singularity to z_0 is at $z = z_1$, then $f(z)$ is analytic inside the circle $|z - z_0| = R$ where $R = |z_1 - z_0|$ (see Fig. 4.22). The Taylor series for $f(z)$ about $z = z_0$ will be convergent for $|z - z_0| < R$ and will be divergent for $|z - z_0| > R$.

Taylor's theorem is a dual purpose result: it states the conditions under which a power series representation for $f(z)$ exists and it gives a method for calculating the coefficients. However, a power series representation of a function about any point z_0 is unique, and therefore alternative methods of calculating the coefficients may be used, all of which will give the same series as Taylor's theorem. Such methods, for example the binomial theorem, are easier to apply than Taylor's theorem and therefore the main purpose of Taylor's theorem in this chapter is to establish the existence of a power series for a given function.

EXAMPLE 1   The functions e^z, $\sin z$ and $\cos z$ are analytic throughout the whole of the z plane therefore their Taylor series are convergent over the whole of the plane.

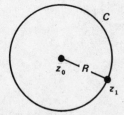

Fig. 4.22   The circle of convergence.

The Taylor series of e^z about $z = 0$ is

$$e^z = 1 + z + \frac{z^2}{2!} + \frac{z^3}{3!} + \ldots + \frac{z^n}{n!} + \ldots,$$

and in particular, when $z = i\theta$,

$$e^{i\theta} = 1 + i\theta - \frac{\theta^2}{2!} - \frac{i\theta^3}{3!} + \ldots \text{ (see exercise 4 of §4.2).}$$

Also

$$\sin z = z - \frac{z^3}{3!} + \frac{z^5}{5!} + \ldots + (-1)^{r-1} \frac{z^{2r-1}}{(2r-1)!} + \ldots,$$

$$\cos z = 1 - \frac{z^2}{2!} + \frac{z^4}{4!} + \ldots + (-1)^{r-1} \frac{z^{2r-2}}{(2r-2)!} + \ldots.$$

The region of convergence of each of these series is $|z| < \infty$.

EXAMPLE 2   The function $(1 + z)^{-2}$ is analytic everywhere except at the point $z = -1$. The Taylor series for $(1 + z)^{-2}$ about $z = 0$ is easily calculated by the binomial theorem and is

$$(1 + z)^{-2} = 1 - 2z + 3z^2 - 4z^3 + \ldots + (-1)^{r+1}(r + 1)z^r + \ldots,$$

which is convergent in $|z| < 1$.

EXAMPLE 3   The function $\log(1 + z)$ has a branch point at $z = -1$ and if the plane is cut from $z = -1$ to infinity along any line, $\log(1 + z)$ is single-valued. There is no singularity of $\log(1 + z)$ other than $z = -1$, therefore the function is analytic at all other points on the cut plane. The Taylor series for $\log(1 + z)$ about $z = 0$, on the principal branch of the function, is

$$\log(1 + z) = z - \frac{z^2}{2} + \frac{z^3}{3} + \ldots + (-1)^{r-1} \frac{z^r}{r} + \ldots,$$

which is convergent for $|z| < 1$.

EXAMPLE 4   The function $f(z) = e^z/z$ has a singularity at $z = 0$ and therefore $f(z)$ has a Taylor series about any point $z = a$, where $a \neq 0$. The radius of convergence of the series is $R = |a|$ and the region of convergence is $|z - a| < R$. Put $u = z - a$ so that $z = u + a$ and

$$\frac{e^z}{z} = \frac{e^{u+a}}{u+a} = \frac{e^a e^u}{a} \left(1 + \frac{u}{a}\right)^{-1}.$$

Now

$$e^u = 1 + u + \frac{u^2}{2!} + \ldots + \frac{u^r}{r!} + \ldots,$$

and

$$\left(1 + \frac{u}{a}\right)^{-1} = 1 - \frac{u}{a} + \left(\frac{u}{a}\right)^2 - \left(\frac{u}{a}\right)^3 + \ldots + (-1)^r \left(\frac{u}{a}\right)^r + \ldots,$$

and therefore

$$\frac{e^{u+a}}{u+a} = \frac{e^a}{a} \left\{ 1 + u \left(1 - \frac{1}{a}\right) + \left(\frac{1}{2} - \frac{1}{a} + \frac{1}{a^2}\right) u^2 + \ldots \right\}$$

$$= \frac{e^a}{a} \left\{ 1 + (z - a) \left(1 - \frac{1}{a}\right) + (z - a)^2 \left(\frac{1}{2} - \frac{1}{a} + \frac{1}{a^2}\right) + \ldots \right\}.$$

In example 4 it is possible to find a series expansion about the point $z = 0$, though it is important to note that it is *not* a Taylor series. The series is

$$\frac{e^z}{z} = \frac{1}{z}\left(1 + z + \frac{z^2}{2!} + \ldots\right) = \frac{1}{z} + 1 + \frac{z}{2!} + \ldots, \tag{21}$$

and it is convergent for $0 < |z| < \infty$. In a similar way the function $z^{-2} \log(1 + z)$, which has a branch point at $z = -1$ and a double pole at $z = 0$, can be expanded about $z = 0$ on the principal branch of $\log(1 + z)$ to give the result

$$\frac{\log(1 + z)}{z^2} = \frac{1}{z} - \frac{1}{2} + \frac{z}{3} + \ldots, \tag{22}$$

a series convergent in the annulus $0 < |z| < 1$. The series (21) and (22) are examples of *Laurent series*, which exist under less stringent conditions than Taylor series. The conditions under which a Laurent series exists are given in *Laurent's theorem*, which will be stated without proof (see Churchill *et al.* [2]).

LAURENT'S THEOREM   Let C_1 and C_2 be circles with centres at $z = z_0$ and radii R_1 and R_2 respectively, where $R_1 > R_2$, and let $\mathscr{R}$ be the annular region bounded by C_1 and C_2. If $f(z)$ is analytic in $\mathscr{R}$ then $f(z)$ can be represented at each point z in $\mathscr{R}$ by the series

$$f(z) = a_0 + a_1(z - z_0) + a_2(z - z_0)^2 + \ldots + a_r(z - z_0)^r + \ldots$$

$$+ \frac{b_1}{(z - z_0)} + \frac{b_2}{(z - z_0)^2} + \ldots + \frac{b_r}{(z - z_0)^r} + \ldots,$$

which can be written alternatively as

$$f(z) = \sum_{n=-\infty}^{\infty} A_n(z - z_0)^n,$$

where $A_n = a_n$ when n is a positive integer or zero and $A_n = b_{-n}$ when n is a negative integer. The coefficients A_n are given by

$$A_n = \frac{1}{2\pi i} \oint_C \frac{f(w)\,dw}{(w - z_0)^{n+1}}, \tag{23}$$

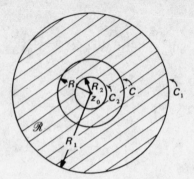

Fig. 4.23   The contours C, C_1, C_2 in Laurent's theorem.

for $n = 0, \pm1, \pm2, \ldots$, where C is a circle with centre at $z = z_0$ and radius R such that $R_2 < R < R_1$.

The region $\mathscr{R}$ and the contour C are shown in Fig. 4.23. The coefficients of the Laurent series are rarely calculated by using the formula (23) of Laurent's theorem; the series (21), for example, was obtained from the known series for e^z. Just as the region of convergence of a Taylor series is the interior of a circle, the region of convergence of a Laurent series is in general an annulus with singularities on the bounding circles. The annulus of convergence of series (21) is $0 < |z| < \infty$.

In general the inner circle C_2 can contain several singularities and the expansion can, if required, be about any one of these, that is, z_0 can be any one of the singularities. Alternatively, it need not be any of the singularities. In this section we shall require, as an aid to integration, Laurent series about isolated singularities and in particular Laurent series convergent in the vicinity of a singularity. That is, if $z = z_0$ is an isolated singularity of $f(z)$, we shall consider only the Laurent series of $f(z)$ about $z = z_0$ convergent in the annulus $0 < |z - z_0| < R$, for some R.

EXAMPLE 5   Find the Laurent series of the function $f(z) = z^{-1}(z-1)^{-2}$ about (a) $z = 0$, and (b) $z = 1$.

(a) The Laurent series of $f(z)$ about $z = 0$ is

$$\frac{1}{z(z-1)^2} = \frac{1}{z}(1-z)^{-2} = \frac{1}{z}\left(1 + 2z + \frac{2.3}{2!}z^2 + \ldots\right)$$

$$= \frac{1}{z} + 2 + 3z + \ldots,$$

which is convergent in the annulus $0 < |z| < 1$ shown as the stippled region in Fig. 4.24.

(b) The Laurent series of $f(z)$ about $z = 1$ is obtained with the help of the substitution $u = z - 1$ and is

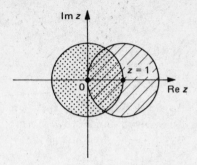

Fig. 4.24   The annuli $0 < |z| < 1$ and $0 < |z-1| < 1$ of example 5.

$$\frac{1}{z(z-1)^2} = \frac{1}{u^2(u+1)} = \frac{1}{u^2}(1+u)^{-1} = \frac{1}{u^2}(1-u+u^2-u^3+\ldots)$$

$$= \frac{1}{u^2} - \frac{1}{u} + 1 - u + \ldots .$$

The required Laurent series is therefore

$$\frac{1}{z(z-1)^2} = \frac{1}{(z-1)^2} - \frac{1}{(z-1)} + 1 - (z-1) + \ldots ,$$

which is convergent in the annulus $0 < |z-1| < 1$, shown as the lined region in Fig. 4.24.

The Laurent series provides a great deal of information about the nature of the function. If $z = z_0$ is an isolated singularity and the Laurent series, valid in the annulus $0 < |z - z_0| < R$, is written in the form

$$f(z) = \sum_{n=0}^{\infty} a_n(z-z_0)^n + \sum_{n=1}^{\infty} b_n(z-z_0)^{-n}, \qquad (24)$$

then the first series on the right-hand side of equation (24) is called *the analytic part of $f(z)$ at $z = z_0$* and the second series is called *the principal part of $f(z)$ at $z = z_0$*. It is possible to distinguish three categories of function by the nature of this Laurent series.

1. If $b_n = 0$ for all n, then the principal part of $f(z)$ at z_0 is zero and the Laurent series has the form

$$f(z) = \sum_{n=0}^{\infty} a_n(z-z_0)^n . \qquad (25)$$

A Laurent series of the form (25) is produced by two kinds of function:
   (a) a function which is analytic at $z = z_0$, and therefore analytic everywhere within $|z - z_0| = R$. The power series expansion of $f(z)$ about z_0 is unique, and is really a Taylor series. Hence a Taylor series is a special kind of Laurent series;

(b) a function which has a removable singularity at $z = z_0$. For example,

$$\frac{\sin z}{z} = \frac{1}{z}\left(z - \frac{z^3}{3!} + \ldots\right) = 1 - \frac{z^2}{3!} + \frac{z^4}{5!}\ldots,$$

which is convergent for all values of z.

2. If $b_n = 0$ for $n > m$ and $b_m \neq 0$, then the principal part of $f(z)$ at $z = z_0$ terminates after m terms and the Laurent series has the form

$$f(z) = \sum_{n=0}^{\infty} a_n(z - z_0)^n + \frac{b_1}{(z - z_0)} + \frac{b_2}{(z - z_0)^2} + \ldots + \frac{b_m}{(z - z_0)^m}$$

which is convergent in $0 < |z - z_0| < R$ and may be written as

$$f(z) = (z - z_0)^{-m}\phi(z),$$

where

$$\phi(z) = \sum_{n=0}^{\infty} a_n(z - z_0)^{n+m} + b_m + b_{m-1}(z - z_0) + \ldots + b_1(z - z_0)^{m-1}.$$

The series $\phi(z)$, which is a power series in $(z - z_0)$, will be convergent and therefore analytic in $|z - z_0| < R$. Further,

$$\lim_{z \to z_0} (z - z_0)^m f(z) = \lim_{z \to z_0} \phi(z) = b_m,$$

and since $b_m \neq 0$ this indicates (see §4.4) that $z = z_0$ is a pole of order m. Hence, *if the principal part of $f(z)$ at $z = z_0$ terminates after the mth term, then $f(z)$ has a pole of order m at $z = z_0$.*

3. If the principal part does not terminate, then $z = z_0$ is said to be an *essential singularity*.

The coefficient $b_1 = A_{-1}$ in a Laurent series has special significance. Equation (23) shows that

$$b_1 = \frac{1}{2\pi i} \oint_C f(z)\,dz, \tag{26}$$

where C is a circle with centre at $z = z_0$ and lying within the annulus of convergence of the Laurent series (24). If Γ is any closed contour which lies within the annulus of convergence, then by the Cauchy–Goursat theorem

$$\oint_{\Gamma} f(z)\,dz = \oint_C f(z)\,dz,$$

and hence from equation (26)

$$\frac{1}{2\pi i} \oint_{\Gamma} f(z)\,dz = b_1.$$

The Laurent series about $z = z_0$ of a function thus provides information which enables us to evaluate the integral of the function around any closed contour lying within the annulus of convergence. The coefficient b_1 is called *the residue* of $f(z)$ at $z = z_0$, and can of course be evaluated by finding the Laurent series. However, the following procedure can prove useful. Multiply equation (24) by $(z - z_0)^m$ and differentiate $m - 1$ times to obtain the equation

$$\frac{d^{m-1}}{dz^{m-1}}[(z - z_0)^m f(z)] = b_1(m - 1)! + \sum_{n=0}^{\infty} a_n(m + n)!(z - z_0)^{n+1}.$$

The result

$$b_1 = \frac{1}{(m-1)!} \lim_{z \to z_0} \frac{d^{m-1}}{dz^{m-1}}[(z - z_0)^m f(z)] \tag{27}$$

then follows. If $z = z_0$ is a simple pole

$$b_1 = \lim_{z \to z_0} [(z - z_0)f(z)],$$

and if $z = z_0$ is a double pole

$$b_1 = \lim_{z \to z_0} \frac{d}{dz}[(z - z_0)^2 f(z)].$$

For $m \geqslant 3$, equation (27) is usually more difficult to handle than the Laurent series. The above theory can be generalized to give the residue theorem:

THE RESIDUE THEOREM   Let $f(z)$ be continuous and analytic on a closed contour C and analytic everywhere within C except at a finite number of isolated singularities $z_1, z_2, \ldots, z_n$. If $\sigma_1, \sigma_2, \ldots, \sigma_n$ denote the residues of $f(z)$ at $z_1, z_2, \ldots, z_n$ respectively, then

$$\oint_C f(z)\, dz = 2\pi i(\sigma_1 + \sigma_2 + \ldots + \sigma_n).$$

Proof   Let each of the points z_j be enclosed by a small circle $C_j, j = 1, 2, \ldots, n$ (see Fig. 4.25). Then the contour C together with the circles C_j form the boundary of a multiply-connected region in which $f(z)$ is analytic. If $\mathscr{C} = C - C_1 - C_2 - \ldots - C_n$, then the Cauchy–Goursat theorem gives

$$\oint_{\mathscr{C}} f(z)\, dz = 0,$$

that is,

$$\oint_C f(z)\, dz = \oint_{C_1} f(z)\, dz + \oint_{C_2} f(z)\, dz + \ldots + \oint_{C_n} f(z)\, dz.$$

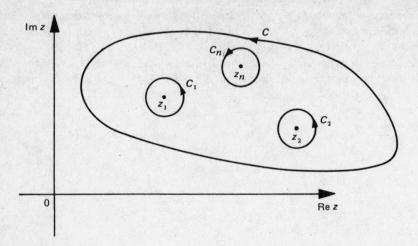

Fig. 4.25   The contours C, C_j for $j = 1, 2$ and n in the proof of the residue theorem.

We see from equation (26) that

$$\oint_{C_j} f(z)\, dz = 2\pi i \sigma_j$$

and therefore

$$\oint_C f(z)\, dz = 2\pi i \sum_{j=1}^{n} \sigma_j .$$

EXAMPLE 6   Evaluate $\displaystyle\oint_C \frac{3z + 1}{z(z + 2)(z + \pi i)^2}\, dz$, where C is the contour $|z| = 3$.

The contour C encloses the simple poles at $z = 0$ and $z = -2$ but excludes the double pole at $z = -\pi i$. The residue at $z = 0$ is

$$\lim_{z \to 0} \left\{ \frac{z(3z + 1)}{z(z + 2)(z + \pi i)^2} \right\} = \frac{3z + 1}{(z + 2)(z + \pi i)^2} \bigg|_{z=0} = -\frac{1}{2\pi^2} ,$$

and the residue at $z = -2$ is

$$\lim_{z \to -2} \left\{ \frac{(z + 2)(3z + 1)}{z(z + 2)(z + \pi i)^2} \right\} = \frac{3z + 1}{z(z + \pi i)^2} \bigg|_{z=-2} = \frac{-5}{-2(-2 + \pi i)^2} .$$

Hence, by the residue theorem,

$$\oint_C f(z)\, dz = 2\pi i \left(-\frac{1}{2\pi^2} + \frac{5}{2(2 - \pi i)^2} \right) .$$

Evaluation of Real Integrals by Application of the Residue Theorem

The main application of the residue theorem is in the evaluation of real integrals. The technique is best demonstrated by examples.

EXAMPLE 7   Evaluate $I = \displaystyle\int_0^{2\pi} \frac{d\theta}{3 - 2\cos\theta}$.

Let $z = e^{i\theta}$, then $dz = iz\,d\theta$ and from equations (9) it can be shown that

$$\cos\theta = \frac{z + z^{-1}}{2} \quad \text{and} \quad \sin\theta = \frac{z - z^{-1}}{2i}.$$

As θ increases from 0 to 2π, z makes one circuit of the circle $|z| = 1$, so that if $z = e^{i\theta}$ is substituted into the required integral, we have

$$I = \int_0^{2\pi} \frac{d\theta}{3 - 2\cos\theta} = \oint_C \frac{dz}{iz\{3 - (z + z^{-1})\}} = -\frac{1}{i}\oint_C \frac{dz}{(z^2 - 3z + 1)},$$

where C is the circle $|z| = 1$. The poles of the integrand are at

$$z = \frac{3 \pm \sqrt{(9 - 4)}}{2} = \frac{3 \pm \sqrt{5}}{2}$$

and each is a simple pole. Only the poles inside C contribute to the integral and therefore we require the residue at $z = \frac{1}{2}(3 - \sqrt{5})$. The required residue is

$$\frac{1}{z - \frac{1}{2}(3 + \sqrt{5})}\,\bigg|_{z=\frac{1}{2}(3-\sqrt{5})} = -\frac{1}{\sqrt{5}},$$

and hence from the residue theorem the real integral I is given by

$$I = -\frac{1}{i}\oint_C \frac{dz}{z^2 - 3z + 1} = \frac{2\pi i}{-i}\left(-\frac{1}{\sqrt{5}}\right) = \frac{2\pi}{\sqrt{5}}.$$

This result can be checked by evaluating the integral using the standard techniques of integral calculus.

The procedure used in example 7 is useful for evaluating integrals of the type

$$\int_0^{2\pi} F(\sin\theta, \cos\theta)\,d\theta.$$

EXAMPLE 8   Evaluate the integral

$$\int_{-\infty}^{\infty} \frac{dx}{x^2 + 1} = \lim_{K\to\infty} \int_{-K}^{K} \frac{dx}{x^2 + 1}.$$

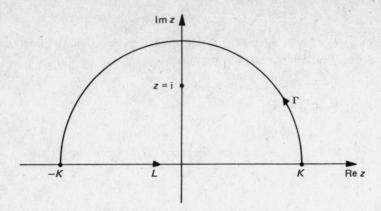

Fig. 4.26   The contour in example 8.

Consider the contour integral

$$\oint_C \frac{dz}{z^2 + 1},$$

with $C = L + \Gamma$, where

L is the line	$y = 0$	and	$-K \leqslant x \leqslant K$,	
Γ is the semicircle	$|z| = K$	and	$0 \leqslant \arg z \leqslant \pi$,	

and $K > 1$. The contours L and Γ are shown in Fig. 4.26. The integrand has poles at $z = \pm i$, and clearly only the pole at $z = i$ is within C. The residue at $z = i$ is

$$\lim_{z \to i} \left(\frac{z - i}{z^2 + 1} \right) = \frac{1}{z + i} \bigg|_{z=i} = \frac{1}{2i},$$

and therefore, by the residue theorem,

$$\oint_C \frac{dz}{z^2 + 1} = \int_L \frac{dx}{x^2 + 1} + \int_\Gamma \frac{dz}{z^2 + 1} = 2\pi i \left(\frac{1}{2i} \right) = \pi, \qquad (28)$$

for all $K > 1$. The required integral is the limit as $K \to \infty$ of the integral along L and from equation (28) is given by

$$\lim_{K \to \infty} \int_L \frac{dx}{x^2 + 1} = \pi - \lim_{K \to \infty} \int_\Gamma \frac{dz}{z^2 + 1}.$$

Bounds for the integral around Γ can be obtained in the following way. Result (e) of example 1 in §4.2 may be used to give

$$|z^2 + 1| = |z^2 - (-1)| \geqslant \big| |z|^2 - |-1| \big|,$$

and on Γ, $|z| = K$ with $K > 1$, and therefore

$$|z^2 + 1| \geqslant |K^2 - 1|$$
$$\geqslant K^2 - 1 .$$

Hence,

$$\left| \frac{1}{z^2 + 1} \right| \leqslant \frac{1}{K^2 - 1} ,$$

and therefore, since the length of Γ is πK, equation (14e) gives the result

$$\left| \int_\Gamma \frac{dz}{z^2 + 1} \right| \leqslant \frac{\pi K}{K^2 - 1} .$$

Since the limit as $K \to \infty$ of the right-hand side of this inequality is zero, we see that

$$\lim_{K \to \infty} \left| \int_\Gamma \frac{dz}{z^2 + 1} \right| = 0 ,$$

and therefore

$$\int_{-\infty}^{\infty} \frac{dx}{x^2 + 1} = \pi .$$

In order to use the residue theorem to evaluate an infinite real integral, it is necessary to choose a suitable function $f(z)$ and to integrate it round an appropriate closed contour C. The contour is then deformed so that C consists of a contour at infinity and a segment (or the whole) of the real axis. The crucial step is to show that the integral along the curve at infinity is zero, leaving the integral along the real axis as the only contribution to the answer. The task of showing that the integral over the contour at infinity is zero is often facilitated by the use of Jordan's lemma, which will be stated without proof (see Whittaker and Watson [4]).

JORDAN'S LEMMA   If Γ is the semicircle $|z| = R$ and $0 \leqslant \arg z \leqslant \pi$, then

$$\lim_{R \to \infty} \int_\Gamma e^{imz} \phi(z) \, dz = 0$$

provided that (a) m is real and positive, and (b) on Γ, $|\phi(z)| \leqslant M(R)$ where $M(R)$ is a function of R such that $M(R) \to 0$ as $R \to \infty$.

EXAMPLE 9   Evaluate $\displaystyle\int_0^{\infty} \frac{x \sin x}{x^2 + a^2} \, dx$, where $a > 0$.

An attempt to integrate

$$f(z) = \frac{z \sin z}{z^2 + a^2}$$

around the contour C in Fig. 4.26 will fail because $|\sin z|$ becomes exponentially large as $|z| \to \infty$ and therefore the integral along Γ will not tend to zero as Γ is deformed to the semicircle at infinity. It is necessary, therefore, to consider

$$I = \oint_C \frac{z e^{iz}}{z^2 + a^2} \, dz \,,$$

where C is the contour in Fig. 4.26, with $K > a$. The integrand has simple poles at $z = \pm ia$, but only the pole at $z = ia$ is enclosed by C. The residue at $z = ia$ is

$$\left. \frac{z e^{iz}}{z + ia} \right|_{z=ia} = \frac{e^{-a}}{2}.$$

and therefore, by the residue theorem,

$$I = \frac{2\pi i e^{-a}}{2} = \pi i e^{-a}.$$

For $K > a$, the triangle inequalities give

$$\left| \frac{z}{z^2 + a^2} \right| \leqslant \frac{K}{K^2 - a^2} \to 0 \quad \text{as } K \to \infty$$

for all arg z, and so, by Jordan's lemma, taking $M(K) = K/(K^2 - a^2)$,

$$\lim_{K \to \infty} \int_\Gamma \frac{z e^{iz}}{z^2 + a^2} \, dz = 0.$$

As $K \to \infty$,

$$\oint_C \frac{z e^{iz}}{z^2 + a^2} \, dz \to \int_{-\infty}^{\infty} \frac{x e^{ix}}{x^2 + a^2} \, dx \,,$$

therefore

$$\int_{-\infty}^{\infty} \frac{x e^{ix}}{x^2 + a^2} \, dx = \pi i e^{-a}. \tag{29}$$

Equating real parts and imaginary parts of equation (29), we obtain the equations

$$\int_{-\infty}^{\infty} \frac{x \cos x}{x^2 + a^2} \, dx = 0 \quad \text{and} \quad \int_{-\infty}^{\infty} \frac{x \sin x}{x^2 + a^2} \, dx = \pi e^{-a} \,,$$

and since $x(x^2 + a^2)^{-1} \sin x$ is an even function of x, the result

$$\int_0^{\infty} \frac{x \sin x}{x^2 + a^2} = \tfrac{1}{2} \pi e^{-a}$$

is obtained.

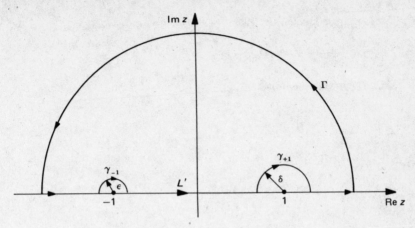

Fig. 4.27   The contour in example 10.

EXAMPLE 10   Evaluate $\displaystyle\int_0^\infty \frac{\cos x}{x^2 - 1}\, dx$.

Consider $I = \displaystyle\oint_C \frac{e^{iz}}{z^2 - 1}\, dz$,

where C is the contour in Fig. 4.26 with $K > 1$. The integrand has poles at $z = \pm 1$ which are on the contour C and therefore the residue theorem cannot be applied immediately. In this case it is necessary to *indent* or deform the contour C so that the poles are excluded (see Fig. 4.27).

The indentations at $z = \pm 1$ are semicircles and C', the indented contour, is defined by $C' = \Gamma + L' + \gamma_{-1} + \gamma_{+1}$ where

L' consists of the portions $-K \leqslant x \leqslant -1 - \epsilon$, $-1 + \epsilon \leqslant x \leqslant 1 - \delta$, $1 + \delta \leqslant x \leqslant K$ of the line $y = 0$,

γ_{-1} is the semicircle $\mid z + 1 \mid = \epsilon$ from $\arg(z + 1) = \pi$ to $\arg(z + 1) = 0$,

γ_{+1} is the semicircle $\mid z - 1 \mid = \delta$ from $\arg(z - 1) = \pi$ to $\arg(z - 1) = 0$

and Γ is the semicircle $\mid z \mid = K$ from $\arg z = 0$ to $\arg z = \pi, K > 1$.

The integrand is analytic within and on C' and so, by the residue theorem,

$$\oint_{C'} \frac{e^{iz}}{z^2 - 1}\, dz = 0 ,$$

that is,

$$\int_{L'} \frac{e^{ix}}{x^2 - 1}\, dx + \int_{\gamma_{-1}} \frac{e^{iz}}{z^2 - 1}\, dz + \int_{\gamma_{+1}} \frac{e^{iz}}{z^2 - 1}\, dz + \int_{\Gamma} \frac{e^{iz}}{z^2 - 1}\, dz = 0 .$$

For $K > 1$, the triangle inequalities give

$$\left| \frac{1}{z^2 - 1} \right| \leqslant \frac{1}{K^2 - 1} \to 0 \quad \text{as } K \to \infty,$$

and therefore, by Jordan's lemma,

$$\lim_{K \to \infty} \int_\Gamma \frac{e^{iz}}{z^2 - 1} \, dz = 0.$$

On γ_{-1}, $z = -1 + \epsilon e^{i\theta}$, therefore

$$\int_{\gamma_{-1}} \frac{e^{iz}}{z^2 - 1} \, dz = \int_\pi^0 \frac{\exp(-i + i\epsilon e^{i\theta}) i\epsilon e^{i\theta}}{\epsilon e^{i\theta} (-2 + \epsilon e^{i\theta})} \, d\theta$$

and

$$\lim_{\epsilon \to 0} \int_\pi^0 \frac{i \exp(-i + i\epsilon e^{i\theta})}{(-2 + \epsilon e^{i\theta})} \, d\theta = \frac{ie^{-i}}{-2} \int_\pi^0 d\theta = \frac{\pi i e^{-i}}{2}.$$

On γ_{+1}, $z = 1 + \delta e^{i\theta}$, therefore

$$\int_{\gamma_{+1}} \frac{e^{iz}}{z^2 - 1} \, dz = \int_\pi^0 \frac{\exp(i + i\delta e^{i\theta}) i\delta e^{i\theta}}{\delta e^{i\theta} (2 + \delta e^{i\theta})} \, d\theta,$$

and

$$\lim_{\delta \to 0} \int_\pi^0 \frac{i \exp(i + i\delta e^{i\theta})}{(2 + \delta e^{i\theta})} \, d\theta = \frac{ie^i}{2} \int_\pi^0 d\theta = -\frac{\pi i e^i}{2}.$$

Therefore in the limit as $K \to \infty$, $\epsilon \to 0$ and $\delta \to 0$,

$$\lim_{\substack{\epsilon, \delta \to 0 \\ K \to \infty}} \int_{L'} \frac{e^{ix}}{x^2 - 1} \, dx + \frac{\pi i e^{-i}}{2} - \frac{\pi i e^i}{2} = 0,$$

which gives the result

$$\int_{-\infty}^\infty \frac{e^{ix}}{x^2 - 1} \, dx = -\frac{\pi}{2i} [e^i - e^{-i}] = -\pi \sin 1.$$

If the real parts of both sides of this equation are considered, we have

$$\int_{-\infty}^\infty \frac{\cos x}{x^2 - 1} \, dx = -\pi \sin 1,$$

and since the integrand is even, the result

$$\int_0^\infty \frac{\cos x}{x^2 - 1} \, dx = -\tfrac{1}{2}\pi \sin 1$$

follows. It should be stated here that

$$\int_0^\infty \frac{\cos x}{x^2 - 1}\, dx$$

is an improper integral (see Whittaker and Watson [4]) because the integrand is infinite at $x = 1$.

Further examples of contour integration are contained in §5.3 where the systematic procedure for inverting Laplace transforms is discussed. In the above examples and those in §5.3, real integrals are evaluated by integrating a single-valued function of a complex variable around a suitable contour. It is sometimes necessary to evaluate integrals where the appropriate function of z possesses a branch point, that is $f(z)$ is multiple-valued. In this case, the choice of contour can be particularly difficult because $f(z)$ is analytic only in a suitably cut plane and the contour must not cross the cut or branch line. Such problems are beyond the scope of this text and the reader is referred to Carrier, Krook and Pearson [7] where several examples are discussed.

Exercises

1. Find the first two terms of the Taylor series about (a) $z = 0$ and (b) $z = \pi/3$ of the functions $\tan z$, $\sec z$.
   State the region of convergence in each case.

2. Find the Laurent series, valid near the stated singularity, for

(a) $\dfrac{e^{3z}}{(z + 2)^2}$, about $z = -2$, (b) $\dfrac{z - \sin z}{z^3}$, about $z = 0$,

(c) $z \exp\left(\dfrac{1}{z - 1}\right)$, about $z = 1$,

(d) $\dfrac{z - 2}{z(z - 3)^3}$, about (i) $z = 0$, (ii) $z = 3$.

In each case specify the type of singularity, the region of convergence and the residue if any.

3. Evaluate the following contour integrals in the counterclockwise sense:

(a) $\oint_C \dfrac{z^2 - 3z}{(z - 1)^2 (z + 4)}\, dz$ where C is the circle $|z| = 3$,

(b) $\oint_C \dfrac{z - \sin z}{z^3}\, dz$ where C is any closed contour enclosing the origin,

(c) $\oint_C z \exp\left(\dfrac{1}{z - 1}\right) dz$ where C is the circle $|z - 1| = 2$,

(d) $\displaystyle\oint_C e^z \csc z \, dz$ where C is the boundary of the rectangular region given by $-5\pi/2 \leqslant x \leqslant 5\pi/2$, $-\pi \leqslant y \leqslant \pi$.

4. Evaluate the following real integrals using the theory of residues:

(a) $\displaystyle\int_0^{2\pi} \frac{\cos\theta}{3 - 2\cos\theta} \, d\theta$,

(b) $\displaystyle\int_0^\infty \frac{dx}{x^4 + 2x^2 + 1}$.

(c) $\displaystyle\int_0^\infty \frac{\cos 3x}{x^2 + 1} \, dx$,

(d) $\displaystyle\int_0^\infty \frac{\sin x}{x} \, dx$.

4.6 CONFORMAL MAPPING

In §4.2, some of the properties of several simple functions $f(z)$ were demonstrated geometrically by finding the region R' of the w plane which resulted from applying the mapping $w = f(z)$ to every point of a region R of the z plane. The function $f(z)$ is then said to map or transform the region R into the region R', or alternatively R' is said to be the image of R under the mapping $w = f(z)$. In this section, we shall find and investigate the properties of a particular class of mappings called *conformal mappings* which are defined as follows.

DEFINITION   A transformation which preserves angles in both magnitude and sense is said to be *conformal.*

The conditions on the function $f(z)$ which ensure that the transformation $w = f(z)$ is conformal are given in the following theorem.

THEOREM 1   If $f(z)$ is analytic and $f'(z) \neq 0$ in a region R, then $w = f(z)$ is a conformal mapping, and infinitesimally small elements at any point z_0 of R are magnified (or reduced) in the w plane by a multiplicative factor $|f'(z_0)|$, and all are rotated through the same angle $\arg f'(z_0)$.

Proof   Consider a curve C in the z plane which passes through the point $z_0 = x_0 + iy_0$, and let the image of C in the w plane be the curve C' which passes through the point w_0, the image of z_0. Let the tangent to C at z_0 be at angle α to the Re z axis and the tangent to C' at w_0 be at angle γ to the Re w axis (see Fig. 4.28). If $f(z)$ is continuous in R and z_1 is a point on C near to z_0, then w_1, the image of z_1, will be near to w_0. Therefore if $f(z)$ is analytic at z_0,

$$f'(z_0) = \lim_{z_1 \to z_0} \left(\frac{f(z_1) - f(z_0)}{z_1 - z_0} \right) = \lim_{z_1 \to z_0} \left(\frac{w_1 - w_0}{z_1 - z_0} \right) = \lim_{z_1 \to z_0} \left(\frac{\rho e^{i\phi}}{r e^{i\theta}} \right),$$

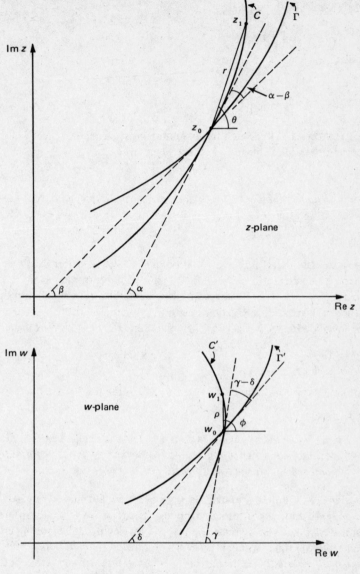

Fig. 4.28 Illustration of Theorem 1.

where $z_1 - z_0 = re^{i\theta}$ and $w_1 - w_0 = \rho e^{i\phi}$. Provided that $f'(z_0) \neq 0$, then $f'(z_0)$ may be written as $f'(z_0) = Me^{i\psi}$, where

$$Me^{i\psi} = \lim_{z_1 \to z_0} \left(\frac{\rho}{r} e^{i(\phi - \theta)} \right),$$

from which it may be seen that

$$M = |f'(z_0)| = \lim_{r \to 0}\left(\frac{\rho}{r}\right),$$ (30a)

and

$$\psi = \arg f'(z_0) = \lim_{r \to 0}(\phi - \theta) = \gamma - \alpha.$$ (30b)

Equation (30a) shows that in a small region containing z_0, small distances r in the z plane correspond to small distances ρ in the w plane, where

$$\rho \simeq |f'(z_0)|\, r.$$ (31)

In other words, *distances are magnified by a factor* $|f'(z_0)|$ *independent of their orientation*. Equation (30b) shows that the tangent to C' at w_0 makes an angle

$$\gamma = \alpha + \arg f'(z_0)$$ (32a)

with the Re w axis and therefore the inclination of C' at w_0 is greater than the inclination of C at z_0 by an amount $\arg f'(z_0)$. If Γ is another curve in the z plane which also passes through z_0 and Γ' is its image in the w plane, then Γ' will pass through w_0. Let the tangent to Γ at z_0 make an angle β with the Re z axis and the tangent to Γ' at w_0 make an angle δ with the Re w axis. Then equation (30b) can be used again to show that

$$\delta = \beta + \arg f'(z_0),$$ (32b)

and if equation (32b) is subtracted from equation (32a) the result

$$\gamma - \delta = \alpha - \beta$$

is obtained. The angle between Γ and C at z_0 is $\alpha - \beta$ and the angle between Γ' and C' at w_0 is $\gamma - \delta$ (see Fig. 4.28), hence *angles are preserved under the transformation in both magnitude and sense, and the transformation is therefore conformal.*

It is important to note that although the angle between two curves is preserved in magnitude and sense under a conformal mapping, the curves are generally rotated. A *small* figure in the z plane will therefore be mapped by a conformal mapping into a *magnified* (or reduced) figure in the w plane which has *approximately the same shape* but which *is usually rotated*. The magnification and rotation will vary from point to point in the plane, however, and therefore large figures in the z plane may look very different from their image figures in the w plane, even though *locally* the angles are preserved.

To illustrate the behaviour at $z = 0$, write $z = re^{i\theta}$ and $w = \rho e^{i\phi}$, so that

$$\rho e^{i\phi} = r^2 e^{2i\theta}.$$

The line $\theta = \theta_0$ is mapped into the line $\phi_0 = 2\theta_0$ and the line $\theta = \theta_1$ maps into the line $\phi_1 = 2\theta_1$, therefore

$$\phi_1 - \phi_0 = 2(\theta_1 - \theta_0).$$

The angle between the two lines through $z = 0$ is thus doubled by the transformation, and $w = z^2$ is therefore not conformal at $z = 0$.

> **THEOREM 2** A conformal mapping $w = f(z)$ from R to R' has a single-valued inverse $z = f^{-1}(w)$ which maps R' to R.

Proof If $w = f(z)$ is conformal in R then $f(z)$ is analytic and $f'(z) \neq 0$ in R. The real and imaginary parts of an analytic function satisfy the Cauchy–Riemann equations and therefore if $w = u + iv$ and $z = x + iy$, where u, v, x and y are real then

$$|f'(z)|^2 = \left(\frac{\partial u}{\partial x} + i\frac{\partial v}{\partial x} \right)\left(\frac{\partial u}{\partial x} - i\frac{\partial v}{\partial x} \right) = \left(\frac{\partial u}{\partial x} \right)^2 + \left(\frac{\partial v}{\partial x} \right)^2,$$

$$= u_x v_y - v_x u_y = \begin{vmatrix} u_x & u_y \\ v_x & v_y \end{vmatrix} = \frac{\partial(u,\, v)}{\partial(x,\, y)},$$

where $\partial(u, v)/\partial(x, y)$ is the Jacobian of the transformation (see §5.2 of Volume 1). The condition $f'(z) \neq 0$ thus implies that the Jacobian of the transformation is non-zero and therefore that there exists an inverse mapping $z = f^{-1}(w)$ (see §5.2 of Volume 1).

Points at which $f'(z)$ is zero are called *critical points* of the transformation and will require special consideration as shown in the following example.

EXAMPLE 2 The mapping $w = z^2$ has a critical point at $z = 0$. The inverse function $z = w^{\frac{1}{2}}$ is single-valued only if the w plane is 'cut' from $w = 0$ to infinity along any line (a branch cut). The mapping $w = z^2$ then has a single-valued inverse at every point in the cut plane. The inverse function $z = w^{\frac{1}{2}}$ has been discussed in detail in §4.3.

Some Simple Conformal Mappings

If Π is a figure in the z plane and Π' is its image in the w plane, where $w = f(z)$, then
(a) if $f(z) = z + p$, where p is complex, Π' is identical in shape to Π but is displaced or translated in the direction of p (see Fig. 4.29).
(b) if $f(z) = e^{i\alpha}z$, where α is real, Π' is identical to Π in shape but is rotated by an angle α (see Fig. 4.30).
(c) if $f(z) = az$, where a is real, Π' has the same angles as Π but has an area which is greater than or less than Π as $a > 1$ or $0 < a < 1$. This is a 'magnifying' transformation (see Fig. 4.31).
The mapping $w = bz + p$ is a combination of the two conformal mappings $s = bz$ and $w = s + p$. This mapping, which is called a *linear transformation*, is a combination of the translation and magnifying transformations if b is real, and a combination of the translation, magnifying and rotation transformations if b is complex. The mapping

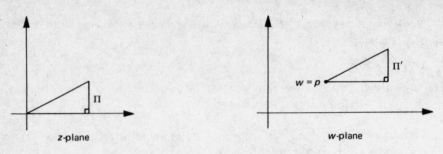

Fig. 4.29   A translation mapping.

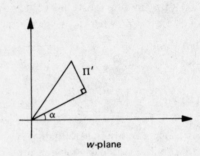

Fig. 4.30   A rotation mapping.

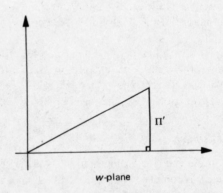

Fig. 4.31   A magnifying mapping.

$w = 1/z$ was considered in §4.3 and maps all points outside the circle $|z| = 1$ into the region $|w| < 1$ and all points in the region $|z| < 1$ into the region $|w| > 1$ (see Fig. 4.32).

The circle $|z| = 1$ is mapped into the circle $|w| = 1$ and circles $|z| = c$ are mapped into circles $|w| = 1/c$. Straight lines are mapped into circles through the origin, as in Fig. 4.32. This mapping is called an *inversion mapping*.

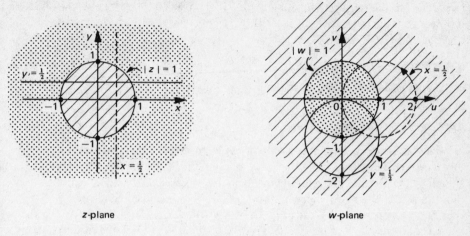

z-plane   w-plane

Fig. 4.32   The mapping $w = 1/z$.

The transformation

$$w = \frac{bz + p}{dz + q},$$

where b, d, p and q are complex, is called the *bilinear transformation* (see Churchill *et al.* [2]) and is a combination of the translation, rotation, magnifying and inversion transformations. It has the property that it maps circles in the z plane into circles or straight lines in the w plane, and straight lines in the z plane into circles or straight lines in the w plane. Other mappings have been considered already in §4.3.

The Transformation of Harmonic Functions

Under the transformation $w = f(z)$, where $w = u + iv$ and $z = x + iy$, the function $\phi(x, y)$ is transformed to the function

$$\phi\{x(u, v), y(u, v)\} = \Phi(u, v).$$

If $w = f(z)$ is conformal in a region R of the z plane, it is easy to show by using the chain rule of partial differentiation (equation (17) of §4.2 in Volume 1) that

$$\frac{\partial^2 \phi}{\partial x^2} + \frac{\partial^2 \phi}{\partial y^2} = |f'(z)|^2 \left(\frac{\partial^2 \Phi}{\partial u^2} + \frac{\partial^2 \Phi}{\partial v^2} \right). \tag{33}$$

If $\phi(x, y)$ is harmonic in R, then the left-hand side of equation (33) is zero. Hence the right-hand side of equation (33) is zero and therefore $\Phi(u, v)$ is harmonic in R', the image of R in the w plane. Further, if $\phi(x, y) = c$ along some curve C in the z plane, where c is a constant, then $\Phi(u, v) = c$ along C', the image of C in the w plane. Alternatively, if $\partial \phi / \partial n = 0$ on C, then $\partial \Phi / \partial n' = 0$ on C', where $\partial / \partial n$ and $\partial / \partial n'$ denote the derivatives normal to the curves C and C' respectively (see §6.4 of Volume 1). This last result is a consequence of the fact that the level curves of ϕ are orthogonal to the level curves of the conjugate function ψ (see §4.4). When $\partial\phi/\partial n = 0$ on C, then C is orthogonal to the level curves of ϕ. Hence C is a level curve of ψ and consequently C' is a level curve of Ψ where

$$\Psi(u, v) = \psi\{x(u, v), y(u, v)\},$$

and the result $\partial\Phi/\partial n' = 0$ on C' follows.

Applications of Conformal Mappings

Many physical problems in engineering can be formulated mathematically as boundary-value problems involving a partial differential equation (see Chapter 7 of Volume 1). Often the partial differential equation is Laplace's equation, and the problem is to find a solution $\phi(x, y)$ in a region R with boundary conditions of the type $\phi(x, y) =$ constant on some portions of the boundary of R and $\partial\phi/\partial n = 0$ on the remainder. It may be that the problem is difficult to solve because the region R has a shape which is difficult to express in a convenient coordinate system. Such a problem may sometimes be simplified by using an appropriate conformal mapping.

Suppose that in the region R, the boundary value problem is

$$\frac{\partial^2\phi}{\partial x^2} + \frac{\partial^2\phi}{\partial y^2} = 0$$

with boundary conditions either

$$\phi = \text{constant} \quad \text{or} \quad \frac{\partial\phi}{\partial n} = 0 \text{ on different parts of the boundary.}$$

If the problem is restated in the region R', the image of R under the conformal mapping $w = f(z)$, where $w = u + iv$ and $z = x + iy$, then

$$\frac{\partial^2\Phi}{\partial u^2} + \frac{\partial^2\Phi}{\partial v^2} = 0$$

with boundary conditions either

$$\Phi = \text{constant} \quad \text{or} \quad \frac{\partial\Phi}{\partial n'} = 0 \text{ on corresponding parts of the boundary,}$$

where $\Phi(u, v) = \phi\{x(u, v), y(u, v)\}$. A skilful choice of the mapping $w = f(z)$ may render the problem in R' more easily solvable than the problem in R, and $\Phi(u, v)$ can be determined. The result

$$\phi = \Phi\{u(x, y), v(x, y)\}$$

can then be obtained.

In order to demonstrate the technique we will consider a boundary value problem for Laplace's equation which is easily solved directly and then show that the solution of a more difficult problem can be obtained by applying a conformal mapping to the configuration.

EXAMPLE 3   Two infinite conducting planes Γ_1 and Γ_2 are maintained at potentials ϕ_1 and ϕ_2 respectively. If Γ_1 occupies the plane $y = 0$ and Γ_2 occupies the plane $y = a$ and the space V between the plates is a vacuum, find the electrostatic potential $\phi(x, y)$ at every point in V given that ϕ satisfies Laplace's equation in V (that is, it is harmonic in V).

The configuration is shown in Fig. 4.33. The symmetry of the problem implies that the electrostatic potential will be a function of y only, therefore the boundary value problem for $\phi = \phi(y)$ is

$$\frac{d^2\phi}{dy^2} = 0 \quad \text{in } V$$

with

$$\phi(y) = \phi_1 \text{ on } \Gamma_1 \quad \text{and} \quad \phi(y) = \phi_2 \text{ on } \Gamma_2.$$

(34)

The solution to this problem is

$$\phi(y) = Ay + B$$

where the constants A and B are determined by the boundary conditions and are

$$A = \frac{1}{a}(\phi_2 - \phi_1) \quad \text{and} \quad B = \phi_1.$$

The potential between the plates is thus

$$\phi(x, y) = \frac{1}{a}\{(\phi_2 - \phi_1)y + a\phi_1\}.$$

(35)

If a conformal mapping $w = u + iv = f(z)$ is applied to the configuration in Fig. 4.33, then Γ_1, Γ_2 and V will be mapped into their images Γ'_1, Γ'_2 and V' in the w plane. A possible image configuration is given in Fig. 4.34. The electrostatic potential $\Phi(u, v)$ in V' is the solution of the boundary value problem

$$\frac{\partial^2\Phi}{\partial u^2} + \frac{\partial^2\Phi}{\partial v^2} = 0 \quad \text{in } V'$$

with

$$\Phi(u, v) = \phi_1 \text{ on } \Gamma'_1 \quad \text{and} \quad \Phi(u, v) = \phi_2 \text{ on } \Gamma'_2,$$

(36)

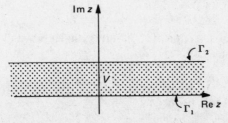

Fig. 4.33   The initial configuration in example 3.

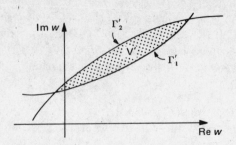

Fig. 4.34 A possible image configuration associated with example 3.

where $\Phi(u, v) = \phi\{x(u, v), y(u, v)\}$. The potential $\Phi(u, v)$ can be obtained from expression (35) by applying the transformation $w = f(z)$ to $\phi(x, y)$ and hence the boundary value problem (36) is solved.

EXAMPLE 4   The conformal mapping

$$w = e^{\pi z/a} \tag{37}$$

maps the configuration in example 3 into the upper half of the w plane. The boundary Γ_1 is mapped into the line $v = 0$ and $u > 0$, and the boundary Γ_2 is mapped into the line $v = 0$ and $u < 0$. The boundary value problem (34) expressed in the w plane is

$$\frac{\partial^2 \Phi}{\partial u^2} + \frac{\partial^2 \Phi}{\partial v^2} = 0 \quad \text{in } v > 0, \ -\infty < u < \infty,$$

with

$$\Phi(u, 0) = \phi_1 \quad \text{for} \quad u > 0 \quad \text{and} \quad \Phi(u, 0) = \phi_2 \quad \text{for} \quad u < 0. \tag{38}$$

It can be shown from equation (37) that

$$x = \frac{a}{2\pi} \log (u^2 + v^2) \qquad \text{and} \qquad y = \frac{a}{\pi} \tan^{-1} \left(\frac{v}{u} \right)$$

with $0 \leqslant \tan^{-1}(v/u) \leqslant \pi$, and therefore the solution to problem (38), obtained from equation (35), is

$$\Phi(u, v) = \pi^{-1}(\phi_2 - \phi_1) \tan^{-1} \left(\frac{v}{u} \right) + \phi_1. \tag{39}$$

EXAMPLE 5   The cross-section of an infinite cylinder is bounded by the curved conductor Π, defined by

$$x^2 + y^2 = 1, \quad \text{and} \quad y > 0,$$

resting on the conductor L, defined by

$$-1 \leqslant x \leqslant 1, \quad \text{and} \quad y = 0.$$

Find the electrostatic potential ϕ in the space R between the conductors if Π is maintained at constant potential ϕ_2, L is maintained at constant potential ϕ_1, and it is assumed that Π and L are insulated from each other along the lines of contact.

The potential ϕ, which is a function of x and y, is the solution of the boundary value problem

$$\frac{\partial^2 \phi}{\partial x^2} + \frac{\partial^2 \phi}{\partial y^2} = 0 \quad \text{in } R$$

with

$$\phi(x, y) = \phi_1 \text{ on } L \quad \text{and} \quad \phi(x, y) = \phi_2 \text{ on } \Pi.$$

(40)

If $z = x + iy$, the conformal mapping

$$w = \left(\frac{1+z}{1-z}\right)^2,$$

(41)

where $w = u + iv$, maps the configuration of this example into the upper half of the w plane. The line L is mapped into the line $v = 0$, $u > 0$ and Π is mapped into the line $v = 0$, $u < 0$. It can be shown from equation (41) that

$$\tan^{-1}\left(\frac{v}{u}\right) = \arg w = 2 \arg\left(\frac{1+z}{1-z}\right) = 2 \tan^{-1}\left(\frac{2y}{1-x^2-y^2}\right),$$

(42)

and therefore the solution of problem (40) can be obtained from equations (39) and (42) as

$$\phi(x, y) = \frac{2}{\pi}(\phi_2 - \phi_1) \tan^{-1}\left(\frac{2y}{1-x^2-y^2}\right) + \phi_1.$$

(43)

The solution to equations (40) can be obtained immediately from the solution to example 3 without reference to the solution of example 4. The configuration in the w plane is really an intermediate stage in the solution, because the solution of example 4 was obtained from the solution to example 3. The configuration of example 5 can be mapped directly into the configuration shown in Fig. 4.33 by applying the combined mapping

$$w = \left(\frac{1+z}{1-z}\right)^2 \quad \text{and} \quad s = \frac{a}{\pi}\log w,$$

that is

$$s = \frac{2a}{\pi}\log\left(\frac{1+z}{1-z}\right),$$

(44)

where $s = r + it$. The s plane is identical to the z plane in example 3 and the solution in the s plane is therefore

$$\phi(r, t) = \frac{1}{a}\{(\phi_2 - \phi_1)t + a\phi_1\},$$

from equation (35). Substituting for t in terms of x and y using equation (44) gives the result (43).

Further examples of the solution of boundary value problems by conformal mapping may be found in Churchill *et al.* [2] and Spiegel [5].

It is not difficult to see that the usefulness of this method depends on finding the appropriate conformal mapping for the problem. Many books dealing with conformal mapping, for example Kober [6], Churchill *et al.* [2] and Spiegel [5], contain lists of conformal mappings and illustrate various regions and their images.

PROBLEMS

1. If $z = \cos\theta + i\sin\theta$, express $z^n + 1/z^n$ and $z^n - 1/z^n$ in terms of θ. Hence show that $\cos^7\theta = (\frac{1}{2})^6 (\cos 7\theta + 7\cos 5\theta + 21\cos 3\theta + 35\cos\theta)$ and express $\cos 5\theta$ in terms of $\cos\theta$.

2. Find all the values of z such that $z^7 = -1$ and hence solve the equation $(w+1)^7 = -(w-1)^7$. Deduce the roots of $x^6 + 21x^4 + 35x^2 + 7 = 0$.

3. Find the indefinite integral $\int x\,e^{ix}\,dx$ and hence show that

$$\int x\cos x\,dx = \cos x + x\sin x + \text{const.}$$

4. If a and b are real, find $\int e^{ax}(\cos bx + i\sin bx)\,dx$ and hence find $\int e^{ax}\cos bx\,dx$ and $\int e^{ax}\sin bx\,dx$.

5. Find all the solutions of $z^n = 1$ where n is a positive integer. If $n = 3$ and the roots are labelled z_1, z_2 and z_3, show that if $z_1 = 1$ then

(a) $z_2 = z_3^2$ and $z_3 = z_2^2$,
(b) $1 + z_2 + z_3 = 0$.

6. Solve the equation $z^4 - 4z^2 + 8z - 4 = 0$ given that $1 + i$ is a root.

7. Show that the solutions of the equation $\sin z = 0$ are all real.

8. If $w = z^2$, find the region of the w plane which is the image of the interior of the rectangle $OPQR$ in the z plane, where O is the point $(0, 0)$, P is the point $(a, 0)$, Q is the point $(a, -b)$, R is the point $(0, -b)$ and a and b are real and positive.

9. Show that $\sin^{-1} z = -i\log\{iz + (1 - z^2)^{1/2}\}$ if $\sin^{-1} 0 = 0$.

10. If R is the annulus $\alpha \leqslant |z| \leqslant \beta$, where $\alpha < \beta$, and $w = \text{Log } z$, find the image of R in the w plane.

11. Use the chain rule of partial differentiation to express the Cauchy–Riemann equations in their polar form

$$u_r = \frac{1}{r}v_\theta, \quad \frac{1}{r}u_\theta = -v_r \quad \text{for } r \neq 0.$$

12. If $f(z) = u(r,\theta) + iv(r,\theta)$ is analytic in a region R which does not include $r = 0$, show that $u(r,\theta)$ satisfies the equation

$$r^2 u_{rr} + r u_r + u_{\theta\theta} = 0$$

throughout R. [This is Laplace's equation in polar coordinates.]

13. Show that the function $u(r, \theta) = \log r$ is harmonic in the region $r > 0$ and $0 \leqslant \theta < 2\pi$ and find the conjugate function $v(r, \theta)$. Express $u + iv$ in the form $f(z)$.

14. Sketch the level curves of $\operatorname{Re} z^2$ and $\operatorname{Im} z^2$. Why are they not orthogonal at the origin?

15. Evaluate

$$\oint_C \frac{e^{3z}\, dz}{(z+2)^2},$$

where C is the circle $|z| = 3$.

16. Show that $e^{\cos\theta} \cos(n\theta - \sin\theta)$ is the real part of $f(z) = e^z z^{-n}$ where $z = e^{i\theta}$, and hence show that

$$\int_0^{2\pi} e^{\cos\theta} \cos(n\theta - \sin\theta)\, d\theta = \frac{2\pi}{n!}.$$

17. If $f(z)$ is analytic inside and on a closed contour C surrounding $z = a$, show, using the residue theorem, that

$$f(a) = \frac{1}{2\pi i} \oint_C \frac{f(z)}{z-a}\, dz$$

where the integral is taken counterclockwise. [This is Cauchy's integral formula.]

18. By application of the residue theorem to the integral of a suitable function of z round the circle $|z| = 1$, evaluate the integral

$$\int_0^{2\pi} \frac{1}{1+a^2 - 2a\cos\theta}\, d\theta$$

when (i) $|a| < 1$, and (ii) $|a| > 1$.

19. (a) Verify that the function $u(x,y) = \sinh x \sin y$ is harmonic, find its complex conjugate function $v(x,y)$ and express $u + iv$ as an analytic function of $z = x + iy$.
   (b) State the location and nature of each of the singularities of the function

$$f(z) = \frac{e^{imz}}{(z^2+1)^3}.$$

Find the first three terms of the Laurent expansion of $f(z)$ about the singularity in the upper half-plane and give the annulus of convergence of the series.

Show that

$$\lim_{R\to\infty}\left|\int_C f(z)\,dz\right|=0\ ,$$

where $f(z)$ is the above function and C is the semicircle $|z|=R,\,0\leqslant\arg z\leqslant\pi$. Hence evaluate the integral

$$\int_0^\infty \frac{\cos mx}{(x^2+1)^3}\,dx\ .$$

20. (a) Use the residue theorem to show that

$$\int_0^{2\pi}\frac{1}{5-4\sin\theta}\,d\theta=\frac{2}{3}\pi\ .$$

(b) By evaluating an integral around a suitable contour in the z plane, show that

$$\int_0^\infty\frac{\sin x}{x(x^2+a^2)}\,dx=\frac{\pi}{2a^2}\,(1-e^{-a}),\qquad(a>0)\ .$$

21. Evaluate

$$\oint_C|z|^2\,dz$$

around the square with vertices at $(0,0),(1,0),(1,1)$ and $(0,1)$. Why is this integral around a closed contour non-zero?

22. A square in the z plane with vertices at $1,2,1+i$ and $2+i$ is mapped into a region of the w plane by the transformation $w=f(z)$. Sketch the region and verify that the interior angles of the transformed region are right angles when

(a) $f(z)=2+i-2z$, (b) $f(z)=z^2$.

23. Explain the term *conformal mapping*.

Show that if $w=f(z)$ is analytic and $g(w)=\phi(u,v)+i\psi(u,v)$ is an analytic function of $w=u+iv$, then $G(z)=g\{f(z)\}=\Phi(x,y)+i\,\Psi(x,y)$ is an analytic function of $z=x+iy$. Verify that the function

$$w=f(z)=\frac{1+iz}{i+z}$$

maps the exterior of the circle $|z|=1$ into the upper half-plane $v>0$. Verify also that, when

$$g(w)=\frac{-i}{\pi}\,\mathrm{Log}\,w\ ,$$

$$\phi(u,0)=\begin{cases}0&(u>0),\\1&(u<0).\end{cases}$$

Use this function $g(w)$ to write down a function $G(z)$ which is analytic outside $|z| = 1$ and such that on $|z| = 1$

$$\Phi = \begin{cases} 0 & (x > 0), \\ 1 & (x < 0). \end{cases}$$

24. (a) Verify that the function $u(x,y) = e^{-2xy} \sin(x^2 - y^2)$ is harmonic, find its complex conjugate $v(x,y)$, and express $u + iv$ as an analytic function of $z = x + iy$.

(b) The function $z = \cosh w$ maps part of the w plane onto the z plane. Express x and y in terms of the real and imaginary parts u and v of w, and so find the curves $u = $ constant, $v = $ constant in the z plane. Verify that, at almost all points of the z plane, these two families of curves cut orthogonally.

Show that the region $u \geqslant 0, 0 \leqslant v \leqslant \pi$ is mapped onto the upper half-plane $y \geqslant 0$. Hence show that the harmonic function $v = \text{Im} \cosh^{-1}(x + iy)$ satisfies on $y = 0$ the boundary conditions $v = 0$ for $x \geqslant 1$, $v = \pi$ for $x \leqslant -1$, $\partial v / \partial y = 0$ for $-1 < x < 1$.

25. *A fluid flow problem:* In a two-dimensional steady flow the velocity components v_x and v_y of the fluid may be derived from a velocity potential function Φ, that is

$$v_x = \frac{\partial \Phi}{\partial x} \quad \text{and} \quad v_y = \frac{\partial \Phi}{\partial y}.$$

If the fluid is incompressible then Φ is harmonic and hence there exists a conjugate function Ψ, called the stream function. The analytic function $W(z) = \Phi + i\Psi$ is called the complex potential. The level curves $\Phi(x,y) = \phi$ and $\Psi(x,y) = \psi$ are called equipotential lines and stream lines respectively, the latter representing the actual paths of the fluid particles.

(a) If an incompressible fluid moves with steady uniform velocity V at angle α to the x axis, find W, Φ and Ψ and the equations of the stream lines and equipotential lines.

(b) An infinitesimally thin plate, parallel to the direction of flow of the fluid will not affect the flow pattern and therefore the complex potential of the flow is the same as if the plate were absent. The conformal mapping $w = \left(z + \dfrac{1}{z} \right)$ maps the circle $|z| = 1$ into the segment $-2 \leqslant u \leqslant 2$ of the line $v = 0$ where $w = u + iv$, and the exterior of the circle $|z| = 1$ into the exterior of the line segment. This mapping, known as the Joukowski transformation, is of importance in aerodynamics (see Milne-Thompson [3]). Use this mapping to obtain the complex potential of the flow past a cylinder in the z plane.

26. (a) The steady temperature field inside a half-plane is governed by Laplace's equation (see §7.6 of Volume 1). If $\Theta(x,y)$ is the temperature at a point (x,y) in the half-plane $x \geqslant 0$,

$$\alpha = \tan^{-1}\left(\frac{y+1}{x}\right) \quad \text{and} \quad \beta = \tan^{-1}\left(\frac{y-1}{x}\right),$$

show that $\Theta = A\alpha + B\beta + C$ is harmonic and find A, B and C such that $A\alpha + B\beta + C$

represents the temperature field inside the half-plane $x \geqslant 0$ with boundary conditions

$$\Theta = t_0 \quad \text{on} \quad x = 0 \quad \text{and} \quad y < -1 \,,$$

$$\Theta = t_1 \quad \text{on} \quad x = 0 \quad \text{and} \quad -1 \leqslant y \leqslant 1 \,,$$

$$\Theta = t_2 \quad \text{on} \quad x = 0 \quad \text{and} \quad y > 1 \,.$$

(b) Use conformal mapping techniques to find the steady-state temperature inside a semi-infinite slab of material occupying the region $-1 \leqslant y \leqslant 1$ and $x \geqslant 0$ with boundary conditions

$$\Theta = \lambda \quad \text{on} \quad y = -1 \quad \text{and} \quad x > 0 \,,$$

$$\Theta = 2\lambda \quad \text{on} \quad y = 1 \quad \text{and} \quad x > 0 \,,$$

$$\Theta = 0 \quad \text{on} \quad x = 0 \quad \text{and} \quad -1 < y < 1 \,.$$

[*Hint:* apply the mapping $w = \sinh(\tfrac{1}{2}\pi z)$ to the solution in part (a).]

BIBLIOGRAPHY

[1]   Lennox, S. C. and M. Chadwick, *Mathematics for Engineers and Applied Scientists*, Heinemann, London (1970).
[2]   Churchill, R. V., J. W. Brown and R. F. Verhey, *Complex Variables and Applications*, McGraw-Hill, New York (1974).
[3]   Milne-Thompson, L. M., *Theoretical Hydrodynamics*, Macmillan, London (1955).
[4]   Whittaker, E. T. and G. N. Watson, *Modern Analysis*, C.U.P., London (1950).
[5]   Spiegel, M. R., *Complex Variables*, Schaum, New York (1964).
[6]   Kober, H., *Dictionary of Conformal Representations*, Dover, New York (1952).
[7]   Carrier, G. F., M. Krook and C. E. Pearson, *Functions of a Complex Variable*, McGraw-Hill, New York (1966).

CHAPTER 5

Integral Transforms

5.1 INTRODUCTION

In Chapter 3 of Volume 1 it was shown that the application of the Laplace transform to linear ordinary differential equations with constant coefficients resulted in algebraic equations which could be easily solved for the transformed dependent variable. It is only one of a number of *integral transforms* which are used in the solution of differential equations. Each has the form

$$\bar{f}(s) = \int_a^b K(s,t)f(t)\,dt,$$

where $\bar{f}(s)$ is the transform of $f(t)$, $K(s,t)$ is the *transform kernel* and a and b are constants. Most often, the interval of integration is infinite or semi-infinite, with $a = -\infty$ or 0 and $b = \infty$.

The most frequently used transforms are in the list below, where the notations are those which are commonly, but not invariably, employed:

(a) *Laplace transform*

$$\bar{f}(s) = \mathscr{L}\{f(t)\} = \int_0^\infty e^{-st}f(t)\,dt .\tag{1}$$

(b) *Fourier transform*

$$F(\xi) = \mathscr{F}\{f(x)\} = \int_{-\infty}^\infty e^{-i\xi x}f(x)\,dx .\tag{2}$$

(c) *Fourier cosine transform*

$$F_c(\xi) = \mathscr{F}_c\{f(x)\} = \int_0^\infty \cos \xi x\, f(x)\,dx .\tag{3}$$

(d) *Fourier sine transform*

$$F_s(\xi) = \mathscr{F}_s\{f(x)\} = \int_0^\infty \sin \xi x\, f(x)\,dx .\tag{4}$$

(e) *Mellin transform*

$$\bar{f}(s) = \mathcal{M}\{f(x)\} = \int_0^\infty x^{s-1} f(x)\, dx \,. \tag{5}$$

(f) *Hankel transform*

$$\bar{f}_\nu(\xi) = \mathcal{H}_\nu\{f(\rho)\} = \int_0^\infty J_\nu(\xi\rho)\, f(\rho)\, d\rho \,, \tag{6}$$

where $J_\nu(\xi\rho)$ is the Bessel function of the first kind, of order ν (see §5.2(b) and §6.5). In most applications of Hankel transforms it is the transform of order zero or, less often, order one (that is, $\nu = 0$ or 1) which is required.

This chapter is concerned chiefly with properties of the Laplace transform additional to those given in Volume 1 and with the properties of the three Fourier transforms. The last section discusses the application of transforms to certain linear partial differential equations, where the usefulness of transforms depends upon the essential property of *linearity*. The discussion of the linearity of the Laplace transform in Volume 1 is equally valid for the other transforms and will not be recapitulated.

It is important to be able to *invert* a transform; that is, to calculate a function $f(t)$ where its transform $\bar{f}(s)$ is known. This can usually be done by means of tables of transform-pairs, sometimes augmented by various properties, as shown in Volume 1 for the Laplace transform. In addition, each transform has an inversion formula which is in the form of another integral transform. Each of the inversion formulae is derived from the following basic theorem.

FOURIER'S INTEGRAL THEOREM   If $\phi(x)$ is piecewise continuous and has a finite number of maxima and minima in $-\infty < x < \infty$, and if $\displaystyle\int_{-\infty}^\infty |\phi(x)|\, dx$ converges, then

$$\tfrac{1}{2}\{\phi(x+0) + \phi(x-0)\} = \frac{1}{\pi} \int_0^\infty \int_{-\infty}^\infty \cos u(x-v)\, \phi(v)\, dv\, du \,, \tag{7}$$

where $\phi(x+0)$ and $\phi(x-0)$ are the right-hand and left-hand limits, respectively, at the point x.

For use in this chapter, equation (7) must be expressed in the alternative form

$$\tfrac{1}{2}\{\phi(x+0) + \phi(x-0)\} = \frac{1}{2\pi} \int_{-\infty}^\infty \int_{-\infty}^\infty e^{iu(x-v)} \phi(v)\, dv\, du \,. \tag{8}$$

If $\phi(x)$ is continuous at x, the value of the integral is simply $\phi(x)$. Proofs of the theorem are to be found in more advanced books on transform theory [1], [2].

5.2 SOME USEFUL FUNCTIONS

We define here several non-elementary functions which are useful because they enable us to express concisely the transforms, or inverse transforms, of some functions which occur frequently. Detailed accounts of the functions, with tables and graphs, are given in the handbook by Abramowitz and Stegun [3], which also has a useful list of Laplace transform pairs.

(a) *The Gamma Function*

This function is defined by the integral

$$\Gamma(\nu) = \int_0^\infty e^{-u} u^{\nu-1} \, du, \tag{9}$$

which is convergent for $\nu > 0$. It has the following properties:

(i) $\Gamma(\nu + 1) = \nu\Gamma(\nu)$ (the *recurrence relation*),
(ii) $\Gamma(n + 1) = n!$ when $n = 1, 2, 3, \ldots$ and also when $n = 0$ if we define $0! = 1$,
(iii) $\Gamma(\tfrac{1}{2}) = \pi^{1/2}$,
(iv) $\Gamma(\nu)\Gamma(1 - \nu) = \pi \operatorname{cosec} \pi\nu$.

Property (i) is obtained by an integration by parts of integral (9) and is a means of extending the definition of $\Gamma(\nu)$ to all values of ν except $\nu = 0, -1, -2, -3, \ldots$ (at which values $\Gamma(\nu)$ becomes infinite). Property (ii) follows from repeated application of property (i) and the identity $\Gamma(1) = 1$, which is easily derived from equation (9). To obtain property (iii), put $\nu = \tfrac{1}{2}$ in equation (9) and let $u = q^2$, so that

$$\Gamma(\tfrac{1}{2}) = 2 \int_0^\infty \exp(-q^2) \, dq \, .$$

The identity then follows from the result of example 8 of §5.2 of Volume 1. The proof of property (iv) is more difficult and will not be given here.

EXAMPLE 1   Show that, for $\nu > -1$, the Laplace transform of t^ν is given by

$$\mathscr{L}\{t^\nu\} = \Gamma(\nu + 1)s^{-\nu-1} \, . \tag{10}$$

Put $t = u/s$ in the transform integral. Then

$$\mathscr{L}\{t^\nu\} = \int_0^\infty e^{-u} \left(\frac{u}{s}\right)^\nu \frac{du}{s} = \frac{1}{s^{\nu+1}} \int_0^\infty e^{-u} u^\nu \, du$$

$$= \Gamma(\nu + 1)s^{-\nu-1} \, .$$

Thus the gamma function provides a compact method of expressing the transform of a fractional power of t.

(b) *Bessel Functions and Modified Bessel Functions*

These functions are solutions of, respectively, equation (86) and equation (89) in §7.7 of Volume 1 (see also §6.5). The Bessel function of the first kind, of order n, $J_n(t)$, has the series representation

$$J_n(t) = (\tfrac{1}{2}t)^n \sum_{k=0}^{\infty} \frac{(-1)^k (\tfrac{1}{2}t)^{2k}}{k!(n+k)!} . \tag{11}$$

The modified Bessel function of the first kind, of order n, $I_n(t)$, has the expansion

$$I_n(t) = (\tfrac{1}{2}t)^n \sum_{k=0}^{\infty} \frac{(\tfrac{1}{2}t)^{2k}}{k!(n+k)!} . \tag{12}$$

Both the above series converge for all finite values of t.

EXAMPLE 2   Show that $\mathscr{L}\{J_0(t)\} = (s^2 + 1)^{-\frac{1}{2}}$.

Transform the series for $J_0(t)$ term by term and so obtain

$$\mathscr{L}\left\{ \sum_{k=0}^{\infty} \frac{(-1)^k (\tfrac{1}{2}t)^{2k}}{(k!)^2} \right\} = \sum_{k=0}^{\infty} \frac{(-1)^k (2k)!}{(k!)^2 \, 2^{2k} s^{2k+1}}$$

$$= \frac{1}{s}\left\{ 1 + \sum_{k=1}^{\infty} \frac{(-1)^k (\tfrac{1}{2})(\tfrac{3}{2}) \ldots (k - \tfrac{1}{2})}{k! \, s^{2k}} \right\}$$

$$= \frac{1}{s}\left(1 + \frac{1}{s^2} \right)^{-\frac{1}{2}} = (s^2 + 1)^{-\frac{1}{2}} .$$

(c) *The Error Function*

The error function erf x is defined by the equation

$$\operatorname{erf} x = 2\pi^{-\frac{1}{2}} \int_0^x e^{-u^2} \, du . \tag{13}$$

Notice that $\operatorname{erf} x \to \pi^{-\frac{1}{2}} \Gamma(\tfrac{1}{2}) = 1$ as $x \to \infty$. The *complementary error function* erfc x is given by

$$\operatorname{erfc} x = 1 - \operatorname{erf} x = 2\pi^{-\frac{1}{2}} \int_x^{\infty} e^{-u^2} \, du . \tag{14}$$

EXAMPLE 3   Show that $\mathscr{L}\{\exp(-\tfrac{1}{4}t^2)\} = \pi^{\frac{1}{2}} \exp(s^2)\operatorname{erfc} s$.

We have

$$\mathscr{L}\{\exp(-\tfrac{1}{4}t^2)\} = \int_0^{\infty} \exp\{-(st + \tfrac{1}{4}t^2)\}dt .$$

But $st + \frac{1}{4}t^2 = (s + \frac{1}{2}t)^2 - s^2$ and so, after substituting $u = s + \frac{1}{2}t$, we find that

$$\mathcal{L}\{\exp(-\tfrac{1}{4}t^2)\} = 2\exp(s^2)\int_s^\infty e^{-u^2}\,du = \pi^{1/2}\exp(s^2)\,\text{erfc }s.$$

(d) *The Exponential, Cosine and Sine Integrals*

These integrals are defined as follows:

Exponential integral

$$E_1(t) = \int_t^\infty u^{-1}e^{-u}\,du, \tag{15}$$

Cosine integral

$$\text{Ci}(t) = -\int_t^\infty u^{-1}\cos u\,du, \tag{16}$$

Sine integral

$$\text{Si}(t) = \int_0^t u^{-1}\sin u\,du. \tag{17}$$

The Laplace transforms of these functions are easily calculated with the aid of the results

$$\mathcal{L}\left\{\int_t^\infty u^{-1}f(u)\,du\right\} = s^{-1}\int_0^s \bar{f}(\sigma)\,d\sigma,$$

$$\mathcal{L}\left\{\int_0^t u^{-1}f(u)\,du\right\} = s^{-1}\int_s^\infty \bar{f}(\sigma)\,d\sigma, \tag{18}$$

where $\bar{f}(s) = \mathcal{L}\{f(t)\}$ (see problems 2 and 3 in Chapter 3 of Volume 1).

Exercises

1. Use properties (i) and (iii) of the gamma function to show that

$$\Gamma(n + \tfrac{1}{2}) = \pi^{1/2}2^{-2n}(2n)!/n! \quad \text{for integer } n.$$

2. Find the Laplace transforms of (a) $t^{-1/2}$, (b) $t^{3/2}$.

3. Use the convolution property of the Laplace transform (see §3.4 of Volume 1) to express the inverse transform of $s^{-\alpha}\bar{f}(s)$, for all $\alpha > 0$, in terms of $f(t)$.

4. Use term-by-term transformation of the series (12) to find the Laplace transform of $I_0(t)$.

5. Show by term-by-term integration that

$$\text{erf}(t^{1/2}) = \frac{2}{\pi^{1/2}}\sum_{n=0}^\infty \frac{(-1)^n t^{n+1/2}}{(2n+1)n!},$$

and hence find its Laplace transform.

6. Use equations (18) to prove that

$$\mathscr{L}\{E_1(t)\} = \frac{\log(1+s)}{s}, \quad \mathscr{L}\{\text{Ci}(t)\} = -\frac{\log(1+s^2)}{2s}, \quad \mathscr{L}\{\text{Si}(t)\} = \frac{\cot^{-1}s}{s}.$$

5.3 THE INVERSE LAPLACE TRANSFORM

As in Volume 1, we write the Laplace transform of a function $f(t)$ as

$$\mathscr{L}\{f(t)\} \equiv \int_0^\infty e^{-st}f(t)\,dt.$$

If the integral converges when Re s is large enough (see §3.1 of Volume 1 for a set of sufficient conditions), a function of s is defined by the equation $\bar{f}(s) = \mathscr{L}\{f(t)\}$ and the Laplace transform is said to exist. Conversely, if a given function $\bar{f}(s)$ is the transform of some function $f(t)$, we may write

$$f(t) = \mathscr{L}^{-1}\{\bar{f}(s)\}$$

and call $f(t)$ the *inverse transform* of $\bar{f}(s)$.

Uniqueness

If the class of inverse transforms is restricted to piecewise continuous functions and if the function $\bar{f}(s)$ has an inverse, $f(t)$, then that inverse is unique except at points of discontinuity. However, at any such point t_0, the right-hand and left-hand limits, $f(t_0 + 0)$ and $f(t_0 - 0)$, are unambiguously defined and it is these limits which are of practical importance in most contexts.

It is usually possible to invert a Laplace transform by the elementary methods given in Volume 1, in conjunction with a table of transform-pairs (Table A5 of the Appendix contains a brief list, but for a comprehensive table see Reference [4]). Sometimes a useful result is obtained by expanding $\bar{f}(s)$ in an infinite series which can then be inverted term by term, as shown later in this section. However, it may be necessary to resort to the inversion formula given in the theorem below. In order to use the formula, we have to consider $\bar{f}(s)$ as a function of a *complex* variable s and to identify the *singularities* of $\bar{f}(s)$ in the complex s plane. In fact, for the inverse transform to exist, there must exist a right half-plane, Re $s \geqslant c$, say, in which $\bar{f}(s)$ is analytic at every point. Consider, for example, the functions (a) $s(s^2 + 2s + 5)^{-1}$ which has simple poles at $s = -1 \pm 2i$ and (b) sinh $s^{1/2}$ cosech $\pi s^{1/2}$ which has simple poles at $s = -1, -4, -9, \ldots$. Both functions are analytic everywhere in a half-plane Re $s \geqslant -1 + \epsilon$ for any $\epsilon > 0$ and so have inverse transforms.

THEOREM 1   If $f(t)$ is piecewise continuous and if $\mathscr{L}\{f(t)\}$ converges for Re $s = c$, then

$$\frac{1}{2\pi i}\int_{c-i\infty}^{c+i\infty} e^{st}\bar{f}(s)\,ds = \begin{cases} 0 & \text{for} \quad t < 0, \\ f(t) & \text{for} \quad t > 0, \end{cases} \tag{19}$$

except at points at which $f(t)$ is not continuous, where the formula gives $\frac{1}{2}\{f(t+0)+f(t-0)\}$.

The definition of $\mathcal{L}\{f(t)\}$ ensures that it converges for all s such that $\mathrm{Re}\ s > c$ so long as it exists when $\mathrm{Re}\ s = c$. It is then possible to show that, considered as a function of the complex variable s, $\bar{f}(s)$ is *analytic* at all points of the half-plane $\mathrm{Re}\ s \geqslant c$. It follows that the contour of integration in equation (19) can be *any line* $\mathrm{Re}\ s = $ constant *which lies to the right of all singularities of $\bar{f}(s)$*.

The details of the proof of the theorem will not be given. It depends upon the use of the *integral theorem* of §5.1 with the function $\phi(v)$ in equation (8) chosen as

$$\phi(v) = \begin{cases} 0 & \text{for} \quad v < 0, \\ e^{-cv}f(v) & \text{for} \quad v > 0, \end{cases}$$

and the substitution $s = c + iu$. The variable x in equation (8) must be changed to t to make the identification complete.

Usually, the easiest way of evaluating the inversion integral (19) is by the contour integration methods of §4.5. When all the singularities of $\bar{f}(s)$ are isolated, the appropriate closed contour is that of the line $\mathrm{Re}\ s = c$ on which $-R \leqslant \mathrm{Im}\ s \leqslant R$, together with the semicircle Γ with centre $s = c$ and radius R, as shown in Fig. 5.1. The method depends on showing that the integral round Γ tends to zero as $R \to \infty$. This will be the case provided $\bar{f}(s)$ satisfies the conditions of the following lemma.

LEMMA   If $|\bar{f}(s)| < M(R)$ on Γ and if $M(R) \to 0$ as $R \to \infty$, then for $t > 0$

$$\lim_{R \to \infty} \int_{\Gamma} e^{st}\bar{f}(s)\ ds = 0.$$

Proof   Put $s = c + iz$. Γ is mapped into the semicircle Γ' (see Fig. 5.2) on which $z = Re^{i\phi}, 0 \leqslant \phi \leqslant \pi$, and the integral becomes

$$ie^{ct}\int_{\Gamma'} e^{izt}\bar{f}(c + iz)\ dz.$$

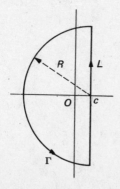

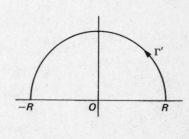

Fig. 5.1   Closed contour $C \equiv L + \Gamma$ in s plane.   **Fig. 5.2**   Contour Γ' in z plane.

This integral satisfies the conditions of Jordan's lemma (see §4.4) and hence tends to zero as $R \to \infty$. Note that this result holds even if, to ensure that $M(R) \to 0$, R must be constrained to take a specified set of values $R_N, N = 1, 2, 3, \ldots$, such that $R_{N+1} > R_N$.

We are now ready to prove the following result.

THEOREM 2   If $\bar{f}(s)$ is analytic everywhere except at a number of isolated singularities in Re $s < c$ and satisfies the conditions of the above lemma, then

$$\mathscr{L}^{-1}\{\bar{f}(s)\} = \text{Sum of the residues of } e^{st}\bar{f}(s) \text{ at all the singularities of } \bar{f}(s).$$

Proof   Let $C = L + \Gamma$, where L and Γ are the contours defined above and shown in Fig. 5.1. When the singularities are finite in number, they will all be enclosed by C if R is chosen sufficiently large. Then, by the residue theorem,

$$\frac{1}{2\pi i} \oint_C e^{st}\bar{f}(s) \, ds = \sum \{\text{Residues of } e^{st}\bar{f}(s) \text{ at singularities of } \bar{f}(s)\}.$$

As $R \to \infty$, the integral round Γ vanishes and the integral along L becomes the required integral. The result follows. When the singularities extend to infinity, as in example 2 below, the semicircle Γ is made to avoid the singularities by constraining R to pass through a specified set of values R_N such that $R_N \to \infty$ as $N \to \infty$. The sum of the residues then becomes an infinite series.

Theorem 2 does not apply if $\bar{f}(s)$ has any singularity which is *not* isolated. In particular, for multi-valued functions (which have branch points among their singularities), more complicated contours than that shown in Fig. 5.1 are necessary (see Doetsch [1] or Sneddon [2]).

EXAMPLE 1   Find $f(t)$ when

$$\bar{f}(s) = \frac{6s^2 + 10s + 2}{s(s+1)(s+2)}.$$

The only singularities of $\bar{f}(s)$ are simple poles at $s = 0, -1, -2$, where the residues of $e^{st}\bar{f}(s)$ are, respectively,

$$\lim_{s \to 0} se^{st}\bar{f}(s) = e^{st} \frac{6s^2 + 10s + 2}{(s+1)(s+2)}\bigg|_{s=0} = 1,$$

$$\lim_{s \to -1} (s+1)e^{st}\bar{f}(s) = e^{st} \frac{6s^2 + 10s + 2}{s(s+2)}\bigg|_{s=-1} = 2e^{-t},$$

$$\lim_{s \to -2} (s+2)e^{st}\bar{f}(s) = e^{st} \frac{6s^2 + 10s + 2}{s(s+1)}\bigg|_{s=-2} = 3e^{-2t}.$$

Then, by the above theorem,

$$f(t) = 1 + 2e^{-t} + 3e^{-2t}.$$

Note that this result may be found equally well by the partial fraction method (see §3.1 of Volume 1).

EXAMPLE 2   Find $\mathscr{L}^{-1}\{\bar{f}(s)\}$ where

$$\bar{f}(s) = \frac{\sinh(\pi s/a)}{s \sinh(\pi s/b)} , \quad \text{and} \quad 0 < b < a.$$

The only singularities of $\bar{f}(s)$ are simple poles at $s = inb$ $(n = 0, \pm 1, \pm 2, \ldots)$, where $\sinh \pi s/b$ is zero. (Note that $s = 0$ is not a *double* pole because $\sinh(\pi s/a)$ is also zero there.) The residue of $e^{st}\bar{f}(s)$ at $s = 0$ is

$$\sigma_0 = \lim_{s \to 0} s e^{st}\bar{f}(s) = \frac{b}{a}$$

and the other residues are given by

$$\sigma_n = \lim_{s \to inb} (s - inb) e^{st}\bar{f}(s), \qquad n = \pm 1, \pm 2, \ldots .$$

By l'Hôpital's rule,

$$\sigma_n = \lim_{s \to inb} \frac{e^{st} \sinh(\pi s/a) + (s - inb)e^{st}\{t \sinh(\pi s/a) + (\pi/a) \cosh(\pi s/a)\}}{\sinh(\pi s/b) + s(\pi/b) \cosh(\pi s/b)}$$

$$= \frac{e^{inbt} \sinh(in\pi b/a)}{in\pi \cosh in\pi} = \frac{e^{inbt} \sin(n\pi b/a)}{n\pi(-1)^n}$$

so that

$$\sigma_n + \sigma_{-n} = \frac{2(-1)^n}{n\pi} \sin(n\pi b/a) \cos nbt .$$

Let Γ_N be the semicircle on which $s = c + R_N e^{i\theta}$ $(\tfrac{1}{2}\pi < \theta < \tfrac{3}{2}\pi)$, where $R_N^2 = c^2 + (N + \tfrac{1}{2})^2 b^2$, and N is a positive integer, so that Γ_N passes through $s = \pm(N + \tfrac{1}{2}) bi$. Then, on Γ_N,

$$|\bar{f}(s)| \to R_N^{-1} \exp\{\pi R_N \mid \cos \theta \mid (a^{-1} - b^{-1})\} \quad \text{as } R_N \to \infty,$$

except at $s = \pm(N + \tfrac{1}{2}) bi$, where $\bar{f}(s) = R_N^{-1}(-1)^N \sin\{(N + \tfrac{1}{2})\pi b/a\}$. The conditions of the above lemma are then satisfied and, by Theorem 2,

$$\mathscr{L}^{-1}\left\{\frac{\sinh(\pi s/a)}{s \sinh(\pi s/b)}\right\} = \frac{b}{a} + \frac{2}{\pi} \sum_{n=1}^{\infty} (-1)^n n^{-1} \sin(n\pi b/a) \cos nbt, \quad 0 < b < a.$$

See example 3 for a different form of this inverse transform.

Inversion of Convergent Series

The following theorem gives the basic result which we require.

THEOREM 3   If $\bar{f}(s)$ can be represented by a series

$$\bar{f}(s) = \sum_{n=0}^{\infty} \bar{u}_n(s)$$

in which each of the transforms

$$\bar{u}_n(s) = \mathscr{L}\{u_n(t)\}$$

exists in a common half-plane Re $s \geqslant c$, and if each of the transforms

$$\bar{v}_n(s) \equiv \mathscr{L}\{|u_n(t)|\}$$

exists in the same half-plane, then the series

$$f(t) = \sum_{n=0}^{\infty} u_n(t)$$

converges and is the inverse of $\bar{f}(s)$.

We have already discussed in §3.6(a) of Volume 1 a particular type of expansion of $\bar{f}(s)$, of the form

$$\bar{f}(s) = \sum_{n=0}^{\infty} \bar{f}_n(s)\, e^{-nas} \tag{20}$$

which, under suitable conditions, has the inverse

$$f(t) = \sum_{n=0}^{\infty} f_n(t - na)\, H(t - na), \tag{21}$$

where $f_n(t) = \mathscr{L}^{-1}\{\bar{f}_n(s)\}$ and $H(t)$ is the Heaviside step function.

EXAMPLE 3   Find an inverse of the form (21) for the transform $\bar{f}(s)$ considered in example 2.

$$\bar{f}(s) = \frac{\sinh(\pi s/a)}{s \sinh(\pi s/b)}$$

$$= \frac{1}{s}\, \frac{e^{\pi s/a} - e^{-\pi s/a}}{e^{\pi s/b} - e^{-\pi s/b}} = \frac{e^{-\pi s/b}(e^{\pi s/a} - e^{-\pi s/a})}{s(1 - e^{-2\pi s/b})}$$

$$= s^{-1}\, e^{-\pi s/b}(e^{\pi s/a} - e^{-\pi s/a}) \sum_{n=0}^{\infty} e^{-2n\pi s/b}$$

$$= s^{-1} \sum_{n=0}^{\infty} \left[\exp\left\{ -\pi s\left(\frac{2n+1}{b} - \frac{1}{a} \right) \right\} - \exp\left\{ -\pi s\left(\frac{2n+1}{b} + \frac{1}{a} \right) \right\} \right],$$

since $0 < b < a$. The inverse transform is

$$f(t) = \sum_{n=0}^{\infty} \left[H\left\{ t - \pi\left(\frac{2n+1}{b} - \frac{1}{a} \right) \right\} - H\left\{ t - \pi\left(\frac{2n+1}{b} + \frac{1}{a} \right) \right\} \right] ,$$

which is a periodic function consisting of a square pulse commencing at $t = \pi(b^{-1} - a^{-1})$ and of duration $2\pi/a$, repeated with period $2\pi/b$.

Another type of series which is easily inverted is the expansion in negative powers of s. As the following example shows, integer powers are not essential.

EXAMPLE 4   Show that

$$f(t) \equiv \mathscr{L}^{-1}\{s^{-\frac{1}{2}}e^{-1/s}\} = (\pi t)^{-\frac{1}{2}} \cos(2t^{\frac{1}{2}}) .$$

For all real $s \neq 0, \bar{f}(s)$ has the expansion

$$\bar{f}(s) = s^{-\frac{1}{2}} \sum_{n=0}^{\infty} (-1)^n \frac{s^{-n}}{n!} = \sum_{n=0}^{\infty} (-1)^n \frac{s^{-(n+\frac{1}{2})}}{n!} ,$$

and hence $f(t) = \sum_{n=0}^{\infty} \frac{(-1)^n t^{n-\frac{1}{2}}}{n!\Gamma(n+\frac{1}{2})}$. But (see exercise 1 of §5.2) $n!\Gamma(n+\frac{1}{2}) = \pi^{\frac{1}{2}}2^{-2n}(2n)!$

and so

$$f(t) = (\pi t)^{-\frac{1}{2}} \sum_{n=0}^{\infty} \frac{(-1)^n (4t)^n}{(2n)!} = (\pi t)^{-\frac{1}{2}} \cos(2t^{\frac{1}{2}}) .$$

Exercises

1. By means of Theorem 2 calculate

(a) $\mathscr{L}^{-1}\left\{ \frac{s^3 + 16}{s^4 - 16} \right\} ,$ (b) $\mathscr{L}^{-1}\left\{ \frac{s}{(s^2 + \omega^2)^2} \right\} .$

2. The only singularities of the function

$$\bar{f}(s) = \frac{\sinh as^{\frac{1}{2}}}{\sinh bs^{\frac{1}{2}}}, \quad \text{where } 0 < a < b,$$

are simple poles at $s = s_n \equiv -n^2 \pi^2 b^{-2}, n = 1, 2, 3, \ldots$. Find the residue of $e^{st}\bar{f}(s)$ at s_n, and hence show that

$$\mathscr{L}^{-1}\{\bar{f}(s)\} = -2\pi b^{-2} \sum_{n=1}^{\infty} (-1)^n n \sin(n\pi a/b) \exp(-n^2 \pi^2 t/b^2) .$$

3. Expand the function

$$\bar{f}(s) = (s - a)^{\frac{1}{2}} - (s - b)^{\frac{1}{2}}$$

in negative powers of s by the binomial theorem and find a series representation of $\mathscr{L}^{-1}\{\bar{f}(s)\}$ by term-by-term inversion. Use the result of exercise 1 of §5.2 to simplify the terms of the series and hence express $\mathscr{L}^{-1}\{\bar{f}(s)\}$ in terms of exponential functions.

5.4 ASYMPTOTIC FORMULAE FOR THE INVERSE LAPLACE TRANSFORM

It is not unusual to find that the procedures outlined in §5.3 for evaluating inverse transforms can be carried through, but that the expression obtained for the inverse is difficult to handle. In some cases the methods may be completely unsuccessful. In both these situations it is often possible to obtain useful information about the limiting behaviour of the inverse transform $f(t)$ as $t \to 0$ or $t \to \infty$ by examining the limiting behaviour of $\bar{f}(s)$.

Two of the most useful asymptotic formulae are given, without proof, in the theorems below. A fairly comprehensive account of such results is given by Doetsch [1].

THEOREM 1   If $\bar{f}(s)$ is the Laplace transform of $f(t)$ and if

$$\bar{f}(s) \to As^{-\lambda} \quad \text{as } s \to +\infty,$$

where A is any non-zero constant and λ is a positive constant, then

$$f(t) \to \frac{At^{\lambda-1}}{\Gamma(\lambda)} \quad \text{as } t \to 0.$$

EXAMPLE 1   Find the limiting form of $f(t)$ as $t \to 0$ when $\bar{f}(s) = \log\{(s+b)/(s+a)\}$, for $0 < a < b$.

$$\bar{f}(s) = \log\frac{1+b/s}{1+a/s} = \left(\frac{b}{s} - \frac{1}{2}\frac{b^2}{s^2} + \dots\right) - \left(\frac{a}{s} - \frac{1}{2}\frac{a^2}{s^2} + \dots\right)$$

$$= \frac{b-a}{s} + O\left(\frac{1}{s^2}\right), \quad s > b,$$

where $O(s^{-\nu})$ indicates a quantity which is not greater than $Ks^{-\nu}$, for some constant K and sufficiently large s. Then, by Theorem 1,

$$f(t) \to b - a \quad \text{as } t \to 0.$$

Reference to Table A5 in the Appendix confirms this result.

EXAMPLE 2   Find the limiting form of $f(t)$ as $t \to 0$ when $\bar{f}(s) = 1/\{s^{1/2}(s-a^2)\}$.

Since $\bar{f}(s) \to s^{-3/2}$ as $s \to \infty$, then

$$f(t) \to \frac{t^{1/2}}{\Gamma(\frac{3}{2})} = \frac{t^{1/2}}{\frac{1}{2}\Gamma(\frac{1}{2})} = \frac{2t^{1/2}}{\pi^{1/2}} \quad \text{as } t \to 0,$$

where properties (i) and (iii) of the Γ-function (§5.2(a)) have been used. This result may be confirmed by examining the inverse transform, which is

$$f(t) = a^{-1} \exp(a^2 t) \operatorname{erf}(at^{1/2}),$$

where $\operatorname{erf} x$ is the error function, defined by equation (13), §5.2(c).

Asymptotic Expansions

Investigation of the behaviour of $f(t)$ as $t \to \infty$ is more difficult and requires some acquaintance with the idea of asymptotic expansions. A good introduction to asymptotic methods is given by Murray [5]. Consider the finite series

$$S_N(z) = \sum_{n=0}^{N-1} a_n z^{-\lambda_n}, \quad \text{where } \lambda_0 < \lambda_1 < \lambda_2 < \dots .$$

If, for *every* positive integer N,

$$F(z) - S_N(z) = O(z^{-\lambda_N}) \qquad \text{as } |z| \to \infty, \tag{22}$$

then we write

$$F(z) \sim \sum_{n=0}^{\infty} a_n z^{-\lambda_n} \qquad \text{as } |z| \to \infty \tag{23}$$

and say that the series (23) is an *asymptotic expansion* of $F(z)$ as $|z| \to \infty$. The following features should be noted:

(a) Equation (22) is essential to the definition of an asymptotic expansion and shows that, if the Nth partial sum, $S_N(z)$, is used as an approximation to $F(z)$ when $|z|$ is large, the error is of the order of the first term omitted.

(b) The region of validity of the expansion may be only a certain range of $\arg z$.

(c) Asymptotic expansions exist for limiting values of z other than infinity. A series in positive powers of $z - z_0$ might be an asymptotic expansion of a function $F(z)$ as $z \to z_0$.

(d) Even though every absolutely convergent series is an asymptotic expansion, some asymptotic expansions are *not* convergent anywhere. For practical purposes, a divergent asymptotic expansion may sometimes be more useful than a convergent series, since fewer terms of the divergent expansion may be sufficient to achieve a desired approximation. However, a divergent expansion is often derived simply because a convergent series cannot be found.

For many purposes, the first term of the expansion is sufficient. When we wish to find the limiting value of an inverse transform $f(t)$ as $t \to 0$, we can use Theorem 1 so long as $\bar{f}(s)$ has the specified behaviour, and the value is just the first term of an asymptotic expansion. The full result is given by Doetsch [6], Chapter 8.

The above definition of an asymptotic expansion of $F(z)$ may be extended by including the possibility that the quotient $F(z)/G(z)$ may have such an expansion, where $G(z)$ is a well-known function such as an exponential or a logarithm. In such a case we write

$$F(z) \sim G(z) \sum_{n=0}^{\infty} a_n z^{-\lambda_n} \quad \text{as } |z| \to \infty. \tag{24}$$

EXAMPLE 3   Find an asymptotic expansion for the exponential integral $E_1(t)$, defined by equation (15), as $t \to \infty$.

Integration by parts gives

$$E_1(t) = \int_t^{\infty} u^{-1} e^{-u} \, du$$

$$= [-u^{-1} e^{-u}]_t^{\infty} - \int_t^{\infty} u^{-2} e^{-u} \, du$$

$$= t^{-1} e^{-t} + [u^{-2} e^{-u}]_t^{\infty} + 2 \int_t^{\infty} u^{-3} e^{-u} \, du$$

$$= e^{-t}[t^{-1} - t^{-2} + 2! t^{-3} - 3! t^{-4} + \ldots + (-1)^{n+1}(n-1)! t^{-n}]$$

$$+ (-1)^n n! \int_t^{\infty} u^{-(n+1)} e^{-u} \, du.$$

The series is not convergent since, for any given t, the nth term tends to infinity as $n \to \infty$. However, the 'remainder' term is

$$E_1(t) - S_N(t) = (-1)^N N! \int_t^{\infty} u^{-(N+1)} e^{-u} \, du$$

and since its modulus satisfies

$$|E_1(t) - S_N(t)| < N! t^{-N-1} \int_t^{\infty} e^{-u} \, du = N! t^{-N-1} e^{-t} = 0(t^{-N-1} e^{-t})$$

the error is of the order of the first term omitted. Consequently, by the definition above, the required asymptotic expansion is

$$E_1(t) \sim e^{-t} \sum_{n=0}^{\infty} (-1)^n n! t^{-(n+1)} \quad \text{as } t \to \infty.$$

Note the essential characteristic that for finite N and sufficiently large t, $S_N(t)$ is a good approximation to $E_1(t)$ and improves as t increases.

The behaviour of an inverse transform $f(t)$ as $t \to \infty$ is often very important, particularly in the study of stability. It transpires that an asymptotic formula for large t depends critically upon the position of the singularity of $\bar{f}(s)$ having the largest real part. The following theorem is applicable when this *dominant singularity*, $s = \alpha$, is either an isolated singularity or a non-logarithmic branch point.

THEOREM 2   If $\bar{f}(s)$ is analytic everywhere in Re $s \geqslant$ Re α except at $s = \alpha$ and if

(1) $\bar{f}(s) \to 0$ as Im $s \to \pm \infty$

in some strip Re $\alpha - \epsilon_1 \leqslant$ Re $s \leqslant$ Re $\alpha + \epsilon_2$, when $\epsilon_1 > 0$, $\epsilon_2 > 0$,

(2) $\bar{f}(s) \sim \sum\limits_{n=0}^{\infty} c_n (s - \alpha)^{\lambda_n}$,   where $\lambda_0 < \lambda_1 < \lambda_2 < \dots$,   (25)

as $s \to \alpha$ in the sector $|\arg(s - \alpha)| \leqslant \frac{1}{2}\pi + \delta$, for some $\delta > 0$, then

$$f(t) \sim e^{\alpha t} \sum_{n=0}^{\infty} \frac{c_n}{\Gamma(-\lambda_n)} t^{-\lambda_n - 1} \quad \text{as } t \to +\infty. \tag{26}$$

If in any term of equation (26) λ_n has one of the values $0, 1, 2, 3, \dots$, then $\Gamma(-\lambda_n)$ becomes infinite and the corresponding term may be omitted. For other positive values of λ_n it is often convenient to use property (iv) of the Γ-function (see §5.2(a)) and to put

$$\{\Gamma(-\lambda_n)\}^{-1} = -\pi^{-1} \sin \pi \lambda_n \, \Gamma(1 + \lambda_n). \tag{27}$$

EXAMPLE 4   Find the asymptotic expansion of $f(t)$ as $t \to \infty$ when $\bar{f}(s) = \exp(-as^{\frac{1}{2}})$.

Since $\bar{f}(s)$ has a branch point at $s = 0$ and is analytic elsewhere, the required expansion is in (non-integer) powers of s and is obtained from the exponential series as

$$\bar{f}(s) = \sum_{n=0}^{\infty} \frac{(-a)^n s^{n/2}}{n!}, \quad |s| < \infty.$$

Then, by Theorem 2,

$$f(t) \sim \sum_{n=0}^{\infty} \frac{(-a)^n}{n!} \frac{t^{-1 - n/2}}{\Gamma(-\frac{1}{2}n)} \quad \text{as } t \to \infty.$$

However, since $\Gamma(-\frac{1}{2}n)$ becomes infinite for $n = 0, 2, 4, \dots$, the expansion reduces to

$$f(t) \sim - \sum_{n=0}^{\infty} \frac{a^{2n+1} t^{-n - 3/2}}{(2n + 1)! \, \Gamma(-n - \frac{1}{2})} \quad \text{as } t \to \infty,$$

which, by equation (27), can be written

$$f(t) \sim \frac{a}{\pi} \sum_{n=0}^{\infty} \frac{a^{2n}(-1)^n \Gamma(n + \frac{3}{2})}{(2n + 1)! \, t^{n + 3/2}} \quad \text{as } t \to \infty.$$

Use of the result of exercise 1 of §5.2 allows this expression to be simplified to

$$f(t) \sim \frac{a}{2\pi^{\frac{1}{2}} t^{\frac{3}{2}}} \sum_{n=0}^{\infty} \frac{(-1)^n a^{2n}}{n! 2^{2n} t^n} \qquad \text{as } t \to \infty .$$

This example is unusual in that the expansion for $f(t)$ is convergent for all $t > 0$. The series is easily expressed as an exponential function and the result is

$$f(t) \sim \frac{a}{2\pi^{\frac{1}{2}} t^{\frac{3}{2}}} \exp\left(-\frac{a^2}{4t}\right), \qquad \text{as } t \to \infty . \tag{28}$$

Reference to Table A5 in the Appendix shows that the asymptotic formula (28) is actually the inverse transform, valid for all $t > 0$.

If $s = \alpha$ is an isolated singularity of $\bar{f}(s)$, the expansion (25) is simply the Laurent series about $s = \alpha$, and the expansion (26) is the residue of $e^{st}\bar{f}(s)$ at $s = \alpha$. In such cases we obtain from Theorem 2 the precise contribution to $f(t)$ which would be obtained from that singularity by means of the contour integration methods of §5.3.

Whatever the nature of the dominant singularity $s = \alpha$, the behaviour of $f(t)$ as $t \to \infty$ will be controlled by the exponential factor $e^{\alpha t}$, unless $\mathrm{Re}\ \alpha = 0$. As $t \to \infty$, $|f(t)|$ increases or decreases exponentially according as $\mathrm{Re}\ \alpha$ is positive or negative. If $\mathrm{Re}\ \alpha = 0$, the expansion is dominated by the first term, which tends to infinity or zero according as $\lambda_0 + 1$ is negative or positive. If $\mathrm{Im}\ \alpha \neq 0$, the growth or decay of $f(t)$ occurs in an oscillatory fashion.

Two Dominant Singularities

Suppose $\bar{f}(s)$ is analytic in $\mathrm{Re}\ s \geqslant \sigma$, except at $s = \sigma + i\tau_1$ and $s = \sigma + i\tau_2$, and that an expansion of the form (25) can be found about each of the two singularities. Then the corresponding expansions of the form (26) can be superposed to obtain an asymptotic expansion of $f(t)$ as $t \to \infty$.

EXAMPLE 5   Find the first term of an asymptotic expansion for $J_0(at)$ as $t \to +\infty$, given that $\mathscr{L}\{J_0(at)\} = (s^2 + a^2)^{-\frac{1}{2}}$.

There are branch points of the function

$$\bar{f}(s) = (s^2 + a^2)^{-\frac{1}{2}} = (s + ia)^{-\frac{1}{2}}(s - ia)^{-\frac{1}{2}}$$

at $s = \pm ia$, both with zero real part. For an expansion about $s = ia$, write

$$\bar{f}(s) = (2ia)^{-\frac{1}{2}} \left(1 + \frac{s - ia}{2ia}\right)^{-\frac{1}{2}} (s - ia)^{-\frac{1}{2}}$$

$$\sim (2a)^{-\frac{1}{2}} e^{-i\pi/4} (s - ia)^{-\frac{1}{2}} \qquad \text{as } s \to ia .$$

For an expansion about $s = -ia$, write

$$\bar{f}(s) = (-2ia)^{-\frac{1}{2}} \left(1 - \frac{s + ia}{2ia}\right)^{-\frac{1}{2}} (s + ia)^{-\frac{1}{2}}$$

$$\sim (2a)^{-\frac{1}{2}} e^{i\pi/4} (s + ia)^{-\frac{1}{2}} \qquad \text{as } s \to -ia .$$

These two asymptotic formulae are the first terms of two expansions of the form (25) and the corresponding first terms in expansions of the form (26) are

$$e^{iat}(2a)^{-\frac{1}{2}}e^{-i\pi/4}\frac{t^{-\frac{1}{2}}}{\Gamma(\frac{1}{2})} = \frac{\exp\{i(at - \frac{1}{4}\pi)\}}{(2\pi at)^{\frac{1}{2}}},$$

$$e^{-iat}(2a)^{-\frac{1}{2}}e^{i\pi/4}\frac{t^{-\frac{1}{2}}}{\Gamma(\frac{1}{2})} = \frac{\exp\{-i(at - \frac{1}{4}\pi)\}}{(2\pi at)^{\frac{1}{2}}}.$$

Addition of these two expressions gives the result

$$J_0(at) \sim \left(\frac{2}{\pi at}\right)^{\frac{1}{2}} \cos(at - \tfrac{1}{4}\pi) \quad \text{as } t \to \infty.$$

This result shows that for large values of at the Bessel function $J_0(at)$ oscillates with period $2\pi/a$, but with amplitude decaying like $t^{-\frac{1}{2}}$.

Exercises

1. Deduce from Theorem 1 that if $\bar{f}(s) = \mathscr{L}\{f(t)\}$ and $\lim\limits_{s \to +\infty} s\bar{f}(s)$ exists, then

$$\lim_{t \to 0} f(t) = \lim_{s \to +\infty} s\bar{f}(s).$$

(This is sometimes called the *initial-value theorem*.)

2. Find an asymptotic expansion for $\mathscr{L}^{-1}\{s^{-1}[1 - \exp\{-(as)^{\frac{1}{2}}\}]\}$ as $t \to +\infty$.

3. If $\bar{f}(s) = s^{-1}\tanh(s^{\frac{1}{2}})$, show that

(a) $f(t) \to 1 \quad$ as $t \to 0$.

(b) $f(t) \sim (\pi t)^{-\frac{1}{2}} \left(1 + \dfrac{1}{6t} + \dfrac{1}{10t^2} + \dots\right) \quad$ as $t \to +\infty$.

4. If

$$\bar{f}(s) = \frac{(s + a)^{\frac{1}{2}} - (s - a)^{\frac{1}{2}}}{(s + a)^{\frac{1}{2}} + (s - a)^{\frac{1}{2}}}$$

find $\lim\limits_{t \to 0} f(t)$ and the first three terms of an asymptotic expansion for $f(t)$ as $t \to +\infty$.

5.5 FOURIER TRANSFORMS

Let x be a point at which $f(x)$ is continuous, and let

$$F(\xi) \equiv \int_{-\infty}^{\infty} e^{-i\xi x} f(x)\, dx, \tag{29}$$

where ξ is a real parameter, then, by equation (8),

$$f(x) = (2\pi)^{-1} \int_{-\infty}^{\infty} e^{ix\xi} F(\xi)\, d\xi. \tag{30}$$

The function $F(\xi)$ is the *Fourier transform* of $f(x)$, while $f(x)$ is the *inverse* Fourier transform of $F(\xi)$. The pair of functions $f(x)$, $F(\xi)$ form a Fourier transform *pair* whose relationship may be expressed symbolically by

$$\mathscr{F}\{f(x)\} = F(\xi), \qquad \mathscr{F}^{-1}\{F(\xi)\} = f(x).$$

Sometimes the transform and inverse are defined with the factor $(2\pi)^{-1}$ in equation (30) 'shared' between them so that each has a factor $(2\pi)^{-\frac{1}{2}}$, thus increasing their symmetry. Another variation in definition is to have a *positive* exponent in the transform and negative in the inverse.

EXAMPLE 1   Find the Fourier transform of x^{-1}.

Since $e^{-i\xi x} = \cos \xi x - i \sin \xi x$ where $\cos \xi x$ is even and $\sin \xi x$ odd, the transform can be written

$$\mathscr{F}_i\{x^{-1}\} \equiv \int_{-\infty}^{\infty} e^{-i\xi x} x^{-1} \, dx = -2i \int_0^{\infty} \sin \xi x \, x^{-1} \, dx.$$

Put $u = \xi x$. Then

$$\mathscr{F}\{x^{-1}\} = -2i \int_0^{\infty} \frac{\sin u}{u} \, du \, \text{sgn} \, \xi,$$

where sgn ξ is the function defined by

$$\text{sgn} \, \xi = \begin{cases} -1 & \text{for} \quad \xi < 0, \\ 1 & \text{for} \quad \xi > 0. \end{cases}$$

The integral may be evaluated as the limit, as $a \to 0$, of the integral in example 9 of §4.5 and it is found that

$$\mathscr{F}\{x^{-1}\} = -i\pi \, \text{sgn} \, \xi.$$

Notice that the inverse transform of sgn ξ cannot be calculated by the formula (30) since the integral is not convergent.

Existence

A *sufficient condition* for the existence of the Fourier transform of a function $f(x)$ is that the integral $\displaystyle\int_{-\infty}^{\infty} |f(x)| \, dx$ should converge. It is not a *necessary* condition, as shown by example 1, where the transform exists although $\displaystyle\int_{-\infty}^{\infty} |x^{-1}| \, dx$ does not converge. However, $f(x)$ does not have a Fourier transform unless $f(x) \to 0$ as $|x| \to \infty$, and it is worth noting that this requirement is much more stringent than the corresponding condition for a *Laplace* transform which requires merely exponential order at ∞ (see §3.1 of Volume 1).

EXAMPLE 2   Find the Fourier transform of $e^{-a|x|}$, where $a > 0$.

$$\mathscr{F}\{e^{-a|x|}\} = \int_{-\infty}^{\infty} e^{-i\xi x}\, e^{-a|x|}\, dx$$

$$= \int_{-\infty}^{\infty} \{\cos \xi x - i \sin \xi x\} e^{-a|x|}\, dx$$

$$= 2 \int_{0}^{\infty} \cos \xi x\, e^{-ax}\, dx$$

since $\cos \xi x$ and $\sin \xi x$ are even and odd, respectively. Hence

$$\mathscr{F}\{e^{-a|x|}\} = 2\,\mathrm{Re} \int_{0}^{\infty} e^{i\xi x}\, e^{-ax}\, dx$$

$$= 2\,\mathrm{Re} \left[\frac{e^{x(i\xi - a)}}{i\xi - a} \right]_{0}^{\infty} = \mathrm{Re}\,(a - i\xi)^{-1}$$

$$= \frac{2a}{\xi^2 + a^2}.$$

Note that $\mathscr{F}\{e^{-ax}\}$ does *not* exist since the integral does not converge as $x \to -\infty$.

Since the integrals in equations (29) and (30) differ only in the sign of the exponent and the interchange of ξ and x, most Fourier transform pairs have a 'companion pair' such that, if the original pair is given by

$$\mathscr{F}\{\phi_1(x)\} = \phi_2(\xi),$$

then its companion pair is given by   (31)

$$\mathscr{F}\{\phi_2(-x)\} = 2\pi\phi_1(\xi).$$

Thus the transform pair obtained in example 2 leads to the companion pair

$$\mathscr{F}\left\{ \frac{2a}{x^2 + a^2} \right\} = 2\pi\, e^{-a|\xi|}$$

or

$$\mathscr{F}\{(x^2 + a^2)^{-1}\} = \pi a^{-1} e^{-a|\xi|}.$$

Fourier Transforms of Derivatives

The following formulae are obtained by integration by parts in the same way as the corresponding results for the Laplace transform in §3.2 of Volume 1. If $\mathscr{F}\{f(x)\}$ exists and if $f(x)$ is continuous, then

$$\mathscr{F}\{f'(x)\} = i\xi\, F(\xi).$$

The general result, for the nth derivative, is that, if $\mathscr{F}\{f(x)\}$ exists and if $f(x)$ and its first $n-1$ derivatives are continuous, then

$$\mathscr{F}\{f^{(n)}(x)\} = (i\xi)^n F(\xi). \tag{32}$$

These results are equally applicable to a function $f(x, y, \ldots)$ of two or more variables. Thus if

$$F(\xi, y, \ldots) = \mathscr{F}\{f(x, y, \ldots)\} \equiv \int_{-\infty}^{\infty} e^{-i\xi x} f(x, y, \ldots)\, dx,$$

then

$$\mathscr{F}\{\partial^n f/\partial x^n\} = (i\xi)^n F(\xi, y, \ldots).$$

Shift Properties

The following results are analogous to the shift properties of the Laplace transform and are easily proved:

$$\mathscr{F}\{e^{iax} f(x)\} = F(\xi - a), \tag{33}$$

$$\mathscr{F}\{f(x - a)\} = e^{-ia\xi} F(\xi). \tag{34}$$

Notice that no step function is required in equation (34).

EXAMPLE 3   Apply the shift properties to $f(x) \equiv e^{-b|x|}$.

Equations (33) and (34) used with the result of example 2 give

$$\mathscr{F}\{e^{iax} e^{-b|x|}\} = 2b\{(\xi - a)^2 + b^2\}^{-1},$$

$$\mathscr{F}\{e^{-b|x-a|}\} = 2b e^{-ia\xi}(\xi^2 + b^2)^{-1}.$$

The Convolution Property

For use with the Fourier transform, the *convolution* $f(x) * g(x)$ of $f(x)$ and $g(x)$ is defined by the *doubly infinite* integral

$$f(x) * g(x) = \int_{-\infty}^{\infty} f(x - u)\, g(u)\, du. \tag{35}$$

By an obvious change of variable it is easy to show that

$$f(x) * g(x) = \int_{-\infty}^{\infty} g(x - u)\, f(u)\, du = g(x) * f(x).$$

This definition of a convolution should not be confused with that used with Laplace transforms. The Fourier transform of $f(x) * g(x)$ is

$$\mathscr{F}\{f(x) * g(x)\} = F(\xi) G(\xi), \tag{36}$$

where $F(\xi) = \mathscr{F}\{f(x)\}$, $G(\xi) = \mathscr{F}\{g(x)\}$. The inverse form of equation (36) is

$$\mathscr{F}^{-1}\{F(\xi)G(\xi)\} = f(x) * g(x) . \tag{37}$$

The proof follows the same lines as that for the corresponding result for the Laplace transform (see Volume 1).

In the same way we can prove parallel results for the convolution of $F(\xi)$ and $G(\xi)$:

$$\mathscr{F}^{-1}\{F(\xi) * G(\xi)\} = 2\pi f(x)g(x) , \tag{38}$$

$$\mathscr{F}\{f(x)g(x)\} = (2\pi)^{-1}F(\xi) * G(\xi) . \tag{39}$$

EXAMPLE 4 Find the Fourier transform of $x^{-1}e^{-a|x|}$.

Use the results of examples 1 and 2 in equation (39):

$$\mathscr{F}\{x^{-1}e^{-a|x|}\} = (2\pi)^{-1}[-\pi i \operatorname{sgn} \xi] * \left[\frac{2a}{\xi^2 + a^2}\right]$$

$$= -ia \int_{-\infty}^{\infty} \operatorname{sgn}(\xi - u)(u^2 + a^2)^{-1} \, du$$

$$= -ia \left\{\int_{-\infty}^{\xi} (u^2 + a^2)^{-1} \, du - \int_{\xi}^{\infty} (u^2 + a^2)^{-1} \, du\right\} .$$

These integrals may be evaluated to give

$$\mathscr{F}\{x^{-1}e^{-a|x|}\} = -2i \tan^{-1}(\xi/a) .$$

Cosine and Sine Transforms

Since the Fourier transform is an integral over $-\infty < x < \infty$, it is not appropriate for use with a function $f(x)$ having a region of interest wholly in $x \geqslant 0$. A similar problem occurs when we wish to find a Fourier *series* representation of a function $f(x)$ defined over a half-period only (see §2.4 of Volume 1). In both cases the difficulty is overcome by proceeding as if the behaviour in the other half-range is either a symmetric or an anti-symmetric reflection of the behaviour in the half-range of definition.

The Cosine Transform

If $f(x)$ is defined in $0 \leqslant x < \infty$, and if

$$\int_0^\infty |f(x)| \, dx < \infty,$$

then the *Fourier cosine transform* $\mathscr{F}_c\{f(x)\}$ exists and is given by

$$\mathscr{F}_c\{f(x)\} \equiv F_c(\xi) = \int_0^\infty \cos \xi x \, f(x) \, dx . \tag{40}$$

The *inverse* cosine transform is given by

$$\mathscr{F}_c^{-1}\{F_c(\xi)\} \equiv f(x) = \frac{2}{\pi}\int_0^\infty \cos x\xi\, F_c(\xi)\, \mathrm{d}\xi.\tag{41}$$

Note that the transform and its inverse are symmetric, apart from the factor $2/\pi$. The transform is sometimes defined completely symmetrically, with the transform and its inverse each having a factor $(2/\pi)^{\frac{1}{2}}$.

If $f_1(x)$ is an *even* function which coincides with $f(x)$ in $0<x<\infty$, its Fourier transform is given by

$$\mathscr{F}\{f_1(x)\} = \int_{-\infty}^\infty e^{-\mathrm{i}\xi x} f_1(x)\, \mathrm{d}x = 2\int_0^\infty \cos \xi x\, f(x)\, \mathrm{d}x,$$

so that

$$\mathscr{F}\{f_1(x)\} = 2F_c(\xi).\tag{42}$$

Since $\cos \xi x$ is an even function of ξ, so is $F_c(\xi)$ and it follows from the inversion formula (41) that

$$\mathscr{F}_c^{-1}\{F_c(\xi)\} = \frac{1}{\pi}\int_{-\infty}^\infty e^{\mathrm{i}x\xi} F_c(\xi)\, \mathrm{d}\xi = 2\mathscr{F}^{-1}\{F_c(\xi)\}.\tag{43}$$

Relation (42), between a Fourier transform and a cosine transform, and relation (43), between the two inverse transforms, are often of practical use.

The Sine Transform

If $f(x)$ is defined in $0<x<\infty$ and if

$$\int_0^\infty |f(x)|\, \mathrm{d}x < \infty,$$

then the *Fourier sine transform* $\mathscr{F}_s\{f(x)\}$ exists and is given by

$$\mathscr{F}_s\{f(x)\} \equiv F_s(\xi) = \int_0^\infty \sin \xi x\, f(x)\, \mathrm{d}x.\tag{44}$$

The *inverse* sine transform is given by

$$\mathscr{F}_s^{-1}\{F_s(\xi)\} \equiv f(x) = \frac{2}{\pi}\int_0^\infty \sin x\xi\, F_s(\xi)\, \mathrm{d}\xi.\tag{45}$$

There is an alternative, symmetric definition such that both the transform and its inverse have a factor $(2/\pi)^{\frac{1}{2}}$.

If $f_2(x)$ is an *odd* function which coincides with $f(x)$ in $0<x<\infty$, its Fourier transform is given by

$$\mathscr{F}\{f_2(x)\} = \int_{-\infty}^\infty e^{-\mathrm{i}\xi x} f_2(x)\, \mathrm{d}x = -2\mathrm{i}\int_0^\infty \sin \xi x\, f(x)\, \mathrm{d}x,$$

so that

$$\mathcal{F}\{f_2(x)\} = -2i\,F_s(\xi). \tag{46}$$

Since $\sin \xi x$ is an odd function, so is $F_s(\xi)$ and the inversion formula (45) gives

$$\mathcal{F}_s^{-1}\{F_s(\xi)\} = \frac{1}{\pi i}\int_{-\infty}^{\infty} e^{ix\xi}F_s(\xi)\,d\xi = -2i\,\mathcal{F}^{-1}\{F_s(\xi)\}. \tag{47}$$

Relations (46) and (47) are often useful.

Care is required in using equation (43) or equation (47) to express a cosine or sine transform as a Fourier transform, because a transform $F_c(\xi)$ does not always appear to be an even function. Similarly a transform $F_s(\xi)$ does not always appear to be an odd function. In such cases, the proper definition for negative values of ξ must be chosen.

EXAMPLE 5   Find the cosine and sine transforms of e^{-ax}.

$$\mathcal{F}_c\{e^{-ax}\} = \int_0^{\infty} \cos \xi x\; e^{-ax}\,dx$$

and use of equation (42) and reference to example 2 shows that

$$\mathcal{F}_c\{e^{-ax}\} = \tfrac{1}{2}\,\mathcal{F}\{e^{-a|x|}\} = \frac{a}{\xi^2 + a^2}.$$

Also $\mathcal{F}_s\{e^{-ax}\} = \displaystyle\int_0^{\infty} \sin \xi x\; e^{-ax}\,dx = \operatorname{Im}\int_0^{\infty} e^{i\xi x}\, e^{-ax}\,dx$. By referring again to example 2, we see that

$$\mathcal{F}_s\{e^{-ax}\} = \operatorname{Im}(a - i\xi)^{-1} = \frac{\xi}{\xi^2 + a^2}.$$

Cosine and Sine Transforms of Derivatives

Integration by parts gives

$$\mathcal{F}_c\{f'(x)\} = [\cos \xi x\, f(x)]_0^{\infty} + \xi \int_0^{\infty} \sin \xi x\, f(x)\,dx$$

$$= -f(0) + \xi\, F_s(\xi), \tag{48}$$

in which the *sine* transform of $f(x)$ now appears. Similarly,

$$\mathcal{F}_s\{f'(x)\} = -\xi\, F_c(\xi), \tag{49}$$

which involves the *cosine* transform. Evidently, problems involving a function and its *first* derivative are not readily amenable to treatment by means of either the cosine or the sine transform. However, the second derivative has transforms

$$\mathcal{F}_c\{f''(x)\} = [\cos \xi x\, f'(x)]_0^\infty + \xi \int_0^\infty \sin \xi x\, f'(x)\, dx$$

$$= -f'(0) - \xi^2 F_c(\xi), \tag{50}$$

where equation (49) has been used, and

$$\mathcal{F}_s\{f''(x)\} = [\sin \xi x\, f'(x)]_0^\infty - \xi \int_0^\infty \cos \xi x\, f'(x)\, dx$$

$$= \xi f(0) - \xi^2 F_s(\xi), \tag{51}$$

which requires use of equation (48).

In general, transforms of derivatives of even orders remain in terms of the original transform, whereas the formulae for the transforms of *odd* orders involve both cosine and sine transforms. The formulae for the fourth derivatives are

$$\mathcal{F}_c\{f^{(4)}(x)\} = \xi^4 F_c(\xi) + \xi^2 f'(0) - f'''(0),$$
$$\mathcal{F}_s\{f^{(4)}(x)\} = \xi^4 F_s(\xi) - \xi^3 f(0) + \xi f''(0). \tag{52}$$

The results given in equations (48) to (52) hold equally well for transforms of *partial* derivatives with respect to x.

A decision on the type of transform appropriate to some problem for which $0 \leqslant x < \infty$ must take account of the behaviour shown in the derivative formulae (48) to (52). Examples of the uses of each are given in §5.6.

There are no simple shift and convolution formulae for the cosine and sine transforms corresponding to those for the Fourier and Laplace transforms. However, it is sometimes advantageous to express a result in terms of Fourier transforms by means of relation (42) or relation (46) in order to use the convolution property of the Fourier transform.

Short tables of Fourier, cosine and sine transforms are in the Appendix. Extensive lists are to be found in specialist books such as [4].

Relation to Fourier Series

In §2.2 of Volume 1 it was shown that the Fourier series representation of a periodic function $f(x)$ takes the form

$$f(x) = \tfrac{1}{2}a_0 + \sum_{n=1}^\infty \left\{ a_n \cos \frac{n\pi x}{L} + b_n \sin \frac{n\pi x}{L} \right\},$$

where $2L$ is the period and the coefficients a_n, b_n are given by equations (12) in §2.2 of Volume 1. In many applications, such as frequency analysis of signals, we are concerned with a time-function $f(t)$ with period T which is related to the *fundamental frequency* $\omega_0/2\pi$ (measured in Hz if t is in seconds) by $T = 2\pi/\omega_0$. The Fourier series for $f(t)$ then takes the form

$$f(t) = \tfrac{1}{2}a_0 + \sum_{n=1}^{\infty} \{a_n \cos n\omega_0 t + b_n \sin n\omega_0 t\},$$

or, by use of the exponential forms of $\cos n\omega_0 t$ and $\sin n\omega_0 t$ (see §4.2),

$$f(t) = \sum_{n=-\infty}^{\infty} c_n e^{in\omega_0 t}, \tag{53}$$

where, if $f(t)$ is real, $c_0 = \tfrac{1}{2}a_0$ and

$$c_n = \begin{cases} \tfrac{1}{2}(a_n - ib_n), & n > 0, \\ \tfrac{1}{2}(a_n + ib_n), & n < 0. \end{cases} \tag{54}$$

From equations (12) in §2.2 of Volume 1 we find that

$$c_n = \frac{1}{T} \int_{-\frac{1}{2}T}^{\frac{1}{2}T} e^{-in\omega_0 t} f(t)\, \mathrm{d}t. \tag{55}$$

In general, the coefficients, $c_1, c_2, c_3, \ldots$ are complex but, by means of equation (54), they give the cosine and sine components of the *frequency spectrum* at the *angular frequencies* $\omega_0, 2\omega_0, 3\omega_0, \ldots$.

If $f(t)$ is a *non*-periodic function, it has no Fourier series representation valid for all t. However, if $f(t)$ is a pulse of finite duration, given by

$$f(t) = \begin{cases} g(t), & \text{for} \quad |t| < a, \\ 0, & \text{for} \quad |t| > a, \end{cases}$$

where $g(t)$ satisfies suitable continuity conditions, then $f(t)$ may be expressed in terms of its Fourier transform $F(\omega)$ as

$$f(t) = \frac{1}{2\pi} \int_{-\infty}^{\infty} e^{i\omega t} F(\omega)\, \mathrm{d}\omega, \tag{56}$$

where

$$F(\omega) = \int_{-a}^{a} g(t) e^{-i\omega t}\, \mathrm{d}t. \tag{57}$$

A *periodic* signal $\phi(t)$ consisting of the same pulse $g(t)$ repeated with period T, where $T = 2\pi/\omega_0 > 2a$, can be expressed by equations (53) and (55) as

$$\phi(t) = \sum_{n=-\infty}^{\infty} c_n e^{in\omega_0 t}, \tag{58}$$

where

$$c_n = \frac{1}{T} \int_{-a}^{a} e^{-in\omega_0 t} g(t)\, \mathrm{d}t. \tag{59}$$

Comparison of equations (56) and (57) on the one hand with equations (58) and (59) on the other shows that $(2\pi)^{-1}F(\omega)\,d\omega$ plays the same part in the integral representation of $f(t)$ as c_n plays in the series representation of $\phi(t)$. Moreover,

$$c_n = T^{-1}F(n\omega_0). \tag{60}$$

The transform $F(\omega)$ is the *continuous frequency spectrum* for the single pulse $f(t)$. In a narrow band of frequencies of width $d\omega$ about any value ω, the spectrum contributes $(2\pi)^{-1}F(\omega)\,d\omega$ to the integral representation of $f(t)$, as shown by equation (56). By contrast, c_n represents the *discrete* frequency spectrum of the periodic signal ϕ as expressed by the series (58).

EXAMPLE 6   Determine the frequency spectrum of the square pulse indicated by the solid line in Fig. 5.3, $f(t) = H(t + \tfrac{1}{2}\pi) - H(t - \tfrac{1}{2}\pi)$, and compare it with the spectrum of the periodic signal $\phi(t)$ consisting of the same pulse repeated with period T, where $T > \pi$. Give the Fourier representation of each function.

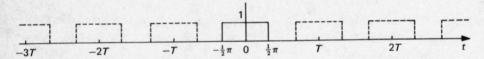

Fig. 5.3   Solid line: single square pulse $f(t)$. Discontinuous *and* solid lines: repeated square pulse $\phi(t)$.

The frequency spectrum of $f(t)$ is given by

$$F(\omega) \equiv \mathscr{F}\{f(t)\} = \int_{-\pi/2}^{\pi/2} e^{-i\omega t}\,dt = \frac{e^{-i\omega\pi/2} - e^{i\omega\pi/2}}{-i\omega}$$

$$= 2\omega^{-1}\sin\tfrac{1}{2}\pi\omega . \tag{61}$$

The periodic function $\phi(t)$ has a discrete frequency spectrum represented by the coefficients c_n. By using equation (61) in relation (60) we find that

$$c_n = \frac{2\sin\tfrac{1}{2}\pi n\omega_0}{n\omega_0 T}, \quad \text{where } \omega_0 = 2\pi/T,$$

and hence

$$c_n = (\pi n)^{-1}\sin\tfrac{1}{2}\pi n\omega_0 . \tag{62}$$

The Fourier integral representation of $f(t)$ is, from equations (56) and (61),

$$f(t) = \pi^{-1}\int_{-\infty}^{\infty} e^{i\omega t}\,\omega^{-1}\sin\tfrac{1}{2}\pi\omega\,d\omega .$$

The Fourier series representation of $\phi(t)$ is, from equations (58) and (62),

$$\phi(t) = \pi^{-1}\sum_{-\infty}^{\infty} e^{in\omega_0 t}\,n^{-1}\sin\tfrac{1}{2}\pi n\omega_0 .$$

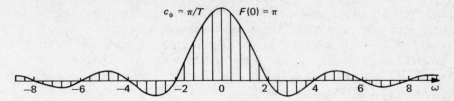

Fig. 5.4 Continuous curve: continuous spectrum $F(\omega) = 2\omega^{-1} \sin \frac{1}{2}\pi\omega$. Vertical lines: discrete spectrum $c_n = (\pi n)^{-1} \sin \frac{1}{2}\pi n\omega_0$.

In Fig. 5.4, the curve represents the continuous spectrum $F(\omega)$, and the vertical lines represent the discrete spectrum c_n with $\omega_0 = 0.4$, with the scales arranged so that the two spectra coincide at $\omega = 0, \pm 0.4, \pm 0.8, \pm 1.2, \ldots$. As the period T increases, ω_0 decreases and the vertical lines in Fig. 5.4 are pushed closer together. In the limit, as $T \to \infty$ and $\omega_0 \to 0$, only one pulse remains on the finite part of the t axis. Then the periodic function $\phi(t)$ becomes the single pulse function $f(t)$, and the discrete spectrum c_n condenses to the continuous spectrum $F(\omega)$.

Exercises

1. Use the substitution $u = x + \frac{1}{2}i\xi$ and the properties of the error function to show that $\mathscr{F}\{\exp(-x^2)\} = \pi^{\frac{1}{2}} \exp(-\frac{1}{4}\xi^2)$.

2. Evaluate $\mathscr{F}\{(x^2 + a^2)^{-1}\}$ by means of the calculus of residues, using a closed contour in the upper half-plane for $\xi < 0$, in the lower half-plane for $\xi > 0$.

3. Use the derivative formula to deduce $\mathscr{F}\{x \exp(-x^2)\}$ from the transform pair of exercise 1.

4. Deduce the cosine transform of $\exp(-x^2)$ from the answer to exercise 1 and the sine transform of $x \exp(-x^2)$ from the answer to exercise 3.

5. Find the frequency spectrum of the single pulse

$$f(t) = \cos t \{H(t + \tfrac{1}{2}\pi) - H(t - \tfrac{1}{2}\pi)\}.$$

Deduce the frequency spectrum of the periodic signal consisting of the same pulse repeated with period 2π (the half-wave rectification of the cosine wave).

5.6 SOLUTION OF LINEAR PARTIAL DIFFERENTIAL EQUATIONS

In Volume 1, it was shown that the application of the Laplace transform to a linear ordinary differential equation often leads directly to an algebraic expression for the transform of the unknown function in terms of s the transform parameter. In a similar way, it is sometimes possible to apply the Laplace transform to a partial differential equation depending on x and t in order to replace the differential dependence on t with an algebraic dependence on s. The transformed equation is an *ordinary* differential equation which is usually solved without difficulty and the final result is obtained by inversion. Similar reductions may be achieved by the use of other transforms. One aim of this section is to show which transforms are apt in various circumstances. To do so, we consider the solution of several well-known equations under the commoner types of boundary and initial conditions. The general approach is illustrated in detail in the first case considered.

The problems tackled in this section may often be solved equally well by the methods of Chapter 7 of Volume 1, or, in the case of Laplace's equation in two dimensions, by the complex variable methods for finding harmonic functions discussed in §4.6.

(a) *Solution of Laplace's Equation in the Half-plane*

A number of physical quantities, including potentials of various kinds, satisfy Laplace's equation. Here, to be specific, we consider the steady two-dimensional temperature distribution $\theta(x, y)$ in the half-plane $y \geq 0$ with specified temperature $\theta(x, 0) = \theta_0(x)$ on the boundary and with $\theta \to 0$ as $x^2 + y^2 \to \infty$. Then $\theta(x, y)$ satisfies the two-dimensional form of Laplace's equation (see §7.6 of Volume 1).

$$\nabla_1^2 \theta \equiv \frac{\partial^2 \theta}{\partial x^2} + \frac{\partial^2 \theta}{\partial y^2} = 0 . \tag{63}$$

Multiply the equation by $e^{-i\xi x}$ and integrate it with respect to x over $-\infty < x < \infty$. Then the equation becomes

$$\mathscr{F} \left\{ \frac{\partial^2 \theta}{\partial x^2} \right\} + \mathscr{F} \left\{ \frac{\partial^2 \theta}{\partial y^2} \right\} = 0 . \tag{64}$$

By equation (32),

$$\mathscr{F} \left\{ \frac{\partial^2 \theta}{\partial x^2} \right\} = -\xi^2 \Theta(\xi, y) , \tag{65}$$

where

$$\Theta(\xi, y) = \mathscr{F} \{\theta(x, y)\} = \int_{-\infty}^{\infty} e^{-i\xi x} \theta(x, y) \, dx ,$$

while

$$\mathscr{F} \left\{ \frac{\partial^2 \theta}{\partial y^2} \right\} = \int_{-\infty}^{\infty} e^{-i\xi x} \frac{\partial^2 \theta}{\partial y^2} \, dy$$

$$= \frac{\partial^2}{\partial y^2} \int_{-\infty}^{\infty} e^{-i\xi x} \theta(x, y) \, dx$$

$$= \frac{\partial^2}{\partial y^2} \Theta(\xi, y) . \tag{66}$$

Substitution of results (65) and (66) into equation (64) gives the transformed equation

$$-\xi^2 \Theta + \frac{\partial^2 \Theta}{\partial y^2} = 0. \tag{67}$$

The conditions on $y = 0$ and at infinity must also be transformed, and give

$$\Theta(\xi, 0) = \Theta_0(\xi) \equiv \mathcal{F}\{\theta_0(x)\}, \tag{68}$$

$$\Theta(\xi, y) \to 0 \quad \text{as} \quad y \to \infty. \tag{69}$$

Since equation (67) contains no derivatives with respect to ξ, it may be treated as an *ordinary* differential equation. However, in place of the two arbitrary constants which would arise in the solution of a true ordinary differential equation, there will be two arbitrary functions of ξ. It is quite usual to write a transformed equation such as equation (67) with an ordinary, rather than a partial, differential coefficient and this practice will be followed subsequently.

The general solution of equation (67) would usually be stated as

$$\Theta(\xi, y) = A(\xi) e^{\xi y} + B(\xi) e^{-\xi y},$$

where $A(\xi)$ and $B(\xi)$ are arbitrary functions of ξ, or the equivalent hyperbolic form. However, since the range of ξ is $(-\infty, \infty)$, condition (69) can be satisfied only if $A(\xi) = 0$ for $\xi > 0$ and $B(\xi) = 0$ for $\xi < 0$. We therefore write the solution in the form

$$\Theta(\xi, y) = C(\xi) e^{|\xi| y} + D(\xi) e^{-|\xi| y},$$

in which case condition (69) gives $C \equiv 0$ and condition (68) gives $D = \Theta_0(\xi)$. Then, by the inversion formula (30),

$$\theta(x, y) = (2\pi)^{-1} \int_{-\infty}^{\infty} e^{ix\xi} \Theta_0(\xi) e^{-|\xi| y} \, d\xi. \tag{70}$$

The convolution property, equation (37), provides an alternative method of expressing the solution. From example 2 of §5.5,

$$\mathcal{F}^{-1}\{e^{-|\xi| y}\} = \frac{1}{\pi} \frac{y}{x^2 + y^2}$$

for $y > 0$, and it follows that

$$\theta(x, y) = \mathcal{F}^{-1}\{\Theta_0(\xi) e^{-|\xi| y}\} = \theta_0(x) * \frac{1}{\pi} \left(\frac{y}{x^2 + y^2}\right)$$

$$= \frac{y}{\pi} \int_{-\infty}^{\infty} \frac{\theta_0(u)}{(x - u)^2 + y^2} \, du \quad \text{for } y > 0. \tag{71}$$

A *fundamental solution* of the problem is obtained by specifying the boundary value $\theta_0(x) = T_0 \delta(x - x_0)$, corresponding to the condition that $\theta = 0$ on $y = 0$ except for a *point source* of heat of strength T_0 at $x = x_0$. Then equation (71) yields

$$\theta(x, y) = \frac{T_0 y}{\pi\{(x - x_0)^2 + y^2\}}.$$

In terms of this fundamental solution, equation (71) represents the integral over the *distribution* of sources $\theta_0(x)$ on $y = 0$.

EXAMPLE 1   Solve equation (63) for $y > 0$ when $\theta \to 0$ as $x^2 + y^2 \to \infty$ and

$$\theta(x, 0) = \begin{cases} T, & |x| < a, \\ 0, & |x| > a. \end{cases} \tag{72}$$

The integral in equation (71) is easily evaluated to give

$$\theta(x, y) = \frac{T}{\pi} \left\{ \tan^{-1}\left(\frac{x + a}{y}\right) - \tan^{-1}\left(\frac{x - a}{y}\right) \right\} \tag{73}$$

where the inverse tangents have values in the interval $(-\tfrac{1}{2}\pi, \tfrac{1}{2}\pi)$. The reader should compare the present method of solution with the complex variable method of solving a similar problem in problem 26 of Chapter 4. Although the formula (71) is not valid for $y = 0$, the boundary values can be recovered from equation (73) by letting $y \to 0$ and using the results

$$\lim_{R \to \infty} \tan^{-1} R = \tfrac{1}{2}\pi, \qquad \lim_{R \to -\infty} \tan^{-1} R = -\tfrac{1}{2}\pi.$$

An alternative method of solution is to find the transform $\Theta_0(\xi)$ of the function (72) and to insert it into the solution in the form (70). The result (73) is then reached by a quite different route. Since $\cos \xi x$ and $\sin \xi x$ are even and odd functions, respectively, we have that

$$\Theta_0(\xi) = \int_{-a}^{a} T\, e^{i\xi x}\, dx = 2T \int_{0}^{a} \cos \xi x\, dx$$

$$= 2T\xi^{-1} \sin \xi a$$

and then, from equation (70),

$$\theta(x, y) = \frac{T}{\pi} \int_{-\infty}^{\infty} e^{-ix\xi}\, \xi^{-1} \sin \xi a\, e^{-|\xi|y}\, d\xi$$

$$= \frac{2T}{\pi} \int_{0}^{\infty} \cos x\xi\, \xi^{-1} \sin \xi a\, e^{-\xi y}\, d\xi. \tag{74}$$

The integral is now in the form of a cosine transform but, written as

$$\theta(x, y) = \frac{T}{\pi} \int_{0}^{\infty} [\sin \xi(x + a) - \sin \xi(x - a)]\xi^{-1}\, e^{-\xi y}\, d\xi,$$

it may be treated as the sum of two *sine* transforms and hence evaluated by referring to Table A8 in the Appendix. The reader should confirm that the result is that given in equation (73).

(b) *Solution of Laplace's Equation in the Quarter-plane*

Suppose $\theta(x, y)$ satisfies Laplace's equation (63) in $x \geqslant 0, y \geqslant 0$, with given boundary conditions on $x = 0$ and $y = 0$, and that $\theta \to 0$ as $x^2 + y^2 \to \infty$. We cannot apply the Fourier transform with respect to x, as in (a), since $\theta(x, y)$ is not defined for $x < 0$. Alternatives are the cosine and sine transforms, which are both suitable for functions defined only in $x \geqslant 0$. The Laplace transform, also appropriate for functions defined in $x \geqslant 0$, turns out to be unsuitable for use with Laplace's equation.

From equation (50), the *cosine transform* of equation (63) with respect to x is

$$-\theta_x(0, y) - \xi^2 \Theta_c(\xi, y) + \frac{d^2 \Theta_c}{dy^2} = 0 , \tag{75}$$

where $\theta_x(0, y)$ denotes $\partial \theta / \partial x$ evaluated on $x = 0$ and

$$\Theta_c(\xi, y) = \mathscr{F}_c\{\theta(x, y)\} .$$

Similarly, from equation (51), the *sine transform* is

$$\xi \theta(0, y) - \xi^2 \Theta_s(\xi, y) + \frac{d^2 \Theta_s}{dy^2} = 0 , \tag{76}$$

where

$$\Theta_s(\xi, y) = \mathscr{F}_s\{\theta(x, y)\}.$$

From §3.2 of Volume 1, the *Laplace transform* of equation (63) is

$$s^2 \bar{\theta}(s, y) - s\theta(0, y) - \theta_x(0, y) + \frac{d^2 \bar{\theta}}{dy^2} = 0 , \tag{77}$$

where

$$\bar{\theta}(s, y) = \mathscr{L}\{\theta(x, y)\} \text{ and } \theta_x = \partial \theta / \partial x.$$

Physically natural boundary conditions for Laplace's equation are that θ or its normal derivative (or possibly a linear combination of them) should be specified at every point of the boundary (see §7.9 of Volume 1). It then follows from equations (75) and (76) that the cosine transform is appropriate for problems in which $\partial \theta / \partial x$ is specified everywhere on $x = 0$ and that the sine transform is appropriate when θ is specified at all points of $x = 0$, for then the term not involving Θ is a known function.

However, equation (77) contains both $\theta(0, y)$ and $\theta_x(0, y)$ and one of them remains undetermined. Since this difficulty cannot be overcome, the Laplace transform method does not lead to a solution.

EXAMPLE 2   Determine the temperature distribution $\theta(x, y)$ in $x \geqslant 0, y \geqslant 0$ when the surface $x = 0$ is insulated, $\theta(x, 0) = \theta_0(x)$ and $\theta \to 0$ as $x^2 + y^2 \to \infty$.

In this case, $\partial\theta/\partial x = 0$ on $x = 0$, so the cosine transform is used and equation (75) becomes

$$\frac{d^2\Theta_c}{dy^2} - \xi^2\Theta_c = 0.$$

The conditions given on $y = 0$ and as $x^2 + y^2 \to \infty$ are transformed to $\Theta_c(\xi, 0) = \Theta_0(\xi)$, $\Theta_c \to 0$ as $y \to \infty$. The solution is

$$\Theta_c(\xi, y) = \Theta_0(\xi)e^{-\xi y}, \tag{78}$$

where

$$\Theta_0(\xi) = \int_0^\infty \cos \xi x\, \theta_0(x)\, dx\,.$$

For definiteness consider the special case

$$\theta_0(x) = \begin{cases} T, & 0 < x < a, \\ 0, & a < x < \infty, \end{cases}$$

which is easily transformed to give

$$\Theta_0(\xi) = T\xi^{-1} \sin a\xi. \tag{79}$$

Substitute the value (79) into equation (78) and use the inversion formula (41). Then

$$\theta(x, y) = \frac{2T}{\pi} \int_0^\infty \cos x\xi\, \xi^{-1} \sin a\xi\, e^{-\xi y}\, d\xi\,.$$

Reference to equation (74) shows that this result is precisely the same as the solution of example 1. This is because the conditions on $y = 0$ in example 1 ensure that $x = 0$ is a line of symmetry and hence that $\partial\theta/\partial x = 0$ on $x = 0$. Thus, the conditions on $x = 0$ for $y > 0$ and on $y = 0$ for $x > 0$ are just those of example 2, in which $\partial\theta/\partial x = 0$ on $x = 0$.

(c) *Solution of Laplace's Equation in the Infinite and Semi-infinite Strip*

The techniques used for the half-plane and quarter-plane, for which $0 \leqslant y < \infty$, may be extended to deal with the infinite and semi-infinite strip, for which $0 \leqslant y \leqslant h$. Instead of the condition $\theta \to 0$ as $x^2 + y^2 \to \infty$, there is now a boundary condition on θ or $\partial\theta/\partial x$ when $y = h$. For the infinite strip $-\infty < x < \infty$ the Fourier transform is used. For the semi-infinite strip $0 \leqslant x < \infty$ there is a choice between the cosine and the sine transform according to the type of condition given for θ on $x = 0$, in the same way as for the quarter plane; that is, the cosine transform is used if $\partial\theta/\partial x$ is given on $x = 0$, but the sine transform is used if θ is given on $x = 0$.

EXAMPLE 3   Solve $\nabla_1^2\theta = 0$ in $0 \leqslant y \leqslant h, x > 0$, when $\theta = 0$ on $x = 0$, $\theta = \theta_0(x)$ on $y = 0$, $\partial\theta/\partial y = \theta_1(x)$ on $y = h$, as shown in Fig. 5.5.

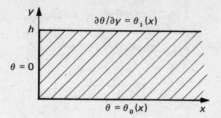

Fig. 5.5 Semi-infinite strip.

If the sine transform is applied to Laplace's equation and the condition $\theta(0, y) = 0$ is used, the resulting equation is

$$\frac{d^2\Theta_s}{dy^2} - \xi^2\Theta_s = 0.\tag{80}$$

Write $\mathscr{F}_s\{\theta_0(x)\} = \Theta_0(\xi)$ and $\mathscr{F}_s\{\theta_1(x)\} = \Theta_1(\xi)$, then the conditions on $y = 0, h$ transform to

$$\Theta_s = \Theta_0(\xi) \quad \text{on } y = 0, \qquad \frac{d\Theta_s}{dy} = \Theta_1(\xi) \quad \text{on } y = h.\tag{81}$$

In strip problems, the solution of equation (80) is best written in terms of hyperbolic functions in the form

$$\Theta_s(\xi, y) = A \cosh \xi y + B \sinh \xi y,\tag{82}$$

where A and B are functions of ξ to be determined from conditions (81). From the first condition,

$$A = \Theta_0(\xi).$$

Differentiation of equation (82) and the use of the second condition shows that

$$\Theta_1(\xi) = A \xi \sinh \xi h + B \xi \cosh \xi h$$

and hence

$$B = \frac{\xi^{-1}\Theta_1(\xi) - \Theta_0(\xi) \sinh \xi h}{\cosh \xi h}.$$

Equation (82) then becomes

$$\Theta_s(\xi, y) = \Theta_0(\xi) \cosh \xi y + \frac{\{\xi^{-1}\Theta_1(\xi) - \Theta_0(\xi) \sinh \xi h\} \sinh \xi y}{\cosh \xi h}$$

$$= \frac{\Theta_0(\xi) \cosh \xi(h - y) + \xi^{-1}\Theta_1(\xi) \sinh \xi y}{\cosh \xi h}.\tag{83}$$

Equation (83) gives the general solution of the transformed problem. As a special case, let θ be zero on $y = 0$ except at x_0, where there is a point source of heat represented by $\theta_0(x) = T_0 \delta(x - x_0)$, and let $\theta_1(x) = 0$ for all x. Then

$$\Theta_0(\xi) = T_0 \int_0^\infty \sin \xi x \, \delta(x - x_0) \, dx = T_0 \sin \xi x_0,$$

$$\Theta_1(\xi) = 0,$$

and equation (83) becomes

$$\Theta_s(\xi, y) = \frac{T_0 \sin \xi x_0 \cosh \xi(h - y)}{\cosh \xi h}.$$

By the inversion formula (45),

$$\theta(x, y) = \frac{2T_0}{\pi} \int_0^\infty \frac{\sin x\xi \, \sin \xi x_0 \, \cosh \xi(h - y)}{\cosh \xi h} \, d\xi$$

$$= \frac{T_0}{\pi} \int_0^\infty \frac{[\cos \xi(x - x_0) - \cos \xi(x + x_0)] \cosh \xi(h - y)}{\cosh \xi h} \, d\xi. \tag{84}$$

Integral (84) may be regarded as composed of two inverse *cosine* transforms, the first with parameter $x - x_0$, the second with parameter $x + x_0$. From Table A7 in the Appendix we find that

$$\int_0^\infty \frac{\cos \xi x \, \cosh \xi(h - y)}{\cosh \xi h} \, d\xi = \frac{\pi}{h} \left\{ \frac{\cos\{\frac{1}{2}\pi(h - y)/h\} \, \cosh(\frac{1}{2}\pi x/h)}{\cos\{\pi(h - y)/h\} + \cosh(\pi x/h)} \right\}$$

$$= \frac{\pi}{h} \left\{ \frac{\sin(\frac{1}{2}\pi y/h) \, \cosh(\frac{1}{2}\pi x/h)}{-\cos(\pi y/h) + \cosh(\pi x/h)} \right\},$$

and hence

$$\theta(x, y) = \frac{T_0 \sin(\frac{1}{2}\pi y/h)}{h} \left\{ \frac{\cosh\{\frac{1}{2}\pi(x + x_0)/h\}}{\cos(\pi y/h) - \cosh\{\pi(x + x_0)/h\}} \right.$$

$$\left. - \frac{\cosh\{\frac{1}{2}\pi(x - x_0)/h\}}{\cos(\pi y/h) - \cosh\{\pi(x - x_0)/h\}} \right\}.$$

Books of tables do not usually list many cosine or sine transforms involving hyperbolic functions and, for most strip problems, another method is required. In many cases the inverse transform may be evaluated by the complex variable methods of §4.5. First the result must be expressed as an inverse *Fourier* transform by relation (43) or (47). The intergrand is then integrated in the *complex* ξ plane over a contour consisting of the real axis closed by an infinite semicircle in the upper half-plane. Just as with the inverse *Laplace* transform of similar functions (see §5.3), the result involves a sum of residues at an infinite number of poles in the ξ plane.

(d) *Diffusion Equation*

Diffusion phenomena, such as heat conduction, are described by equation (2) in §7.1 of Volume 1. When diffusion is entirely in the x-direction, the equation reduces to

$$\frac{\partial^2 \theta}{\partial x^2} = \frac{1}{\kappa} \frac{\partial \theta}{\partial t}. \tag{85}$$

If the boundary conditions depend on time, or if the medium extends to infinity in the x-direction, equation (85) cannot be solved by the method of §7.5 of Volume 1 and transform methods should be considered. Consider the temperature $\theta(x, t)$ in a thin bar which is insulated at the sides and has thermal diffusivity κ. The bar is subject to some *initial* condition at $t = 0$, so that $\theta(x, 0)$ is specified for $0 \leqslant x \leqslant a$, where a is the length, which may be infinite. There must also be a boundary condition at each end, specifying either θ or $\partial\theta/\partial x$ (or possibly a linear combination of them) as functions of t.

When the bar is semi-infinite, it is possible to use the cosine or sine transform with respect to x, the choice depending upon the type of condition at $x = 0$, as with Laplace's equation. If the bar is finite the cosine and sine transforms are not suitable and we resort to the Laplace transform with respect to t. Since the Laplace transform is usually more sucessful with semi-infinite bars also, the use of the other transforms will not be discussed.

Application of the Laplace transform to equation (85) and the use of the initial condition in the derivative formula (see §3.2 of Volume 1) give

$$\frac{d^2 \bar{\theta}}{dx^2} = \frac{1}{\kappa} \{s\bar{\theta} - \theta(x, 0)\},$$

where $\bar{\theta}(x, s) = \mathscr{L}\{\theta(x, t)\}$. The general solution of this equation can be stated in the alternative forms

$$\bar{\theta}(x, s) = A \exp\{-(s/\kappa)^{\frac{1}{2}}x\} + B \exp\{(s/\kappa)^{\frac{1}{2}}x\} + \bar{g}(x, s), \tag{86}$$

$$\bar{\theta}(x, s) = C \cosh(s/\kappa)^{\frac{1}{2}}x + D \sinh(s/\kappa)^{\frac{1}{2}}x + \bar{g}(x, s), \tag{87}$$

where $\bar{g}(x, s)$ is a particular integral of the equation and A, B, C, D are functions of s to be determined by the boundary conditions. A general form for $\bar{g}(x, s)$ is given by the indefinite integral (see §1.7 of Volume 1)

$$\bar{g}(x, s) = (\kappa s)^{-\frac{1}{2}} \int^x \theta(u, 0) \sinh\{(s/\kappa)^{\frac{1}{2}}(x - u)\} \, du.$$

Equation (86) is suitable in the case of a semi-infinite bar $0 \leqslant x < \infty$, when the usual requirement that $\theta(x, t) \to 0$ as $x \to \infty$ implies that $B \equiv 0$. The boundary conditions for a finite bar are more suited to the form (87).

EXAMPLE 4   Find the temperature distribution $\theta(x, t)$ in a semi-infinite bar $0 \leqslant x < \infty$ given that $\theta(x, 0) = 0$ for all x, $\theta(0, t) = \theta_0(t)$ and $\theta(x, t) \to 0$ as $x \to \infty$.

The condition $\theta(x, 0) = 0$ implies that $\bar{g}(x, s) \equiv 0$. Use, in equation (86), of the other conditions gives $A = \bar{\theta}_0(s)$ and $B \equiv 0$, so that $\bar{\theta}$ is given by

$$\bar{\theta}(x, s) = \bar{\theta}_0(s) \exp\{-(s/\kappa)^{\frac{1}{2}}x\}.$$

Now from Table A5 in the Appendix we have

$$\mathcal{L}^{-1}\{\exp[-(s/\kappa)^{\frac{1}{2}}x]\} = \tfrac{1}{2}(\kappa\pi)^{-\frac{1}{2}}xt^{-\frac{3}{2}}\exp(-x^2/4\kappa t)$$

and then the use of the convolution property of the Laplace transform (see §3.4(g) of Volume 1), gives the result

$$\theta(x,t) = \frac{x}{2(\kappa\pi)^{\frac{1}{2}}}\int_0^t \theta_0(t-u)\,\frac{\exp(-x^2/4\kappa u)}{u^{\frac{3}{2}}}\,du.$$

If $\theta_0(t) = T_0$, a constant, the integral can be simplified by putting $p = \tfrac{1}{2}x(\kappa u)^{-\frac{1}{2}}$ with the result

$$\theta(x,t) = 2T_0\pi^{-\frac{1}{2}}\int_{\frac{1}{2}x(\kappa t)^{-\frac{1}{2}}}^{\infty} e^{-p^2}\,dp,$$

which can be expressed in terms of the complementary error function defined by equation (14), as

$$\theta(x,t) = T_0\,\mathrm{erfc}\{\tfrac{1}{2}x(\kappa t)^{-\frac{1}{2}}\}.$$

(e) Wave Equation

The equation

$$\frac{\partial^2 v}{\partial x^2} = \frac{1}{c^2}\frac{\partial^2 v}{\partial t^2} \tag{88}$$

governs many kinds of one-dimensional waves (see §7.2 of Volume 1). It is possible to solve some problems of wave propagation in semi-infinite media by applying the cosine or sine transform to equation (88), but the Laplace transform is more generally successful.

EXAMPLE 5   Obtain an expression for the transverse motion $v(x,t)$ of a stretched string with ends at $x = 0$ and $x = l$ such that $v = 0$, $\partial v/\partial t = 0$ everywhere at $t = 0$, $v(l,t) = 0$ and $v(0,t) = v_0(t)$ for $t > 0$.

Apply the Laplace transform with respect to t to equation (88), using the derivative formula to transform $\partial^2 v/\partial t^2$ (see §3.2 of Volume 1). The transformed equation is

$$\frac{d^2\bar{v}}{dx^2} = \frac{s^2}{c^2}\bar{v}, \tag{89}$$

where $\bar{v}(x,s) = \mathcal{L}\{v(x,t)\}$, and the transformed boundary conditions are $\bar{v}(0,s) = \bar{v}_0(s)$, $\bar{v}(l,s) = 0$. The appropriate form of general solution of equation (89) is

$$\bar{v}(x,s) = A\,\cosh(xs/c) + B\,\sinh(xs/c).$$

The boundary conditions imply that $A = \bar{v}_0(s)$ and

$$A\,\cosh(ls/c) + B\,\sinh(ls/c) = 0$$

and it follows that

$$\bar{v}(x, s) = \bar{v}_0(s)\{\cosh(xs/c) - \coth(ls/c)\sinh(xs/c)\}$$
$$= \bar{v}_0(s)\bar{f}(s),$$

where

$$\bar{f}(s) = \frac{\sinh\{(l - x)s/c\}}{\sinh(ls/c)}.$$

Now $\bar{f}(s)$ can be expanded (see example 3 of §5.3) in the form

$$\bar{f}(s) = \sum_{n=0}^{\infty} [\exp\{-(2nl + x)s/c\} - \exp\{-(2nl + 2l - x)s/c\}]$$

and so

$$\bar{v}(x, s) = \sum_{n=0}^{\infty} \bar{v}_0(s)[\exp\{-(2nl + x)s/c\} - \exp\{-(2nl + 2l - x)s/c\}].$$

Then, by the second shift property (see §3.4(b) of Volume 1 and equation 21),

$$v(x, t) = \sum_{n=0}^{\infty} \left\{ v_0 \left(t - \frac{2nl + x}{c} \right) H \left(t - \frac{2nl + x}{c} \right) \right.$$
$$\left. - v_0 \left(t - \frac{2(n + 1)l - x}{c} \right) H \left(t - \frac{2(n + 1)l - x}{c} \right) \right\}.$$

This is a solution of D'Alembert's type (see §7.2 of Volume 1). It clearly shows that $v(x, t)$ is the result of the superposition of the original wave $v_0(t - x/c)$, given by $n = 0$ in the first term, and successive reflections at $x = 0$ and $x = l$, given by putting $n = 1, 2, 3, \ldots$ in the first term and $n = 0, 1, 2, 3, \ldots$ in the second term, respectively.

(f) *Biharmonic Equation*

Many plane problems in classical elasticity can be reduced to that of solving the biharmonic equation

$$\nabla_1^4 \phi \equiv \frac{\partial^4 \phi}{\partial x^2} + 2\frac{\partial^4 \phi}{\partial x^2 \partial y^2} + \frac{\partial^4 \phi}{\partial y^4} = 0, \tag{90}$$

in which the Airy stress function ϕ is related to the components of stress in the plane by

$$\sigma_x = \frac{\partial^2 \phi}{\partial y^2}, \quad \sigma_y = \frac{\partial^2 \phi}{\partial x^2}, \quad \tau_{xy} = -\frac{\partial^2 \phi}{\partial x \partial y}. \tag{91}$$

Half-plane or quarter-plane problems of elastic equilibrium are often amenable to treatment by Fourier transforms or by cosine or sine transforms.

EXAMPLE 6   Find the stress distribution in the half-plane $y > 0$ when $\sigma_y = s(x)$ and $\tau_{xy} = 0$ on $y = 0$ and there is zero stress at infinity.

Let

$$\mathscr{F}\{\phi(x,y)\} = \int_{-\infty}^{\infty} e^{-i\xi x}\phi(x,y)\,dx = \Phi(\xi,y).$$

Then the Fourier transform of equation (90) is

$$\xi^4\Phi - 2\xi^2\frac{d^2\Phi}{dy^2} + \frac{d^4\Phi}{dy^4} = 0 \tag{92}$$

and the conditions on $y = 0$ become, by means of equations (91),

$$-\xi^2\Phi = \mathscr{F}\{s(x)\} \equiv S(\xi), \quad i\xi\frac{d\Phi}{dy} = 0, \quad \text{on } y = 0. \tag{93}$$

The condition at infinity is satisfied if $\Phi \to 0$ as $y \to \infty$. The solution of equation (92) which tends to zero as $y \to \infty$ is

$$\Phi = (A + By)e^{-|\xi|y},$$

where A and B are to be determined from conditions (93). The result is

$$\Phi(\xi,y) = -S(\xi)\xi^{-2}(1 + y\,|\,\xi\,|)e^{-|\xi|y}.$$

The transforms of the stress components are

$$\mathscr{F}\{\sigma_x\} = \frac{d^2\Phi}{dy^2} = S(\xi)(1 - y\,|\,\xi\,|)e^{-|\xi|y},$$

$$\mathscr{F}\{\sigma_y\} = -\xi^2\Phi = S(\xi)(1 + y\,|\,\xi\,|)e^{-|\xi|y}, \tag{94}$$

$$\mathscr{F}\{\tau_{xy}\} = i\xi\frac{d\Phi}{dy} = S(\xi)iy\xi\,e^{-|\xi|y}.$$

Formal solutions can now be obtained by using the convolution property, equation (37), and the results

$$\mathscr{F}^{-1}\{e^{-|\xi|y}\} = \frac{y}{\pi(x^2 + y^2)}, \quad \mathscr{F}^{-1}\{|\,\xi\,|\,y\,e^{-|\xi|y}\} = \frac{y(y^2 - x^2)}{\pi(x^2 + y^2)^2},$$

$$\mathscr{F}^{-1}\{i\xi y\,e^{-|\xi|y}\} = -\frac{2xy^2}{\pi(x^2 + y^2)^2}. \tag{95}$$

Then, for example,

$$\sigma_y = \frac{2y^3}{\pi}\int_{-\infty}^{\infty}\frac{s(x-u)}{(u^2 + y^2)^2}\,du. \tag{96}$$

If $s(x)$ is a *point force* at $x = a$, given by $s(x) = s_0\delta(x - a)$, it follows from equation (96) that

$$\sigma_y = \frac{2s_0y^3}{\pi\{(x-a)^2 + y^2\}^2}.$$

Point force solutions play the same part in elasticity as the impulse response in a linear time-dependent system, discussed in §3.7(a) of Volume 1.

Use of Mellin and Hankel Transforms

The *Mellin transform* is useful for solving certain differential equations, such as Laplace's equation, in polar coordinates in an infinite sector or 'wedge' of the plane. If $\nabla_1^2 u$ is expressed in polar coordinates (see equation (76) in §7.6 of Volume 1) and if $u(\rho, \phi) \to 0$ as $\rho \to \infty$, the equation can be transformed with respect to ρ. Use of the formula for the Mellin transform of a derivative (see Sneddon [2]) produces the result

$$\frac{d^2\bar{u}}{d\phi^2} + s^2\bar{u} = 0, \tag{97}$$

where $\bar{u}(s, \phi) = \mathcal{M}\{u(\rho, \phi)\}$, as defined by equation (5). The general solution of equation (97) is easily obtained. It involves two arbitrary functions of the transform parameter s which are determined from the conditions at the boundaries of the sector, ϕ_1 and ϕ_2 say. The inversion formula is an integral in the complex s plane.

The *Hankel* transform can be used for solving Laplace's equation under conditions of symmetry about the z axis either in a half-space $0 \leqslant z < \infty$ or in an infinite thick plate or slab $0 \leqslant z \leqslant a$. In such cases, Laplace's equation in cylindrical polar coordinates, equation (83) in §7.7 of Volume 1, reduces to the equation

$$\frac{\partial^2 u}{\partial\rho^2} + \frac{1}{\rho}\frac{\partial u}{\partial\rho} + \frac{\partial^2 u}{\partial z^2} = 0. \tag{98}$$

So long as $u \to 0$ as $\rho \to \infty$, the application of the Hankel transform of order zero, with respect to ρ, leads to the equation

$$\frac{d^2\bar{u}_0}{dz^2} - \xi^2\bar{u}_0 = 0, \tag{99}$$

where $\bar{u}_0(\xi, z) = \mathcal{H}_0\{u(\rho, z)\}$, as defined by equation (6). The general solution of equation (99) is elementary and the complete solution for $\bar{u}_0$ is obtained by using the transforms of the boundary conditions.

The uses and properties of the Mellin and Hankel transforms are discussed in detail in a number of books such as Sneddon [2]. The tables compiled by Erdélyi and others contain extensive lists of Mellin transforms (Vol. 1 [4]) and Hankel transforms (Vol. 2 [8]).

Exercises

1. The steady temperature $\theta(x, y)$ in the half-plane $y > 0$ satisfies equation (63). Given that $\theta \to 0$ as $x^2 + y^2 \to \infty$ and that, on $y = 0$, the heat flux is such that

$$\frac{\partial\theta}{\partial y} = \begin{cases} -k & \text{for} & -a < x < 0 \\ k & \text{for} & 0 < x < a, \\ 0 & \text{for} & |x| > a, \end{cases}$$

show that

$$\theta(x,y) = -2k\pi^{-1} \int_0^\infty \xi^{-2}(1 - \cos \xi a) \sin \xi x \, e^{-\xi y} \, d\xi.$$

2. Determine the steady temperature distribution $\theta(x,y)$ in the quarter-plane $x > 0$, $y > 0$ when $\theta \to 0$ as $x^2 + y^2 \to \infty$, $\theta(0, y) = 0$ and

$$\theta(x, 0) = \begin{cases} 0 & \text{for} \quad x < a \quad \text{and} \quad x > b, \\ T & \text{for} \quad a < x < b. \end{cases}$$

3. Find the Fourier transform of the steady temperature $\theta(x, y)$ in the infinite strip $0 < y < h$, $-\infty < x < \infty$ when $\theta(x, h) = 0$ and $\theta(x, 0) = \theta_0(x)$. Write the solution in the form

$$\theta(x,y) = \mathscr{F}^{-1}\{\Theta_0(\xi)\Phi(\xi, y)\}$$

and evaluate

$$\phi(x,y) \equiv \mathscr{F}^{-1}\{\Phi(\xi, y)\}$$

by the calculus of residues. Hence find a series representation for $\theta(x, y)$ when $\theta_0(x) = \cos x \, \{H(x + \frac{1}{2}\pi) - H(x - \frac{1}{2}\pi)\}$.

4. Find the Laplace transform of the solution $\theta(x, t)$ of the diffusion equation (85) in the bar $0 \leqslant x \leqslant 1$ when $\theta(x, 0) = 0$, $\theta(0, t) = T$ and $\partial\theta/\partial x = 0$ on $x = 1$. Use the complex inversion formula to express $\theta(x, t)$ as an infinite series.

5. Calculate the stress components in the half-plane $y > 0$ when, in example 6,

$$s(x) = \begin{cases} P & \text{for} \quad |x| < a, \\ 0 & \text{for} \quad |x| > a. \end{cases}$$

PROBLEMS

1. Find the inverse Laplace transforms of

  (a) $s^{-\frac{1}{2}}(s - a)^{-1}$, (b) $(s^3 + a^3)^{-1}$.

2. Find two different series representations of $\mathscr{L}^{-1}\{s^{-2} \sinh as \operatorname{sech} bs\}$, where $0 < a < b$, by (a) using the complex inversion formula and (b) term-by-term inversion of an expansion in powers of e^{-bs}.

3. Find the first three terms of an asymptotic expansion of $f(t)$ as $t \to \infty$, where

$$\mathscr{L}\{f(t)\} = \frac{(s + a)^{\frac{1}{2}} - s^{\frac{1}{2}}}{(s + a)^{\frac{1}{2}} + s^{\frac{1}{2}}},$$

and determine $\lim_{t \to 0} f(t)$.

4. Find the single pulse $f(t)$ which has frequency spectrum

$$F(\omega) = \omega^{-2} \sin^2 \pi\omega,$$

and hence derive the periodic signals with frequency spectra such that

(a) $c_n = \pi^{-1} n^{-2} \sin^2 \frac{1}{2}\pi n$,   (b) $c_n = \pi^{-1} n^{-2} \sin^2 \frac{1}{3}\pi n$.

5. The temperature $\theta(x, t)$ in a layer $0 < x < d$ undergoing a chemical reaction satisfies the equation

$$\frac{\partial \theta}{\partial t} = \frac{\partial^2 \theta}{\partial x^2} - \alpha^2 \theta$$

where α is a real constant. If $\theta(x, 0) = 0$ for all x, and if $\theta(0, t) = T_0$ and $\theta(d, t) = T_1$ for $t > 0$, find the Laplace transform of $\theta(x, t)$. Find the inverse transform by means of the complex inversion formula.

6. When a sound wave is propagated with spherical symmetry, the excess pressure $p(r, t)$ satisfies the equation

$$\frac{\partial^2}{\partial r^2} (rp) = \frac{1}{c^2} \frac{\partial^2}{\partial t^2} (rp).$$

A medium in $a < r < b$ has $p = 0$ for $t \leqslant 0$ and has boundary conditions $p(a, t) = 0$ and $p(b, t) = p_1 e^{-\lambda t}$ for $t > 0$. Find the Laplace transform $\bar{p}(r, s)$, expand it in a series of exponential functions and invert term by term in order to determine $p(r, t)$.

7. Find the steady temperature distribution in an infinite strip $0 < y < h$, $-\infty < x < \infty$ when the temperature is zero on $y = 0$ except for a point source of heat represented by $T_0 \delta(x)$ and the surface $y = h$ is perfectly insulated.

8. The temperature $\theta(x, y)$ in a semi-infinite strip $0 \leqslant x < \infty$, $-1 \leqslant y \leqslant 1$ reaches a steady state under the boundary conditions $\theta = 0$ on $y = \pm 1$ $(x > 0)$ and $\theta = -\frac{1}{2}\lambda(y + 3)$ on $x = 0$ $(-1 < y < 1)$. Show that the sine transform of θ is given by

$$\Theta_s(\xi, y) = \frac{\lambda}{2\xi} \left\{ \frac{3 \cosh \xi y}{\cosh \xi} + \frac{\sinh \xi y}{\sinh \xi} - y - 3 \right\}$$

$$= \frac{\lambda}{\xi} \left\{ \frac{2 \sinh \xi(1 + y) + \sinh \xi(1 - y)}{\sinh 2\xi} - \frac{y + 3}{2} \right\}$$

and hence find $\theta(x, y)$ with the help of Table A8 in the Appendix. By adding the linear temperature distribution $\frac{1}{2}\lambda(y + 3)$ to $\theta(x, y)$, find the solution for the boundary values

$$\theta = \lambda \quad \text{on } y = -1 \quad \text{for} \quad x > 0,$$

$$\theta = 2\lambda \quad \text{on } y = 1 \quad \text{for} \quad x > 0,$$

$$\theta = 0 \quad \text{on } x = 0 \quad \text{for} \quad -1 < y < 1,$$

as in problem 26(b) of Chapter 4.

BIBLIOGRAPHY

[1]   Doetsch, G., *Introduction to the Theory and Application of the Laplace Transformation*, Springer, Berlin (1974).

[2]   Sneddon, I. N., *The Use of Integral Transforms*, McGraw-Hill, New York (1972).

[3]   Abramowitz, M., and I. A. Stegun, *Handbook of Mathematical Functions*, Dover, New York (1965)

[4]   Erdélyi, A., W. Magnus, F. Oberhettinger and F. G. Tricomi, *Tables of Integral Transforms*, Vol. 1, McGraw-Hill, New York (1954).

[5]   Murray, J. D., *Asymptotic Analysis*, Oxford (1974).

[6]   Doetsch, G., *Handbuch der Laplace-Transformation*, Band 2, Birkhäuser, Basel (1955).

[7]   Whittaker, E. T., and G. N. Watson, *A Course of Modern Analysis*, Cambridge (1952).

[8]   Erdélyi, A., W. Magnus, F. Oberhettinger and F. G. Tricomi, *Table of Integral Transforms*, Vol. 2, McGraw-Hill, New York (1954).

CHAPTER 6

Ordinary Differential Equations

6.1 INTRODUCTION

The linear second-order equation with constant coefficients has been studied in detail in Chapter 1 of Volume 1. In this chapter we are concerned mainly with the solution of linear equations of second order with non-constant coefficients. Examples of such equations are Bessel's equation and Legendre's equation, each of which arises in Chapter 7 of Volume 1 in the solution of partial differential equations by separation of variables. Certain general properties of the solutions of linear equations are considered in §6.2 and §6.3 whilst §§6.4, 6.5 and 6.6 are devoted to methods of obtaining the solutions.

The linear equations which occur in engineering frequently arise as approximations to situations governed by non-linear equations in which the non-linearity is small. The perturbation method of solution considered in §6.7 provides a means of approximating to the solution of such equations in terms of the solutions of their linear counterparts.

For the general non-linear equations, no analytic methods of solution exist and it is necessary to employ numerical or other approximate methods. The considerations of §6.8 form an introduction to the qualitative study of the behaviour of the solutions. This is an important prerequisite to any attempt at an approximate solution by numerical methods.

6.2 THE LINEAR HOMOGENEOUS EQUATION

A differential equation is said to be linear if the dependent variable y and its derivatives occur in the first degree with coefficients depending on the independent variable x only. Thus, the general linear equation of order n for a function $y(x)$ is

$$a_0(x)y^{(n)} + a_1(x)y^{(n-1)} + \ldots + a_{n-1}(x)y' + a_n(x)y = f(x).$$

Here, and throughout this chapter, the prime denotes differentiation with respect to x. Thus

$$y' = y'(x) = \frac{dy}{dx}, \; y'' = y''(x) = \frac{d^2y}{dx^2}, \ldots, y^{(n)} = y^{(n)}(x) = \frac{d^ny}{dx^n}.$$

The following treatment deals predominantly with equations of second order, but most of the results are readily generalized to equations of any order. When the function $f(x)$ on the right-hand side is identically zero the differential equation is said to be homogeneous, otherwise the equation is termed inhomogeneous. This section contains some general results relating to the solution of linear homogeneous equations.

The Superposition Principle

Consider the equation

$$(1 + x^2)y'' + xy' - y = 0.\tag{1}$$

It is easily seen that $y = x$ is a solution, and it may be verified by substitution in the differential equation that $y = (1 + x^2)^{\frac{1}{2}}$ is another solution. Then the function $y = c_1 x + c_2 (1 + x^2)^{\frac{1}{2}}$ is also a solution, for all values of the constants c_1 and c_2. Thus

$$y' = c_1 + \frac{c_2 x}{(1 + x^2)^{\frac{1}{2}}}, \quad y'' = \frac{c_2}{(1 + x^2)^{\frac{3}{2}}}$$

which when substituted in equation (1) give

$$(1 + x^2)y'' + xy' - y$$

$$= \frac{c_2}{(1 + x^2)^{\frac{1}{2}}} + c_1 x + \frac{c_2 x^2}{(1 + x^2)^{\frac{1}{2}}} - c_1 x - c_2 (1 + x^2)^{\frac{1}{2}} \equiv 0.$$

This result is an example of the *superposition principle* (see also §7.1 of Volume 1). The principle states that if $y = u_1(x), y = u_2(x), \ldots, y = u_r(x)$, are each solutions of a homogeneous linear equation, then any *linear combination* (see §1.3) $y = c_1 u_1(x) + c_2 u_2(x) + \ldots + c_r u_r(x)$ is also a solution for all values of the constants $c_1, c_2, \ldots, c_r$.

Initial Value Problem

If a solution of equation (1) is required for which $y = 3$ when $x = 0$, then one such solution is $y = 3(1 + x^2)^{\frac{1}{2}}$. It is clear that $y = 3(1 + x^2)^{\frac{1}{2}} + c_1 x$ is also such a solution for all values of the constant c_1. If in addition, however, it is required that $y' = 5$ at $x = 0$, then only the solution for which $c_1 = 5$ will satisfy this additional condition. The two *initial conditions* $y = 3, y' = 5$ at $x = 0$, pick out one particular solution $y = 5x + 3(1 + x^2)^{\frac{1}{2}}$ and it can be proved that this is the only solution of the differential equation which will satisfy these initial conditions. It should be noticed that it is not possible to prescribe arbitrary values to any further derivatives of y at $x = 0$. Thus it follows from the differential equation (1) that, for all values of x

$$y'' = \frac{y - xy'}{(1 + x^2)}.$$

Putting $x = 0, y = 3, y' = 5$ in this equation determines the second derivative at $x = 0$ as $(y'')_{x=0} = (y)_{x=0} = 3$. Moreover by repeatedly differentiating equation (1) it is possible to determine the value of each derivative of y at $x = 0$ in terms of the values of y and y' at $x = 0$.

Similar results hold for all homogeneous linear equations. Thus, for an equation of order n, a particular solution is obtained by prescribing y and its first $(n - 1)$ derivatives at $x = 0$. The problem of obtaining the solution satisfying these conditions is known as the *initial value problem* or *Cauchy's problem*. It may be proved that for the homogeneous linear equation a solution always exists and is unique provided $a_0(x) \neq 0$ at $x = 0$.

General Solution

The solution $y = c_1 x + c_2(1 + x^2)^{1/2}$ of equation (1) has the properties that $y = c_2$, $y' = c_1$, at $x = 0$. By choosing the constants c_1 and c_2 appropriately, it is possible to obtain the solution of the Cauchy problem, for any initial values. Moreover every solution of the equation is obtained from the solution $y = c_1 x + c_2(1 + x^2)^{1/2}$ by an appropriate choice of c_1 and c_2. The solution $y = c_1 x + c_2(1 + x^2)^{1/2}$ is termed the *general solution* of the differential equation (1).

Since $y = x$ is a solution of equation (1) so also is $y = 5x$ and hence by the superposition principle $y = c_1 x + c_2(5x)$ is a solution for all values of c_1 and c_2. But this solution cannot be made to satisfy arbitrary initial conditions at $x = 0$. The reason is that $y = x$ and $y = (5x)$ are *linearly dependent* (see §1.3), the second solution being a simple multiple of the first. Quite generally a set of functions $\varphi_1(x), \varphi_2(x), \ldots, \varphi_r(x)$ is said to be linearly dependent if there exist constants $\alpha_1, \alpha_2, \ldots, \alpha_r$ such that the equation

$$\alpha_1 \varphi_1(x) + \alpha_2 \varphi_2(x) + \ldots + \alpha_r \varphi_r(x) = 0$$

is satisfied for all values of x, with at least one of the constants $\alpha_1, \alpha_2, \ldots, \alpha_r$ being non-zero. If the only values of $\alpha_1, \alpha_2, \ldots, \alpha_r$ for which this equation is satisfied are $\alpha_1 = 0, \alpha_2 = 0, \ldots, \alpha_r = 0$, then the functions $\varphi_1(x), \varphi_2(x), \ldots, \varphi_r(x)$ are *linearly independent* (see §1.3). To obtain the general solution of the nth order equation, it is necessary to obtain n linearly independent solutions. Then the general solution is a linear combination of these.

If a set of n solutions $u_1(x), u_2(x), \ldots, u_n(x)$ is known, there arises the problem of determining whether or not they are linearly independent. To do this, consider the solution $y(x)$ formed by the linear combination

$$y(x) = c_1 u_1(x) + c_2 u_2(x) + \ldots + c_n u_n(x). \tag{2}$$

Let this be required to satisfy the initial conditions that

$$y(\bar{x}) = k_0, \, y'(\bar{x}) = k_1, \, y''(\bar{x}) = k_2, \ldots, y^{(n-1)}(\bar{x}) = k_{n-1}, \quad \text{at } x = \bar{x},$$

where $k_0, k_1, \ldots, k_{n-1}$ are specified constants. These conditions will be satisfied provided the constants $c_1, c_2, \ldots, c_n$ satisfy the system of linear simultaneous equations

$$
\begin{aligned}
c_1 u_1(\bar{x}) &+ c_2 u_2(\bar{x}) &+ \ldots + c_n u_n(\bar{x}) &= k_0, \\
c_1 u_1'(\bar{x}) &+ c_2 u_2'(\bar{x}) &+ \ldots + c_n u_n'(\bar{x}) &= k_1, \\
&\vdots \\
c_1 u_1^{(n-1)}(\bar{x}) &+ c_2 u_2^{(n-1)}(\bar{x}) &+ \ldots + c_n u_n^{(n-1)}(\bar{x}) &= k_{n-1}.
\end{aligned}
$$

It is shown in §8.4 of Volume 1 that these equations have a unique solution for $c_1, c_2, \ldots, c_n$ provided the *Wronskian determinant* $W(x)$ given by

$$
W(x) = \begin{vmatrix}
u_1(x) & u_2(x) & \ldots & u_n(x) \\
u_1'(x) & u_2'(x) & \ldots & u_n'(x) \\
\vdots & \vdots & \vdots\vdots\vdots & \vdots \\
u_1^{(n-1)}(x) & u_2^{(n-1)}(x) & \ldots & u_n^{(n-1)}(x)
\end{vmatrix}, \tag{3}
$$

is non-zero at $x = \bar{x}$. In this case the functions $u_1(x), u_2(x), \ldots, u_n(x)$ are linearly independent. It can be proved that if $W(\bar{x})$ is non-zero, then $W(x)$ is non-zero for all values of x with the possible exception of certain isolated values (see §6.5).

Applying these ideas to equation (1) we find that the Wronskian for the two solutions $u_1(x) = x, u_2(x) = (1 + x^2)^{\frac{1}{2}}$ is non-zero for all x and the solutions are linearly independent. On the other hand the Wronskian for $u_1(x) = x$ and $u_2(x) = 5x$ is identically zero, showing that these solutions are linearly dependent and that $c_1 u_1 + c_2 u_2 = (c_1 + 5c_2)x$ is *not* the general solution.

Boundary Value Problem

The Cauchy problem is not the only problem arising in the solution of differential equations. Thus it may be necessary to obtain the solution of equation (1) satisfying certain *boundary conditions*, for example the conditions $y = 3$ when $x = 0$ and $y = -4$ when $x = 1$. When these conditions are applied to the general solution $y = c_1 x + c_2(1 + x^2)^{\frac{1}{2}}$ there results the particular solution $y = -(3\sqrt{2} + 4)x + 3(1 + x^2)^{\frac{1}{2}}$. Again, taking as boundary conditions $y' = 1$ at $x = 0$, $y = 0$ at $x = 2$, gives rise to the solution

$$y = x - \frac{2}{\sqrt{5}}(1 + x^2)^{\frac{1}{2}}.$$ In each case there is a unique non-trivial solution satisfying the boundary conditions. On the other hand, the only solution of equation (1) satisfying the boundary conditions $y = 0$ at $x = 0$, $y' = 0$ at $x = -1$, corresponds to $c_1 = c_2 = 0$, which gives the trivial solution $y = 0$.

Consider now the equation

$$(1 + x^2)y'' - 2xy' + 2y = 0 \tag{4}$$

subject to the boundary conditions

$$y' = 1 \quad \text{at } x = 0, \qquad y = 1 \quad \text{at } x = 1.$$

Equation (4) has the general solution $y = c_1 x + c_2(1 - x^2)$. (The reader should verify this by substitution into equation (4).) Applying the boundary conditions leads to the equation $c_1 = 1$ and places no restriction on the constant c_2. There exists an infinity of solutions $y = x + c_2(1 - x^2)$, which satisfy the boundary conditions. However there is no solution of equation (4) which satisfies the boundary conditions $y = 1$ at $x = 1$ and $y = 1$ at $x = -1$, since these conditions lead to the incompatible equations $c_1 = 1$ and $c_1 = -1$.

These examples show the variety of possibilities which arise in the study of boundary value problems. There may be only the trivial solution, a unique solution, an infinity of solutions or no solution at all. This is in marked contrast to the case of the initial value problem, which always has a unique solution.

Exercises

1. Verify that $y = u_1(x) = x^2 - 4/3$ and $y = u_2(x) = (1 + x)^{\frac{1}{2}}$ each satisfy the differential equation

$$2(3x^2 + 5x + 2)y'' - (9x + 10)y' + 6y = 0 ,$$

and show that these solutions are linearly independent.

2. Solve the differential equation of exercise 1 subject to each of the following sets of initial conditions

(a) $y = 3$, $y' = 0$,   at $x = 0$,
(b) $y = 1$, $y' = 6$,   at $x = -1$,
(c) $y = 0$, $y' = 1$,   at $x = 2/\sqrt{3}$.

3. Verify that the Wronskian $W(x)$ of the functions $u_1(x)$ and $u_2(x)$ given in exercise 1 satisfies the first-order linear differential equation

$$2(3x^2 + 5x + 2)W' - (9x + 10)W = 0 .$$

4. Solve the differential equation of exercise 1 subject to each of the following sets of boundary conditions:

(a) $y = 2$ at $x = 0$, $y' = -3$ at $x = 2$,
(b) $y' = 0$ at $x = 0$, $y' = -5$ at $x = 1$,
(c) $y = 0$ at $x = 2/\sqrt{3}$, $y' = 0$ at $x = 2/3$,
(d) $y' = 0$ at $x = 0$, $y = 0$ at $x = 2/\sqrt{3}$.

6.3 THE LINEAR INHOMOGENEOUS EQUATION

To obtain the general solution of the inhomogeneous equation

$$a_0(x)y^{(n)} + a_1(x)y^{(n-1)} + \ldots + a_n(x)y = f(x) \tag{5}$$

it is necessary to know any one solution, together with the general solution of the corresponding homogeneous equation. Then if $v(x)$ is one solution of equation (5) the general solution is

$$y = v(x) + c_1 u_1(x) + c_2 u_2(x) + \ldots + c_n u_n(x) \tag{6}$$

where $c_1, c_2, \ldots, c_n$ are arbitrary constants and $y = u_1(x), y = u_2(x), \ldots, y = u_n(x)$ are n linearly independent solutions of the homogeneous form of equation (5). This solution consists of the sum of the *particular integral* $v(x)$ and the *complementary function* $c_1 u_1(x) + c_2 u_2(x) + \ldots + c_n u_n(x)$. Equation (6) will yield the solution of the Cauchy problem for equation (5) for any given set of initial conditions.

EXAMPLE 1   The reader should verify that $v(x) = \frac{1}{3}(x^2 + 2)$ is a particular integral of the equation

$$(1 + x^2)y'' + xy' - y = x^2 .$$

Adding the complementary function $y = c_1 x + c_2(1 + x^2)^{\frac{1}{2}}$ (§6.2) gives the general solution $y = \frac{1}{3}(x^2 + 2) + c_1 x + c_2(1 + x^2)^{\frac{1}{2}}$. Imposing the initial conditions $y = 2, y' = -5$ at $x = 0$ gives the particular solution $y = \frac{1}{3}(x^2 + 2) - 5x + \frac{4}{3}(1 + x^2)^{\frac{1}{2}}$.

If the complementary function of equation (5) is known, a particular integral $v(x)$ can be determined by the *method of variation of parameters*. This method will be described for the second-order equation

$$a_0(x)y'' + a_1(x)y' + a_2(x)y = f(x) , \tag{7}$$

but may readily be extended to equations of any order.

Let the complementary function of equation (7) be $y = c_1 u_1(x) + c_2 u_2(x)$. The object of the method is to determine functions $v_1(x)$ and $v_2(x)$ such that $y = v_1(x)u_1(x) + v_2(x)u_2(x)$ is a particular integral of (7). With this assumed form for y the first derivative is given by

$$y' = v_1(x)u_1'(x) + v_2(x)u_2'(x) + v_1'(x)u_1(x) + v_2'(x)u_2(x) .$$

If this is again differentiated there results an expression for y'' which involves the unknown functions $v_1(x)$, $v_2(x)$ and their first and second derivatives. Substitution into equation (7) would then lead to one second-order differential equation for these two unknown functions. If, however, the functions $v_1(x)$ and $v_2(x)$ are made to satisfy the condition

$$v_1'(x)u_1(x) + v_2'(x)u_2(x) = 0 , \tag{8}$$

then the expression for y' becomes

$$y' = v_1(x)u_1'(x) + v_2(x)u_2'(x) .$$

This does not involve derivatives of v_1 and v_2. As a result the second derivative of y is

$$y'' = v_1'(x)u_1'(x) + v_2'(x)u_2'(x) + v_1(x)u_1''(x) + v_2(x)u_2''(x) ,$$

which involves $v_1(x)$, $v_2(x)$ and their first derivatives only. Substituting these expressions for y, y' and y'' into equation (7) gives

$$v_1(x)\{a_0 u_1'' + a_1 u_1' + a_2 u_1\} + v_2(x)\{a_0 u_2'' + a_1 u_2' + a_2 u_2\}$$
$$+ a_0(x)[v_1'(x)u_1'(x) + v_2'(x)u_2'(x)] = f(x) .$$

Since $u_1(x)$ and $u_2(x)$ satisfy the homogeneous form of equation (7), the terms in braces vanish and the equation simplifies to

$$v_1'(x)u_1'(x) + v_2'(x)u_2'(x) = f(x)/a_0(x) . \tag{9}$$

Equations (8) and (9) together form a pair of linear algebraic equations for $v_1'(x)$ and $v_2'(x)$. Straightforward elimination yields expressions for $v_1'(x)$ and $v_2'(x)$ which may be readily integrated to give

$$v_1(x) = \int \frac{f(x)}{a_0(x)} \frac{u_2(x)\, dx}{(u_2 u_1' - u_1 u_2')} ,$$

$$v_2(x) = \int \frac{f(x)}{a_0(x)} \frac{u_1(x)\, dx}{(u_1 u_2' - u_2 u_1')} .$$

The arbitrary constants of integration in $v_1(x)$ and $v_2(x)$ give rise to a term in y of the form $c_1 u_1(x) + c_2 u_2(x)$ which corresponds to the complementary function. Thus the method yields not simply a particular integral but the general solution.

EXAMPLE 2   Obtain a particular integral of

$$(1 + x^2)y'' - 2xy' + 2y = 3x(1 + x^2).$$

The complementary function is the general solution $y = c_1 x + c_2(1 - x^2)$ of equation (4). This leads to the choice of a trial solution in the form

$$y = xv_1(x) + (1 - x^2)v_2(x).$$

Differentiating with respect to x gives

$$y' = v_1(x) - 2xv_2(x) + xv_1'(x) + (1 - x^2)v_2'(x).$$

The derivatives v_1' and v_2' may be eliminated from this expression by imposing the condition

$$xv_1'(x) + (1 - x^2)v_2'(x) = 0. \tag{10}$$

This gives

$$y' = v_1(x) - 2xv_2(x).$$

Differentiating again with respect to x gives

$$y'' = -2v_2(x) + v_1'(x) - 2xv_2'(x).$$

These expressions when substituted into the differential equation lead to the condition

$$(1 + x^2)[-2v_2(x) + v_1'(x) - 2xv_2'(x)] - 2x[v_1(x) - 2xv_2(x)]$$
$$+ 2[xv_1(x) + (1 - x^2)v_2(x)] = 3x(1 + x^2).$$

On rearranging, this becomes

$$v_1(x)\{-2x + 2x\} + v_2(x)\{-2(1 + x^2) + 4x^2 + 2(1 - x^2)\}$$
$$+ (1 + x^2)v_1'(x) - 2x(1 + x^2)v_2'(x) = 3x(1 + x^2),$$

and since the terms in braces vanish this reduces to

$$v_1'(x) - 2xv_2'(x) = 3x. \tag{11}$$

It is convenient to solve equations (10) and (11) for $v_2'(x)$ to obtain

$$v_2'(x) = \frac{-3x^2}{(1 + x^2)} = -3 + \frac{3}{(1 + x^2)}.$$

This equation may be integrated immediately to give

$$v_2(x) = -3x + 3 \tan^{-1}x + a_2$$

where a_2 is an arbitrary constant. Substituting into equation (10) then leads after some simplification to the expression

$$v_1'(x) = -3x + \frac{6x}{(1+x^2)}.$$

This integrates to give

$$v_1(x) = -\tfrac{3}{2}x^2 + 3\log(1+x^2) + a_1,$$

where a_1 is an arbitrary constant. The general solution is then given by

$$y = xv_1(x) + (1-x^2)v_2(x)$$
$$= \tfrac{3}{2}x(x^2-2) + 3x\log(1+x^2) + 3(1-x^2)\tan^{-1}x + a_1x + a_2(1-x^2).$$

Exercises

1. Obtain the general solution of the differential equation

$$(1+x^2)y'' - 2xy' + 2y = x^2 + 1.$$

(For the complementary function, see the solution of equation (4), §6.2.)

2. Solve the differential equation of exercise 1 subject to each of the following sets of initial or boundary conditions.

    (a) $y = 0$, $y' = 0$,   at $x = 0$,

    (b) $y = 0$, $y' = 5$,   at $x = -1$,

    (c) $y = 2$ at $x = 0$, $y = 0$ at $x = 1$,

    (d) $y = 0$ at $x = -1$, $y = 0$ at $x = 1$.

3. Obtain the general solution of the differential equation

$$(1+x^2)y'' + xy' - y = (1+x^2)^{-\frac{1}{2}}.$$

(For the complementary function, see the solution of equation (1), §6.2.)

6.4 THE LINEAR EQUATION. SOLUTION IN SERIES

It is known that, under certain conditions of differentiability, a function $y(x)$ may be expanded as a power series in x in the form

$$y(x) = y(0) + xy'(0) + \frac{x^2}{2!}y''(0) + \ldots + \frac{x^n}{n!}y^{(n)}(0) + \ldots,$$

which is its Taylor series about $x = 0$. Moreover it has been shown in §6.2 that, for a second-order equation, if y and y' are given at $x = 0$, all higher derivatives are determined by the differential equation and equations derived from it by repeated differentiation. This suggests solving for $y(x)$ as an infinite series. For example, consider again the equation (1)

$$(1 + x^2)y'' + xy' - y = 0, \tag{1}$$

and differentiate this equation p times using Leibnitz' theorem to obtain

$$(1 + x^2)y^{(p+2)}(x) + (2p + 1)xy^{(p+1)}(x) + (p^2 - 1)y^{(p)}(x) = 0,$$

which is valid for $p \geqslant 0$. At $x = 0$ this reduces to

$$y^{(p+2)}(0) = -(p + 1)(p - 1)y^{(p)}(0). \tag{12}$$

This *recurrence relation* gives

$$y^{(2)}(0) = -(1)(-1)y(0) = y(0)$$
$$y^{(3)}(0) = -(2)(0)y'(0) = 0$$
$$y^{(4)}(0) = -(3)(1)y^{(2)}(0) = -3y(0)$$

and, in general,

$$y^{(2k)}(0) = -(2k - 1)(2k - 3)y^{(2k-2)}(0)$$
$$= (2k - 1)(2k - 3)(2k - 3)(2k - 5)y^{(2k-4)}(0)$$
$$= (-1)^{k-1}(2k - 1)(2k - 3)^2(2k - 5)^2 \ldots (3)^2(1)y(0),$$

whilst

$$y^{(2k+1)}(0) = 0 \quad \text{for } k > 0.$$

Thus, substituting into the Taylor series for $y(x)$ gives

$$y(x) = y(0) + xy'(0) + \frac{x^2}{2!}y(0) - 3\frac{x^4}{4!}y(0) + \ldots$$

$$+ \frac{x^{2k}}{(2k)!}(-1)^{k-1}(2k - 1)(2k - 3)^2(2k - 5)^2 \ldots (3)^2(1)y(0) + \ldots,$$

or, on rearranging,

$$y(x) = y'(0)x + y(0)\left\{1 + \frac{x^2}{2!} - \frac{3x^4}{4!} + \ldots \right.$$

$$\left. + (-1)^{k-1}(2k - 1)(2k - 3)^2(2k - 5)^2 \ldots (3)^2(1)\frac{x^{2k}}{(2k)!} + \ldots\right\}.$$

In this form it is clear that there are two arbitrary parameters $y(0)$ and $y'(0)$ in the solution for $y(x)$ which is a linear combination of the infinite series and the function x. By applying the ratio test, the series may be shown to be convergent for $|x| < 1$. In this interval it has the sum $(1 + x^2)^{\frac{1}{2}}$ so that $y = c_1 x + c_2(1 + x^2)^{\frac{1}{2}}$ satisfies equation (1) for arbitrary c_1 and c_2 when $|x| < 1$. However, it is readily verified that although the series is not convergent for $|x| \geqslant 1$ the function $(1 + x^2)^{\frac{1}{2}}$ will satisfy the differential equation for all values of x and the general solution obtained here agrees with that quoted in §6.2.

An alternative method of obtaining these solutions, and the one commonly employed in practice, is to assume a solution in series form

$$y = \sum_{r=0}^{\infty} a_r x^r,$$

where the coefficients a_r are as yet undetermined. If it is assumed that this series may be differentiated term by term there results

$$y' = \sum_{r=0}^{\infty} r a_r x^{r-1}, \qquad y'' = \sum_{r=0}^{\infty} r(r-1) a_r x^{r-2}.$$

Substitution into equation (1) gives

$$(1+x^2)y'' + xy' - y = (1+x^2) \sum_{r=0}^{\infty} r(r-1) a_r x^{r-2}$$

$$+ x \sum_{r=0}^{\infty} r a_r x^{r-1} - \sum_{r=0}^{\infty} a_r x^r = 0.$$

This equation must hold for all values of x and thus the constant term and the coefficient of each distinct power of x must vanish. It is convenient to write the equation in terms of four separate sums in the form

$$\sum_{r=0}^{\infty} r(r-1) a_r x^{r-2} + \sum_{r=0}^{\infty} r(r-1) a_r x^r + \sum_{r=0}^{\infty} r a_r x^r - \sum_{r=0}^{\infty} a_r x^r = 0.$$

Notice that in the first two sums the terms corresponding to $r = 0$ and $r = 1$ vanish and that in the third sum the term corresponding to $r = 0$ vanishes. The non-zero contributions to the constant term arise only from the terms corresponding to $r = 2$ in the first sum and $r = 0$ in the fourth sum and lead to the equation

$$2a_2 - a_0 = 0.$$

The coefficient of x is obtained by taking $r = 3$ in the first sum and $r = 1$ from the other three. There are non-zero contributions from the first, third and fourth sums, and the condition that the coefficient of x should vanish gives the equation

$$6a_3 + a_1 - a_1 = 0.$$

In the general case the coefficient of x^n is obtained by taking $r = n + 2$ in the first sum and $r = n$ in the other three. In the case $n \geqslant 2$, there are contributions from all four sums and the coefficient will vanish provided that

$$(n+2)(n+1)a_{n+2} + n(n-1)a_n + na_n - a_n = 0.$$

These equations may be solved to give

$$a_2 = \tfrac{1}{2} a_0, \quad a_3 = 0, \quad a_{n+2} = -\frac{(n-1)}{(n+2)} a_n.$$

From these it may be seen that there are two solutions. One involves even powers of x only and the coefficient of x^{2k} is given by

$$a_{2k} = \frac{(-1)^{k-1}(2k-1)(2k-3)^2(2k-5)^2 \dots (3)^2(1)}{(2k)!} a_0$$

This gives an infinite series whose sum is $a_0(1+x^2)^{\frac{1}{2}}$ for $|x| < 1$. The second solution is $y = a_1 x$ and the general solution is $y = a_0(1+x^2)^{\frac{1}{2}} + a_1 x$ where a_0 and a_1 are arbitrary constants.

As a second example consider the differential equation

$$(x+2)(x-1)y'' + (3x+5)y' - (x^2+2)y = 0 . \tag{15}$$

As before, assume a solution of the form

$$y = \sum_{r=0}^{\infty} a_r x^r .$$

Differentiating the series term by term and substituting in equation (15) leads to

$$(x+2)(x-1) \sum_{r=2}^{\infty} r(r-1)a_r x^{r-2} + (3x+5) \sum_{r=1}^{\infty} ra_r x^{r-1}$$

$$- (x^2+2) \sum_{r=0}^{\infty} a_r x^r = 0 .$$

This equation is satisfied provided the constant term and the coefficient of each power of x separately vanish. Rewriting this equation as separate sums gives

$$\sum_{r=2}^{\infty} r(r-1)a_r x^r + \sum_{r=0}^{\infty} r(r-1)a_r x^{r-1} - 2\sum_{r=2}^{\infty} r(r-1)a_r x^{r-2}$$

$$+ 3\sum_{r=1}^{\infty} ra_r x^r + 5\sum_{r=1}^{\infty} ra_r x^{r-1} - \sum_{r=0}^{\infty} a_r x^{r+2} - 2\sum_{r=0}^{\infty} a_r x^r = 0 .$$

Equating the constant term on the left-hand side to zero gives

$$-4a_2 + 5a_1 - 2a_0 = 0 . \tag{16}$$

Equating the coefficient of x on the left-hand side to zero gives

$$2a_2 - 12a_3 + 3a_1 + 10a_2 - 2a_1 = 0 , \tag{17}$$

and equating the coefficient of x^n to zero leads to the equation

$$n(n-1)a_n + (n+1)na_{n+1} - 2(n+2)(n+1)a_{n+2}$$

$$+ 3na_n + 5(n+1)a_{n+1} - a_{n-2} - 2a_n = 0 . \tag{18}$$

Note that equation (18) is valid only for $n \geqslant 2$ since a_{n-2} is not defined for $n < 2$.

Equation (16) determines a_2 in terms of a_0 and a_1 as

$$a_2 = \tfrac{5}{4}a_1 - \tfrac{1}{2}a_0.$$

Equation (17) determines a_3 in terms of a_0, a_1, on using equation (16), as

$$a_3 = a_2 + \tfrac{1}{12}a_1 = \tfrac{4}{3}a_1 - \tfrac{1}{2}a_0.$$

All other values of $a_n (n \geqslant 4)$ may be determined recursively from the *recurrence relation* derived from equation (18)

$$a_{n+2} = \frac{(n+5)}{2(n+2)} a_{n+1} + \frac{(n^2 + 2n - 2)}{2(n+2)(n+1)} a_n - \frac{a_{n-2}}{2(n+2)(n+1)}, \quad \text{for } n \geqslant 2.$$

The constants a_0 and a_1 are not determined and correspond to the two arbitrary constants in the general solution of the second-order equation. Choosing $a_0 = 1$ and $a_1 = 0$, there results

$$a_2 = -\tfrac{1}{2}, a_3 = -\tfrac{1}{2}, a_4 = -\tfrac{29}{48}, a_5 = -\tfrac{31}{48},$$

and one solution may be written formally as

$$y = u_1(x) = 1 - \frac{x^2}{2} - \frac{x^3}{2} - \frac{29x^4}{48} - \frac{31x^5}{48} + \ldots. \tag{19}$$

Again, putting $a_0 = 0$ and $a_1 = 1$ gives

$$a_2 = \tfrac{5}{4}, \quad a_3 = \tfrac{4}{3}, \quad a_4 = \tfrac{71}{48}, \quad a_5 = \tfrac{191}{120},$$

and a second solution is formally

$$y = u_2(x) = x + \frac{5x^2}{4} + \frac{4x^3}{3} + \frac{71x^4}{48} + \frac{191x^5}{120} + \ldots. \tag{20}$$

Equations (19) and (20) give valid solutions provided the series are convergent. In this example, it is not possible to write down an explicit expression for the general term of either of these series, and the examination of their convergence is accordingly more difficult. No attempt will be made here to examine convergence, but in the following section we state a general criterion concerning this question.

This technique of solution in series may also be applied to solve the inhomogeneous equation provided the terms on the right-hand side are either polynomials or functions which can be expanded as power series in x (see exercise 4 below).

Exercises

1. By repeated differentiation of the equation

$$y'' + xy = 0,$$

obtain the Taylor series expansion for the function y satisfying this equation and the initial conditions $y = 1, y' = 1$, at $x = 0$.

2. Obtain the general solution of the differential equation of exercise 1 as a linear combination of two infinite series and examine the convergence of the two series.

3. Obtain the recurrence relation between the coefficients in the series solution of the differential equation

$$(x + 2)y'' - xy' + 4y = 0$$

and write down the first five terms in each of two linearly independent series solutions.

4. Use the method of solution in series to solve the equation

$$y'' + 3xy' + (1 - x^2)y = 1 + x^2$$

subject to the initial conditions that $y = 1, y' = 0$ at $x = 0$.

6.5 THE LINEAR EQUATION. METHOD OF FROBENIUS

The method of solution in series, described in §6.4, is not valid for all linear equations. Consider as a further example the equation

$$x^2 y'' + 4xy' + y = 0 . \tag{21}$$

Proceeding as before, substitute $y = \sum_{r=0}^{\infty} a_r x^r$ to obtain

$$x^2 \sum_{r=2}^{\infty} r(r-1)a_r x^{r-2} + 4x \sum_{r=1}^{\infty} ra_r x^{r-1} + \sum_{r=0}^{\infty} a_r x^r = 0 .$$

Equating the constant term to zero gives $a_0 = 0$. Putting the coefficient of x equal to zero gives $a_1 = 0$. By continuing this process it is found that all the coefficients a_r vanish, and no solution of the assumed form exists.

Returning to the original procedure in which the solution is expanded as a Taylor series, it is seen immediately that the differential equation (21) fails to determine y'' at $x = 0$ in terms of y and y' at $x = 0$, because the coefficient of y'' vanishes at this point. In such situations the point $x = 0$ is said to be a *singular point* of the differential equation. Equation (21) is an example of Euler's equation, discussed in §1.10 of Volume 1. This equation has solutions of the form $y = x^p$ provided that

$$p(p - 1)x^p + 4px^p + x^p = (p^2 + 3p + 1)x^p = 0 .$$

This is satisfied for $p_1 = -\dfrac{3}{2} + \dfrac{\sqrt{5}}{2}$ or $p_2 = -\dfrac{3}{2} - \dfrac{\sqrt{5}}{2}$, and the general solution is $y = c_1 x^{p_1} + c_2 x^{p_2}$.

A slightly different equation is

$$x^2 y'' + 4xy' + (1 - x^2)y = 0 , \tag{22}$$

which also has a singular point at $x = 0$. It may again be shown that no power series

solution exists and since equation (22) is not an example of Euler's equation there are
no solutions of the form $y = x^p$. However, for values of x close to zero the coefficient
of y is approximately equal to 1 and it seems reasonable to expect that the solutions
behave like the solutions of equation (21) as x tends to zero. This leads to a search for
solutions of the form $y = x^p u(x)$ where $u(x)$ tends to a finite non-zero limit as x tends
to zero. Assuming that $u(x)$ may be expanded in a power series in x leads to the
possibility of solutions of the form

$$y = x^p \cdot \sum_{r=0}^{\infty} a_r x^r = \sum_{r=0}^{\infty} a_r x^{r+p}$$

where the index p and the coefficients a_r are as yet undetermined. If this series can be
differentiated term by term, there results

$$y' = \sum_{r=0}^{\infty} (r+p)a_r x^{r+p-1}, \quad y'' = \sum_{r=0}^{\infty} (r+p)(r+p-1)a_r x^{r+p-2}.$$

Substituting this trial solution into equation (22) gives

$$x^2 \sum_{r=0}^{\infty} (p+r)(p+r-1)a_r x^{p+r-2} + 4x \sum_{r=0}^{\infty} (p+r)a_r x^{p+r-1}$$

$$+ (1-x^2) \sum_{r=0}^{\infty} a_r x^{p+r}$$

$$= \sum_{r=0}^{\infty} (p+r)(p+r-1)a_r x^{p+r} + 4 \sum_{r=0}^{\infty} (p+r)a_r x^{p+r}$$

$$+ \sum_{r=0}^{\infty} a_r x^{p+r} - \sum_{r=0}^{\infty} a_r x^{p+r+2} = 0. \tag{23}$$

For this equation to be satisfied the coefficient of each individual power of x must
vanish. The lowest power of x is x^p and the vanishing of its coefficient gives

$$p(p-1)a_0 + 4pa_0 + a_0 = (p^2 + 3p + 1)a_0 = 0.$$

This equation involves only the first coefficient a_0 and is satisfied by $a_0 = 0$ which
violates the requirement that $u(x)$ tends to a non-zero limit as $x \to 0$. The only
alternative is that p must satisfy the equation

$$(p^2 + 3p + 1) = 0. \tag{24}$$

Equating the coefficient of x^{p+1} to zero gives

$$(p+1)pa_1 + 4(p+1)a_1 + a_1 = 0, \tag{25}$$

and in general the coefficient of x^{p+n} vanishes provided that

$$(p+n)(p+n-1)a_n + 4(p+n)a_n + a_n - a_{n-2} = 0, \quad \text{for } n \geqslant 2. \tag{26}$$

Thus equation (23) is satisfied if p takes one of the two values obtained from equation (24), and if the coefficients a_1, a_n satisfy the *recurrence relations* arising from equations (25) and (26), namely

$$(p^2 + 5p + 5)a_1 = 0 ,$$

$$a_n = \frac{a_{n-2}}{\{(p+n)^2 + 3(p+n) + 1\}} = \frac{a_{n-2}}{\{p^2 + 3p + 1 + n^2 + 2pn + 3n\}}$$

$$= \frac{a_{n-2}}{n(n + 2p + 3)} , \quad \text{for } n \geqslant 2 .$$

Equation (24) is termed the *indicial equation* of equation (22) and its roots are the values $p_1 = -\dfrac{3}{2} + \dfrac{\sqrt{5}}{2}$ and $p_2 = -\dfrac{3}{2} - \dfrac{\sqrt{5}}{2}$ which arise in the solution of equation (21).

Taking $p = p_1$, the recurrence relations become

$$(1 + \sqrt{5})a_1 = 0 ,$$

$$a_n = \frac{a_{n-2}}{n(n + \sqrt{5})} ,$$

which yield

$$a_1 = 0 = a_3 = a_5 = \ldots = a_{2k+1} = \ldots ,$$

$$a_2 = \frac{a_0}{2(2 + \sqrt{5})} , \quad a_4 = \frac{a_2}{4(4 + \sqrt{5})} = \frac{a_0}{8(2 + \sqrt{5})(4 + \sqrt{5})} ,$$

$$a_{2k} = \frac{a_{2k-2}}{2k(2k + \sqrt{5})} = \frac{a_0}{(2)(4) \ldots (2k)(2 + \sqrt{5})(4 + \sqrt{5}) \ldots (2k + \sqrt{5})}$$

$$= \frac{a_0}{2^k k!(2 + \sqrt{5})(4 + \sqrt{5}) \ldots (2k + \sqrt{5})} .$$

Choose $a_0 = 1$, then the solution is written formally as

$$y = u_1(x) \equiv x^{(-3+\sqrt{5})/2} \left\{ 1 + \sum_{k=1}^{\infty} \frac{\left(\dfrac{x^2}{2}\right)^k}{k!(2k + \sqrt{5})(2k - 2 + \sqrt{5}) \ldots (2 + \sqrt{5})} \right\} .$$

Similarly by taking $p = p_2$ in equations (25) and (26), a second solution is obtained with coefficients given by

$$a_1 = a_3 = \ldots = a_{2k+1} = \ldots = 0 ,$$

$$a_2 = \frac{a_0}{2(2 - \sqrt{5})} , \quad a_4 = \frac{a_0}{8(2 - \sqrt{5})(4 - \sqrt{5})} ,$$

$$a_{2k} = \frac{a_0}{2^k k!(2k - \sqrt{5})(2k - 2 - \sqrt{5}) \ldots (2 - \sqrt{5})} .$$

With the choice $a_0 = 1$ this solution may be written as

$$y = u_2(x) = x^{(-3-\sqrt{5})/2} \left\{ 1 + \sum_{k=1}^{\infty} \frac{\left(\dfrac{x^2}{2}\right)^k}{k!(2k - \sqrt{5})(2k - 2 - \sqrt{5}) \ldots (2 - \sqrt{5})} \right\}.$$

It is easily shown that the series in the expressions for $u_1(x)$ and $u_2(x)$ are convergent for all finite x so that $u_1(x)$ and $u_2(x)$ are defined for all finite and non-zero values of x. These two solutions are linearly independent and give the general solution $y = c_1 u_1(x) + c_2 u_2(x)$.

This illustrates the method of Frobenius which is valid for linear equations that reduce to the form of an Euler equation as $x \to 0$. For such equations the origin is said to be a *regular singular point*. The general second-order equation

$$a_0(x)y'' + a_1(x)y' + a_2(x)y = 0, \tag{27}$$

has a singular point at $x = 0$ if $\{a_0(x)/a_2(x)\} \to 0$ as $x \to 0$. If in addition the limits α and β given by

$$\lim_{x \to 0} \left\{ \frac{xa_1(x)}{a_0(x)} \right\} = \alpha, \quad \lim_{x \to 0} \left\{ \frac{x^2 a_2(x)}{a_0(x)} \right\} = \beta$$

exist, equation (27) may be approximated near $x = 0$ by the Euler equation

$$x^2 y'' + \alpha x y' + \beta y = 0, \tag{28}$$

and so the origin is a regular singular point. Equation (22) satisfies these criteria with $\alpha = 4$ and $\beta = 1$.

EXAMPLE 1   Solve $x^2 y'' + xy' + (x^2 - v^2)y = 0$, (Bessel's equation of order v) and examine the case when v is an integer.

The Frobenius method leads to the indicial equation

$$p^2 - v^2 = 0$$

and the recurrence relations

$$\{(p + 1)^2 - v^2\}a_1 = 0, \quad \{(p + n)^2 - v^2\}a_n + a_{n-2} = 0 \quad \text{for } n \geqslant 2.$$

The indicial equation has roots $p = \pm v$ and the recurrence relations give

$$a_1 = a_3 = \ldots = a_{2k+1} = \ldots = 0,$$

$$a_{2k} = \frac{-a_{2k-2}}{4k(p + k)} = \ldots = \frac{(-1)^k a_0}{2^{2k} k!(p + k)(p + k - 1) \ldots (p + 1)}.$$

The choice $p = v$ with $a_0 = \{\Gamma(v + 1)2^v\}^{-1}$ leads to the solution $y = J_v(x)$, where

$$J_v(x) = \sum_{r=0}^{\infty} \frac{(-1)^r \left(\dfrac{x}{2}\right)^{2r+v}}{r!\Gamma(v + r + 1)}$$

is the Bessel function of the first kind of order ν (see [2]) and $\Gamma(s)$ is the gamma function (see §5.2). Provided that ν is not an integer or zero the general solution is given by $y = c_1 J_\nu(x) + c_2 J_{-\nu}(x)$.

When ν is an integer, $\nu = m$ say, the choice $p = m$ leads to the solution $J_m(x)$. With the choice $p = -m$ however, the recurrence relation for $n = 2m$ gives $a_{2m-2} = 0$ which can be satisfied only when $a_0 = a_2 = \ldots = a_{2m-2} = 0$. The resulting series is a multiple of $J_m(x)$ and the method fails to give two linearly independent solutions.

This example illustrates the possible breakdown of the Frobenius method whenever the roots of the indicial equation are equal or differ by an integer. The technique for dealing with this situation is outside the scope of this chapter but may be found for example in Boyce and Di Prima [1].

It is now possible to return to the consideration of the convergence of the series method of solution discussed in §6.4. Recall the differential equation (15)

$$(x + 2)(x - 1)y'' + (3x + 5)y' - (x^2 + 2)y = 0, \tag{15}$$

for which we obtained the series solutions in §6.4 without examining their convergence. Note that the coefficient of y'' vanishes at $x = 1$ and $x = -2$ and that these two points are therefore singular points of the differential equation. At the origin $(x = 0)$ on the other hand the coefficient of the second derivative is non-zero and the origin is said to be an *ordinary point* of the differential equation. It is possible to prove that in such cases the series solutions in powers of x are convergent in every interval $|x| < d$ where d is a positive constant such that the circle $|z| = d$ in the complex plane contains no singular point of the differential equation (see Chapter 4). Thus in the case of equation (15) the solutions are convergent for $|x| < 1$. They may or may not be convergent for other values of x, the theorem gives no information on this point. The same point is illustrated in the solution of equation (1) in §6.4. This equation has singular points in the complex plane at $z = \pm i$ and the series solution is convergent for $|x| < 1$. These singular points, at which the coefficient of the highest derivative vanishes, are the isolated points at which the Wronskian also vanishes, as referred to in §6.2.

Exercises

1. Determine which of the following equations have regular singular points at the origin:

  (a) $x^3 y'' + x^2(x + 1)y' - 2y = 0$,

  (b) $x^3 y'' + x^2(x + 1)y' - 2xy = 0$,

  (c) $x(x - 3)y'' + 2y' + (x + 5)y = 0$.

2. Obtain the indicial equations and recurrence relations for each of the following equations:

  (a) $x^2(x + 2)y'' - 3xy' + (x - 1)y = 0$,

  (b) $3xy'' + (1 + x)y' + 2y = 0$.

3. Solve the differential equation

$$2xy'' - 3y' + y = 0.$$

6.6 THE LINEAR EQUATION. EIGENVALUE PROBLEMS

In §6.2 the boundary value problem associated with a differential equation was examined briefly. This section consists of a more detailed examination of such problems. For a second-order equation, whose general solution involves two arbitrary constants, the boundary value problem involves prescribing the value of either y or y', or some linear combination of the two, at two distinct values of x. When both these prescribed values are zero the problem is known as the *homogeneous boundary value problem* (irrespective of whether or not the governing differential equation is homogeneous). Otherwise the boundary value problem is said to be inhomogeneous.

The general *inhomogeneous boundary value problem* may always be reduced to the solution of a homogeneous boundary value problem. Thus consider the second-order equation

$$a_0(x)y'' + a_1(x)y' + a_2(x)y = f(x) \tag{29}$$

subject to the inhomogeneous boundary conditions

$$y = A \quad \text{at} \quad x = a, \quad y' = B \quad \text{at} \quad x = b. \tag{30}$$

First choose any function $v(x)$ which satisfies the boundary conditions (30). A convenient choice is the linear function $v = A + B(x - a)$. Then write $y(x) = v(x) + u(x)$, so that $u(x)$ must satisfy the differential equation

$$a_0(x)\frac{d^2u}{dx^2} + a_1(x)\frac{du}{dx} + a_2(x)u = f(x) - Ba_1(x) - a_2(x)\{A + B(x - a)\}. \tag{31}$$

Moreover, the boundary conditions on $u(x)$ are

$$u = 0 \quad \text{at} \quad x = a, \quad \frac{du}{dx} = 0 \quad \text{at} \quad x = b, \tag{32}$$

which are homogeneous. This analysis shows that it is necessary to discuss only the case of homogeneous boundary conditions.

We begin by examining the homogeneous equation subject to homogeneous boundary conditions. Clearly this will always have the trivial solution $y = 0$, and the question of interest is whether or not non-trivial solutions exist. Consider, for example, the equation

$$y'' + y = 0, \tag{33}$$

which has general solution $y = c_1\cos x + c_2\sin x$. Suppose that the boundary conditions are $y = 0$ at $x = 0$ and $y = 0$ at $x = a$, then c_1 and c_2 must satisfy

$$c_1 = 0, \quad c_1\cos a + c_2\sin a = 0. \tag{34}$$

Unless a is such that $\sin a = 0$, the only possibility is $c_1 = c_2 = 0$, giving the trivial solution $y = 0$. If however a has one of the discrete values $\pm\pi, \pm 2\pi, \pm 3\pi, \ldots$ the constant c_2 is undetermined and the boundary value problem has an infinity of non-trivial solutions $y = c_2 \sin x$.

As a second example consider equation (4) of §6.1,

$$(1 + x^2)y'' - 2xy' + 2y = 0 . \tag{4}$$

This has the general solution $y = c_1 x + c_2(1 - x^2)$. The boundary conditions $y = 0$ at $x = 0, y = 0$ at $x = 1$, are satisfied only if $c_1 = c_2 = 0$, giving the trivial solution. On the other hand the boundary conditions $y = 0$ at $x = -1, y = 0$ at $x = 1$, are satisfied by $y = c_2(1 - x^2)$ for all values of c_2.

A different example is provided by the differential equation

$$y'' + \lambda y = 0 \tag{35}$$

subject to the boundary conditions $y = 0$ at $x = 0, y = 0$ at $x = a$. This is a problem of the type which occurs frequently in Chapter 7 of Volume 1 in the analysis of vibrating systems. The general solution of equation (35) is $y = c_1 \cos \lambda^{1/2} x + c_2 \sin \lambda^{1/2} x$. This when substituted into the boundary conditions gives

$$c_1 = 0, \quad c_2 \sin \lambda^{1/2} a = 0 . \tag{36}$$

For non-trivial solutions to exist it is necessary that $c_2 \neq 0$, so that λ must satisfy the *eigenvalue equation*

$$\sin \lambda^{1/2} a = 0 \tag{37}$$

(cf. equation (22) of §7.2 of Volume 1). Thus whenever λ takes one of the *eigenvalues* (or *characteristic values*) $\lambda = n^2 \pi^2/a^2$, where $n = 1, 2, \ldots$, there exists an infinity of non-trivial solutions $y = c_2 \sin \lambda^{1/2} x$ to the boundary value problem. Corresponding to each eigenvalue $\lambda = n^2 \pi^2/a^2$ the solution $\sin(n\pi x/a)$ is termed the *eigenfunction* or *characteristic function*.

If the boundary conditions are replaced by the conditions $y' = 0$ at $x = 0, y = 0$ at $x = a$, there results a different set of equations

$$c_2 = 0, \quad c_1 \cos \lambda^{1/2} a = 0 \tag{38}$$

giving a different set of eigenvalues $\lambda = (n + \frac{1}{2})^2 \pi^2/a^2, n = 0, 1, 2, \ldots$, and associated eigenfunctions $\cos(n + \frac{1}{2})\pi x/a$.

The *general eigenvalue problem* in which the equation

$$a_0(x)y'' + a_1(x)y' + a_2(x)y = -\lambda y \tag{39}$$

is to be solved subject to homogeneous boundary conditions such as

$$y = 0 \quad \text{at } x = 0 \text{ and at } x = a \tag{40}$$

forms a branch of mathematics known as Sturm-Liouville theory (see Boyce and Di Prima [1]). The theory gives rise to a method for the solution of the inhomogeneous equation (29). The method uses two results which relate to the (infinite) set of eigenfunctions $\varphi_1(x), \varphi_2(x), \ldots \varphi_r(x), \ldots$ of equations (39) and (40).

RESULT 1   The eigenfunctions $\varphi_1(x), \varphi_2(x), \ldots \varphi_r(x), \ldots$ satisfy the *orthogonality relation*

$$\int_0^a \omega(x)\varphi_r(x)\varphi_s(x)\, dx = 0 \qquad r \neq s$$

where $\omega(x)$ is a weighting function given by

$$\omega(x) = \frac{1}{a_0(x)} \exp\left\{\int^x \frac{a_1(x)}{a_0(x)}\, dx\right\}.$$

RESULT 2   Every function $f(x)$ which is continuous in $0 \leqslant x \leqslant a$ may be represented in $(0, a)$ by an infinite series in the $\varphi_r(x)$ of the form

$$f(x) = \sum_{r=1}^{\infty} b_r \varphi_r(x).$$

The coefficients b_r in this series expansion are derived by multiplying both sides by $\omega(x)\varphi_s(x)$ for any value of x and integrating from $x = 0$ to $x = a$. This gives

$$\int_0^a f(x)\, \omega(x)\varphi_s(x)\, dx = \sum_{r=1}^{\infty} b_r \int_0^a \omega(x)\varphi_r(x)\varphi_s(x)\, dx$$

$$= b_s \int_0^a \omega(x)\varphi_s^2(x)\, dx,$$

where Result 1 has been used in order to evaluate the integrals on the right-hand sides. Thus

$$b_s = \frac{\displaystyle\int_0^a f(x)\, \omega(x)\varphi_s(x)\, dx}{\displaystyle\int_0^a \omega(x)\varphi_s^2(x)\, dx}. \tag{41}$$

With these results it is possible to solve the inhomogeneous equation subject to homogeneous boundary conditions and this will be illustrated by means of the following example.

EXAMPLE 1   Solve

$$y'' + y = 1 - x \tag{42}$$

subject to the conditions

$$y = 0 \quad \text{at } x = 0 \text{ and } x = 1. \tag{43}$$

To solve this, consider the associated eigenvalue problem

$$y'' + y = -\lambda y, \quad \text{or} \quad y'' + (1 + \lambda)y = 0,$$

with the boundary conditions (43). By referring to the solutions of equations (35) and (37) it is seen that the eigenvalues λ_r and the associated eigenfunctions $\varphi_r(x)$ are given by $\lambda_r = r^2\pi^2 - 1$, and $\varphi_r = \sin r\pi x, r = 1, 2, \ldots$. Since, by Result 2, any function may be expanded in an infinite series of these eigenfunctions in the interval $0 < x < 1$, it is appropriate to write

$$(1 - x) = \sum_{r=1}^{\infty} b_r \sin r\pi x, \quad y(x) = \sum_{r=1}^{\infty} c_r \sin r\pi x, \tag{44}$$

so that

$$y'' + y = \sum_{r=1}^{\infty} (-\lambda_r)c_r \sin r\pi x.$$

Thus substituting into equation (42) and comparing coefficients we find that

$$b_r = -\lambda_r c_r = (1 - r^2\pi^2)c_r, \quad r = 1, 2, \ldots. \tag{45}$$

However, equation (41) gives the coefficients b_r as

$$b_r = \frac{\displaystyle\int_0^1 (1 - x) \sin r\pi x \, dx}{\displaystyle\int_0^1 \sin^2 r\pi x \, dx} = \frac{2}{r\pi}.$$

From equations (44) and (45) the solution is then found as

$$y = \sum_{r=1}^{\infty} \frac{2 \sin r\pi x}{r\pi(1 - r^2\pi^2)}. \tag{46}$$

Since $(1 - x)$ is a particular integral of equation (42), the solution may be found by the methods of Chapter 1 of Volume 1 as

$$y = 1 - x - \cos x + \cot 1 \sin x. \tag{47}$$

Equations (46) and (47) appear to give two different solutions. This is not the case, and the reader should verify that the right-hand side of equation (46) is the Fourier sine series (see §2.4 of Volume 1) of the solution (47) in the interval $0 < x < 1$.

This example shows that for equation (42) the eigenfunction method is essentially the same as the Fourier series procedure in Chapter 2 of Volume 1. For more general equations (39) the eigenfunction expansion is a natural generalization of the Fourier series expansion. This method of solution of the inhomogeneous equation as a series in the eigenfunctions is sometimes more useful than the direct method of obtaining particular integrals, and arises naturally in the solution of boundary value problems for partial differential equations (see Chapter 7 of Volume 1).

Exercises

1. Write the inhomogeneous boundary value problem

$$y'' + 2y' + 5y = 0,$$

$$y = 1 \quad \text{at } x = 0, \quad y' = 3 \quad \text{at } x = 1$$

as a homogeneous boundary value problem for another differential equation having the same left-hand side.

2. Show that the eigenvalues of the differential equation

$$y'' + 2y' + y = -\lambda y$$

subject to the boundary conditions

$$y = 0 \quad \text{at } x = 0, \quad y' = 0 \quad \text{at } x = 1$$

are given by the roots of the equation

$$\lambda^{\frac{1}{2}} = \tan \lambda^{\frac{1}{2}}.$$

3. Find the eigenvalues and associated eigenfunctions of the differential equation in exercise 2 subject to the boundary conditions

$$y = 0 \quad \text{at } x = 0 \text{ and } x = 1.$$

Verify that the eigenfunctions are orthogonal with the weighting function $\omega(x) = e^{2x}$.

6.7 THE PERTURBATION METHOD

Up to now we have dealt solely with linear equations, but in this section we consider a method of solution which is valid for both linear and non-linear equations. The class of equations to which this method applies is characterized by the presence in the equations of a parameter ϵ, the equations being such that it is possible to obtain solutions for the case when $\epsilon = 0$. Many equations arising in engineering situations are of this kind, the equations being in general non-linear and involving a parameter ϵ in such a way that the equation becomes linear when $\epsilon \to 0$. As an example, consider the vibrations about the equilibrium position of a mass m attached to a spring whose stiffness k varies according to $k = k_0(1 + \epsilon x^2)$, where x is the displacement from the equilibrium position. Then the equation of motion is

$$m \frac{d^2 x}{dt^2} + k_0(1 + \epsilon x^2)x = 0,$$

which is a non-linear equation for x as a function of t. In the case when $\epsilon = 0$ this reduces to the well-known linear equation of simple harmonic motion

$$m \frac{d^2 x}{dt^2} + k_0 x = 0,$$

corresponding to vibrations of a mass m attached to a spring of constant stiffness k_0. Clearly, the solution of the non-linear equation will involve the parameter ϵ, and must reduce to the solution of the linear equation when $\epsilon = 0$. If the solution is written as $x = u(t, \epsilon)$, then under appropriate differentiability conditions the function $u(t, \epsilon)$ may be expanded in powers of ϵ to give

$$x = u_0(t) + \epsilon u_1(t) + \epsilon^2 u_2(t) + \ldots,$$

where $u_0(t)$ is the solution of the linear equation. In this example it is natural to use t to represent the independent variable (time) and to use x for the dependent variable (displacement). For the remainder of this section the independent variable will be denoted by x and the dependent variable by y, as in the preceding sections.

Our example suggests that, for any differential equation for $y(x)$ involving a parameter ϵ, it may be possible to obtain a solution of the form

$$y(x, \epsilon) = \sum_{r=0}^{\infty} \epsilon^r y_r(x),$$

where the $y_r(x)$ are solutions of simpler differential equations than that for y itself.

EXAMPLE 1   Solve the equation $y'' + (1 + \epsilon x)y = 0$ subject to the initial conditions $y = 1, y' = 0$ at $x = 0$.

Put

$$y = \sum_{r=0}^{\infty} \epsilon^r y_r(x),$$

so that

$$y' = \sum_{r=0}^{\infty} \epsilon^r y_r'(x), \quad y'' = \sum_{r=0}^{\infty} \epsilon^r y_r''(x).$$

Substituting into the differential equation gives

$$\sum_{r=0}^{\infty} \epsilon^r y_r''(x) + \sum_{r=0}^{\infty} \epsilon^r y_r(x) + \sum_{r=0}^{\infty} \epsilon^{r+1} x y_r(x) = 0.$$

This equation will be satisfied provided the terms independent of ϵ vanish, and the coefficient of each distinct power of ϵ vanishes. Terms independent of ϵ arise by putting $r = 0$ in the first two sums in this equation and these vanish if $y_0(x)$ satisfies the differential equation

$$y_0'' + y_0 = 0.$$

For $n \geqslant 1$ the coefficient of ϵ^n is obtained by putting $r = n$ in the first two sums and $r = n - 1$ in the third. This vanishes provided $y_n(x)$ satisfies the inhomogeneous differential equation

$$y_n'' + y_n = -x y_{n-1}.$$

The initial conditions are obtained by equating the coefficients of each power of ϵ on both sides of the equations

$$\sum_{r=0}^{\infty} \epsilon^r y_r(0) = 1, \quad \text{and} \quad \sum_{r=0}^{\infty} \epsilon^r y_r'(0) = 0.$$

This yields the system of initial conditions

$$y_0(0) = 1, \quad y_0'(0) = 0,$$

$$y_n(0) = 0, \quad y_n'(0) = 0, \quad \text{for } n \geqslant 1.$$

The solution of the differential equation for $y_0(x)$ satisfying the given initial conditions is $y_0(x) = \cos x$. The differential equation for $y_1(x)$ then becomes

$$y_1''(x) + y_1(x) = -x \cos x,$$

and the solution satisfying the initial conditions is

$$y_1(x) = -\tfrac{1}{4}x \cos x + \tfrac{1}{4}(1 - x^2) \sin x.$$

The differential equation for $y_2(x)$ is

$$y_2''(x) + y_2(x) = \tfrac{1}{4}x^2 \cos x - \tfrac{1}{4}x(1 - x^2) \sin x.$$

The solution of this satisfying the initial conditions $y_2(0) = y_2'(0) = 0$ is

$$y_2(x) = -\tfrac{1}{32}(x^4 - 7x^2) \cos x + \tfrac{1}{96}(10x^3 - 21x) \sin x.$$

Proceeding in this way it is possible to build up the solution to any required power of ϵ. In many situations ϵ is a small parameter ($\epsilon \ll 1$) and it is only necessary to determine the first few terms in the series in order to obtain a good approximation to the solution (at least for some range of values of x). In this particular problem the solution up to terms of order ϵ^2 has the form

$$y = \{1 - \tfrac{1}{4}\epsilon x - \tfrac{1}{32}\epsilon^2(x^4 - 7x^2)\} \cos x + \{\tfrac{1}{4}\epsilon(1 - x^2) + \tfrac{1}{96}\epsilon^2(10x^3 - 21x)\} \sin x.$$

The results obtained in this particular example are typical of the method in general. Thus the assumption of an infinite series solution in powers of ϵ leads to an infinite system of differential equations which may be solved recursively. The first of these, the equation for y_0, is obtained from the original equation on putting $\epsilon = 0$. The remaining equations for $y_1, y_2, \ldots$ are inhomogeneous linear equations. The method is known as the *perturbation method*.

The perturbation method requires some modification when it is applied to eigenvalue problems. Again the solution for y may be expanded in the form of a perturbation series, but in addition the eigenvalues λ also turn out to involve the parameter ϵ. This suggests that for eigenvalue problems it is appropriate to look for solutions of the form

$$y = \sum_{r=0}^{\infty} \epsilon^r y_r(x)$$

with the eigenvalue $\lambda(\epsilon)$ having the form

$$\lambda(\epsilon) = \sum_{r=0}^{\infty} \epsilon^r \lambda_r.$$

The use of these expressions in an eigenvalue problem will lead to a system of differential equations for the functions $y_r(x)$. The solutions of these equations will involve the parameters λ_r whose values are then determined from the boundary conditions. For further details of the technique see Carrier and Pearson [5].

Exercises

1. Obtain the first two terms in the perturbation solution of the equation

$$(1 + \epsilon \sin t)\frac{d^2x}{dt^2} - 4x = 0$$

subject to the initial conditions $x = 1$, $dx/dt = 2$ at $t = 0$.

2. Obtain the first two terms in the perturbation solution of the non-linear equation

$$\frac{d^2x}{dt^2} + x(1 - \epsilon x^2) = 0$$

given that $x = 0$ and $dx/dt = 1$ at $t = 0$.

3. Use the perturbation method to determine the eigenvalues of the equation

$$\frac{d^2y}{dx^2} + \lambda(1 + \epsilon x)y = 0$$

subject to $y = 0$ at $x = 0$ and at $x = 1$. Obtain the answer correct to terms of order ϵ^2.

6.8 NON-LINEAR EQUATIONS

First-order Equations

In this final section we consider methods of examining the solution of non-linear equations. The simplest non-linear equation is the first-order equation

$$\frac{dy}{dx} = f(x, y). \tag{48}$$

A solution $y = \phi(x)$ of equation (48) may be represented by a curve in the x, y plane known as an *integral curve* of the equation. For particular forms of the function $f(x, y)$, methods of solution have been given in Chapter 1 of Volume 1. There is no general analytical method of solving equation (48) and for specific problems it is frequently necessary to use numerical methods (see Chapter 7). Before attempting a numerical solution it is pertinent to ask whether or not a solution exists and under what conditions a solution is unique. The answer to these questions is contained in the following theorem (see for example Boyce and Di Prima [1] Chapter 2).

> THEOREM   If $f(x, y)$ and $\partial f/\partial y$ exist and are continuous in some region of the x, y plane and (x_0, y_0) is any point in this region, then there exists a unique solution $y = \phi(x)$ of equation (48) passing through the point (x_0, y_0).

A point (x_0, y_0) at which the conditions of this theorem are satisfied is called an *ordinary point* of the differential equation (48). With the aid of this theorem it is possible to sketch the solutions and obtain some information on their behaviour. It is advisable to carry out this process before performing any numerical calculations.

In geometrical terms the differential equation (48) defines the slope of the integral curve at any point (x, y) for which $f(x, y)$ exists. At every such point it is possible to draw a line element representing the direction of this tangent at that point. The set of line elements thus obtained is called the *direction field* of the equation. Consider the specific example

$$\frac{dy}{dx} = y(3 - 2y). \tag{49}$$

Here $f(x, y) = y(3 - 2y)$ is a non-linear function of y which is independent of x and is continuous for all y. Further, $\partial f/\partial y = (3 - 4y)$ is also continuous for all y, and so equation (49) has a unique solution through every point of the x, y plane.

The most convenient way of plotting the direction field is by sketching the *isoclines*, the family of curves on each of which $dy/dx = f(x, y)$ is a constant. For equation (49) the integral curves have zero slope ($dy/dx = 0$) on the curve $y(3 - 2y) = 0$, which consists of the two straight lines $y = 0$ and $y = \frac{3}{2}$. The integral curves have unit slope ($dy/dx = 1$) on $y(3 - 2y) = 1$. This consists of the two straight lines $y = \frac{1}{2}$ and $y = 1$. The isocline on which $dy/dx = -2$ is $y(3 - 2y) = -2$ which consists of the two straight lines $y = 2$ and $y = -\frac{1}{2}$. In this way it is possible to build up the direction field of equation (49) as shown in Fig. 6.1, where some of the line elements giving the direction field are shown. Notice that the slope has its maximum value $dy/dx = \frac{9}{8}$ at $y = \frac{3}{4}$.

Since every point of the plane is an ordinary point of equation (49), there is one and only one integral curve through each point. The form of the integral curve through (x_0, y_0) may be sketched as a sequence of short line elements with each element having the direction of the tangent field at its starting point (see §1.2 of Volume 1). In this way it is seen that the lines $y = 0$ and $y = \frac{3}{2}$ represent solutions of equation (49). Consider now the integral curve passing through the point $(0, \frac{1}{2})$. The slope of the tangent increases from 1 at $y = \frac{1}{2}$ to $\frac{9}{8}$ at $y = \frac{3}{4}$ and then decreases to zero at $y = \frac{3}{2}$. Since all points of the line $y = \frac{3}{2}$ are ordinary points, the integral curve cannot meet this line at any finite value of x, and so the line $y = \frac{3}{2}$ must be an asymptote as $x \to \infty$. Likewise it is found that as $x \to -\infty$ the integral curve is asymptotic to $y = 0$. Similar arguments hold for every curve lying between $y = 0$ and $y = \frac{3}{2}$. In the same way it is possible to sketch the form of integral curves lying above the solution $y = \frac{3}{2}$ and below the solution $y = 0$. The former have $y = \frac{3}{2}$ as an asymptote as $x \to \infty$, the latter have

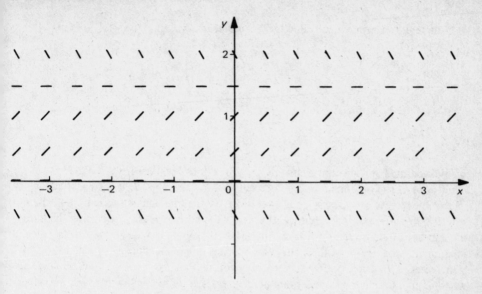

Fig. 6.1 Direction field for equation (49).

$y = 0$ as an asymptote as $x \to -\infty$. A few examples of these curves are sketched in Fig. 6.2. Equation (49) may be integrated by separating the variables (Chapter 1, Volume 1) and the reader should verify that the solutions are as shown in Fig. 6.2.

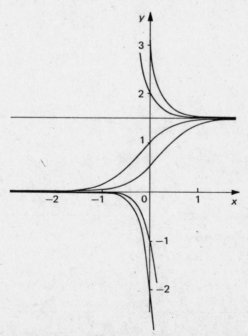

Fig. 6.2 Integral curves of equation (49).

A different example is provided by the equation

$$\frac{dy}{dx} = y(4 - y^2)^{1/2}. \tag{50}$$

Here $f(x, y) = y(4 - y^2)^{1/2}$ is defined only for $|y| \leqslant 2$. Further, as

$$\frac{\partial f}{\partial y} = (4 - y^2)^{1/2} - \frac{y^2}{(4 - y^2)^{1/2}},$$

$\partial f/\partial y$ is defined and continuous for $|y| < 2$ but does not exist for $y = \pm 2$. The conditions of the theorem are therefore satisfied for all $|y| < 2$. It is clear that each of the lines $y = 0$, $y = +2$, $y = -2$ is a solution. By the uniqueness theorem, no other solution can intersect $y = 0$, but the theorem gives no information regarding the lines $y = \pm 2$. The direction field of Fig. 6.3 indicates that $y = 0$ is an asymptote to all the integral curves as $x \to -\infty$. Each curve approaches one of the lines $y = +2$ or $y = -2$ as x increases, with slope tending to zero. It is not possible from the theorem to determine whether any given curve touches one of these lines at a finite value of x or approaches it asymptotically at infinity.

Equation (50) is integrable by the methods of Chapter 1, Volume 1 and its solutions in addition to $y = 0$ and $y = \pm 2$ are

$$x = C - \tfrac{1}{2} \log \left\{ \frac{1 + (1 - y^2/4)^{1/2}}{y} \right\} \quad \text{for } 0 < y < 2, \tag{51a}$$

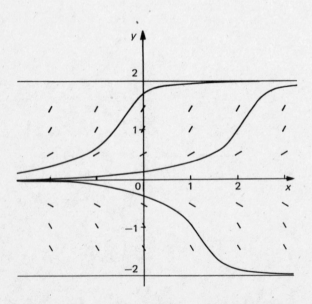

Fig. 6.3　Direction field and integral curves of equation (50).

and

$$x = D - \tfrac{1}{2} \log \left\{ \frac{1 + (1 - y^2/4)^{\frac{1}{2}}}{-y} \right\} \quad \text{for } -2 < y < 0 \,. \tag{51b}$$

These meet the lines $y = \pm 2$ at the finite points $x = C + \tfrac{1}{2}\log 2$ and $x = D + \tfrac{1}{2}\log 2$ respectively. In this case the solutions $y = +2$ and $y = -2$ are said to be envelopes of the family of integral curves given by equations (51), (see §4.5, Volume 1).

Second-order Equations

Consider now the non-linear second-order equation

$$\frac{d^2 x}{dt^2} = f\left(t, x, \frac{dx}{dt}\right)$$

for the function x of the independent variable t. With the introduction of a new variable $y(t)$ defined by $y = dx/dt$, this equation may be replaced by the pair of equations

$$\frac{dx}{dt} = y, \qquad \frac{dy}{dt} = f(t, x, y).$$

Whenever the function $f(t, x, y)$ does not depend explicitly on t (i.e., $f(t, x, y) \equiv f(x, y)$) these equations are said to form an *autonomous system*. This situation arises quite frequently in vibrations of mechanical and electrical systems. A particular example is the equation

$$\frac{d^2 \theta}{dt^2} + \frac{g}{l} \sin \theta = 0, \tag{52}$$

which governs oscillations of a simple pendulum consisting of a rigid weightless rod of length l with a mass at one end free to rotate in a plane about the other end (see Fig. 6.4(a)). Equation (52) is a non-linear autonomous equation for the angle θ as a function of time t. (The linearized form is the equation of simple harmonic motion, and is obtained by approximating $\sin \theta$ by θ for small values of θ.)

For the autonomous system

$$\frac{dx}{dt} = y, \qquad \frac{dy}{dt} = f(x, y) \tag{53}$$

the solution $x(t), y(t)$ may be used to plot a curve in the x, y plane specified by the parametric representation $x = x(t), y = y(t)$. The curve may also be obtained by eliminating t to obtain a differential equation for y as a function of x only. Since $\dfrac{dy}{dx} = \dfrac{dy/dt}{dx/dt}$ this equation is

$$\frac{dy}{dx} = \frac{f(x, y)}{y}. \tag{54}$$

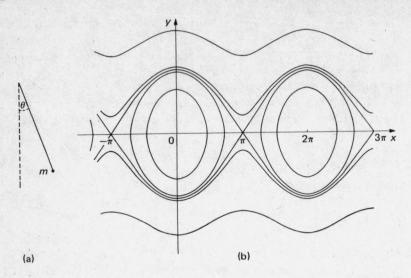

Fig. 6.4 (a) The simple pendulum.   (b) Phase plane trajectories of the simple pendulum.

(a)   (b)

(Notice that elimination of t is not possible for the non-autonomous equation where $f = f(t, x, y)$.) The integral curves of equation (54) give a representation of the solutions of the original second-order equation in the x, y plane. This plane is termed the *phase plane* of the second-order equation and the curves are termed the *phase plane trajectories*. If the phase plane solution $y = \phi(x)$, for which $\phi(x_0) = y_0$, is known, then the solution of the original equation satisfying the initial conditions $x = x_0$, $dx/dt = y_0$ at $t = 0$ may be obtained by integrating the equation $dx/dt = y$ to give

$$t = \int_{x_0}^{x} \frac{dx}{\phi(x)}.$$ (55)

This phase plane technique may be used to solve equation (52). The corresponding pair of equations are, putting $\theta = x$,

$$\frac{dx}{dt} = y, \qquad \frac{dy}{dt} = -\frac{g}{l} \sin x.$$

This is an autonomous system. The phase plane trajectories are the solutions of the equation

$$\frac{dy}{dx} = -\frac{g}{l} \frac{\sin x|}{y}.$$

This is an equation with variables separable (see Chapter 1 of Volume 1) whose solutions are the one parameter family of curves

$$y^2 = C + \frac{2g}{l} \cos x,$$

where C is an arbitrary constant. Some of these phase plane trajectories are plotted in Fig. 6.4(b).

No solutions exist for values of C less than $-2g/l$. For values of C in the range $-2g/l < C < 2g/l$, the trajectories are closed curves and the motion is periodic. The highest point $(\theta = \pi)$ is never reached and the pendulum oscillates about the lowest point $(\theta = 0)$. For values of C greater than $2g/l$, the angular displacement θ $(= x)$ increases indefinitely, with the angular velocity $\dot{\theta}$ $(= y)$ varying periodically. The motion consists of a succession of complete revolutions about the point of support. The trajectory corresponding to $C = 2g/l$ is termed a *separatrix* since it separates the region of periodic solutions from the region of non-periodic solutions.

The constant C is determined from the initial conditions $x = x_0, y = y_0$ at $t = 0$ as $C = y_0^2 - (2g/l)\cos x_0$, and the phase plane trajectory for this initial value problem is given by

$$y^2 = y_0^2 + \frac{2g}{l}(\cos x - \cos x_0).$$

To obtain the solution as a function of time it is necessary to integrate the equation $dx/dt = y$ which gives (cf. equation 55)

$$t = \int_{x_0}^x \frac{dx}{y} = \int_{x_0}^x \frac{dx}{\left\{y_0^2 + \frac{2g}{l}(\cos x - \cos x_0)\right\}^{1/2}}.$$

This is an elliptic integral giving t as a function of x and values may be obtained from a set of tables (see e.g. Abramowitz and Stegun [2]). For the particular case of $y_0 = 2(g/l)^{1/2}, x_0 = 0$ we have $C = 2g/l$ leading to

$$y^2 = \frac{2g}{l}(1 + \cos x) = \frac{4g}{l}\cos^2\frac{x}{2}$$

and

$$t = \tfrac{1}{2}\left(\frac{l}{g}\right)^{1/2}\int_0^x \frac{dx}{\cos x/2} = \left(\frac{l}{g}\right)^{1/2}\log\left(\sec\frac{x}{2} + \tan\frac{x}{2}\right).$$

These may be simplified to give

$$\sin\frac{x}{2} = \tanh\left\{t\left(\frac{g}{l}\right)^{1/2}\right\}, \quad y = 2\left(\frac{g}{l}\right)^{1/2}\operatorname{sech}\left\{t\left(\frac{g}{l}\right)^{1/2}\right\},$$

from which it is seen that $x \to \pi, y \to 0$ as $t \to \infty$. These initial conditions correspond to the pendulum leaving its lowest point with initial angular velocity $2(g/l)^{1/2}$ which is just sufficient to take it up to its highest point in an infinite time, and the trajectory forms part of the separatrix.

Critical Points

The points $x = 0, y = n\pi, n = 0, \pm1, \pm2, \ldots$ all correspond to equilibrium points at which $d\theta/dt = d^2\theta/dt^2 = 0$. At these points the equation for the trajectories has the indeterminate form

$$\frac{dy}{dx} = \frac{0}{0},$$

and the uniqueness theorem fails to hold. Thus, more than one trajectory may pass through these points, which are termed *critical points* of the equation. For the general autonomous equations

$$\frac{dx}{dt} = y, \quad \frac{dy}{dt} = f(x, y),$$

the critical points are given by $y = 0, f(x, y) = 0$. These correspond to equilibrium positions of the system, and the nature of the solution close to these points is of particular interest, since it serves to indicate whether or not the equilibrium point is stable.

It is often possible to examine the behaviour of the solution close to the critical points without solving the differential equation for the trajectories. Assume for simplicity that $x = 0, y = 0$ is a critical point, so that $f(0, 0) = 0$. Expanding $f(x, y)$ by means of Taylor's theorem (see §4.2 of Volume 1) gives

$$f(x, y) = f(0, 0) + x \left(\frac{\partial f}{\partial x}\right)_0 + y \left(\frac{\partial f}{\partial y}\right)_0 + \frac{x^2}{2} \left(\frac{\partial^2 f}{\partial x^2}\right)_0 + xy \left(\frac{\partial^2 f}{\partial x \partial y}\right)_0$$

$$+ \frac{y^2}{2} \left(\frac{\partial^2 f}{\partial y^2}\right)_0 + \dots .$$

For sufficiently small values of x and y this may be approximated by

$$f(x, y) = ax + by,$$

where $a = \left(\dfrac{\partial f}{\partial x}\right)_0$ and $b = \left(\dfrac{\partial f}{\partial y}\right)_0$. Then it seems reasonable to suppose that close to the critical point the system behaves like the equations

$$\frac{dx}{dt} = y, \quad \frac{dy}{dt} = ax + by.$$

This is a system of linear simultaneous equations whose solutions are obtained by the methods of Chapter 1 of Volume 1. The solutions are

$$x = A\,e^{\lambda_1 t} + B\,e^{\lambda_2 t}, \quad y = \lambda_1 A\,e^{\lambda_1 t} + \lambda_2 B\,e^{\lambda_2 t}$$

where $\lambda_1 = \frac{1}{2}(b + (b^2 + 4a)^{1/2})$, $\lambda_2 = \frac{1}{2}(b - (b^2 + 4a)^{1/2})$ and A and B are arbitrary constants. The character of these solutions depends on the values of a and b.

EXAMPLE 1   When $a = -2$ and $b = -3$, so that $\lambda_1 = -1, \lambda_2 = -2$ then $x = Ae^{-t} + Be^{-2t}$ and $y = -Ae^{-t} - 2Be^{-2t}$. If $B = 0$ the trajectory is the straight line $y = -x$ through the critical point and $x \to 0, y \to 0$ as $t \to \infty$. If $A = 0$ the trajectory is $y = -2x$, another straight line through the origin and $x \to 0, y \to 0$ as $t \to \infty$. Every other trajectory tends to the origin as $t \to \infty$, in such a way that

$$\frac{y}{x} = \frac{-(1 + 2Be^{-t}/A)}{(1 + Be^{-t}/A)} \to -1 \ .$$

Thus all trajectories except that for $A = 0$ are asymptotic to $y = -x$ at the critical point. The critical point is called a *node*, and since all trajectories approach it as $t \to \infty$ the node is said to be *stable* (Fig. 6.5(a)).

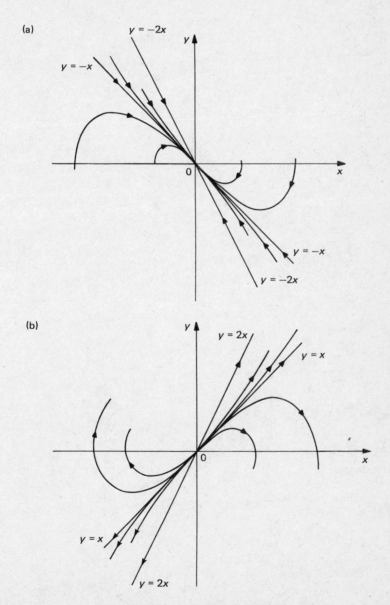

Fig. 6.5   (a) Stable node, $(a = -2, b = -3)$.   (b) Unstable node, $(a = -2, b = 3)$.

EXAMPLE 2   When $a = -2$ and $b = 3$, so that $\lambda_1 = 2$, $\lambda_2 = 1$ then $x = Ae^{2t} + Be^t$,
$y = 2Ae^{2t} + Be^t$ There are two straight line trajectories $y = 2x$ and $y = x$ which pass
through the critical point. All other trajectories pass through the critical point and are
asymptotic to $y = x$ there, so that the critical point is again a node. In this case the
trajectories approach the node as $t \to -\infty$ and move away from the node as t increases.
The node is said to be *unstable* (see Fig. 6.5(b)).

    The general classification of critical points is given below and illustrated in
Fig. 6.6.

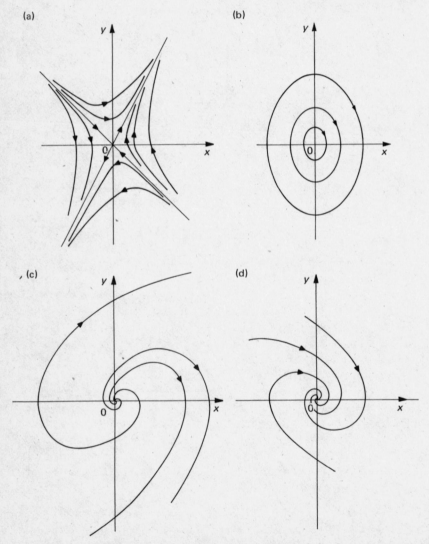

Fig. 6.6 (a) Saddle point. ($a = 2, b = 1$).   (b) Centre, ($a = -2, b = 0$).
(c) Unstable focus ($a = -1, b = 1$).   (d) Stable focus, ($a = -1, b = -1$).

Case 1 $a > 0$ *Saddle point* which is always unstable (Fig. 6.6(a))
Case 2 $0 > a \geqslant -b^2/4$ *Node*, stable for $b < 0$, unstable for $b > 0$ (Fig. 6.5)
Case 3 $0 > a, b = 0$ *Centre*, neutrally stable (Fig. 6.6(b))
Case 4 $-b^2/4 > a$ *Focus*, unstable for $b > 0$, stable for $b < 0$ (Fig. 6.6(c), (d))

As an example of the use of this analysis we examine the problem of the simple pendulum (see Fig. 6.4(a)) immersed in a resisting medium whose resistance is proportional to the velocity. The equation of motion becomes

$$\frac{d^2\theta}{dt^2} + k \frac{d\theta}{dt} + \frac{g}{l} \sin \theta = 0 ,$$

where $k > 0$. Putting $\theta = x$, $d\theta/dt = y$ gives the autonomous system

$$\frac{dx}{dt} = y, \quad \frac{dy}{dt} = -ky - \frac{g}{l} \sin x .$$

The critical points of this system are given by $y = 0$, $\sin x = 0$, which gives $x = n\pi$, $n = 0, \pm 1, \pm 2, \ldots$. To examine the behaviour at the general critical point $x = n\pi$, $y = 0$, put $X = x - n\pi$, $Y = y$. Then

$$\sin x = \sin(X + n\pi) = \sin n\pi \cos X + \cos n\pi \sin X \simeq (-1)^n X$$

for $|X| \ll 1$. The equivalent linear system of equations becomes

$$\frac{dX}{dt} = Y, \quad \frac{dY}{dt} = -kY - \frac{g}{l}(-1)^n X .$$

Comparing these with the general case gives $a = (-1)^{n+1} g/l, b = -k$. For odd values of n this gives $a > 0$ and the critical points at $x = \pm\pi, \pm 3\pi, \ldots, \pm(2k+1)\pi, \ldots$ are all saddle points and therefore unstable. These correspond to the equilibrium position in which the pendulum is directly above the point of support. The critical points for which $n = 0$ or n is even have $a = -g/l < 0, b = -k$, and correspond to the equilibrium positions in which the pendulum is directly below its point of support. There are then two cases to consider. If $k^2 \geqslant 4g/l$ the critical point is a stable node. This corresponds to heavy damping where the pendulum on being displaced slightly from its equilibrium position returns directly to the equilibrium point. For light damping $k^2 < 4g/l$, the critical point is a stable focus and the motion is damped simple harmonic. Both processes require an infinite time before the pendulum reaches equilibrium.

The considerations of this section, whilst they do not give solutions to the non-linear equations, furnish valuable information about the behaviour of the solutions. In particular they can often be used to determine whether or not a periodic solution exists, or whether or not an equilibrium point is stable. For further details of these methods the reader is referred to the books by Minorsky [3] and Hayashi [4].

Exercises

1. Plot the direction field to the differential equation

$$\frac{dy}{dx} = x^2 + y^2$$

and determine the set of points (x_0, y_0) through each of which the solution is unique. Sketch the form of the integral curves.

2. Find the points (x_0, y_0) (if any) through which the solution of the equation

$$\frac{dy}{dx} = xy^{\frac{1}{2}}$$

may not be unique. Integrate the equation and plot the integral curves.

3. Write the differential equation

$$\frac{d^2x}{dt^2} + x(1 - \epsilon x^2) = 0 \quad (\epsilon > 0)$$

as an autonomous system and obtain the equations of the phase plane trajectories. Sketch the curves for the case $\epsilon = 2$.

4. Examine the nature of the critical points of the differential equation

$$\frac{d^2x}{dt^2} + k^2 \frac{dx}{dt} + p^2(x - x^2) = 0 \,,$$

distinguishing between the cases $4p^2 \leqslant k^4$ and $4p^2 > k^4$.

PROBLEMS

1. Verify that $y = 3x + 2$ and $y = (1 - x)^{-1}$ are both solutions of the differential equation

$$(1 - x)(1 - 6x)y'' + 2(3x + 2)y' - 6y = 0 \,,$$

and show that they are linearly independent. Hence obtain the solution of the equation for which $y = 5, y' = -3$, at $x = 0$.

2. Use the solutions of the homogeneous equation in problem 1 to obtain a particular integral of the equation

$$(1 - x)(1 - 6x)y'' + 2(3x + 2)y' - 6y = (1 - 6x)^2 \,.$$

Find the solution of this equation for which $y = 5, y' = -3$, at $x = 0$.

3. Show that $y = c_1(x^2 + 2) + c_2\sqrt{x}$ is the complementary function of the equation

$$2x(3x^2 - 2)y'' - (9x^2 + 2)y' + 6xy = 6x(3x^2 - 2)^2 \,.$$

Hence obtain a particular integral and the general solution of the equation.

4. Show that $y = (1 - x)^{-1}$ is a solution of the differential equation

$$2(1 + 3x)(1 - x^2)y'' - (9x^2 + 14x + 9)y' + (3x + 5)y = 0 \,.$$

By putting $y = u(x)(1 - x)^{-1}$ in the differential equation show that there results a first-order equation for $u'(x)$. Hence determine a second solution of the differential equation and verify that the two solutions are linearly independent. (This is an example of a general technique. Thus, if $f_1(x)$ is one solution of a second-order equation, putting $y = u(x)f_1(x)$ leads to another solution.)

5. Obtain two linearly independent series solutions of the differential equation

$$(1 + x^2)y'' + xy' - 3y = 0 ,$$

giving the general term in each series.

6. Legendre's equation of order α is

$$(1 - x^2)y'' - 2xy' + \alpha(\alpha + 1)y = 0 .$$

The equation arises in the solution of Laplace's equation in spherical polar coordinates using the method of separation of variables (see Chapter 7 of Volume 1). Obtain two linearly independent series solutions of this equation. Show that when α is an integer n, one of these solutions reduces to a polynomial of degree n.

7. The Legendre polynomials $P_n(x)$ are given by the relation

$$P_n(x) = \frac{1}{2^n n!} \frac{d^n}{dx^n} [(x^2 - 1)^n] .$$

Verify that these satisfy the differential equation of problem 6 with $\alpha = n$.

8. Find the series solution of the differential equation

$$2(1 + 3x)(1 - x^2)y'' - (9x^2 + 14x + 9)y' + (3x + 5)y = 0 ,$$

which satisfies the condition $y = 1$, $y' = 1$ at $x = 0$. Compare this solution with that given in problem 4.

9. Use the method of Frobenius to solve the differential equation

$$2x(3x^2 - 2)y'' - (9x^2 + 2)y' + 6xy = 0$$

and compare the results with the solutions given in problem 3.

10. Solve by the method of Frobenius

$$3x^2 y'' - xy' + (1 + 2x)y = 0 .$$

11. Show that the method of Frobenius fails to give two solutions to the differential equation

$$3x^2 y'' - y' + (1 + 2x)y = 0$$

and give the reason for this.

12. Use the method of Frobenius to obtain two linearly independent solutions of the equation

$$x^2 y'' + (x^2 - \alpha^2 + \tfrac{1}{4})y = 0$$

when α is not an integer. What happens to these solutions when α is an integer?

13. Use the method of Frobenius to obtain a series solution of Bessel's equation of order zero

$$x^2 y'' + xy' + x^2 y = 0$$

and examine the convergence of this series.

14. Show that $\lambda = 0$ and $\lambda = 4 + n^2 \pi^2$ give the eigenvalues of the differential equation

$$\frac{d^2 y}{dx^2} + 4\frac{dy}{dx} + \lambda y = 0$$

subject to the conditions $dy/dx = 0$ at $x = 0$ and $x = 1$.

15. Show that the eigenvalues λ_n of the equation

$$\frac{d^2 y}{dx^2} + \lambda y = 0$$

subject to the boundary conditions $y = 0$ at $x = 0$, $dy/dx = ky$ at $x = 1$ satisfy the equation $\sqrt{\lambda} = k \tan \sqrt{\lambda}$. By plotting $v = u/k$ and $v = \tan u$, verify that this equation has an infinite number of roots. Show also that if $\varphi_r(x)$ and $\varphi_s(x)$ are the eigenfunctions corresponding to two distinct eigenvalues λ_r and λ_s then

$$\int_0^1 \varphi_r(x)\varphi_s(x)\,dx = 0 \ .$$

16. The equation of motion for a vibrating rod of viscoelastic material is

$$E\frac{\partial^2 u}{\partial x^2} + \mu\frac{\partial^3 u}{\partial x^2 \partial t} = \rho\frac{\partial^2 u}{\partial t^2}$$

where E, μ and ρ are constants. A rod of length L of this material is set vibrating with its ends free and the resulting displacement has the form $u = y(x)e^{pt}$ where p is a complex constant and $y(x)$ satisfies the equation

$$(c^2 + pK)\frac{d^2 y}{dx^2} - p^2 y = 0 \quad \left(c^2 = \frac{E}{\rho}, K = \frac{\mu}{\rho}\right)$$

and the boundary conditions $dy/dx = 0$ at $x = 0$ and $x = L$. Find the possible values of p and show that each solution decays exponentially with time.

17. Use the perturbation method to solve the equation

$$\frac{d^2 y}{dx^2} + \epsilon y = 0$$

with $y(0) = 0$, $y'(0) = 1$ and compare this solution with that obtained by solving the equation directly.

18. Find the first three terms in the perturbation solution of the non-linear equation

$$\frac{d^2 y}{dx^2} + \epsilon y\frac{dy}{dx} + 4y = 0$$

if $y(0) = 1$ and $y'(0) = 0$.

19. Show that the lowest eigenvalue of Mathieu's Equation

$$y'' + (\lambda - 2\epsilon \cos x)y = 0$$

with $y(0) = 0$, $y(\pi) = 0$ is given by

$$\lambda = 1 - \epsilon - \frac{\epsilon^2}{16} + 0(\epsilon^3).$$

20. Find correct to order ϵ^2 the lowest eigenvalue of the non-linear equation

$$\frac{d^2y}{dx^2} + \lambda(y - \epsilon y^3) = 0$$

with $y'(0) = 0$, $y(1) = 0$. (Note that the eigenvalue varies with the amplitude of the solution.)

21. Plot the isoclines and hence sketch the form of the integral curves for the following differential equations

(a) $y' = 2x - 3y$ (b) $y' = \dfrac{y - 1}{x}$.

Verify your results by solving the equations.

22. Show that there are two straight lines through the origin which satisfy the differential equation

$$\frac{dy}{dx} = \frac{3x + 2y}{x + 2y}.$$

Plot the isoclines and sketch the form of all other integral curves.

23. Plot the isoclines and hence sketch the integral curves of the equation

$$y' = (1 - y^2)^{\frac{1}{2}}.$$

Examine the behaviour as $y \to \pm 1$ by solving the equation.

24. The value R of an electrical resistance varies linearly with temperature. When a constant potential V is placed across the resistance the current causes heating and the resistance R varies with time according to the differential equation

$$\frac{dR}{dt} = \frac{aV^2}{R} - k(R - R_0),$$

where a, k and R_0 are constants. Sketch the integral curves and show that the resistance tends to the constant value

$$\bar{R} = \frac{R_0 + \left(R_0^2 + \dfrac{4aV^2}{k}\right)^{\frac{1}{2}}}{2} \qquad \text{as } t \to \infty.$$

25. The capacitance C of a capacitor varies with the charge q and is given by $C = C_0 + C_1 q^2$ where C_0 and C_1 are constants. The capacitor is connected in series to a resistance R and inductance L to form a complete circuit. The equation for the charge

q in the circuit is then

$$L\frac{d^2q}{dt^2} + R\frac{dq}{dt} + \frac{q}{C_0 + C_1 q^2} = 0 .$$

Examine the nature of the equilibrium point in terms of the constants L, R and C_0. Sketch the phase plane trajectories when $L = R = 1$, $C_0 = 2$ and $C_1 = \frac{1}{2}$.

26. Examine the equilibrium points of the equation

$$\frac{d^2x}{dt^2} + k\frac{dx}{dt} + x(1 - \mu x^2) = 0$$

for all $\mu > 0$ and all values of k positive and negative.

27. Determine the nature of the equilibrium points of the equation

$$\frac{d^2x}{dt^2} + (1 - x^2)\frac{dx}{dt} + x(1 - x^2) = 0 .$$

BIBLIOGRAPHY

[1]   Boyce, W. E., and R. C. Di Prima, *Elementary Differential Equations and Boundary Value Problems*, Wiley, New York (1969).

[2]   Abramowitz, M., and I. A. Stegun, *Handbook of Mathematical Functions*, Dover, New York (1965).

[3]   Minorsky, N., *Non-linear Oscillations*, D. van Nostrand, New York (1962).

[4]   Hayashi, C., *Non-linear Oscillations in Physical Systems*, McGraw-Hill, New York (1964).

[5]   Carrier, G. F., and C. E. Pearson, *Ordinary Differential Equations*, Blaisdell Publishing Company, Waltham, Mass. (1968).

CHAPTER 7

Numerical Solution of Differential Equations

7.1 INTRODUCTION

It has been pointed out in Chapter 6 that there is no general analytical method available for solving non-linear differential equations. Although for non-linear equations the qualitative approach described in §6.8 does provide useful information about the existence and uniqueness of the solutions, it does not yield accurate results and so numerical methods must be used to obtain solutions. Even for those differential equations which may be solved analytically, it is often difficult or impractical to use the analytic solutions and a direct numerical method of solution is to be preferred.

Many of the numerical methods for solving ordinary differential equations require that the equation be rewritten as a system of first-order equations. An nth-order ordinary differential equation having the form

$$\frac{d^n y}{dx^n} = f\left(x; y, \frac{dy}{dx}, \ldots, \frac{d^{n-1}y}{dx^{n-1}}\right),$$

is exactly equivalent to the system of first-order equations

$$\frac{dz_1}{dx} = z_2,$$

$$\frac{dz_2}{dx} = z_3,$$

$$\ldots$$

$$\frac{dz_n}{dx} = f(x; z_1, z_2, \ldots, z_{n-1}).$$

For example, the second-order equation

$$m\frac{d^2 x}{dt^2} + k\left(\frac{dx}{dt}\right)^2 + n^2 x = f(t),$$

may be rewritten as the system

$$\frac{dz_1}{dt} = z_2, \qquad \frac{dz_2}{dt} = \frac{1}{m}\{f(t) - n^2 z_1 - kz_2^2\}.$$

Problems involving ordinary differential equations divide into two classes; initial value problems and boundary value problems (see §6.2). In this chapter the principal types of method available for the solution of ordinary differential equations are described. In particular the various methods for initial value problems are described in detail for the typical problem

$$\frac{dy}{dx} = f(x, y) \quad \text{with} \quad y(x_0) = y_0,$$

(1)

and may be readily extended to apply to a system of n first-order equations.

The choice of numerical algorithm for a given problem will depend upon the complexity of the function $f(x, y)$ as well as on the means of computation that is available. In the treatment of each numerical method account is taken of the accuracy of the calculated function values. The various ways that errors occur in numerical calculations are discussed in §9.1 of Volume 1. A direct estimate of the error per step is available for some methods while for others it may be necessary to repeat the computations with a smaller step-length to obtain this information. For those methods where the calculations proceed step by step over a range of values of the independent variable it is particularly important to estimate the magnitude of the cumulative error. The cumulative error is not in general the sum of the individual truncation errors of each step. Finally, there is the question of instability. This is the phenomenon by which small errors in one step of the computation cause increasingly large errors as the computations proceed. Instability may arise because the numerical algorithm itself is of higher order than the differential equation it represents, thus introducing a spurious solution which eventually completely swamps the correct solution. A second type of instability (see §7.3) can occur when one part of the solution decays very much faster than another part. This is called a partial instability as it can be removed by using a smaller step-length.

Although iterative methods are usually suitable only for automatic computation, the iterative methods of this chapter are suitable for use on a desk calculator as they require fewer calculations of the right-hand side $f(x, y)$. The single step methods usually require much more computation and smaller step-lengths and are more convenient for automatic computation. Single step methods do have an advantage in that the size of step may be easily varied.

The numerical solution of a differential equation is obtained as a tabulation of function values and throughout this chapter the notation

for $x = x_0(h)x_n$,

is used to mean that the values of the dependent variable are required at $x = x_0$, $x_0 + h, x_0 + 2h$, up to $x_0 + nh = x_n$.

7.2 THE TAYLOR SERIES METHOD

Any sufficiently smooth function can be expressed as a Taylor series and this is the basis of the Taylor series method. It is useful when the differential equation is readily differentiated to give formulae for the higher derivatives of the unknown function of x. Using the convenient notation

$$y(x_0) \equiv y_0, \quad \left.\frac{dy}{dx}\right|_{x_0} \equiv y'(x_0) \equiv y'_0,$$

$$\left.\frac{d^2y}{dx^2}\right|_{x_0} \equiv y''(x_0) \equiv y''_0, \quad \text{etc.,}$$

and

$$y(x_1) \equiv y_1, \quad h = x_1 - x_0,$$

the value of $y(x)$ at $x = x_1$ may be written as

$$y_1 = y_0 + hy'_0 + \frac{h^2}{2!} y''_0 + \frac{h^3}{3!} y'''_0 + \dots. \tag{2}$$

Equation (1) can be differentiated successively to give

$$\frac{d^2y}{dx^2} = \frac{\partial f}{\partial x} + \frac{\partial f}{\partial y}\frac{dy}{dx} = \frac{\partial f}{\partial x} + f\frac{\partial f}{\partial y},$$

$$\frac{d^3y}{dx^3} = \frac{\partial^2 f}{\partial x^2} + 2\frac{\partial^2 f}{\partial x \partial y}\frac{dy}{dx} + \frac{\partial^2 f}{\partial y^2}\left(\frac{dy}{dx}\right)^2 + \frac{\partial f}{\partial y}\frac{d^2y}{dx^2},$$

and so on, and this enables the individual terms of the Taylor series (2) to be calculated. When sufficient terms have been found the series is summed to find y_1. To calculate y_2, the value of y at $x = x_0 + 2h$, the above procedure is repeated starting with the new value y_1 at $x = x_1$.

An important feature of the method is that changing the sign of h provides a back check on the computations as the series should then give the previously computed value. For example, starting from $y(x_1) = y_1$,

$$y_2 = y(x_1 + h) = y_1 + hy'_1 + \frac{h^2}{2!}y''_1 + \frac{h^3}{3!}y'''_1 + \dots,$$

and changing the sign of h gives

$$y_0 = y(x_1 - h) = y_1 - hy'_1 + \frac{h^2}{2!}y''_1 - \frac{h^3}{3!}y'''_1 + \dots,$$

which should give a value of y_0 agreeing with the given initial value.

In practice it is convenient to use the *reduced derivatives*

$$\tau_i^n = \frac{h^n}{n!} y^{(n)}(x_i),$$

which are the individual terms of the series. Also it is convenient to sum the odd and even terms separately as

$$S_1 = y_1 + \tau_1^2 + \tau_1^4 + \dots,$$

and

$$S_2 = \tau_1^1 + \tau_1^3 + \tau_1^5 + \dots,$$

so that

$$y_2 = S_1 + S_2 ,$$

and

$$y_0 = S_1 - S_2 .$$

EXAMPLE 1   Solve by the Taylor series method the initial value problem

$$\frac{dy}{dx} = xy + x^2 \quad \text{with } y(0) = 1 ,$$

for $x = 0(0.1)0.3$ to an accuracy of four decimal places.

Repeated differentiation of the equation

$$y' = xy + x^2 ,$$

gives

$$y'' = xy' + y + 2x ,$$
$$y''' = xy'' + 2y' + 2 , \tag{3}$$
$$y'''' = xy''' + 3y'' ,$$

and

$$y^{(n)} = xy^{(n-1)} + (n-1)y^{(n-2)} \quad \text{for } n > 3 .$$

This last equation may be put in terms of the reduced derivatives by multiplying by $h^n/n!$ to give, at $x = x_i$,

$$\tau_i^n = x_i \frac{h}{n} \tau_i^{n-1} + (n-1) \frac{h^2}{n(n-1)} \tau_i^{n-2}$$

$$= \frac{h}{n} (x_i \tau_i^{n-1} + h\tau_i^{n-2}) . \tag{4}$$

In this example, once the first four terms of the Taylor series have been found subsequent terms are obtained using the recurrence formula (4). The computations may be recorded in tabular form as shown in Table 7.1.

The calculation proceeds by using the given initial value $y(0) = 1$ and equations (3) to calculate the first three derivatives of y giving

$$y'(0) = 0, \quad y''(0) = 1, \quad y'''(0) = 2 .$$

It follows that, with $h = 0.1$, the first four terms of the Taylor series become

$$y_0 = 1 , \quad \tau_0^1 = hy'(0) = 0 ,$$

$$\tau_0^2 = \frac{h^2}{2} y''(0) = 0.005 ,$$

$$\tau_0^3 = \frac{h^3}{6} y'''(0) = \frac{0.001}{6} \times 2 = 0.00033 ,$$

TABLE 7.1

x	0	0.1	0.2
i	0	1	2
y_i	1	1.00534	1.02288
τ_i^1	0	0.01105	0.02446
τ_i^2	0.005	0.00608	0.00736
τ_i^3	0.00033	0.00039	0.00046
τ_i^4	0.00001	0.00002	0.00002
S_1	1.00501	1.01144	1.03026
S_2	0.00033	0.01144	0.02492

and these are entered in the first column of Table 7.1. Setting $n = 4$ in the recurrence formula (4) gives

$$\tau_0^4 = \frac{h}{4}(x_0 \tau_0^3 + h\tau_0^2)$$

$$= \frac{0.1}{4}(0 \times 0.00033 + 0.1 \times 0.005)$$

$$= 0.00001 ,$$

and no further terms are needed to give the required accuracy. The sums of the odd and even terms are shown in the table and give

$$y(-0.1) = S_1 - S_2 = 1.00468 ,$$

$$y(0.1) = S_1 + S_2 = 1.00534 .$$

Thus 1.00534 becomes the first entry in the next column of the table. Equations (3) are then used to calculate $y'(0.1), y'(0.1), y''(0.1)$ and the second column of the table is completed. It follows that

$$y(0.2) = 1.01144 + 0.01144 = 1.02288 ,$$

with the back check

$$y(0) = 1.01144 - 0.01144 = 1.$$

In exactly the same way the third column is completed to give

$$y(0.3) = 1.03026 + 0.02492 = 1.05518 ,$$

with the back check

$$y(0.1) = 1.03026 - 0.02492 = 1.00534 .$$

Therefore, to four decimal places,

$$y(0.1) = 1.0053, \quad y(0.2) = 1.0229, \quad y(0.3) = 1.0552 .$$

Second-order Equation

For a second-order equation

$$\frac{d^2y}{dx^2} = g\left(x, y, \frac{dy}{dx}\right),$$

where $y(x_0) = y_0$ and $y'(x_0) = y'_0$ are given, it is necessary to compute the two series

$$y_{i+1} = y_i + hy'_i + \frac{h^2}{2!}y''_i + \frac{h^3}{3!}y'''_i + \dots ,$$

$$y'_{i+1} = \qquad y'_i + hy''_i + \frac{h^2}{2!}y'''_i + \dots .$$

These may be written in terms of the reduced derivatives as

$$y_{i+1} = S_1 + S_2, \qquad hy'_{i+1} = T_1 + T_2 ,$$

where S_1 and S_2 are the sums of the odd and even terms as before and

$$T_1 = \tau_i^1 + 3\tau_i^3 + 5\tau_i^5 + \dots ,$$
$$T_2 = 2\tau_i^2 + 4\tau_i^4 + \dots .$$

The back check is provided by

$$y_{i-1} = S_1 - S_2 \quad \text{and} \quad hy'_{i-1} = T_1 - T_2 .$$

The Taylor series method may similarly be used without additional difficulty for the solution of a system of ordinary differential equations (see problem 2).

The remainder after n terms of the Taylor series (see §4.2 of Volume 1) is

$$\frac{y^{(n+1)}(\xi)}{(n+1)!} h^{n+1}$$

for some ξ satisfying $x_i < \xi < x_{i+1}$, and this expression cannot be explicitly computed since ξ is unknown. It is usual to truncate the Taylor series when the contribution of the last term, to the number of decimal places required, is negligible. However, this criterion is not sufficient to ensure that the sum of the remaining terms is not significant.

The advantages of the Taylor series method are that large step-lengths may often be used, it can be applied to non-linear equations, it is self-starting and there is a simple and effective back check. The main disadvantage is that the derivatives may be difficult to calculate and to program for automatic computation.

Exercises

1. Use the Taylor series method to find the numerical solution, correct to *four* decimal places, of

$$\frac{dy}{dx} = xy + 2, \quad \text{with} \quad y(0) = 0 ,$$

for the range $x = 0(0.2)0.4$.

2. Use the Taylor series method to obtain to *four* decimal places the numerical solution for y at $x = 1.2$ and $x = 1.4$ if

$$\frac{d^2 y}{dx^2} = xy + x, \quad \text{with} \quad y(1) = 0.5, \quad y'(1) = 0 .$$

7.3 RUNGE–KUTTA METHODS

The Runge–Kutta methods are a group of methods that are easily programmed for automatic computation. They have the advantage of being self-starting as the new function value is calculated using only the immediately preceding value. The common feature of the methods is that in order to advance one step the function $f(x, y)$ is calculated at several intermediate points of the interval. Throughout this section the theory and formulae will be written down for the calculation advancing from the point x_0 to x_1. For the next step the formulae are used afresh with a new x_0, equal to the previous x_1, and so on.

A Simple Example

If the differential equation (1) is formally integrated from x_0 to x then

$$y = y_0 + \int_{x_0}^{x} f\{s, y(s)\} \, ds . \tag{5}$$

Thus the original differential equation may be replaced by an integral equation where the unknown function $y(x)$ occurs on the left-hand side and under the integral sign on the right. The simplest approximation for the integral is to assume $f\{s, y(s)\}$ is constant over the interval x_0 to x_1 so that

$$y_1 = y_0 + hf(x_0, y_0) . \tag{6}$$

This is the Euler formula and the right-hand side is, of course, the first two terms of the Taylor series. Formula (6) can be improved by approximating the integral in equation (5) using the trapezoidal rule to give

$$y_1 = y_0 + \frac{h}{2} \{f(x_0, y_0) + f(x_1, y_1)\} .$$

But the right-hand side now contains y_1 and to obtain an explicit formula for y_1 the Euler formula (6) is used in the right-hand side. The resulting formula may then be written

$$y_1 = y_0 + \tfrac{1}{2}(k_1 + k_2) , \tag{7}$$

where

$$k_1 = hf(x_0, y_0) ,$$
$$k_2 = hf(x_0 + h, y_0 + k_1) .$$

Written in this way (7) is a simple formula of the *Runge–Kutta type*. It is a second-order formula because when expanded in powers of h the formula matches term by term the Taylor series up to terms of $O(h^2)$; that is, the error at each step is $O(h^3)$.

Second-order Runge–Kutta Formulae

The general Runge–Kutta formula of second order has the form

$$y_1 = y_0 + \alpha_1 k_1 + \alpha_2 k_2 \,,$$

where

$$k_1 = hf(x_0, y_0), \quad k_2 = hf(x_0 + \beta h, y_0 + \gamma k_1) \,,$$

and $\alpha_1, \alpha_2, \beta, \gamma$ are constants. The constants are chosen to ensure that the error is of order h^3. The first step is to expand k_2 in powers of h, remembering that it is a Taylor series expansion in two variables (see §4.2 of Volume 1) giving

$$k_2 = h \left\{ f(x_0, y_0) + \beta h \frac{\partial f}{\partial x}(x_0, y_0) + \gamma h f_0 \frac{\partial f}{\partial y}(x_0, y_0) + O(h^2) \right\} \,,$$

where $f_0 = f(x_0, y_0)$.

The expansion of y_1 is then

$$y_1 = y_0 + \alpha_1 h f(x_0, y_0) + \alpha_2 h \left\{ f_0 + \beta h \frac{\partial f}{\partial x}(x_0, y_0) + \gamma h f_0 \frac{\partial f}{\partial y}(x_0, y_0) \right\} + O(h^3)$$

$$= y_0 + (\alpha_1 + \alpha_2) h f(x_0, y_0) + \alpha_2 \beta h^2 \frac{\partial f}{\partial x}(x_0, y_0) + \alpha_2 \gamma h^2 f_0 \frac{\partial f}{\partial y}(x_0, y_0) + O(h^3) \,.$$

The ordinary Taylor series expansion for y_1 is

$$y_1 = y_0 + h f(x_0, y_0) + \frac{h^2}{2} \left\{ \frac{\partial f}{\partial x}(x_0, y_0) + f_0 \frac{\partial f}{\partial y}(x_0, y_0) \right\} + O(h^3) \,,$$

and term-by-term comparison gives the following equations for the constants

$$\alpha_1 + \alpha_2 = 1 \,,$$

$$\alpha_2 \beta = \tfrac{1}{2} \,,$$

$$\alpha_2 \gamma = \tfrac{1}{2} \,.$$

These are three equations to determine the four unknowns $\alpha_1, \alpha_2, \beta$ and γ. Thus, choosing the value of one constant fixes the values of the remaining three. The choice of $\beta = 1$ implies that $\alpha_2 = \tfrac{1}{2}, \alpha_1 = \tfrac{1}{2}, \gamma = 1$ which gives the formula (7) already obtained. The choice of $\alpha_2 = 1$ implies that $\alpha_1 = 0, \beta = \tfrac{1}{2}$ and $\gamma = \tfrac{1}{2}$ giving the elegant formula

$$y_1 = y_0 + k_2, \quad \text{where} \quad k_2 = hf(x_0 + \tfrac{1}{2}h, y_0 + \tfrac{1}{2}hf_0) \,.$$

Third-order Runge-Kutta Formulae

The general form of these formulae is

$$y_1 = y_0 + \alpha_1 k_1 + \alpha_2 k_2 + \alpha_3 k_3 \,,$$

where

$$k_1 = hf(x_0, y_0),$$

$$k_2 = hf(x_0 + \beta_1 h, y_0 + \gamma k_1),$$

$$k_3 = hf(x_0 + \beta_2 h, y_0 + \delta_1 k_1 + \delta_2 k_2).$$

The relationships between the eight constants $\beta_1, \beta_2, \gamma, \delta_1, \delta_2, \alpha_1, \alpha_2$ and α_3 are found by expansion of the above formulae in powers of h followed by a term-by-term comparison with the standard Taylor series expansion up to terms of $O(h^3)$. As was found previously with the second-order formulae the unknown constants are not determined uniquely by these equations and there is some freedom of choice in the formulae.

A typical third-order formula, due to Kutta, is

$$y_1 = y_0 + \tfrac{1}{6}(k_1 + 4k_2 + k_3),$$

where

$$k_1 = hf(x_0, y_0)$$

$$k_2 = hf(x_0 + \tfrac{1}{2}h, y_0 + \tfrac{1}{2}k_1),$$

$$k_3 = hf(x_0 + h, y_0 - k_1 + 2k_2).$$

Fourth-order Runge-Kutta Formulae

A widely used formula is the standard fourth-order formula

$$y_1 = y_0 + \tfrac{1}{6}(k_1 + 2k_2 + 2k_3 + k_4),$$

where

$$k_1 = hf(x_0, y_0),$$

$$k_2 = hf(x_0 + \tfrac{1}{2}h, y_0 + \tfrac{1}{2}k_1),$$

$$k_3 = hf(x_0 + \tfrac{1}{2}h, y_0 + \tfrac{1}{2}k_2),$$

$$k_4 = hf(x_0 + h, y_0 + k_3).$$

The error per step is $O(h^5)$ and the formula is derived by employing Taylor series expansions as before. Note that the third-order formulae require three evaluations of $f(x, y)$ per step and the fourth-order formulae four evaluations of $f(x, y)$. However, there are no fifth-order formulae involving five evaluations per step as it is found that the number of equations to determine the constants far exceeds the number of unknowns.

EXAMPLE 1   Solve by the standard fourth-order Runge-Kutta formula the initial value problem

$$\frac{dy}{dx} = xy + x^2 \quad \text{with} \quad y(0) = 1$$

for $x = 0(0.1)0.3$.

TABLE 7.2

i	x	y	f(x, y)	k_i	K
1	0	1	0	0	
2	0.05	1	0.05250	0.00525	
3	0.05	1.00262	0.05263	0.00526	
4	0.1	1.00526	0.11053	0.01105	0.00535
1	0.1	1.00535	0.11054	0.01105	
2	0.15	1.01088	0.17413	0.01741	
3	0.15	1.01406	0.17461	0.01746	
4	0.2	1.02281	0.24456	0.02446	0.01754
1	0.2	1.02289	0.24458	0.02446	
2	0.25	1.03512	0.32128	0.03213	
3	0.25	1.03895	0.32224	0.03222	
4	0.3	1.05511	0.40653	0.04065	0.03230
1	0.3	1.05519			

Table 7.2 shows a convenient layout for this method where, for this problem, $h = 0.1$ and

$$f(x, y) = xy + x^2 .$$

The table starts at $x_0 = 0$ with the initial value $y_0 = 1$ which gives $f(0, 1) = 0$ and $k_1 = 0$. The second row, to find k_2, has

$$x_0 + \tfrac{1}{2}h = 0.05 \quad \text{and} \quad y_0 + \tfrac{1}{2}k_1 = 1 ,$$

giving

$$k_2 = 0.1f(0.05, 1) = 0.00525 .$$

In the third row

$$x_0 + \tfrac{1}{2}h = 0.05 \quad \text{and} \quad y_0 + \tfrac{1}{2}k_2 = 1.00262 ,$$

giving

$$k_3 = 0.1f(0.05, 1.00262) = 0.00526 .$$

Similarly

$$k_4 = hf(x_0 + h, y_0 + k_3)$$

$$= 0.1f(0.1, 1.00526) = 0.01105 .$$

From these values of k_1, k_2, k_3 and k_4 the quantity

$$K = (k_1 + 2k_2 + 2k_3 + k_4)/6$$

$$= 0.00535 .$$

When added to the initial value of y this yields

$$y(0.1) = 1.00535,$$

and this is the new initial value for the next step. The whole procedure is repeated to find $y(0.2)$, and so on. The reader is warned that it is easy to make the mistake of adding $\frac{1}{2}k_2$ or k_3 on to the previous y value entered in the table and not to the first or initial value. This means that either $y_0 + \frac{1}{2}k_1 + \frac{1}{2}k_2$ or $y_0 + \frac{1}{2}k_2 + k_3$ is used incorrectly to compute k_3 and k_4 respectively. Finally it may be noted that this example 1 is the same as example 1 in §7.2 where the same function values were obtained by the Taylor series method.

The usual method of determining the accuracy of the solution when using an ordinary Runge-Kutta type formula is to repeat the computations using a smaller step length.

Systems of Equations

The Runge-Kutta formulae are readily generalized for systems of equations. In particular, the standard fourth-order formulae for the system

$$\frac{dy_r}{dx} = f_r(x, y_1, y_2, \ldots y_n), \ r = 1, 2, \ldots, n,$$

are

$$y_r(x_0 + h) = y_r(x_0) + \tfrac{1}{6}(k_{r1} + 2k_{r2} + 2k_{r3} + k_{r4}), \tag{8}$$

where

$$k_{r1} = hf_r(x_0, y_1, y_2, \ldots, y_n),$$
$$k_{r2} = hf_r(x_0 + \tfrac{1}{2}h, y_1 + \tfrac{1}{2}k_{11}, y_2 + \tfrac{1}{2}k_{21}, \ldots, y_n + \tfrac{1}{2}k_{n1}),$$
$$k_{r3} = hf_r(x_0 + \tfrac{1}{2}h, y_1 + \tfrac{1}{2}k_{12}, y_2 + \tfrac{1}{2}k_{22}, \ldots, y_n + \tfrac{1}{2}k_{n2}),$$
$$k_{r4} = hf_r(x_0 + h, y_1 + k_{13}, y_2 + k_{23}, \ldots, y_n + k_{n3}).$$

EXAMPLE 2   Solve the second-order equation

$$\frac{d^2y}{dx^2} = xy^2 + \frac{dy}{dx},$$

with the initial values $y(1) = 1, y'(1) = 0$ for $x = 1(0.2)1.4$ accurate to four decimal places.

The equation is first written as a system of two first-order equations

$$\frac{dy}{dx} = z, \quad \frac{dz}{dx} = xy^2 + z,$$

so that $f_1 = z$, and $f_2 = xy^2 + z$.

TABLE 7.3

i	x	y	z	k_{1i}	k_{2i}	K_1	K_2
1	1	1	0	0	0.2		
2	1.1	1.0	0.1	0.02	0.24		
3	1.1	1.01	0.12	0.024	0.2484		
4	1.2	1.024	0.2484	0.0497	0.3013	0.0229	0.2464
1	1.2	1.0229	0.2464	0.0493	0.3004		
2	1.3	1.0476	0.3966	0.0793	0.3647		
3	1.3	1.0626	0.4288	0.0858	0.3793		
4	1.4	1.1088	0.6257	0.1251	0.4694	0.0841	0.3763
1	1.4	1.1070	0.6227				

Table 7.3 shows the results obtained by using a step-length of $h = 0.2$. The scheme is similar to that used for example 1 with extra columns included because of the two dependent variables of this example. The first row of the table contains the initial values

$$x_0 = 1, \quad y_0 = 1, \quad z_0 = 0,$$

giving $k_{11} = 0.2 f_1(1, 1, 0) = 0$, $\quad k_{21} = 0.2 f_2(1, 1, 0) = 0.2$.

The entries in the second row are

$$x_0 + \tfrac{1}{2}h = 1.1, \quad y_0 + \tfrac{1}{2}k_{11} = 1.0, \quad z_0 + \tfrac{1}{2}k_{21} = 0.1,$$

which give $k_{12} = 0.2 f_1(1.1, 1.0, 0.1) = 0.02$, $k_{22} = 0.2 f_2(1.1, 1.0, 0.1) = 0.24$. In a similar manner k_{13}, k_{23}, k_{14} and k_{24} are calculated. From these values the quantities

$$K_1 = (k_{11} + 2k_{12} + 2k_{13} + k_{14})/6 = 0.0229,$$

$$K_2 = (k_{21} + 2k_{22} + 2k_{23} + k_{24})/6 = 0.2464$$

are found. Therefore

$$y(1.2) = 1 + 0.0229 = 1.0229, \quad z(1.2) = 0 + 0.2464 = 0.2464,$$

which are the starting values for the next step. If the calculations are repeated with the smaller step-length of $h = 0.1$ the results of Table 7.4 are obtained. These results serve to confirm the accuracy of the first calculations.

TABLE 7.4

x	y	z
1.1	1.0054	0.1107
1.2	1.0230	0.2464
1.3	1.0557	0.4138
1.4	1.1071	0.6228

Stability and Errors

A disadvantage of the ordinary Runge–Kutta methods is that there is no simple formula for the error term which would be a guide to the choice of step length. A theoretical estimate of the cumulative error can be obtained if it is assumed that the error is proportional to h^q, where q is the order of the method used. If y_{2r} and y_{1r} denote the values of y at $x = x_0 + 2rh$ obtained in steps of h and $2h$ respectively, then

$$y \simeq y_{2r} + Ah^q,$$

and

$$y \simeq y_{1r} + A(2h)^q,$$

where A is the same constant in each case. It follows that

$$y \simeq y_{2r} + \frac{1}{t-1}(y_{2r} - y_{1r}),$$

where $t = 2^q$. Thus the estimate of cumulative error is

$$\frac{1}{t-1}(y_{2r} - y_{1r}),$$

and for a fourth-order formula the estimate becomes

$$\frac{1}{15}(y_{2r} - y_{1r}).$$

However, a method known as *Runge–Kutta–Merson* provides, by use of one extra calculation of $f(x, y)$, an error estimate which may be used to control the step size automatically (see Mayers [1] pp. 16–27). The formulae for this method are

$$y_1 = y_0 + \tfrac{1}{6}(k_1 + 4k_4 + k_5),$$

where

$$k_1 = hf(x_0, y_0),$$
$$k_2 = hf(x_0 + \tfrac{1}{3}h, y_0 + \tfrac{1}{3}k_1),$$
$$k_3 = hf(x_0 + \tfrac{1}{3}h, y_0 + \tfrac{1}{6}k_1 + \tfrac{1}{6}k_2),$$
$$k_4 = hf(x_0 + \tfrac{1}{2}h, y_0 + \tfrac{1}{8}k_1 + \tfrac{3}{8}k_3),$$
$$k_5 = hf(x_0 + h, y_0 + \tfrac{1}{2}k_1 - \tfrac{3}{2}k_3 + 2k_4).$$

The error estimate for this formula is

$$E \simeq \tfrac{1}{30}(2k_1 - 9k_3 + 8k_4 - k_5),$$

and E is exact when $f(x, y)$ is linear in x and y.

A partial instability may occur with Runge–Kutta methods when one part of the solution decays very much faster than another. This phenomenon is illustrated in the following example.

TABLE 7.5

x	y	z
0	2	0
0.2	2.1937	−0.5563
0.4	2.5609	−1.2203
0.6	3.1484	−2.0508

TABLE 7.6

x	y	z
0	2	0
0.1	1.1783	0.6314
0.2	0.8935	0.7440
0.3	0.7613	0.7204
0.4	0.6759	0.6647
0.5	0.6081	0.6050
0.6	0.5492	0.5484

EXAMPLE 3

$$\frac{dy}{dx} = -8y + 7z, \quad \frac{dz}{dx} = 7y - 8z, \quad \text{with} \quad y(0) = 2, \quad z(0) = 0 .$$

This pair of first-order equations has the solutions

$$y = e^{-x} + e^{-15x} \quad \text{and} \quad z = e^{-x} - e^{-15x}. \tag{9}$$

Because e^{-15x} decays to zero very quickly one might expect to be able to choose a step-length of, say, $h = 0.2$. With $h = 0.2$ the results of Table 7.5 are obtained using the standard fourth-order formulae (8), a table of numbers which are clearly wrong as can be seen from (9) which show that z must be positive for all $x > 0$.
Using a step-length of $h = 0.1$ the results shown in Table 7.6 are obtained. These are much better though still not very accurate as the exact values at $x = 0.1$ are

$$y = 1.12797 \quad \text{and} \quad z = 0.68171 .$$

In fact a much smaller step-length is required to attain any real degree of accuracy.

The explanation is quite simple. The fourth-order formula matches the Taylor series up to terms of $O(h^4)$ so that $e^{-\lambda h}$ is approximated by

$$1 - \lambda h + \tfrac{1}{2}\lambda^2 h^2 - \tfrac{1}{6}\lambda^3 h^3 + \tfrac{1}{24}\lambda^4 h^4 .$$

When $h = 0.2$ and $\lambda = 1$ this gives

$$e^{-0.2} \simeq 0.818731 ,$$

which is very good as it is in error by 0.000002. However when $\lambda = 15$ and $h = 0.2$ the approximation is

$$e^{-3} \simeq 1.375,$$

which is nowhere near to the exact value of 0.0498.

This phenomenon is called a *partial instability* because a reduction of step size resolves the difficulty. Equations of this type are termed 'stiff' and the situation can easily occur that, in order to attain stability, h becomes unacceptably small.

Exercises

1. Use the standard fourth-order Runge–Kutta formula for the initial value problem

$$\frac{dy}{dx} = \frac{1}{y} + x \quad \text{with} \quad y(0) = 1,$$

to find the value of $y(0.4)$ first in one step ($h = 0.4$) and then in two steps ($h = 0.2$).

2. Use a third-order Runge–Kutta formula to obtain, correct to three decimal places, the numerical solution at $x = 0.1$ and $x = 0.2$ of

$$\frac{dy}{dx} = y^2 + x^2,$$

given that $y = 1$ when $x = 0$.

3. Derive the relations between the constants a, b, c, d and e such that

$$y_1 \equiv y(x_0 + h) \simeq y_0 + ak_1 + bk_2 + ck_3,$$

with

$$k_1 = hf(x_0, y_0), \quad k_2 = hf(x_0 + dh, y_0 + dk_1),$$
$$k_3 = hf(x_0 + eh, y_0 + ek_2),$$

is a *third*-order Runge–Kutta formula for the numerical solution of $dy/dx = f(x, y)$ with $y(x_0) = y_0$ given.

Use Heun's formula (given by $a = \frac{1}{4}, b = 0, c = \frac{3}{4}, d = \frac{1}{3}, e = \frac{2}{3}$) to obtain, correct to three decimal places, the numerical solution at $x = 0.1$ of

$$\frac{dy}{dx} - 2xy = \log_{10}(2 + x),$$

given that $y = 1$ when $x = 0$.

7.4 ITERATIVE METHODS

Predictor-corrector Methods

The methods considered in §7.2 and §7.3 integrate the differential equation over a single interval using only the function value at the beginning of the interval. Predictor-corrector methods make use of previously computed values and normally involve two fresh computations of $f(x, y)$ at each step. Starting at $x = x_0$ with the value y_0, the next value is first 'predicted' by a formula which does not involve $f(x_1, y_1)$. The accuracy of this 'predicted' value is then improved using a 'corrector' formula which incorporates the approximate predicted value of $f(x_1, y_1)$. It may sometimes be necessary to use the corrector formula more than once to obtain a specified accuracy.

The simple Runge–Kutta formula (7) may be regarded as being not only an example of a direct method, but also as a simple predictor-corrector procedure with the Euler formula (6)

$$y_1^* = y_0 + hf(x_0, y_0), \tag{10}$$

as the predictor and

$$y_1^{**} = y_0 + \tfrac{1}{2}h\{f(x_0, y_0) + f(x_1, y_1^*)\}, \tag{11}$$

as the corrector. The superscripts * and ** are used to distinguish the predicted and corrected values of y. However the error in y_1^* is $O(h^2)$ and in y_1^{**} it is $O(h^3)$ and no estimate of the magnitude of the error in y_1^{**} is available. To make the error in the predictor formula $O(h^3)$ the next term of the Taylor series may be included to give

$$y_1^* = y_0 + hf_0 + \tfrac{1}{2}h^2 f_0',$$

where $f_0 \equiv f(x_0, y_0)$ and $f_0' \equiv df/dx \ (= \partial f/\partial x + f\partial f/\partial y)$ evaluated at (x_0, y_0); f_0' is then approximated by

$$f_0' = \frac{1}{h}(f_0 - f_{-1}) + O(h),$$

to give the predictor

$$y_1^* = y_0 + \tfrac{1}{2}h(3f_0 - f_{-1}). \tag{12}$$

Expanding formula (12) in powers of h gives

$$y_1^* = y_0 + \tfrac{1}{2}h\{3f_0 - (f_0 - hf_0' + \tfrac{1}{2}h^2 f_0'' - \ldots)\},$$

and if y_1 is the exact value of $y(x_0 + h)$ then

$$y_1 - y_1^* = \tfrac{5}{12}h^3 f_0'' + O(h^4).$$

Similarly, from equation (11)

$$y_1 - y_1^{**} = -\tfrac{1}{12}h^3 f_0'' + O(h^4).$$

It follows that

$$y_1 \simeq y_1^{**} - \tfrac{1}{6}(y_1^{**} - y_1^*),$$

and $\tfrac{1}{6}(y_1^{**} - y_1^*)$ gives an indication of the magnitude of the error. When the predicted and corrected values agree to as many decimal places as the desired accuracy then this indicates that a larger step size may be used. This change may be made by selecting the appropriate values of $f(x, y)$ from those already found.

Adams–Bashforth Formulae

These formulae are derived by using the Newton backward-difference formula (see §11.3 of Volume 1) to approximate $f(x, y)$ in the integral equation (5). Thus, for the predictor, $f(x, y)$ is replaced by

$$f = f_0 + p\nabla f_0 + \tfrac{1}{2}p(p + 1)\nabla^2 f_0 + \tfrac{1}{6}p(p + 1)(p + 2)\nabla^3 f_0 + \dots , \tag{13}$$

where

$$p = (x - x_0)/h, \quad \nabla f_0 = f_0 - f_{-1},$$

$$\nabla^2 f_0 = \nabla f_0 - \nabla f_{-1} = f_0 - 2f_{-1} + f_{-2}, \text{etc.},$$

and integrating from $p = 0$ to $p = 1$ gives

$$y_1^* = y_0 + h(f_0 + \tfrac{1}{2}\nabla f_0 + \tfrac{5}{12}\nabla^2 f_0 + \tfrac{3}{8}\nabla^3 f_0 + \tfrac{251}{720}\nabla^4 f_0 + \dots). \tag{14}$$

The value $f_1^* \equiv f(x_1, y_1^*)$ can then be calculated and the backward differences ∇f_1^*, $\nabla^2 f_1^*, \dots$ found. The corrector formula uses these new differences by replacing $f(x, y)$ in equation (5) by

$$f = f_1^* + q\nabla f_1^* + \tfrac{1}{2}q(q + 1)\nabla^2 f_1^* + \tfrac{1}{6}q(q + 1)(q + 2)\nabla^3 f_1^* + \dots$$

where $q = (x - x_1)/h$, and integrating from $q = -1$ to $q = 0$. This gives

$$y_1^{**} = y_0 + h(f_1^* - \tfrac{1}{2}\nabla f_1^* - \tfrac{1}{12}\nabla^2 f_1^* - \tfrac{1}{24}\nabla^3 f_1^* - \tfrac{19}{720}\nabla^4 f_1^* - \dots). \tag{15}$$

Formulae (14) and (15) are the *Adams–Bashforth formulae*. In practice the formulae must be truncated because the number of terms is restricted by the number of backward differences available at $x = x_0$. If second and higher-order differences are ignored the simple formulae (12) and (11) are recovered. If third and higher-order differences are ignored the formulae become

$$y_1^* = y_0 + \tfrac{1}{12}h(23f_0 - 16f_{-1} + 5f_{-2}),$$

and

$$y_1^{**} = y_0 + \tfrac{1}{12}h(5f_1^* + 8f_0 - f_{-1}).$$

The estimate of the error is then $\tfrac{1}{10}(y_1^{**} - y_1^*)$.

Note that because the predictor-corrector methods require information from several previous points, not only must this information be stored, but a different method, say Taylor series or Runge–Kutta, is needed as a *starting procedure*.

EXAMPLE 1   Advance the calculation of the solution of

$$\frac{dy}{dx} = xy + x^2,$$

by two steps using the Adams–Bashforth formulae and the starting values $y(-0.1) = 1.0047, y(0) = 1, y(0.1) = 1.0053$ and $y(0.2) = 1.0229$ to an accuracy of four decimal places.

TABLE 7.7

x	y	f(x,y)	∇f	∇²f	∇³f
−0.1	1.0047	−0.09047			
			9047		
0	1	0		2006	
			11053		346
0.1	1.0053	0.11053		2352	
			13405		(440)
					441
0.2	1.0229	0.24458		(2792)	
				2793	
			(16197)		(564)
			16198		
0.3	(1.05517)	(0.40655)		(3357)	
	1.05521	0.40656			
			(19555)		
0.4	(1.10529)	(0.60211)			
	1.10534				

For this method the values of

$$f(x, y) = xy + x^2$$

are first calculated for the four starting values given and a finite-difference table constructed as shown in Table 7.7.

The predicted value of y at $x = 0.3$ is

$$y^*(0.3) = 1.0229 + 0.1(0.24458 + \tfrac{1}{2} \times 0.13405 + \tfrac{5}{12} \times 0.02352 + \tfrac{3}{8} \times 0.00346)$$

$$= 1.05517.$$

This predicted value is entered in the table, $f(x, y)$ calculated, and the predicted backward differences found. All these predicted values are shown in parentheses in the table. The corrected value is then given by

$$y^{**}(0.3) = 1.0229 + 0.1(0.40655 - \tfrac{1}{2} \times 0.16197 - \tfrac{1}{12} \times 0.02792 - \tfrac{1}{24} \times 0.00440)$$

$$= 1.05521.$$

This corrected value is entered into the table and $f(x, y)$ and the backward differences calculated. As the predicted and corrected values differ by only 4×10^{-5} no further correction is required. The next step is to calculate $y^*(0.4)$ and $y^{**}(0.4)$ in a similar way, giving

$$y^*(0.4) = 1.05521 + 0.1(0.40655 + \tfrac{1}{2} \times 0.16198 + \tfrac{5}{12} \times 0.02793 + \tfrac{3}{8} \times 0.00441),$$

$$= 1.10529,$$

and

$$y^{**}(0.4) = 1.05521 + 0.1(0.60211 - \tfrac{1}{2} \times 0.19555 - \tfrac{1}{12} \times 0.03357 - \tfrac{1}{24} \times 0.00564)$$

$$= 1.10534.$$

In this example the predicted and corrected values agree to the four decimal places required and so at each step the corrector formula is used only once. In fact the error estimate when the fourth and higher differences are neglected is approximately $0.07(y_1^{**} - y_1^*)$. Therefore $y(0.3) = 1.0552$ and $y(0.4) = 1.1053$ to four decimal places.

Milne's Formulae

A different approach is to integrate the differential equation (1) from a previous point $x_s (s < 0)$ to give

$$y_1 = y_s + \int_{x_s}^{x_1} f(t, y(t))\, dt \, ,$$

and approximate the integral using Simpson's rule. If s is set equal to -3 then two approximations may be written down using step-lengths of $2h$ and h in turn, namely

$$y_1 = y_{-3} + \tfrac{2}{3}h(f_{-3} + 4f_{-1} + f_1)$$

and

$$y_1 = y_{-3} + \tfrac{1}{3}h(f_{-3} + 4f_{-2} + 2f_{-1} + 4f_0 + f_1) \, .$$

To construct a predictor formula the unknown value f_1 is eliminated between these equations to give

$$y_1^* = y_{-3} + \tfrac{4}{3}h(2f_{-2} - f_{-1} + 2f_0) \, . \tag{16}$$

The corrector formula is obtained by setting s equal to -1 and Simpson's rule gives

$$y_1^{**} = y_{-1} + \tfrac{1}{3}h(f_{-1} + 4f_0 + f_1^*) \, . \tag{17}$$

Both the predictor and corrector have errors of $O(h^5)$ and the error estimate is $(y_1^{**} - y_1^*)/29$.

Milne's formulae (16) and (17) are simple to use and require four function values. They are very accurate but the method is often unstable. The instability is present because the numerical approximation to the equation is of a higher order than the original differential equation and an additional solution is introduced which may eventually dominate the true solution.

For example, consider the equation

$$\frac{dy}{dx} = -y \, ,$$

which has the exact solution $y = Ae^{-x}$. Assuming that the predicted and corrected values of y do converge then the Milne corrector formula gives

$$y_{n+1} = y_{n-1} + \tfrac{1}{3}h(y'_{n-1} + 4y'_n + y'_{n+1}) \, ,$$

or

$$\left(1 + \frac{h}{3}\right)y_{n+1} + \frac{4h}{3}y_n - \left(1 - \frac{h}{3}\right)y_{n-1} = 0 \, ,$$

because $y'_{n-1} = -y_{n-1}$, $y'_n = -y_n$ and $y'_{n+1} = -y_{n+1}$. This difference equation relating the values at three neighbouring points (see §3.6 of Volume 1) has the general solution

$$y_n = A\alpha^n + B\beta^n,$$

where

$$\alpha = \left\{ -\tfrac{2}{3}h + \left(1 + \frac{h^2}{3}\right)^{\!\frac{1}{2}} \right\} \Big/ \left(1 + \frac{h}{3}\right), \quad \beta = \left\{ -\tfrac{2}{3}h - \left(1 + \frac{h^2}{3}\right)^{\!\frac{1}{2}} \right\} \Big/ \left(1 + \frac{h}{3}\right)$$

and A and B are arbitrary constants. Expansion in powers of h shows that the first term corresponds to the actual solution e^{-nh} up to terms of $O(h^4)$ but the second term has $|\beta| > 1$ for all $h > 0$ and is an increasing solution of the difference equation. This unwanted solution will always dominate the true solution of the differential equation no matter how small the coefficient B. The presence of this instability is independent of h, that is, it cannot be removed by using a smaller step size. It is for this reason that Milne's method should only be used with great caution.

EXAMPLE 2   Advance the calculation of the solution of

$$\frac{dy}{dx} = xy + x^2$$

by two steps using Milne's formulae and the starting values $y(-0.1) = 1.00468$, $y(0) = 1$, $y(0.1) = 1.00534$ and $y(0.2) = 1.02288$ (see example 1).

The starting values of x, y and $f(x, y)$ are conveniently arranged in tabular form (Table 7.8).

The predicted values (in parentheses) and corrected values shown in the table are obtained as follows:

$$y^*(0.3) = 1.00468 + \tfrac{4}{3} \times 0.1 \, (0 - 0.11053 + 2 \times 0.24458) = 1.05516,$$

$$y^{**}(0.3) = 1.00534 + \tfrac{1}{3} \times 0.1 (0.11053 + 4 \times 0.24458 + 0.40655) = 1.05519,$$

$$y^*(0.4) = 1 + \tfrac{4}{3} \times 0.1 \, (2 \times 0.11053 - 0.24458 + 2 \times 0.40656) = 1.10528,$$

$$y^{**}(0.4) = 1.02288 + \tfrac{1}{3} \times 0.1 \, (0.24458 + 4 \times 0.40656 + 0.60211) = 1.10531.$$

TABLE 7.8

x	y	$f(x, y)$
−0.1	1.00468	−0.09047
0	1	0
0.1	1.00534	0.11053
0.2	1.02288	0.24458
0.3	(1.05516)	(0.40655)
	1.05519	0.40656
0.4	(1.10528)	(0.60211)
	1.10531	

The predictor-corrector methods are good for desk computation as they usually involve only two calculations of $f(x, y)$ per step and they also provide a direct check on the error per step. The Adams—Bashforth formulae have the additional advantage of being inherently stable. The disadvantages for automatic computation are that a special starting procedure is required, the methods make heavy demands on store and it is awkward to change the step length.

Deferred-correction Method

The method calculates an approximate solution over the whole range of interest, and then this solution is improved in one or more stages. This method, unlike the previous ones, uses difference formulae to approximate the differential equation. Although the difference formulae are inherently less accurate than the integration formulae used in the predictor-corrector methods, the method of computing the corrections enables an accurate solution to be found.

The method is illustrated for the linear differential equation

$$\frac{dy}{dx} + P(x)y = Q(x), \quad y(x_0) = y_0, \tag{18}$$

when the solution is required for $x = x_0(h)x_n$.

It can be shown (see exercise 3 of §11.5 of Volume 1) that

$$\tfrac{1}{2}h(y'_r + y'_{r+1}) = \delta y_{r+\frac{1}{2}} + \tfrac{1}{12}\delta^3 y_{r+\frac{1}{2}} - \tfrac{1}{120}\delta^5 y_{r+\frac{1}{2}} + \dots$$

This may be used with equation (18) to give

$$(1 + \tfrac{1}{2}hP_{r+1})y_{r+1} - (1 - \tfrac{1}{2}hP_r)y_r + Cy_{r+\frac{1}{2}} = \tfrac{1}{2}h(Q_r + Q_{r+1}), \tag{19}$$

where $Q_r = Q(x_r)$, $P_r = P(x_r)$, and

$$Cy_{r+\frac{1}{2}} = \tfrac{1}{12}\delta^3 y_{r+\frac{1}{2}} - \tfrac{1}{120}\delta^5 y_{r+\frac{1}{2}} + \dots$$

Equation (19) is then rearranged to give

$$y_{r+1} = \frac{(1 - \tfrac{1}{2}hP_r)y_r + \tfrac{1}{2}h(Q_r + Q_{r+1}) - Cy_{r+\frac{1}{2}}}{1 + \tfrac{1}{2}hP_{r+1}}. \tag{20}$$

The method of calculation is to neglect the term $Cy_{r+\frac{1}{2}}$ in equation (20). This equation then expresses y_{r+1} explicitly in terms of y_r and the known function values of $P(x)$ and $Q(x)$. Starting with y_0 a value for y_1 is calculated which is then used to calculate y_2 and so on. In this way approximate values of y are found throughout the range. In fact the values of y must be extended beyond the ends of the range x_0 to x_n if a difference table is to be constructed to determine all the n correction terms $Cy_{r+\frac{1}{2}}$. The extension to y_{n+1} and y_{n+2} is made directly by using the formula (20) without the correction term, whilst to calculate y_{-1} and y_{-2} the formula must be rearranged to express y_r in terms of y_{r+1}. A difference table is then constructed and the correction terms $Cy_{r+\frac{1}{2}}$ calculated. These values are used in the right-hand side of equation (20) and new, improved, values for y are calculated. This process is repeated until the required accuracy is obtained.

Note that it is sufficient for the values of successive corrections to be the same. It is also worth noting that if $y_r^{(1)}$ represents the first approximation to the solution it eases the computation if y_r is written as

$$y_r = y_r^{(1)} + \eta_r .$$

The formulae for η_s, the corrections to the first approximation, are then

$$\eta_{r+1} = \frac{(1 - \tfrac{1}{2}hP_r)\eta_r - Cy_{r+\frac{1}{2}}^{(1)}}{1 + \tfrac{1}{2}hP_r} ,$$

and fewer significant figures are needed to compute these corrections.

EXAMPLE 3   Solve the initial value problem

$$\frac{dy}{dx} = xy + x^2 \quad \text{where} \quad y(0) = 1 ,$$

with an accuracy of five decimal places, over the range $x = 0(0.1)0.5$ using the method of deferred correction.

For this example

$$P(x) = -x \quad \text{and} \quad Q(x) = x^2 ,$$

so that equation (20) becomes

$$y_{r+1} = \frac{(1 + \tfrac{1}{2}hx_r)y_r + \tfrac{1}{2}h(x_r^2 + x_{r+1}^2) - Cy_{r+\frac{1}{2}}}{1 - \tfrac{1}{2}hx_{r+1}} .$$

TABLE 7.9

x	$y^{(1)}$	$\delta y^{(1)}$	$\delta^2 y^{(1)}$	$\delta^3 y^{(1)}$	$Cy_{r+\frac{1}{2}}^{(1)}$
−0.1	1.00452				
		−452			
0	1		1005		
		553		218	18
0.1	1.00553		1223		
		1776		258	22
0.2	1.02329		1481		
		3257		309	26
0.3	1.05586		1790		
		5047		371	31
0.4	1.10633		2161		
		7208		457	38
0.5	1.17841		2618		
		9826			
0.6	1.27667				

The term $Cy_{r+\frac{1}{2}}$ is neglected and the calculation proceeds as follows:

$$y_1^{(1)} = y(0.1) = (1 \times 1 + 0.0005)/0.995 = 1.00553,$$

$$y_2^{(1)} = y(0.2) = (1.005 \times 1.00553 + 0.0025)/0.990 = 1.02329,$$

$$y_3^{(1)} = y(0.3) = (1.010 \times 1.02329 + 0.0065)/0.985 = 1.05586,$$

$$y_4^{(1)} = y(0.4) = (1.015 \times 1.05586 + 0.0125)/0.980 = 1.10633,$$

$$y_5^{(1)} = y(0.5) = (1.020 \times 1.10633 + 0.0205)/0.975 = 1.17841,$$

and to extend the table by one value at each end

$$y_6^{(1)} = y(0.6) = (1.025 \times 1.17841 + 0.0305)/0.970 = 1.27667,$$

$$y_{-1}^{(1)} = y(-0.1) = (1 \times 1 - 0.0005)/0.995 = 1.00452.$$

The difference table based on these values is shown in Table 7.9.

The corrections η_r to the first approximation $y_r^{(1)}$ are computed by the formula

$$\eta_{r+1} = \frac{(1 + \frac{1}{2}hx_r)\eta_r - Cy_{r+\frac{1}{2}}^{(1)}}{1 - \frac{1}{2}hx_{r+1}}, \quad \text{with} \quad \eta_0 = 0:$$

$$\eta_1 = (1 \times 0 - 0.00018)/0.995 = -0.00018,$$

$$\eta_2 = (-1.005 \times 0.00018 - 0.00022)/0.990 = -0.00041,$$

$$\eta_3 = (-1.010 \times 0.00041 - 0.00026)/0.985 = -0.00068,$$

$$\eta_4 = (-1.015 \times 0.00068 - 0.00031)/0.980 = -0.00102,$$

$$\eta_5 = (-1.020 \times 0.00102 - 0.00038)/0.975 = -0.00146.$$

These corrections are shown in Table 7.10. Their third differences are sufficiently small for the correction terms $C\eta_{r+\frac{1}{2}}$ not to affect the fifth decimal place. Therefore no further correction is necessary and the solution to an accuracy of five decimal places is shown in the right-hand column of Table 7.10.

TABLE 7.10

x	η	$\delta\eta$	$\delta^2\eta$	$\delta^3\eta$	$y^{(1)} + \eta$
0	0				1
		-18			
0.1	-0.00018		5		1.00535
		-23		-1	
0.2	-0.00041		4		1.02288
		-27		3	
0.3	-0.00068		7		1.05518
		-34		3	
0.4	-0.00102		10		1.10531
		-44			
0.5	-0.00146				1.17695

The deferred-correction method is well suited for the solution of linear equations and may be executed on a desk machine or programmed for automatic computation. It is a stable method and has the advantage of avoiding the cumulative error associated with step-by-step methods. However it does have the disadvantage that in order to construct a difference table y must be computed beyond both ends of the range.

Exercises

1. Use the Adams–Bashforth predictor-corrector formulae to continue to $x = 0.4$ the solution, correct to four decimal places, of

$$\frac{dy}{dx} - y = \log_{10}(2 + x),$$

given the starting values

x:	-0.2	-0.1	0	0.1
y:	0.7684	0.8773	1.0000	1.1379.

2. The function y satisfies the differential equation

$$\frac{dy}{dx} = y - x^2, \quad y(0) = 1,$$

and the following starting values have been calculated

$$y(0.2) = 1.2186, \quad y(0.4) = 1.4682, \quad y(0.6) = 1.7379.$$

Continue the integration to $x = 1$ correct to three decimal places and compare with the exact solution $y = x^2 + 2x + 2 - e^x$.

3. Use the method of deferred correction to solve, correct to four decimal places,

$$\frac{dy}{dx} - y = \log_{10}(2 + x), \quad y(0) = 1,$$

for the range $x = 0(0.1)0.4$.

7.5 BOUNDARY VALUE PROBLEMS

The methods of the previous sections are not directly applicable to boundary value problems because they depend upon all the conditions being known at the same value of x. One way of overcoming this difficulty is to use the step-by-step methods already described for initial value problems; systematically searching for the unspecified initial conditions which give a solution that correctly matches the boundary conditions specified at the other end of the range. Alternatively the deferred-correction method can be adapted to solve boundary value problems.

When the differential equation is linear, use can be made of the special properties of linear equations which are described in §§6.2 and 6.3. These are that the general solution of a given inhomogeneous linear equation is the sum of a particular integral and the complementary function, and that the complementary function is a linear combination of linearly independent solutions of the corresponding homogeneous equation. These independent solutions may be computed by using the methods for initial value problems with suitable choices of initial values. The required solution is then a linear combination of these solutions chosen to fit all the required boundary values.

Trial and Error or Shooting Method

Suppose, for example, that the equation

$$\frac{d^2 y}{dx^2} = f\left(x, y, \frac{dy}{dx}\right),$$

is to be solved subject to the boundary conditions

$$y(x_0) = Y_0, \quad y(x_n) = Y_n.$$

This is equivalent to the system

$$\frac{dy}{dx} = z, \quad \frac{dz}{dx} = f(x, y, z),$$

and

$$y(x_0) = Y_0, \quad y(x_n) = Y_n.$$

This system of two first-order equations could now be solved (by using a Runge–Kutta formula, for example) if the value of z at x_0 were known. The method is to choose two trial values $z_0^{(1)}$ and $z_0^{(2)}$ for $z(x_0)$ and solve in each case. The resulting values $y_n^{(1)}$ and $y_n^{(2)}$ at $x = x_n$ will not in general equal Y_n. However, these two trials usually enable a much better estimate for $z(x_0)$ to be made, from which trial a still better initial value can be found, and so on. It is usual to use linear interpolation at each stage. Thus the third trial starts with the value

$$z(x_0) = z_0^{(2)} - \frac{y_n^{(2)} - Y_n}{y_n^{(2)} - y_n^{(1)}} \left(z_0^{(2)} - z_0^{(1)}\right). \tag{21}$$

For many boundary value problems a suitable choice for the first two trial values $z_0^{(1)}$ and $z_0^{(2)}$ will be suggested by the physical situation the equation models. When no other indication is available a natural choice for $z_0^{(1)}$ is

$$z_0^{(1)} = \frac{Y_n - Y_0}{x_n - x_0}.$$

The resulting value $y_n^{(1)}$ will overestimate the boundary value Y_n by $y_n^{(1)} - Y_n$ and a suitable choice for $z_0^{(2)}$ is then

$$z_0^{(2)} = \frac{Y_n - (y_n^{(1)} - Y_n) - Y_0}{x_n - x_0}$$

$$= \frac{2Y_n - y_n^{(1)} - Y_0}{x_n - x_0}. \tag{22}$$

EXAMPLE 1   Solve the boundary value problem

$$\frac{d^2 y}{dx^2} + xy^2 = 0 \quad \text{with} \quad y(0) = 0, \quad y(1) = 1,$$

for $x = 0(0.1)1$ by the trial and error method.

The equation is written as the system

$$\frac{dy}{dx} = z, \quad \frac{dz}{dx} = -xy^2,$$

and $y(0) = 0, y(1) = 1$.

With $z_0^{(1)} = 1$ as the first trial value the standard fourth-order Runge–Kutta formulae give $y_n^{(1)} = 0.9514$. A second trial value by formula (22) is

$$z_0^{(2)} = \frac{2 \times 1 - 0.9514 - 0}{1 - 0} = 1.0486,$$

and this gives $y_n^{(2)} = 0.9952$. The interpolation formula (21) then gives for the third trial value

$$z_0^{(3)} = 1.0486 - \frac{0.9952 - 1}{0.9952 - 0.9514}(1.0486 - 1) = 1.0539.$$

The solution over the whole range with this starting value is shown in Table 7.11. In this case the boundary value $y(1)$ has been met with an accuracy of the numerical method used. To make any further improvement a smaller step-length and more decimal figures are required.

The trial and error method is laborious but may be used with advantage for automatic computation.

TABLE 7.11

x	y	z
0	0	1.05390
0.1	0.10539	1.05387
0.2	0.21076	1.05346
0.3	0.31604	1.05165
0.4	0.42099	1.04680
0.5	0.52522	1.03660
0.6	0.62804	1.01816
0.7	0.72846	0.98807
0.8	0.82514	0.94258
0.9	0.91634	0.87787
1.0	0.99995	0.79033

Direct Finite-difference or Deferred-correction Method

For this method the first and second derivatives are replaced by the central-difference formulae (see §11.5 of Volume 1)

$$y_r' = \frac{1}{2h}(y_{r+1} - y_{r-1}) + \frac{1}{h}(-\tfrac{1}{6}\mu\delta^3 y_r + \tfrac{1}{30}\mu\delta^5 y_r + \ldots),$$

and

$$y_r'' = \frac{1}{h^2}(y_{r+1} - 2y_r + y_{r-1}) + \frac{1}{h^2}(-\tfrac{1}{12}\delta^4 y_r + \tfrac{1}{90}\delta^6 y_r - \ldots),$$

where

$$\mu\delta^s y_r = \tfrac{1}{2}(\delta^s y_{r-\frac{1}{2}} + \delta^s y_{r+\frac{1}{2}}).$$

The boundary values are incorporated directly in the equations for y_r.

For the linear boundary value problem

$$\frac{d^2 y}{dx^2} + p(x)\frac{dy}{dx} + q(x)y = k(x), \quad y(x_0) = y_0, \quad y(x_n) = y_n,$$

the finite-difference approximation is

$$(1 - \tfrac{1}{2}hp_r)y_{r-1} - (2 - h^2 q_r)y_r + (1 + \tfrac{1}{2}hp_r)y_{r+1} = h^2 k_r - Cy_r$$

$$(r = 1, 2, \ldots, n - 1), \quad (23)$$

where

$$Cy_r = (-\tfrac{1}{12}\delta^4 y_r + \tfrac{1}{90}\delta^6 y_r - \ldots) + hp_r(-\tfrac{1}{6}\mu\delta^3 y_r + \tfrac{1}{30}\mu\delta^5 y_r + \ldots),$$

$$p_r = p(x_r), \quad q_r = q(x_r) \quad \text{and} \quad k_r = k(x_r).$$

These are $n - 1$ equations in the $n - 1$ unknowns $y_1, y_2, \ldots, y_{n-1}$, as y_0 and y_n are known. In matrix notation they may be written as

$$\mathbf{AY} = \mathbf{D} - \mathbf{CY}, \quad (24)$$

where $\mathbf{A}$ is a banded matrix of width three of the form

$$\mathbf{A} = \begin{pmatrix} b_1 & c_1 & 0 & 0 & . & . & 0 \\ a_2 & b_2 & c_2 & 0 & . & . & 0 \\ 0 & a_3 & b_3 & c_3 & . & . & 0 \\ . & . & . & . & . & . & . \\ . & . & . & 0 & a_{n-2} & b_{n-2} & c_{n-2} \\ 0 & . & . & . & 0 & a_{n-1} & b_{n-1} \end{pmatrix}, \quad \mathbf{CY} = \begin{pmatrix} Cy_1 \\ Cy_2 \\ \vdots \\ Cy_{n-1} \end{pmatrix}$$

and $\mathbf{D}$ contains the remaining terms. Note that the term $\mathbf{CY}$ depends upon the unknown values of $\mathbf{Y}$ and may be made small by a sufficiently small choice of h. The difficulty arises that if h is made small enough for the term $\mathbf{CY}$ to be neglected, then in order to cover the same range, the order n of the equations (24) may become very large indeed, with a correspondingly large increase in computation time.

A solution to the difficulty is to use the deferred-correction approach. If the term CY is neglected then the first approximation $Y^{(1)}$ is the solution of

$$AY^{(1)} = D.$$

The term $CY^{(1)}$ is then computed and the second approximation $Y^{(2)}$ is given by the solution of

$$AY^{(2)} = D - CY^{(1)}.$$

The process is repeated until two successive approximations are equal to the required accuracy (usually in about two iterations).

It is more convenient to write

$$Y^{(2)} = Y^{(1)} + \eta^{(1)}$$

so that

$$A\eta^{(1)} = -CY^{(1)},$$

and further corrections satisfy

$$A\eta^{(r+1)} = -C\eta^{(r)}.$$

As is usual in deferred-correction methods it is necessary to extend the table by a few values above and below the range of interest in order to be able to compute all the correction terms.

EXAMPLE 2　　Solve the boundary value problem

$$\frac{d^2 y}{dx^2} + xy = 0, \quad y(0) = 0, \quad y(1) = 1,$$

by the deferred-correction method with $h = 0.2$.

The finite-difference approximation of this equation is

$$y_{r-1} - (2 - h^2 x_r)y_r + y_{r+1} = -Cy_r, \tag{25}$$

where

$$Cy_r = -\tfrac{1}{12}\delta^4 y_r + \tfrac{1}{90}\delta^6 y_r - \dots .$$

With $h = 0.2$ the system of equations (25) becomes

$$-1.992y_1 + y_2 = -Cy_1,$$
$$y_1 - 1.984y_2 + y_3 = -Cy_2,$$
$$y_2 - 1.976y_3 + y_4 = -Cy_3,$$
$$y_3 - 1.968y_4 = -Cy_4 - 1.$$

TABLE 7.12

x	$y^{(1)}$		$\delta^2 y^{(1)}$		$\delta^4 y^{(1)}$	$'\delta^6 y^{(1)}$	Cy_r	$\eta^{(1)}$	$y^{(1)} + \eta^{(1)}$
−0.4	−0.43580								
		21877							
−0.2	−0.21703		−174						
		21703		174					
0	0		0		−349			0	0
		21703		−175		9			
0.2	0.21703		−175		−340	−3	28	0.00054	0.21757
		21528		−515		6			
0.4	0.43231		−690		−334	49	28	0.00080	0.43311
		20838		−849		55			
0.6	0.64069		−1539		−279	19	23	0.00076	0.64145
		19299		−1128		74			
0.8	0.83368		−2667		−205	58	18	0.00048	0.83416
		16632		−1333		132			
1	1.0		−4000		−73			0	1
		12632		−1406					
1.2	1.12632		−5406						
		7226							
1.4	1.19858								

The solution of this system of equations, neglecting the correction terms $-Cy_r$, may be found by a direct elimination method (see §10.2 of Volume 1 and also problem 3 of that Chapter) and is shown in Table 7.12.

The values above and below the range $[0, 1]$ are found by the formulae

$$y_{r-1} = (2 - h^2 x_r)y_r - y_{r+1},$$

and

$$y_{r+1} = (2 - h^2 x_r)y_r - y_{r-1},$$

which are obtained from equation (25).

When the first corrections $\eta^{(1)}$ are differenced the Table 7.13 is obtained. These differences are sufficiently small for no further correction to be necessary and the corrected solution is shown in the last column of Table 7.12.

The above finite-difference approach is well suited to the solution of linear differential equations. The method may be used for non-linear differential equations but then gives rise to non-linear algebraic equations for which there are no direct methods of solution.

Exercises

1. Write down the equations governing the deferred-correction solution of

$$\frac{d^2 y}{dx^2} + y = 0,$$

TABLE 7.13

x	$\eta^{(1)}$		$\delta^2\eta$		$\delta^4\eta$
0	0				
		54			
0.2	0.00054		−28		
		26		−2	
0.4	0.00080		−30		8
		−4		6	
0.6	0.00076		−24		−2
		−28		4	
0.8	0.00048		−20		
		−48			
1.0	0				

for the range $x = 0(0.2)0.8$ given that $y(0) = 0$, $y(0.8) = 1$. Find the solution correct to four decimal places and compare with the exact solution $y = \sin x/\sin 0.8$.

2. Find the deferred-correction solution, accurate to three decimal places, of

$$\frac{d^2y}{dx^2} + x^2y = 1,$$

for the range $x = 0(0.2)1$ given that $y(0) = -0.2$, $y(1) = 1.2$.

7.6 PARTIAL DIFFERENTIAL EQUATIONS

Finite-difference methods for the solution of partial differential equations, where the unknown function u is a function of x and y, depend upon dividing the appropriate region of the x, y plane with a mesh and writing down an approximation to the equation at each point in terms of values of u at that point and at neighbouring mesh points. The approximations for the second derivatives are given by

$$\frac{\partial^2 u}{\partial x^2} = \frac{1}{h^2}\{u(x - h, y) - 2u(x,y) + u(x + h, y)\} + O(h^2)$$

and   (26)

$$\frac{\partial^2 u}{\partial y^2} = \frac{1}{k^2}\{u(x, y - k) - 2u(x,y) + u(x, y + k)\} + O(k^2)$$

where h and k are the mesh sizes in the x and y directions respectively. For the first derivatives, one of the following relations

$$\frac{\partial u}{\partial x} = \frac{1}{2h}\{u(x + h, y) - u(x - h, y)\} + O(h^2) \quad \text{(central difference formula)},$$

$$\frac{\partial u}{\partial x} = \frac{1}{h}\{u(x + h, y) - u(x, y)\} + O(h) \quad \text{(forward difference formula)}, \quad (27)$$

or

$$\frac{\partial u}{\partial x} = \frac{1}{h}\{u(x,y) - u(x-h,y)\} + O(h) \quad \text{(backward difference formula)},$$

may be used. Frequently the independent variables will be (x, t) instead of (x, y), where t denotes time.

One-dimensional Diffusion Equation

The equation

$$\frac{\partial u}{\partial t} = \frac{\partial^2 u}{\partial x^2}, \tag{28}$$

is called the one-dimensional diffusion equation and governs such physical phenomena as unsteady heat conduction in a rod, decay of radioactivity, diffusion of vorticity in a viscous fluid, etc. Analytic solutions of this equation are considered in §7.5 of Volume 1. Typical conditions for the solution $u(x, t)$ of equation (28) are

$$u(x, 0) = f(x) \quad \text{in} \quad a \leqslant x \leqslant b \quad \text{(initial condition)},$$

and

$$u(a, t) = g(t), \quad u(b, t) = h(t) \quad \text{for} \quad t > 0 \quad \text{(boundary conditions)}.$$

The solution is then determined in the region of the x, t plane given by $a \leqslant x \leqslant b$, $t \geqslant 0$.

The x, t plane is subdivided into equal rectangles with sides of length $\delta x = h$ and $\delta t = k$ as shown in Fig. 7.1. The value of u at a typical mesh point (rh, sk), where r and

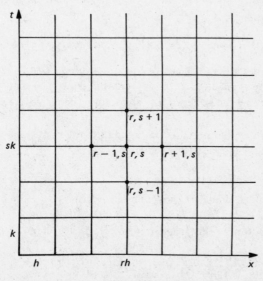

Fig. 7.1

s are integers, is denoted by $u_{r,s}$, so that

$$u_{r,s} \equiv u(rh, sk).$$

Equation (28) is approximated by the finite-difference formulae (26) and (27) to give

$$\frac{1}{k}(u_{r,s+1} - u_{r,s}) = \frac{1}{h^2}(u_{r+1,s} - 2u_{r,s} + u_{r-1,s})$$

or

$$u_{r,s+1} = u_{r,s} + \alpha(u_{r-1,s} - 2u_{r,s} + u_{r+1,s}) \tag{29}$$

where $\alpha = k/h^2$.

This finite-difference equation (29) determines the value of $u_{r,s+1}$ in terms of the known values on the sth row. It is thus an *explicit formula*.

EXAMPLE 1   Use the explicit formula (29) to find the solution of equation (28) subject to the conditions

$$u(x, 0) = 4x(1 - x) \quad \text{for } 0 \leqslant x \leqslant 1$$

and

$$u(0, t) = u(1, t) = 0 \quad \text{for } t > 0.$$

This problem is symmetric about $x = 0.5$ so the solution is necessary only for $0 \leqslant x \leqslant 0.5$. If the choice of $h = 0.1$ and $\delta t = k = 0.001$ is made then $\alpha = 0.1$ and equation (29) becomes

$$u_{r,s+1} = \tfrac{1}{10}(u_{r-1,s} + 8u_{r,s} + u_{r+1,s}). \tag{30}$$

The initial values are

$$u_{0,0} = 0, \quad u_{1,0} = 0.36, \quad u_{2,0} = 0.64, \quad u_{3,0} = 0.84, \quad u_{4,0} = 0.96, \quad u_{5,0} = 1.0.$$

These values, with equation (30), enable the values of $u_{r,1}$ ($r = 1, 2, \ldots, 10$) to be determined since by symmetry $u_{6,s} = u_{4,s}$, etc. Equation (30) is used again to calculate the values of $u_{r,2}$ using the values of $u_{r,1}$ and so on. The results are shown in Table 7.14.

If in order to reduce the amount of computation the larger time step $\delta t = 0.005$ is used then $\alpha = 0.5$ and equation (29) becomes

$$u_{r,s+1} = \tfrac{1}{2}(u_{r-1,s} + u_{r+1,s}). \tag{31}$$

The results using this formula are shown in Table 7.15.

The analytic solution of this problem is (see §7.5 of Volume 1)

$$u(x, t) = \frac{32}{\pi^2} \sum_{n=0}^{\infty} \frac{\sin(2n + 1)\pi x}{(2n + 1)^3} \exp\{-(2n + 1)^2 \pi^2 t\},$$

TABLE 7.14

s	t	x = 0	0.1	0.2	0.3	0.4	0.5
0	0	0	0.3600	0.6400	0.8400	0.9600	1.0000
1	0.001	0	0.3520	0.6320	0.8320	0.9520	0.9920
2	0.002	0	0.3448	0.6240	0.8240	0.9440	0.9840
3	0.003	0	0.3382	0.6161	0.8160	0.9360	0.9760
4	0.004	0	0.3322	0.6083	0.8080	0.9280	0.9680
5	0.005	0	0.3266	0.6007	0.8000	0.9200	0.9600
.		.			.		
10	0.010	0	0.3030	0.5650	0.7608	0.8801	0.9200
.		.		.		.	
20	0.020	0	0.2676	0.5047	0.6878	0.8022	0.8410
.		.		.		.	
100	0.100	0	0.1193	0.2268	0.3122	0.3670	0.3859

TABLE 7.15

s	t	x = 0	0.1	0.2	0.3	0.4	0.5
0	0	0	0.3600	0.6400	0.8400	0.9600	1.0000
1	0.005	0	0.3200	0.6000	0.8000	0.9200	0.9600
2	0.010	0	0.3000	0.5600	0.7600	0.8800	0.9200
3	0.015	0	0.2800	0.5300	0.7200	0.8400	0.8800
4	0.020	0	0.2650	0.5000	0.6850	0.8000	0.8400
5	0.025	0	0.2500	0.4750	0.6500	0.7625	0.8000
.		.		.		.	
20	0.100	0	0.1170	0.2222	0.3062	0.3595	0.3785

and the Table 7.16 shows a comparison of the finite-difference solutions given above with values computed using this formula.

It is clear that although the second of the two finite-difference solutions is not as accurate as the first it would be acceptable for most practical purposes. If an even larger time step were chosen, say $t = 0.01$, then $\alpha = 1$ and equation (29) becomes

$$u_{r,s+1} = u_{r-1,s} - u_{r,s} + u_{r+1,s} .$$

The first six steps of the calculation using this finite-difference equation are shown in Table 7.17 and may be seen to diverge rapidly from the previous solutions.

TABLE 7.16

	Analytic solution at x = 0.5	Finite-difference solution at x = 0.5 $\delta t = 0.001$	% error	Finite-difference solution at x = 0.5 $\delta t = 0.005$	% error
t = 0.010	0.9200	0.9200	0	0.9200	0
t = 0.050	0.6296	0.6306	0.16	0.6250	0.73
t = 0.100	0.3846	0.3859	0.34	0.3785	1.6

TABLE 7.17

s	t	$x =$ 0	0.1	0.2	0.3	0.4	0.5
0	0	0	0.36	0.64	0.84	0.96	1.00
1	0.01	0	0.28	0.56	0.76	0.88	0.92
2	0.02	0	0.28	0.48	0.68	0.80	0.84
3	0.03	0	0.20	0.48	0.60	0.72	0.76
4	0.04	0	0.28	0.32	0.60	0.64	0.68
5	0.05	0	0.04	0.56	0.36	0.64	0.60
6	0.06	0	0.52	−0.16	0.84	0.32	0.68

It can be proved (see Smith [2], Ch. 3) that the explicit method is valid only for $0 < \alpha \leqslant \frac{1}{2}$ and this constraint means that a very small time step must be used. The situation may be much improved by use of the *Crank–Nicolson* implicit method. In this method the term $\partial^2 u / \partial x^2$ is replaced by the mean of its approximations on the $(s + 1)$th and sth rows to give

$$\frac{1}{k}(u_{r,s+1} - u_{r,s}) = \frac{1}{2h^2}(u_{r+1,s+1} - 2u_{r,s+1} + u_{r-1,s+1} + u_{r+1,s} - 2u_{r,s} + u_{r-1,s}),$$

or

$$-\alpha u_{r-1,s+1} + (2 + 2\alpha)u_{r,s+1} - \alpha u_{r+1,s+1} = \alpha u_{r-1,s} + (2 - 2\alpha)u_{r,s} + \alpha u_{r+1,s}. \quad (32)$$

This gives a set of linear equations for the values on the $(s + 1)$th row in terms of the known values on the sth row.

EXAMPLE 2　　Use the Crank–Nicolson implicit method to solve the problem of example 1.

A convenient choice of value for α is $\alpha = 1$ which corresponds to $h = 0.1$ and $\delta t = k = 0.01$ and equation (32) becomes

$$-u_{r-1,s+1} + 4u_{r,s+1} - u_{r+1,s+1} = u_{r-1,s} + u_{r+1,s}.$$

The values of u at the first time step satisfy the equations

$$
\begin{aligned}
4u_{1,1} - u_{2,1} & & = 0 \quad + 0.64, \\
-u_{1,1} + 4u_{2,1} - u_{3,1} & & = 0.36 + 0.84, \\
- u_{2,1} + 4u_{3,1} - u_{4,1} & & = 0.64 + 0.96, \qquad (33) \\
- u_{3,1} + 4u_{4,1} - u_{5,1} & & = 0.84 + 1.00, \\
- 2u_{4,1} + 4u_{5,1} & & = 0.96 + 0.96.
\end{aligned}
$$

TABLE 7.18

s	t	x = 0	0.1	0.2	0.3	0.4	0.5
0	0	0	0.3600	0.6400	0.8400	0.9600	1.0000
1	0.01	0	0.3014	0.5657	0.7615	0.8804	0.9202
2	0.02	0	0.2676	0.5048	0.6885	0.8030	0.8417
3	0.03	0	0.2399	0.4548	0.6231	0.7300	0.7665
4	0.04	0	0.2165	0.4110	0.5646	0.6626	0.6963
5	0.05	0	0.1958	0.3721	0.5117	0.6011	0.6319
.	.	.	.	.	.	.	.
10	0.10	0	0.1197	0.2275	0.3135	0.3685	0.3875

This system may be solved by direct elimination (see problem 3 of Chapter 10 of Volume 1) to give

$$u_{1,1} = 0.3014, \quad u_{2,1} = 0.5657, \quad u_{3,1} = 0.7615, \quad u_{4,1} = 0.8804, \quad u_{5,1} = 0.9202.$$

The system of equations to determine the $u_{r,2}$ has exactly the same form as the system (33) except that $u_{r,1}$ are used to compute the right-hand sides. The results of the calculations are shown in Table 7.18. The accuracy of this solution is comparable with the accuracy given by the explicit method which uses ten times the number of time steps.

Elliptic Equations

Equations of this type govern problems in potential theory, steady heat flow, torsion of elastic cylinders, fluid flow down pipes, etc. The solution of an elliptic equation is determined by specifying the value of the unknown function or its normal derivative on a closed curve. The boundary values determine the unknown function everywhere inside the closed curve. An important elliptic equation in two dimensions is the Poisson equation

$$\frac{\partial^2 u}{\partial x^2} + \frac{\partial^2 u}{\partial y^2} = F(x,y) ,$$

which has been discussed in §7.8 of Volume 1. When $F = 0$ the equation is known as Laplace's equation in two dimensions. Using the usual finite-difference approximations with a square mesh of side h, the equation is approximated by

$$u_{r+1,s} + u_{r,s+1} + u_{r-1,s} + u_{r,s-1} - 4u_{r,s} = h^2 F_{r,s} , \tag{34}$$

where

$$F_{r,s} = F(rh, sh) .$$

This formula is applied to all the interior mesh points to give a set of equations for all the unknown values.

EXAMPLE 3　　Solve the Poisson equation

$$\frac{\partial^2 u}{\partial x^2} + \frac{\partial^2 u}{\partial y^2} = x^2 + y^2$$

in the square $|x| \leqslant 1, |y| \leqslant 1$ subject to the conditions

$$u = 0 \text{ on } x = \pm 1, \qquad \text{and} \quad u = 1 - x^2 \text{ on } y = \pm 1.$$

The problem is symmetric with respect to the x and y axes so that it is only necessary to consider the first quadrant $x \geqslant 0, y \geqslant 0$.

Figure 7.2 shows a finite-difference mesh with $h = 0.25$. It is convenient to re-label the mesh points as indicated in the figure, the symmetry of the problem being shown in the pattern of labelling. The finite-difference approximation (34) applied to each mesh point gives the set of equations

$$
\begin{aligned}
-4u_1 \ +2u_2 \qquad\qquad\qquad\quad\ +u_5 &= -0.9648, \\
u_1 \ -4u_2 \ + u_3 \qquad\qquad\quad +u_6 &= -0.8984, \\
u_2 \ -4u_3 \ + u_4 \ +u_7 &= -0.6992, \\
u_3 \ -4u_4 \qquad\quad +u_8 &= -0.3672, \\
u_1 \ -4u_5 \ +2u_6 \qquad\qquad\qquad +u_9 &= 0.0156, \\
u_2 \ + u_5 \ -4u_6 \ + u_7 \qquad\qquad +u_{10} &= 0.0195, \\
u_3 \qquad\ + u_6 \ -4u_7 \ + u_8 \ +u_{11} &= 0.0313, \\
u_4 \qquad\qquad + u_7 \ -4u_8 \ +u_{12} &= 0.0508, \\
u_5 \ -4u_9 \ +2u_{10} \qquad\qquad\qquad +u_{13} &= 0.0039, \\
u_6 \ + u_9 \ -4u_{10} + u_{11} \qquad\qquad +u_{14} &= 0.0078, \\
u_7 \qquad + u_{10} -4u_{11} + u_{12} +u_{15} &= 0.0195, \\
u_8 \qquad\qquad + u_{11} -4u_{12} +u_{16} &= 0.0391, \\
2u_9 \ -4u_{13} + 2u_{14} \qquad\qquad\qquad\qquad &= 0, \\
2u_{10} + u_{13} -4u_{14} + u_{15} \qquad\qquad &= 0.0039, \\
2u_{11} \qquad + u_{14} -4u_{15} + u_{16} &= 0.0156, \\
2u_{12} \qquad\qquad + u_{15} -4u_{16} &= 0.0352.
\end{aligned}
$$

The solution of this system of equations is

$$
\begin{aligned}
u_1 &= 0.6664, & u_2 &= 0.6159, & u_3 &= 0.4709, & u_4 &= 0.2487, \\
u_5 &= 0.4688, & u_6 &= 0.4288, & u_7 &= 0.3166, & u_8 &= 0.1576, \\
u_9 &= 0.3667, & u_{10} &= 0.3333, & u_{11} &= 0.2413, & u_{12} &= 0.1159, \\
u_{13} &= 0.3355, & u_{14} &= 0.3042, & u_{15} &= 0.2188, & u_{16} &= 0.1039.
\end{aligned}
$$

Problems having boundary conditions expressed in terms of derivatives of the

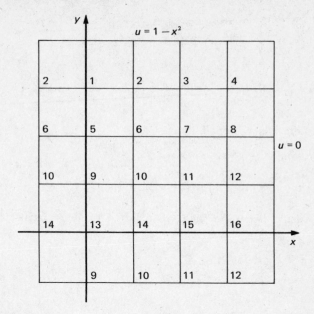

Fig. 7.2

dependent variable may also be solved numerically. The technique involves use of a row of mesh points external to the region and is described in detail in Smith [2], Chapter 5.

Hyperbolic Equations

Many types of wave phenomena are governed by hyperbolic partial differential equations. Equations of this type have the special property that at every point in the plane there are directions (characteristics) along which the equation may be replaced by ordinary differential equations. A discussion of the simplest of these equations, the one-dimensional wave equation, is given in §7.2 of Volume 1 though the full description of the numerical solution of hyperbolic equations by the method of characteristics is beyond the scope of this chapter (see Smith [2], Ch. 4). However, the method used above for the one-dimensional diffusion equation may often be used when the initial conditions of the problem are continuous.

Exercises

1. Calculate a finite-difference solution of the equation

$$\frac{\partial u}{\partial t} = \frac{\partial^2 u}{\partial x^2} \quad \text{for } 0 \leqslant x \leqslant 1, \quad t \geqslant 0,$$

satisfying the initial condition

$$u(x, 0) = \sin^2 \pi x$$

and boundary conditions

$$u(0, t) = u(1, t) = 0 \quad \text{for all } t > 0 .$$

2. The function u satisfies the equation

$$\frac{\partial^2 u}{\partial x^2} + \frac{\partial^2 u}{\partial y^2} = 0 \quad \text{for } 0 \leqslant x \leqslant 1, \quad 0 \leqslant y \leqslant 1 ,$$

and is subject to the boundary conditions

$$u = 1 \quad \text{on} \quad y = \pm 1 ,$$

$$\frac{\partial u}{\partial x} = u \quad \text{on} \quad x = +1, \quad \frac{\partial u}{\partial x} = -u \quad \text{on} \quad x = -1 .$$

Using a square mesh of side 0.25 obtain a finite-difference approximation to the solution.

PROBLEMS

1. Use the Taylor series method as a starting procedure, and the Adams–Bashforth formulae to find the solution, correct to three decimal places, of

$$\frac{dy}{dx} = y + x^2 \quad \text{with} \quad _R \, y(0) = 1 ,$$

for $x = 0(0.2)1$.

2. Use the Taylor series method to solve the second-order system

$$\frac{dy}{dx} = x(y + z), \quad \frac{dz}{dx} = x(y - z)$$

where $y(0) = 1, z(0) = 0$ for $x = 0(0.2)0.6$.

3. Show that the most general second-order Runge–Kutta formulae for the numerical solution of the system of two first-order ordinary differential equations

$$\frac{dy}{dx} = f(x, y, z), \quad \frac{dz}{dx} = g(x, y, z) ,$$

where $y(x_0)$ and $z(x_0)$ are given, are

$$y(x_0 + h) = y(x_0) + (1 - \alpha)k_1 + \alpha k_2 ,$$

$$z(x_0 + h) = z(x_0) + (1 - \beta)l_1 + \beta l_2 ,$$

where

$$k_1 = hf(x_0, y_0, z_0), \quad k_2 = hf(x_0 + \tfrac{1}{2}h/\alpha, y_0 + \tfrac{1}{2}k_1/\alpha, z_0 + \tfrac{1}{2}l_1/\alpha) ,$$

$$l_1 = hg(x_0, y_0, z_0), \quad l_2 = hg(x_0 + \tfrac{1}{2}h/\beta, y_0 + \tfrac{1}{2}k_1/\beta, z_0 + \tfrac{1}{2}l_1/\beta) ,$$

and α and β are arbitrary constants. [The Taylor-series expansion of $F(x, y, z)$ is

$$F(x_0 + a, y_0 + b, z_0 + c) = F(x_0, y_0, z_0) + aF_x + bF_y + cF_z$$
$$+ \tfrac{1}{2}(a^2F_{xx} + b^2F_{yy} + c^2F_{zz} + 2abF_{xy}$$
$$+ 2bcF_{yz} + 2caF_{zx}) \ldots,$$

where the partial derivatives $F_x, F_y, F_z, F_{xx}, \ldots$ etc. are all evaluated at (x_0, y_0, z_0).]
Hence solve, correct to two decimal places, the second-order differential equation

$$\frac{d^2y}{dx^2} = 1 - xy^2, \quad y(1) = 1, \quad y'(1) = 2$$

for y at $x = 0.9, 1.1, 1.2$.

4. Write down the finite-difference approximation of Laplace's equation in plane polar coordinates,

$$\frac{\partial^2 u}{\partial r^2} + \frac{1}{r}\frac{\partial u}{\partial r} + \frac{1}{r^2}\frac{\partial^2 u}{\partial \theta^2} = 0,$$

where the mesh points are the points of intersection of the circles $r = ih$ ($i = 1, 2, \ldots$) and the straight lines $\theta = j\delta\theta$ ($j = 0, 1, 2, \ldots$).

5. Obtain a numerical solution of the initial value problem

$$\frac{dy}{dx} = \frac{3x + 2y}{x + 2y}, \quad y(0.2) = 0,$$

for $x = 0.2(0.2)2$. [Compare problem 22 of Chapter 6.]

6. Solve the initial value problem

$$\frac{dy}{dx} = (1 - y^2)^{\frac{1}{2}}, \quad y(0) = 0,$$

for $x = 0(0.1)1$. [Compare problem 23 of Chapter 6.]

7. Find a numerical solution of the second-order equation

$$\frac{d^2y}{dx^2} + xy = 0 \quad \text{with} \quad y(0) = 1, \quad y'(0) = 1,$$

for $x = 0(0.2)0.6$. [Compare exercise 1 of §6.4.]

8. Use a suitable numerical method to find the solution of the equation

$$\frac{d^2y}{dx^2} + \epsilon y \frac{dy}{dx} + 4y = 0, \quad \text{with} \quad y(0) = 1, \quad y'(0) = 0,$$

for the cases when $\epsilon = 0.2$, and $\epsilon = 2$. Compare the numerical solution with the perturbation solution found in problem 18 of Chapter 6.

9. Solve the one-dimensional diffusion equation

$$\frac{\partial u}{\partial t} = \frac{\partial^2 u}{\partial x^2} \quad \text{in} \quad 0 \leqslant x \leqslant 1,$$

for $0 \leqslant t \leqslant 0.1$ subject to the initial conditions

$$u(x, 0) = 0 \quad 0 < x < 1,$$

and the boundary conditions

$$\frac{\partial u}{\partial x} = u - 1 \quad \text{at} \quad x = 0, \quad t \geqslant 0,$$

$$\frac{\partial u}{\partial x} = -u + 1 \quad \text{at} \quad x = 1, \quad t \geqslant 0.$$

BIBLIOGRAPHY

[1]   Mayers, D. F., *Methods of Runge–Kutta type. Numerical solution of Ordinary and Partial Differential Equations*, Fox, L. (ed.), Pergamon, Oxford (1962).
[2]   Smith, G. D., *Numerical Solution of Partial Differential Equations*, Oxford University Press, London (1969).

FURTHER READING

Fröberg, C.-E., *Introduction to Numerical Analysis*, Addison-Wesley, Reading, Mass. (1965).
Gerald, C. F., *Applied Numerical Analysis*, Addison-Wesley, Reading, Mass. (1970).
Modern Computing Methods, H.M.S.O., London (1961).
Noble, B., *Numerical Methods: 2*, Oliver and Boyd, Edinburgh (1964).
Scheid, F., *Numerical Analysis*, Schaum's Outline Series, McGraw-Hill, New York (1968).
Williams, P. W., *Numerical Computation*, Nelson, London (1972).

Variational Methods

8.1 INTRODUCTION

A typical example of the kind of problem to be examined in this chapter is that of finding the function $\bar{u}(x)$ which gives the minimum value of the integral

$$I[u] = \int_a^b F\{x, u(x), u'(x)\}\, dx, \tag{1}$$

under certain subsidiary conditions on $u(x)$. In equation (1) the integrand $F\{x, u(x), u'(x)\}$ is a known function of three variables and has continuous first and second partial derivatives with respect to these variables. Here and throughout this chapter the prime denotes differentiation with respect to x. The value of the integral clearly depends on the choice of the function $u(x)$ and $I[u]$ is termed a *functional* of $u(x)$. To define the problem precisely it is necessary to specify a class of functions to which $u(x)$ must belong. We shall suppose $u(x)$ has continuous first and second derivatives in $a \leqslant x \leqslant b$ and it is then said to belong to the class of C_2 functions. We denote by $\bar{u}(x)$ the particular C_2 function for which the functional (1) achieves its minimum value (subject to any additional conditions of the problem). This notation should not be confused with that for the Laplace transform.

The basic problem of the *calculus of variations* is to find the C_2 function $\bar{u}(x)$ which minimizes the functional $I[u]$ subject to the boundary conditions

$$u(a) = \alpha, \quad u(b) = \beta. \tag{2}$$

Other boundary conditions are possible and in many problems the functional has a more general form than that in equation (1). For some functionals, there is no C_2 function $\bar{u}(x)$ which gives the required minimum, and it is necessary to bear in mind that the techniques developed in this chapter may not always lead to a solution. However, these minimization problems frequently arise in engineering or physics and it is then often obvious when a solution exists. Some examples which illustrate the wide range of physical problems that admit this formulation are given here and in §8.2.

EXAMPLE 1   Perhaps the simplest example is to determine the shortest path between two points (a, α), (b, β) in the x, y plane.

The arc length along a path $y = u(x)$ joining these points is

$$s[u] = \int_a^b \{1 + [u'(x)]^2\}^{\frac{1}{2}}\, dx$$

where $u(a) = \alpha, u(b) = \beta$. The problem is to select $u(x)$ so that $s[u]$ is minimized.

EXAMPLE 2   Determine the path taken by a ray of light which travels from (a, α) to (b, β) in the x, y plane when the speed of light c is a function of position, $c = c(x, y)$.

By Fermat's principle the path will be such as to minimize the travel time T. Let $y = u(x)$ be any path joining the two points, so that $u(x)$ satisfies the conditions (2). Then T is given by

$$T[u] = \int_a^b \frac{\{1 + [u'(x)]^2\}^{\frac{1}{2}}}{c\{x, u(x)\}} \, dx \, .$$

The problem is to minimize $T[u]$ subject to the boundary conditions (2).

EXAMPLE 3   Determine the deformation of a heavy uniform cylinder of isotropic elastic material which stands vertically on a horizontal base.

Let the length of the cylinder be l, its area of cross-section A, its density ρ, and let the x axis be vertically upwards with the base at $x = 0$. If $u(x)$ denotes the upward displacement, the strain is $u'(x)$ and the strain energy density is $\frac{1}{2}E[u'(x)]^2$ where E is the Young's modulus of the material. The work done per unit volume against the external forces in this displacement is $\rho g u$, where g is the acceleration of gravity. The change in potential energy of the system due to the displacement is

$$P[u] = A \int_0^l \{\tfrac{1}{2}E[u'(x)]^2 + \rho g u(x)\} \, dx$$

and the theorem of minimum potential energy states that the solution minimizes $P[u]$. In this case the only boundary condition on $u(x)$ is $u(0) = 0$.

Some problems do not arise naturally as minimization problems, but they may be converted into such a form.

EXAMPLE 4   Express the problem of solving the differential equation

$$\frac{d^2 y}{dx^2} = 5e^x \, ,$$

subject to the boundary conditions $y(0) = 1, y(1) = 0$, as a minimization problem.

Let $y = \bar{u}(x)$ be the solution. Let $u(x)$ be any other differentiable function which satisfies the boundary conditions but not necessarily the differential equation. Since $\bar{u}(x)$ satisfies the differential equation it follows that

$$\int_0^1 \{u(x) - \bar{u}(x)\}\{\bar{u}''(x) - 5e^x\} \, dx = 0 \, .$$

Integration by parts gives

$$[(u - \bar{u})\bar{u}']_0^1 - \int_0^1 (u' - \bar{u}')\bar{u}' \, dx - \int_0^1 5 e^x (u - \bar{u}) \, dx = 0 \, ,$$

and the first term vanishes since $(u - \bar{u}) = 0$ at $x = 0$ and $x = 1$. Use of the identity

$$u'\bar{u}' = \tfrac{1}{2}(u')^2 + \tfrac{1}{2}(\bar{u}')^2 - \tfrac{1}{2}(u' - \bar{u}')^2$$

then gives the result

$$I[u] = I[\bar{u}] + \tfrac{1}{2} \int_0^1 (u' - \bar{u}')^2 \, dx \, , \tag{3}$$

where

$$I[u] = \int_0^1 \{\tfrac{1}{2}(u')^2 + 5u\, e^x\} \, dx \, .$$

The last term in equation (3) is positive or zero and it follows that $I[\bar{u}] \leqslant I[u]$, so that the solution $\bar{u}$ minimizes the functional $I[u]$.

The technique of example 4 may be applied to the general linear second-order equation

$$a_0(x)\frac{d^2 y}{dx^2} + a_1(x)\frac{dy}{dx} + a_2(x)y = f(x) \, ,$$

which can always be written in the form

$$\frac{d}{dx}\left\{p(x)\frac{dy}{dx}\right\} + q(x)y = h(x) \, ,$$

where

$$p(x) = \exp\left\{\int^x \frac{a_1(s)}{a_0(s)}\, ds\right\} \, , \qquad q(x) = \frac{a_2(x)}{a_0(x)}\, p(x) \, ,$$

$$h(x) = \frac{f(x)}{a_0(x)}\, p(x) \, .$$

The function $y = \bar{u}(x)$ which satisfies this equation subject to the boundary conditions $y = \alpha$ at $x = a$ and $y = \beta$ at $x = b$, is such as to give a stationary value to the integral

$$I[u] = \int_a^b \{p(x)[u'(x)]^2 - q(x)[u(x)]^2 + 2h(x)u(x)\} \, dx \, .$$

Similar techniques are frequently applied to convert partial differential equations into variational problems and examples are given in §8.3.

There are two well-defined approaches to solving the minimization problem. In the first of these, the condition that the functional (1) is stationary with respect to small perturbations of $u(x)$ about the solution $\bar{u}(x)$, leads to an ordinary differential equation for $\bar{u}(x)$. The problem is then reduced to solving the differential equation subject to the appropriate boundary conditions (2). The solution may be obtained either analytically, by using standard integration techniques, or numerically by using the methods of Chapter 7. Functionals of a more general form than that in equation (1) can lead to systems of ordinary differential equations, or to partial differential equations. Section 8.2 is devoted to the derivation of these differential equations for some standard forms of functionals.

The second approach to solving the minimization problem is examined in §8.3. In this direct approach the functional is evaluated for a class of *test functions* $u_n(x)$ involving a number n of arbitrary parameters and these parameters are then chosen so as to minimize the integral. If the exact solution $\bar{u}(x)$ is a member of the class for some choice of the parameters then the exact solution is obtained. Otherwise the method gives an approximate solution and the value of the integral is greater than the true minimum. The powerful finite element method, which is widely used in solving problems in solid mechanics, is a particular case of this direct method. In addition to providing a method for solving the minimization problem, the direct approach leads to approximate methods of solving differential equations whenever these can be replaced by equivalent variational problems as in example 4.

8.2 THE CALCULUS OF VARIATIONS

The Euler–Lagrange Equation

Let $u(x)$ be a C_2 function which satisfies the boundary conditions (2) namely $u(a) = \alpha, u(b) = \beta$, then $u(x)$ is termed an admissible function. We seek the minimizing function $\bar{u}(x)$ from among this class of admissible functions. An admissible function which is 'close' to the function $\bar{u}(x)$ may be expressed as $u(x) = \bar{u}(x) + \epsilon\eta(x)$ where the parameter ϵ is small compared with 1, (see Fig. 8.1). Since $u(x)$ and $\bar{u}(x)$ satisfy the same boundary conditions, then $\eta(x)$ must be an arbitrary C_2 function satisfying $\eta(a) = 0$, and $\eta(b) = 0$.

For a *given function* $\eta(x)$, the functional $I[\bar{u} + \epsilon\eta]$ is a function of ϵ which takes its minimum value when $\epsilon = 0$. Hence we can determine a necessary condition for the existence of the minimum. The functional $I[\bar{u} + \epsilon\eta]$ is given by

$$I[\bar{u} + \epsilon\eta] = \int_a^b F(x, \bar{u} + \epsilon\eta, \bar{u}' + \epsilon\eta')\,dx \ ,$$

and on expanding the integrand using Taylor's theorem this becomes

$$I[\bar{u} + \epsilon\eta] = I[\bar{u}] + \epsilon I_1[\bar{u}] + O(\epsilon^2) \tag{4}$$

where

$$I_1[\bar{u}] = \int_a^b \left\{ \eta(x)\frac{\partial F}{\partial u} + \eta'(x)\frac{\partial F}{\partial u'} \right\}\,dx \ ,$$

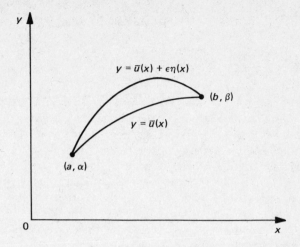

Fig. 8.1 A curve close to the minimizing curve $y = \bar{u}(x)$.

and $\dfrac{\partial F}{\partial u}$, and $\dfrac{\partial F}{\partial u'}$ are evaluated at $\epsilon = 0$. The quantity $\epsilon I_1[\bar{u}]$ is termed the *first variation* of $I[\bar{u}]$. For a given $\eta(x)$, the expression (4) is a power series in ϵ and since $I[\bar{u} + \epsilon \eta] - I[\bar{u}]$ must be strictly positive for $\epsilon > 0$ and $\epsilon < 0$ then the term of order ϵ must vanish. Consequently a necessary condition which must be satisfied by $\bar{u}(x)$ is that

$$I_1[\bar{u}] = \int_a^b \left\{ \eta(x) \frac{\partial F}{\partial u} + \eta'(x) \frac{\partial F}{\partial u'} \right\} \, dx = 0 \,. \tag{5}$$

In order to obtain a useful result from the condition (5) it is necessary to make use of the following lemma:

LEMMA   If the function $\phi(x)$ is continuous in $a \leqslant x \leqslant b$, and if

$$\int_a^b \phi(x) \eta(x) \, dx = 0 \,,$$

for all C_2 functions $\eta(x)$ which vanish at a and b, then $\phi(x)$ is identically zero in $[a, b]$.

The condition (5) may be put in the appropriate form by integrating the second term in braces by parts so that (5) becomes

$$\int_a^b \left\{ \frac{\partial F}{\partial u} - \frac{d}{dx} \left(\frac{\partial F}{\partial u'} \right) \right\} \eta(x) \, dx + \left[\eta(x) \frac{\partial F}{\partial u'} \right]_a^b = 0 \,. \tag{6}$$

The last term vanishes by virtue of the boundary conditions on $\eta(x)$ and use of the lemma then gives

$$\frac{\partial F}{\partial u} - \frac{d}{dx}\left(\frac{\partial F}{\partial u'}\right) = 0 . \tag{7}$$

This is a differential equation with solution $u = \bar{u}(x)$ and is known as the *Euler–Lagrange equation* for the minimization problem. Equation (7) gives the necessary condition for a *stationary* value of $I[u]$ and may correspond to a local maximum, local minimum or point of inflexion. In many problems it is a stationary value of the functional that is required. If the problem is strictly a minimization problem, sufficient conditions for a minimum may be derived (see Craggs [1]) or it may be possible to argue from physical considerations that the solution is a minimum.

EXAMPLE 1   Solve example 1 of §8.1, namely find the shortest path between the points $(a, \alpha), (b, \beta)$. This is the problem of finding the path $y = \bar{u}(x)$ which minimizes

the integral $\displaystyle\int_a^b \{1 + [u'(x)]^2\}^{\frac{1}{2}}\, dx$, subject to $u(a) = \alpha$ and $u(b) = \beta$.

Since $F \equiv \{1 + [u'(x)]^2\}^{\frac{1}{2}}$, the corresponding Euler–Lagrange equation is

$$\frac{d}{dx}\left(\frac{u'(x)}{\{1 + [u'(x)]^2\}^{\frac{1}{2}}}\right) = 0$$

which implies that $u'(x)$ is a constant. Hence the optimum curve is $\bar{u} = Ax + B$ where A and B are constants of integration which may be determined from the boundary conditions. Thus the shortest path is the straight line joining the two points and has the equation

$$\bar{u} - \beta = (\beta - \alpha)\left(\frac{x - b}{b - a}\right) .$$

Integrals of the Euler–Lagrange Equation

The Euler–Lagrange equation (7) is a second order non-linear ordinary differential equation for the optimum curve $y = \bar{u}(x)$. The two constants of integration which are produced on integration of equation (7) may be determined by the boundary conditions (2). In general it is difficult to integrate equation (7) but certain particular cases are straightforward.

(a) If $F\{x, u(x), u'(x)\}$ is independent of $u'(x)$ then equation (7) becomes $\partial F/\partial u = 0$ which is an algebraic equation for u in terms of x.

(b) If $F\{x, u(x), u'(x)\}$ does not depend on $u(x)$ explicitly (see example 1), then the Euler–Lagrange equation becomes

$$\frac{d}{dx}\left(\frac{\partial F}{\partial u'}\right) = 0 ,$$

giving $\partial F/\partial u' = A$, where A is an arbitrary constant. This equation may be solved for $u'(x)$ in terms of x and A and hence $u(x)$ may be found by integration.

(c) If $F\{x, u(x), u'(x)\}$ does not depend *explicitly* on x, then $F = F\{u(x), u'(x)\}$ and equation (5) is

$$\frac{\partial F}{\partial u} - \frac{d}{dx}\left(\frac{\partial F}{\partial u'}\right) = \frac{\partial F}{\partial u} - \frac{\partial^2 F}{\partial u \partial u'} u'(x) - \frac{\partial^2 F}{\partial u'^2} u''(x) = 0 .$$

Multiplying by $u'(x)$ gives

$$u'(x)\frac{\partial F}{\partial u} - \frac{\partial^2 F}{\partial u \partial u'} [u'(x)]^2 - \frac{\partial^2 F}{\partial u'^2} u'(x)u''(x) = 0 ,$$

which may be written in the form

$$\frac{d}{dx}\left\{F - u'(x)\frac{\partial F}{\partial u'}\right\} = 0 ,$$

since F does not depend explicitly on x. This equation has the first integral

$$F - u'(x)\frac{\partial F}{\partial u'} = A \tag{8}$$

where A is an arbitrary constant. This is now a first-order equation involving only $u'(x)$ and $u(x)$. From equation (8) it is possible in principle to find $u'(x)$ as a function of $u(x)$ and A in the form $u'(x) = \phi\{u(x), A\}$. Hence

$$x = \int \frac{1}{\phi(u, A)} \, du + B$$

which gives an explicit expression for x in terms of u.

EXAMPLE 2   *The Brachistochrone.* This problem was posed by Johann Bernoulli in 1696. It is required to find the curve joining two given points such that a particle moving along the curve under gravity and without friction descends from the higher point to the lower point in least time. The curve is known as the *brachistochrone*. It is convenient to take the x axis as the vertical axis and the y axis horizontally. If the particle moves from $(0, 0)$ to (a, α) along the curve $y = u(x)$, the time of descent is

$$t = \frac{1}{(2g)^{1/2}} \int_0^a \left\{\frac{1 + [u'(x)]^2}{x}\right\}^{1/2} dx$$

and this is to be minimized subject to $u(0) = 0, u(a) = \alpha$ (see Fig. 8.2). Since F is independent of $u(x)$, then the Euler–Lagrange equation has the integral $\frac{\partial F}{\partial u'} = A$ which gives

$$\frac{u'(x)}{\{1 + [u'(x)]^2\}^{1/2} x^{1/2}} = A .$$

Solving for $u'(x)$ yields the equation

$$\frac{du}{dx} = \left(\frac{A^2x}{1 - A^2x}\right)^{\frac{1}{2}}.$$

This integral may be evaluated by using the substitution $A^2x = \sin^2 \theta$. Then in terms of the parameter θ, $A^2u = \theta - \frac{1}{2} \sin 2\theta + B$. If the value $\theta = 0$ corresponds to the point $(0, 0)$, then the constant B is zero. The parametric equations of the brachistochrone are

$$A^2x = \sin^2 \theta = \tfrac{1}{2}(1 - \cos 2\theta),$$

$$A^2\bar{u} = \tfrac{1}{2}(2\theta - \sin 2\theta).$$

The constant A^2 and the upper limit for the parameter θ must be chosen so that the curve passes through the point (a, α). The brachistochrone belongs to the family of curves called cycloids.

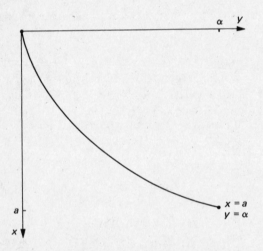

Fig. 8.2   The brachistochrone.

EXAMPLE 3   Suppose the speed of light in example 2 of §8.1 is a function of y only so that $c = c(y)$. The problem is to find the path $y = u(x)$ which minimizes

$$\int_a^b \frac{\{1 + [u'(x)]^2\}^{\frac{1}{2}}}{c\{u(x)\}} \, dx$$

subject to the conditions (2).

In this case $F = \{1 + [u'(x)]^2\}^{\frac{1}{2}}/c\{u(x)\}$ does not depend explicitly on x, and so the Euler–Lagrange equation (7) has the integral (8), namely

$$\frac{\{1 + [u'(x)]^2\}^{\frac{1}{2}}}{c\{u(x)\}} - \frac{[u'(x)]^2}{\{1 + [u'(x)]^2\}^{\frac{1}{2}}c\{u(x)\}} = A.$$

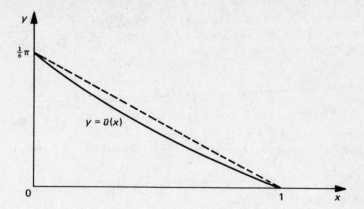

Fig. 8.3 A light ray in an inhomogeneous medium. The dashed curve is the straight line through the end points.

Solving for $u'(x)$ yields the equation

$$\frac{du}{dx} = \frac{\{[c(u)]^2 - B^2\}^{\frac{1}{2}}}{c(u)}$$

in which B is an arbitrary constant.

This equation may be integrated analytically when $c(u)$ has certain special forms. The case when $c(u) = c_0(1 - ku)$ is considered in problem 1. If $c(u) = \cos u$, the above equation integrates to give

$$\sinh^{-1}\left(\frac{\sin u}{(B^2 - 1)^{\frac{1}{2}}}\right) = x + C.$$

Hence

$$\sin u' = D \sinh(x + C)$$

in which C and D are arbitrary constants. If, for example, the ray passes through the points $x = 0, u = \frac{1}{6}\pi$ and $x = 1, u = 0$, then the optimum path is

$$\sin \bar{u} = \frac{\sinh(1 - x)}{2 \sinh 1}.$$

This path is shown on Fig. 8.3. Note that the ray does not travel in a straight line.

Free Boundaries and Natural Boundary Conditions

In some problems it is required to determine the minimum of the functional $I[u]$ of equation (1) when $u(x)$ is not subject to boundary conditions. The arguments used to derive the Euler–Lagrange equation remain valid as far as equation (6) which must now hold for all C_2 functions $\eta(x)$. Among these functions $\eta(x)$ there is the sub-class of C_2 functions which vanish at a and b. For this sub-class the last term in equation (6) vanishes and the requirement that the integral should vanish leads again to the Euler–Lagrange equation (7). Hence a necessary condition for equation (6) to be satisfied for all $\eta(x)$ is that $\bar{u}(x)$ satisfies the same Euler–Lagrange equation as before. Equation (6) then reduces to

$$\left[\eta(x)\frac{\partial F}{\partial u'}\right]_a^b = \eta(b)\left(\frac{\partial F}{\partial u'}\right)_{x=b} - \eta(a)\left(\frac{\partial F}{\partial u'}\right)_{x=a} = 0. \tag{9}$$

Since $\eta(x)$ is arbitrary, the values $\eta(a)$ and $\eta(b)$ are also arbitrary and independent of each other, so that equation (9) is satisfied only if $\bar{u}(x)$ satisfies the boundary conditions

$$\frac{\partial F}{\partial u'} = 0 \quad \text{at } x = a \text{ and } x = b.$$

These are termed the *natural boundary conditions* of the variational problem (1) and arise in connection with any *free boundary* on which no boundary condition is prescribed. Clearly it is possible to have problems in which one boundary condition is prescribed and the other free – these give rise to the Euler–Lagrange equation (7) with one natural boundary condition arising at the free boundary.

EXAMPLE 4   Solve example 3 of §8.1.

Here u is specified to be zero at $x = 0$, but u is not specified at $x = l$ so that $x = l$ is a free boundary. Since $F\{x, u(x), u'(x)\} = A\{\frac{1}{2}E[u'(x)]^2 + \rho g u(x)\}$ the derivatives are $\partial F/\partial u = A\rho g$, $\partial F/\partial u' = AEu'(x)$. The natural boundary condition is then $\partial F/\partial u' = AEu' = 0$ at $x = l$, corresponding to the vanishing of the stress at the upper end. The Euler–Lagrange equation is

$$E\frac{d^2 u}{dx^2} - \rho g = 0,$$

and the solution satisfying both the specified boundary condition at $x = 0$ and the free boundary condition at $x = l$ is

$$\bar{u} = \frac{\rho g}{2E}\{(x - l)^2 - l^2\}.$$

Hence the displacement is a quadratic function of the height x and the stress in the column is a linear function of height as simple mechanics indicates.

Modified Boundary Conditions

Consider now the problem of minimizing the functional

$$J[u] = \int_a^b F\{x, u(x), u'(x)\}\, dx + Au(a) - Bu(b)$$

where A and B are known constants and $x = a$ and $x = b$ are free boundaries. The requirement that the first variation of $J[u]$ should vanish when $u = \bar{u}(x)$ leads to the condition

$$\int_a^b \left\{ \frac{\partial F}{\partial u} - \frac{d}{dx}\left(\frac{\partial F}{\partial u'}\right) \right\} \eta(x)\, dx + \eta(b)\left\{ \left(\frac{\partial F}{\partial u'}\right)_{x=b} - B \right\} - \eta(a)\left\{ \left(\frac{\partial F}{\partial u'}\right)_{x=a} - A \right\} = 0,$$

which must hold for all C_2 functions $\eta(x)$. This equation is satisfied provided $\bar{u}(x)$ satisfies the Euler–Lagrange equation

$$\frac{\partial F}{\partial u} - \frac{d}{dx}\left(\frac{\partial F}{\partial u'}\right) = 0,$$

and the natural boundary conditions

$$\frac{\partial F}{\partial u'} = A \quad \text{at } x = a, \qquad \frac{\partial F}{\partial u'} = B \quad \text{at } x = b.$$

Thus by adding boundary terms to $I[u]$ in order to form $J[u]$ it is possible to modify the natural boundary conditions without changing the Euler–Lagrange equation. More generally it may be shown that for given functions $\phi(u)$ and $\psi(u)$ the variational problem of minimizing

$$J[u] = \int_a^b F(x, u, u')\, dx + \psi\{u(a)\} - \phi\{u(b)\}$$

leads again to the Euler–Lagrange equation (7) and to the natural boundary conditions

$$\frac{\partial F}{\partial u'} = \frac{d\psi}{du} \quad \text{at } x = a, \qquad \frac{\partial F}{\partial u'} = \frac{d\phi}{du} \quad \text{at } x = b. \tag{10}$$

EXAMPLE 5   Solve example 3 of §8.1 when the cylinder supports a load W uniformly distributed over its upper surface.

The potential energy $\hat{P}[u]$ consists of the strain energy plus the work done on the external forces and is given by

$$\hat{P}[u] = A \int_0^l \{ \tfrac{1}{2} E[u'(x)]^2 + \rho g u(x) \}\, dx + Wu(l).$$

This differs from the functional of example 4 by the term $Wu(l)$ and the boundary conditions are now

$$u = 0 \quad \text{at } x = 0, \qquad \frac{\partial F}{\partial u'} = AEu'(x) = -W \quad \text{at } x = l.$$

The free boundary condition corresponds to the condition that the tensile stress is $-W/A$ at $x = l$. The Euler–Lagrange equation is as before

$$E\frac{d^2u}{dx^2} - \rho g = 0$$

and the optimal solution is

$$\bar{u} = \frac{\rho g}{2E} x(x - 2l) - \frac{Wx}{EA} .$$

Variable End Point and Transversality

Another class of problem arises when one of the end points is constrained to lie on some curve $y = f(x)$, say. It is then required to minimize

$$K[u] = \int_a^{\hat{x}} F\{x, u(x), u'(x)\} \, dx$$

subject to $u(a) = \alpha$ and the condition that $u(\hat{x}) = f(\hat{x})$. Here it must be borne in mind that $\hat{x}$ is not a fixed point. The requirement that the first variation of $K[u]$ should vanish leads to the Euler–Lagrange equation (7) subject to $u(a) = \alpha$ and the following conditions which will hold at $x = \hat{x}$:

$$(\bar{u}' - f') \frac{\partial F}{\partial u'} - F = 0, \quad \bar{u}(x) = f(x), \quad \text{at } x = \hat{x}. \tag{11}$$

The first of these conditions is termed the *transversality condition* and is a relation between the gradient $\bar{u}'(x)$ of the optimum curve and the gradient $f'(x)$ of the given curve at $x = \hat{x}$. These conditions are sufficient to determine the arbitrary constants of integration of (7) and the variable end point $\hat{x}$.

EXAMPLE 6   Find the path of shortest distance from the origin to the rectangular hyperbola $xy = 4$.

In this problem $y = f(x) = 4/x$ is the given curve and the functional is

$$I = \int_0^{\hat{x}} \{1 + [u'(x)]^2\}^{\frac{1}{2}} \, dx .$$

Since the integrand is a function of $u'(x)$ only, the Euler–Lagrange equation has a first integral

$$\frac{\partial F}{\partial u'} = u'(x)\{1 + [u'(x)]^2\}^{-\frac{1}{2}} = A ,$$

where A is an arbitrary constant. This implies that $u'(x)$ is constant so that $\bar{u} = Bx + C$. The boundary condition $\bar{u}(0) = 0$ implies $C = 0$. The conditions (11) at $\hat{x}$ are then $B\hat{x} = 4/\hat{x}$ and the transversality condition

$$\frac{(\bar{u}' - f')\bar{u}'}{\{1 + (\bar{u}')^2\}^{\frac{1}{2}}} - \{1 + (\bar{u}')^2\}^{\frac{1}{2}} = \frac{B(B + 4/\hat{x}^2)}{(1 + B^2)^{\frac{1}{2}}} - (1 + B^2)^{\frac{1}{2}} = 0 .$$

From the transversality condition we obtain $4B/\hat{x}^2 = 1$ and this together with the first condition gives $B = 1$, $\hat{x} = \pm 2$. The shortest path from the origin to the hyperbola is therefore the line $y = x$ which meets the hyperbola orthogonally at $(2, 2)$ and $(-2, -2)$.

Integral Constraints

One of the oldest and best known problems of the variational calculus is the *isoperimetric problem* of determining the maximum area that can be enclosed between the x axis and a curve of fixed length l starting at the point $(0, 0)$ and ending at $(a, 0)$. Let $y = u(x)$ be the equation of any curve through these points. Then it is required to maximize the area

$$A[u] = \int_0^a u(x)\, dx$$

subject to $u(0) = u(a) = 0$ and the condition that

$$\int_0^a \{1 + [u'(x)]^2\}^{1/2}\, dx = l.$$

A more general problem of this kind is to minimize the functional $I[u]$ of equation (1) subject to an integral constraint of the form

$$K[u] \equiv \int_a^b G\{x, u(x), u'(x)\}\, dx = l. \tag{12}$$

The solution may be required subject to fixed boundary conditions of the form (2), or to natural boundary conditions associated with free boundaries, or to transversality conditions associated with some boundary curve. In each case the approach consists of defining a new functional $H[u]$ by the relation

$$H[u] \equiv I[u] + \lambda K[u] = \int_a^b (F + \lambda G)\, dx \equiv \int_a^b L\{x, u(x), u'(x)\}\, dx \tag{13}$$

where λ is an arbitrary *Lagrange multiplier* (cf. §4.4 of Volume 1). The condition that $H[u]$ be stationary leads to the Euler–Lagrange equation

$$\frac{\partial L}{\partial u} - \frac{d}{dx}\left(\frac{\partial L}{\partial u'}\right) = 0 \tag{14}$$

for the *Lagrange* function

$$L\{x, u(x), u'(x)\} = F\{x, u(x), u'(x)\} + \lambda G\{x, u(x), u'(x)\}.$$

The solution of the second-order differential equation (14) involves the parameter λ in addition to the usual two arbitrary constants, and these three quantities may be determined by using the appropriate boundary conditions and the integral constraint (12).

EXAMPLE 7 Solve the isoperimetric problem defined above.

Here the Lagrange function is

$$L = u(x) + \lambda\{1 + [u'(x)]^2\}^{1/2}.$$

The Euler–Lagrange equation is

$$1 - \lambda \frac{\mathrm{d}}{\mathrm{d}x}\left(\frac{u'(x)}{\{1 + [u'(x)]^2\}^{\frac{1}{2}}}\right) = 0,$$

which is to be solved subject to $u(0) = u(a) = 0$ and the integral constraint. Integrating this equation gives

$$\frac{\lambda u'(x)}{\{1 + [u'(x)]^2\}^{\frac{1}{2}}} = x + C$$

which solves to give

$$u'(x) = \pm(x + C)\{\lambda^2 - (x + C)^2\}^{-\frac{1}{2}},$$

and

$$u(x) = \mp\{\lambda^2 - (x + C)^2\}^{\frac{1}{2}} + D.$$

The boundary conditions imply that $C = -\frac{1}{2}a$, $D = \pm(\lambda^2 - \frac{1}{4}a^2)^{\frac{1}{2}}$. The positive sign in the expression for $u(x)$ corresponds to a curve lying above the x axis and the negative sign to a curve lying below the x axis. The former gives a positive area and yields the required maximum, the latter gives a negative area which is the minimum. The curves are arcs of a circle with centre at $(\frac{1}{2}a, D)$ and radius λ as illustrated in Fig. 8.4. The value of λ is determined from the expression for the arc length l which is obtained from the integral constraint or may be calculated directly from Fig. 8.4a and Fig. 8.4b as

$$l = \begin{cases} 2\lambda \sin^{-1} a/2\lambda & \text{for} \quad l \leqslant \pi a/2, \\ 2\lambda(\pi - \sin^{-1} a/2\lambda) & \text{for} \quad l \geqslant \pi a/2. \end{cases}$$

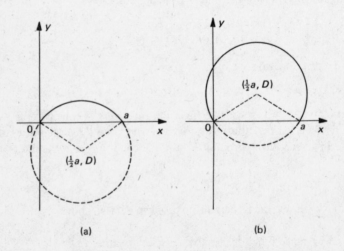

(a)   (b)

Fig. 8.4   Isoperimetric curves for example 7.

EXAMPLE 8   As an example of a problem with an integral constraint and a free end condition, consider a heavy inextensible flexible cable of length l which has one end held at $(0, 0)$, the other end being attached by a frictionless ring to a vertical wire $x = a$.

The curve $y = \bar{u}(x)$ taken up by the cable will minimize the potential energy

$$P[u] = \int_{x=0}^{x=a} \sigma g u(x) \, ds = \int_0^a \sigma g u(x)\{1 + [u'(x)]^2\}^{\frac{1}{2}} \, dx$$

subject to the constraints $u(0) = 0$ and $\int_0^a \{1 + [u'(x)]^2\}^{\frac{1}{2}} \, dx = l$. Here σ is the mass per unit length of the cable and g the acceleration due to gravity. The Lagrange function for this problem is

$$L(x, u, u') = \sigma g \{u(x) + \lambda\}\{1 + [u'(x)]^2\}^{\frac{1}{2}} \,,$$

and does not depend explicitly on x. The Euler–Lagrange equation thus has a first integral

$$L - u' \frac{\partial L}{\partial u'} = \frac{\sigma g\{u(x) + \lambda\}}{\{1 + [u'(x)]^2\}^{\frac{1}{2}}} = C\sigma g \,,$$

where C is an arbitrary constant. This equation may be solved for $u'(x)$ to give

$$u'(x) = \frac{\{[u(x) + \lambda]^2 - C^2\}^{\frac{1}{2}}}{C} \,.$$

Hence, on integration,

$$u(x) = C \cosh\left(\frac{x + D}{C}\right) - \lambda$$

where C, D and λ are to be determined from the boundary conditions and the integral constraint. The free end condition at $x = a$ is

$$\frac{\partial L}{\partial u'} = \sigma g \frac{\{u(a) + \lambda\}u'(a)}{\{1 + [u'(a)]^2\}^{\frac{1}{2}}} = 0 \tag{15}$$

which can only be satisfied by $u'(a) = 0$. This gives $D = -a$ and the other boundary condition gives $\lambda = C \cosh(a/C)$ where C is obtained from the integral condition as a root of the equation $C \sinh(a/C) = l$. The curve is a catenary with a horizontal tangent at the point where it is attached to the wire by the frictionless ring.

More General Integrands

The method used here in order to derive the Euler–Lagrange equations may be applied to more general integrals than that given by equation (1). The following cases cover most situations.

(a) The integrand involves derivatives of $u(x)$ of order higher than the first,

$$I[u] = \int_a^b F\{x, u(x), u'(x), \ldots, u^{(n)}(x)\}\, dx .$$ (16)

The Euler–Lagrange equation is

$$\frac{\partial F}{\partial u} - \frac{d}{dx}\left(\frac{\partial F}{\partial u'}\right) + \frac{d^2}{dx^2}\left(\frac{\partial F}{\partial u''}\right) - \ldots + (-1)^n \frac{d^n}{dx^n}\left(\frac{\partial F}{\partial u^{(n)}}\right) = 0 .$$ (17)

(b) The integrand depends on several unknown functions $v_1(x), v_2(x), \ldots, v_n(x)$,

$$I[v_1, v_2, \ldots, v_n] = \int_a^b F(x, v_1, v_2, \ldots, v_n, v_1', v_2', \ldots, v_n')\, dx .$$ (18)

The functions $\bar{v}_1, \bar{v}_2, \bar{v}_3, \ldots, \bar{v}_n$ which minimize the integral I are the solutions of the system of simultaneous Euler–Lagrange equations

$$\frac{\partial F}{\partial v_r} - \frac{d}{dx}\left(\frac{\partial F}{\partial v_r'}\right) = 0, \quad r = 1, 2, \ldots, n .$$ (19)

(c) The function u is a function of more than one independent variable $x_1, x_2, \ldots, x_n$,

$$I[u] = \int_V F(x_1, x_2, \ldots, x_n, u, u_1, u_2, \ldots, u_n)\, dV ,$$ (20)

where $u_r = \partial u/\partial x_r$ for $r = 1, 2, \ldots, n$ and the integral is over the volume V contained within some surface S in n-dimensional space. The Euler–Lagrange equation for the minimizing function $\bar{u}(x_1, x_2, \ldots, x_n)$ is the partial differential equation

$$\frac{\partial F}{\partial u} - \frac{\partial}{\partial x_1}\left(\frac{\partial F}{\partial u_1}\right) - \frac{\partial}{\partial x_2}\left(\frac{\partial F}{\partial u_2}\right) - \cdots - \frac{\partial}{\partial x_n}\left(\frac{\partial F}{\partial u_n}\right) = 0 .$$ (21)

Extensions of these results are given in more specialized texts on this subject, for example Forray [2], Courant and Hilbert [3].

Exercises

1. Derive the optimum curves which minimize $\int_0^1 F\, dx$ and pass through the points $(0, 0)$, $(1, 2)$ where F has the following forms

(a) $F = x^2 + [u'(x)]^2$,
(b) $F = [u(x)]^2 + [u'(x)]^2$,
(c) $F = [u'(x)]^2 + x^3 u(x)$.

2. Determine the path of the light ray from the point $(0, 0)$ to the point $(1, 1)$ in the x, y plane if the speed of light is $c(x, y) = c_0(1 + px)$ where c_0 and p are constants.

3. Determine the curve with prescribed end points $(-1, 2), (1, 2)$ which is such that if this curve is revolved around the x axis a surface of minimal area results. The surface area of revolution of the curve $y = u(x)$ about the x axis is

$$2\pi \int_{-1}^{1} u(x)\{1 + [u'(x)]^2\}^{\frac{1}{2}} \, dx \ .$$

4. A comet follows a hyperbolic orbit given by the equation $y^2 = 3x^2 + 12x + 9$ where the sun lies at the focus $(0, 0)$. Use the method of example 6 to determine the point of nearest approach to the sun.

5. *Dido's problem.* Find the curve of length l which is such that the area enclosed between the curve and the x axis is a maximum where one end of the curve is fixed at the origin and the other end is at a variable point on the x axis. Show that the optimum curve is a semicircle, a result which Dido is reputed to have known, see Kline [4], Ch. 24.

6. Show that the Euler–Lagrange equation corresponding to a stationary value of the integral

$$\int_{0}^{a} \{[u''(x)]^2 - \omega^2 \, [u(x)]^2\} \, dx$$

is

$$\frac{d^4 u}{dx^4} - \omega^2 u = 0 \ .$$

This equation arises in the vibration of beams.

7. Show that the Euler–Lagrange equation corresponding to a stationary value of the integral

$$\iint_{A} \left\{ \left(\frac{\partial u}{\partial x}\right)^2 + \left(\frac{\partial u}{\partial y}\right)^2 + 2g(x, y)u(x, y) \right\} dx \, dy \ ,$$

where u is a function of two variables x, y defined in the area A, is Poisson's equation

$$\frac{\partial^2 u}{\partial x^2} + \frac{\partial^2 u}{\partial y^2} = g(x, y) \ .$$

8. Show that the Euler–Lagrange equation corresponding to a stationary value of the integral

$$\iint_{A} \left\{ \left(\frac{\partial^2 u}{\partial x^2} + \frac{\partial^2 u}{\partial y^2}\right)^2 - 2p(x, y)u(x, y) \right\} dx \, dy \ ,$$

where u is a function of two variables x, y defined in the area A, is the inhomogeneous biharmonic equation

$$\frac{\partial^4 u}{\partial x^4} + 2 \frac{\partial^4 u}{\partial x^2 \partial y^2} + \frac{\partial^4 u}{\partial y^4} = p(x, y) .$$

8.3 DIRECT METHODS

This section is concerned with direct methods for solving the minimization problem and with the application of these methods to the solution of differential equations. It is convenient to develop the basic method with reference to the problem of minimizing the integral $I[u]$ given by equation (1) subject to the boundary conditions (2).

The Rayleigh–Ritz Method

The basis of the method is to approximate the solution by the *test function $u_n(x)$* given by

$$u_n(x) = \phi_0(x) + C_1 \phi_1(x) + C_2 \phi_2(x) + \ldots + C_n \phi_n(x) . \tag{22}$$

Here $\phi_0(x)$ is chosen to satisfy the boundary conditions (2) and $\phi_1(x), \phi_2(x), \ldots, \phi_n(x)$ are known functions which vanish at $x = a$ and $x = b$ so that $u_n(x)$ satisfies equations (2) for all values of the parameters $C_1, C_2, \ldots, C_n$. When this expression for $u_n(x)$ is substituted in the integral (1) and the integration is carried out, the functional $I[u_n]$ becomes an ordinary function $F_n(C_1, C_2, \ldots, C_n)$ of the parameters. The stationary points of this function are given by the system of equations

$$\frac{\partial F_n}{\partial C_1} = 0, \quad \frac{\partial F_n}{\partial C_2} = 0, \quad \ldots, \quad \frac{\partial F_n}{\partial C_n} = 0,$$

and the solution of this system gives the set of values $C_1 = \bar{C}_1, C_2 = \bar{C}_2, \ldots, C_n = \bar{C}_n$. When these values are substituted into the expression (22) there results the function $\bar{u}_n(x)$ which produces the minimum value of $I[u_n]$ for all $u_n(x)$ belonging to the class of functions defined by equation (22).

In this way it is possible to construct a sequence of approximations $\bar{u}_1(x)$, $\bar{u}_2(x), \ldots, \bar{u}_r(x), \ldots$, which give the minimum of the functional for $n = 1, 2, \ldots, r, \ldots$. Since for all values of r the function $\bar{u}_{r-1}(x)$ is a member of the class of functions $u_r(x)$ (corresponding to $C_r = 0$), it follows that the value of the integral given by $\bar{u}_r(x)$ is less than or equal to the value given by $\bar{u}_{r-1}(x)$ so that

$$I[\bar{u}_1] \geqslant I[\bar{u}_2] \ldots \geqslant I[\bar{u}_{r-1}] \geqslant I[\bar{u}_r] \ldots .$$

Thus the sequence $\{I[\bar{u}_n]\}$ is monotone decreasing and is bounded below by the exact minimum $I[\bar{u}]$. It follows that the sequence converges to a limit. Provided the infinite set of functions $\phi_0(x), \phi_1(x), \ldots, \phi_n(x), \ldots$ is *complete* then it can be proved that the limit of the sequence is the exact minimum $I[\bar{u}]$. The set is said to be complete if any continuous function satisfying the boundary conditions can be approximated to any given accuracy by a linear combination of the functions $\phi_0(x), \phi_1(x), \ldots,$

$\phi_n(x), \ldots$. One example of a complete set is the set of polynomials, and another example is that set of sine and cosine functions which give the Fourier series of any function over the interval $a \leqslant x \leqslant b$. It does not follow that the convergence of the sequence $\{I[\bar{u}_n]\}$ implies that the sequence $\{\bar{u}_n(x)\}$ converges to $\bar{u}(x)$.

EXAMPLE 1   Use the Rayleigh–Ritz method to minimize

$$I[u] = \int_0^1 \left\{ \frac{1}{2}\left(\frac{du}{dx}\right)^2 + 5u(x)e^x \right\} dx$$

subject to $u(0) = 1, u(1) = 3$.

Choose $\phi_0(x) = 1 + 2x$ to satisfy the boundary conditions. Since $\phi_1(x), \phi_2(x), \ldots$ are functions which must vanish at $x = 0$ and at $x = 1$, they are chosen to be the polynomials

$$\phi_1(x) = x(x - 1), \quad \phi_2(x) = x^2(x - 1), \ldots .$$

Then

$$u_1(x) = 1 + 2x + C_1 x(x - 1),$$

and

$$I[u_1] = F_1(C_1) = 2 + \tfrac{1}{6}C_1^2 + 5\{1 + e + C_1(3 - e)\}.$$

This has a stationary value at $\bar{C}_1 = -4.225773$ and gives $I[\bar{u}_1] = 19.2505$. For the second approximation

$$u_2(x) = 1 + 2x + C_1 x(x - 1) + C_2 x^2(x - 1),$$

and

$$I[u_2] = F_2(C_1, C_2) = 2 + \tfrac{1}{6}C_1^2 + \tfrac{1}{15}C_2^2 + \tfrac{1}{6}C_1 C_2$$
$$+ 5\{1 + e + C_1(3 - e) + C_2(3e - 8)\}.$$

This function has a stationary value at $\bar{C}_1 = -3.526452, \bar{C}_2 = -1.398646$ for which $I[\bar{u}_2] = 17.5665$. The third approximation is given by

$$u_3(x) = 1 + 2x + C_1 x(x - 1) + C_2 x^2(x - 1) + C_3 x^3(x - 1),$$

which yields

$$I[u_3] = F_3(C_1, C_2, C_3) = 2 + \tfrac{1}{6}C_1^2 + \tfrac{1}{15}C_2^2 + \tfrac{3}{70}C_3^2 + \tfrac{1}{6}C_1 C_2 + \tfrac{1}{10}C_2 C_3 + \tfrac{1}{10}C_3 C_1$$
$$+ 5\{1 + e + C_1(3 - e) + C_2(3e - 8) + C_3(30 - 11e)\}.$$

The stationary value is given by

$$\bar{C}_1 = -3.596109, \quad \bar{C}_2 = -1.050358, \quad \bar{C}_3 = -0.348282$$

which correspond to $I[\bar{u}_3] = 17.56597$. The close agreement between this value and $I[\bar{u}_2]$ suggests that the sequence is converging rapidly. The exact solution to the problem is obtained by solving the differential equation of example 4 of §8.1 and is

TABLE 8.1

x	$\bar{u}_1(x)$	$\bar{u}_2(x)$	$\bar{u}_3(x)$	$\bar{u}(x)$
0	1	1	1	1
0.1	0.819681	0.870037	0.866584	0.866714
0.2	0.723877	0.791021	0.788782	0.788732
0.3	0.712588	0.771344	0.772062	0.771871
0.4	0.785815	0.819398	0.822725	0.822560
0.5	0.943558	0.943575	0.947910	0.947902
0.6	1.185815	1.152266	1.155591	1.155749
0.7	1.512588	1.453862	1.454576	1.454777
0.8	1.923877	1.856755	1.854513	1.854577
0.9	2.419681	2.369337	2.365881	2.365747
1.0	3	3	3	3

given by

$$\bar{u}(x) = 5e^x - (5e - 7)x - 4.$$

The minimum value of the integral is $I[\bar{u}] = 17.56596$. The optimal functions $\bar{u}_1(x)$, $\bar{u}_2(x)$, $\bar{u}_3(x)$, $\bar{u}(x)$ are tabulated in Table 8.1 and it will be seen that in this case the sequence $\{\bar{u}_n(x)\}$ is converging to the exact solution $\bar{u}(x)$.

Finite Elements

As the order n of the approximation $u_n(x)$ in the Rayleigh–Ritz method becomes large, the algebra involved in evaluating the integral can become prohibitive. In order to reduce the work involved but still to use a large number of parameters the range of integration may be divided into a number of sub-ranges or *finite elements*. In each of these elements a simple polynomial is assumed for $u_n(x)$ in such a way as to ensure continuity between elements, and the integral is evaluated as the sum of the integrals over each element.

EXAMPLE 2   Use finite elements to minimize

$$I[u] = \int_0^1 \left\{ \left(\frac{du}{dx}\right)^2 + x^3 u \right\} dx,$$

with $u(0) = 3$, $u(1) = 1$.

First divide the range $0 \leqslant x \leqslant 1$ into two equal elements in each of which $u_1(x)$ is assumed to be linear in x so that

$$u_1(x) = \begin{cases} 3 + C_1 x & \text{for } 0 \leqslant x \leqslant \frac{1}{2}, \\ 1 + (4 + C_1)(1 - x) & \text{for } \frac{1}{2} < x \leqslant 1. \end{cases}$$

Here $u_1(x)$ is continuous at $x = \frac{1}{2}$ and satisfies the boundary conditions. The integral is evaluated as the sum of separate integrals over the two ranges and is given by

$$I[u_1] = \frac{1}{2}C_1^2 + \frac{1}{2}(4 + C_1)^2 + \frac{9}{32} + \frac{13}{320}(4 + C_1) + \frac{1}{160}C_1.$$

This has a minimum value of 4.3495 at $\bar{C}_1 = -2.0234$. To obtain an improved approximation the range is divided into 3 equal intervals in each of which a linear function is used to give

$$u_2(x) = \begin{cases} 3 + C_1 x & \text{for } 0 \leqslant x \leqslant \frac{1}{3}, \\ 3 + C_1(\frac{2}{3} - x) + C_2(x - \frac{1}{3}) & \text{for } \frac{1}{3} < x \leqslant \frac{2}{3}, \\ 1 + (6 + C_2)(1 - x) & \text{for } \frac{2}{3} < x \leqslant 1. \end{cases}$$

This is continuous at $x = \frac{1}{3}$ and $x = \frac{2}{3}$ and satisfies the boundary conditions at $x = 0$ and $x = 1$. The integral $I[u_2]$ has a minimum value of 4.3492 for $\bar{C}_1 = -2.0247$ and $\bar{C}_2 = -4.0401$. This process of subdivision can be continued. The exact solution is readily obtained as

$$\bar{u}(x) = 3 - \tfrac{81}{40}x + \tfrac{1}{40}x^5$$

and the minimum of the integral is $I[\bar{u}] = 4.3489$.

Partial Differential Equations

The direct method of obtaining the approximate minimum of the functional $I[u]$ can be employed to obtain approximate solutions of differential equations provided the differential equation can be replaced by an appropriate variational problem. The partial differential equation

$$\frac{\partial^2 u}{\partial x^2} + \frac{\partial^2 u}{\partial y^2} = g(x, y),$$

which is known as Poisson's equation, has wide application in physics and engineering. It is frequently required to solve this equation in some region A of the x, y plane subject to the condition that $u(x, y) = 0$ on the bounding curve C of A. It is possible to show that this problem is equivalent to minimizing the integral

$$I[u] = \iint_A \frac{1}{2} \left\{ \left(\frac{\partial u}{\partial x}\right)^2 + \left(\frac{\partial u}{\partial y}\right)^2 + 2gu \right\} \, dxdy,$$

subject to the condition that $u = 0$ on C (see exercise 7 of §8.2).

EXAMPLE 3   Poisson's equation with $g(x, y) = k$ (a constant) arises in the problems of torsion of a cylinder and of slow viscous flow through a pipe. Use the Rayleigh–Ritz method to solve the equation when the curve C is the ellipse

$$\frac{x^2}{a^2} + \frac{y^2}{b^2} = 1.$$

Since $u(x, y)$ is to vanish on C a suitable choice of test function is

$$u_1(x, y) = C_1 \left(\frac{x^2}{a^2} + \frac{y^2}{b^2} - 1\right),$$

which gives

$$I[u_1] = \frac{\pi ab}{2} \left\{ C_1^2 \left(\frac{1}{a^2} + \frac{1}{b^2} \right) - kC_1 \right\} .$$

The minimum value of this is $-\pi k^2 a^3 b^3 / 8(a^2 + b^2)$ for $\bar{C}_1 = ka^2 b^2 / 2(a^2 + b^2)$. It is easily verified that $\bar{u}_1(x, y)$ is the exact solution. In this particular example the obvious choice of test function $u_1(x, y)$ contains the exact solution of the problem. In general the method will give an approximate solution only.

EXAMPLE 4   Obtain an approximate solution of Poisson's equation

$$\frac{\partial^2 u}{\partial x^2} + \frac{\partial^2 u}{\partial y^2} = 1 ,$$

in the square $-1 \leqslant x \leqslant 1, -1 \leqslant y \leqslant 1$ subject to the condition $u = 0$ on the boundary.

Rewriting the problem as a variational problem and choosing the test function

$$u_1(x, y) = C_1(1 - x^2)(1 - y^2)$$

gives $I[u_1] = 2.8444 C_1^2 + 0.8889 C_1$ which has a minimum value of $I[\bar{u}_1] = -0.0695$ for $C_1 = -0.1562$. The solution must be symmetric with respect to each of the lines $x = 0, y = 0, x = y$, so that it must involve even powers of x and y only and be symmetric in the two variables. An improved trial function satisfying the boundary conditions as well as these symmetry requirements is

$$u_2(x, y) = (1 - x^2)(1 - y^2)\{C_1 + C_2(x^2 + y^2)\} .$$

This gives a minimum value $I[\bar{u}_2] = -0.0702$ for $C_1 = -0.1461, C_2 = -0.0296$. The procedure may be repeated until convergence is attained. In this case the exact solution is an infinite series (see §7.8 of Volume 1) and $I[\bar{u}] = -0.0704$.

A two-dimensional finite element approach is frequently useful in problems of this type which involve awkwardly shaped boundaries. In particular the finite element method is often employed in the direct solution of problems in elasticity (see, for example, Zienkiewicz [5]).

Eigenvalue Problems

The Sturm–Liouville problem (see §6.6) is to determine the values of λ for which there are non-zero solutions of the general linear second-order differential equation

$$\frac{d}{dx} \left(p(x) \frac{du}{dx} \right) + \{q(x) + \lambda r(x)\}u(x) = 0 \tag{23}$$

which satisfy the boundary conditions $u(0) = 0, u(1) = 0$. In equation (23), $p(x), q(x)$ and $r(x)$ are known functions. The Sturm–Liouville problem is equivalent to finding the stationary values of the functional

$$I[u] = \int_0^1 \{p(x)[u'(x)]^2 - q(x)[u(x)]^2\} \, dx$$

subject to the integral constraint

$$K[u] = -\int_0^1 r(x)[u(x)]^2 dx = -1.$$

The Lagrange multiplier λ is then the eigenvalue parameter λ of equation (23).

As a special case consider the problem of solving

$$\frac{d^2 u}{dx^2} + \lambda u = 0 \qquad (24)$$

subject to $u(0) = 0$, $u(1) = 0$. Here the functional is

$$I[u] = \int_0^1 \left(\frac{du}{dx}\right)^2 dx$$

and the constraint is

$$K[u] = -\int_0^1 u^2 dx = -1,$$

so that the Lagrange functional $H[u]$ is

$$H[u] = \int_0^1 \left\{\left(\frac{du}{dx}\right)^2 - \lambda u^2\right\} dx.$$

Then it is readily verified that equation (24) is the Euler–Lagrange equation for $H[u]$.

If the test functions are chosen to be the polynomials $\phi_0(x) = 0$, $\phi_1(x) = x(1-x)$, $\phi_2(x) = x^2(1-x), \ldots$, the first approximation $u_1 = C_1 x(1-x)$ gives a stationary value of $H[u_1]$ when $\lambda = 10$, $\bar{C}_1 = \sqrt{30}$. The second approximation gives two possible solutions:

$$\lambda = 10, \quad \bar{C}_1 = \sqrt{30}, \quad \bar{C}_2 = 0,$$

or

$$\lambda = 42, \quad \bar{C}_1 = \sqrt{210}, \quad \bar{C}_2 = -2\sqrt{210}.$$

These approximate eigenvalues are to be compared with the exact values $\pi^2 = 9.8696$ and $4\pi^2 = 39.4784$.

An alternative choice of test functions is $\phi_0(x) = 0$, $\phi_1(x) = \sin \pi x$, $\phi_2(x) = \sin 2\pi x$, $\ldots, \phi_n(x) = \sin n\pi x, \ldots$, so that

$$u_n(x) = C_1 \sin \pi x + C_2 \sin 2\pi x + \ldots + C_n \sin n\pi x.$$

The Lagrange functional is then

$$H[u_n] = \tfrac{1}{2} \sum_{r=1}^n \pi C_r^2 \{r^2 \pi^2 - \lambda\},$$

and this is stationary provided

$$C_r(r^2 \pi^2 - \lambda) = 0, \quad r = 1, 2, \ldots, n.$$

This has n solutions $\lambda_r = r^2 \pi^2$ for the eigenvalues, corresponding to the choices $C_p = 0$ for $p \neq r$. In this case they are the exact eigenvalues and yield the corresponding eigenfunctions $\sin r\pi x$.

As an example of a fourth-order system consider the beam vibration equation (see §7.2 of Volume 1),

$$\frac{d^4 u}{dx^4} + \lambda u = 0$$

with $u(0) = u'(0) = u(1) = u'(1) = 0$. This is equivalent to finding the stationary values of

$$I[u] = \int_0^1 \left(\frac{d^2 u}{dx^2}\right)^2 dx$$

subject to the constraint

$$K[u] = \int_0^1 u^2 \, dx = 1 \; .$$

The Lagrange functional is then

$$H[u] = \int_0^1 \left\{ \left(\frac{d^2 u}{dx^2}\right)^2 + \lambda u^2 \right\} \, dx \; .$$

The functions $\phi_0(x) = 0$, $\phi_1(x) = x^2(1-x)^2$, $\phi_2(x) = x^3(1-x)^2, \ldots, \phi_r(x) = x^{r+1}(1-x)^2$ form a set of polynomials satisfying the boundary conditions. The first approximation $u_1(x) = C_1 x^2(1-x^2)$ leads to $H[u_1] = \frac{1}{5} C_1^2 \{4 + \frac{1}{126}\lambda\}$. The stationary value is given by $\frac{2}{5} C_1 \{4 + \frac{1}{126}\lambda\} = 0$ corresponding to $\lambda = -504$ compared with the exact value of $\lambda = -p_1^4 = -(4.73)^4 = -500$ obtained in §9.4 of Volume 1. This process may be continued to give additional eigenvalues and an improved approximation.

Exercises

1. Use the test function $u_2(x) = \phi_0 + C_1 \phi_1 + C_2 \phi_2$ where

$$\phi_0(x) = 1 + x, \quad \phi_1(x) = (1 - x^2), \quad \phi_2(x) = x(1 - x^2),$$

to obtain an approximate minimum of the integral

$$I[u] = \int_{-1}^1 [\tfrac{1}{2}\{u'(x)\}^2 + 3u \sin \pi x] \, dx$$

subject to $u(-1) = 0$, $u(1) = 2$.

2. Solve exercise 1 by using the trigonometric functions

$$\phi_0(x) = 1 + \sin\tfrac{1}{2}\pi x, \quad \phi_1(x) = \sin \pi x, \quad \phi_2(x) = \sin 2\pi x,$$

and compare the results with the exact solution of the Euler–Lagrange equations.

3. Find the value of the constant C_1 so that $u_1(x, y) = C_1(x^2 - a^2)(y^2 - b^2)$ is an approximate solution of Poisson's equation for $g(x, y) = 2$, in the region bounded by the rectangle $x = \pm a$, $y = \pm b$.

4. Use the test function $u_2(x) = (C_1 \sin \pi x + C_2 \sin 2\pi x) e^{-x}$ to obtain approximate solutions of the eigenvalue problem

$$\frac{d^2 u}{dx^2} + 2 \frac{du}{dx} + \lambda u = 0$$

subject to $u(0) = u(1) = 0$.

Take $I[u] = \displaystyle\int_0^1 e^{2x} u'^2 \, dx$, $K[u] = \displaystyle\int_0^1 e^{2x} u^2 \, dx = 1$, and compare the approximate solution with the exact solution of the differential equation.

PROBLEMS

1. Show that, if the speed of light in the x, y plane decreases linearly with height y according to the relation $c(x, y) = c_0(1 - ky)$ where c_0 and k are constants, then the ray from the point $(0, 0)$ to the point $(1, 0)$ is an arc of a circle. (This accounts for mirages.)

2. A river has two parallel banks $x = 0$ and $x = a$. The water flows parallel to the banks with the speed $v(x)$ which depends on the distance x from the left bank. A man with a boat at the point A on the left-hand bank wishes to cross the river and reach the point B on the opposite bank in the shortest possible time. Assume B is a distance b upstream from A. Suppose the man can row the boat with a speed V relative to the water and, having reached the opposite bank, can run along the bank with a speed kV where $k > 1$. The problem is to determine the path along which the boat should be rowed in order that the time of travel from A to B is minimized.

Show that at position x along the optimum path the steering angle ψ relative to the direction of flow is given by

$$\cos \psi = V / \{v(x) + kV\} .$$

3. Show that the problem of determining the shortest path on the surface $z = h(x, y)$ between the two points (x_0, y_0, z_0), (x_1, y_1, z_1) reduces to determining the minimizing curve for the integral

$$\int_{x_0}^{x_1} \left\{ 1 + [u'(x)]^2 + \left[\frac{\partial h}{\partial x} + u'(x) \frac{\partial h}{\partial u} \right]^2 \right\}^{\frac{1}{2}} dx$$

where the path is $y = u(x)$, $z = h(x, u(x))$.

In general this problem is difficult to solve. Show that when the surface is a plane, say $z = 2x + 3y$, the minimizing curve is a straight line.

If $h = x^2$, which corresponds to a valley of parabolic section, show that the minimizing curve joining the points $(-1, 0, 1)$ and $(1, 2, 1)$ is given by

$$y = \tfrac{1}{7}(3x + 4x^3) + 1, \quad z = x^2 .$$

4. Show that the surface of revolution having least area and joining the two circles, each of radius a, located at $x = \pm k$ is obtained by revolving the curve $y = c \cosh x/c$ about the x axis where the constant c is given by the equation $a = c \cosh k/c$. (Note that there is no C_2 minimizing function when $a < 1.509k$.)

5. The drag D on a body of revolution in a fluid flowing with hypersonic speed is given by

$$\frac{D}{K} = \int_0^a \frac{uu'^3}{1 + u'^2} \, dx + \tfrac{1}{2}[u(0)]^2 .$$

Here K is a constant, a is the length of the body, $u(x)$ is the radius of the body at a distance x from the forward end and $u(a) = b$ is its maximum radius. Show that for minimum drag the natural boundary condition at $x = 0$ is $u'(x) = 1$ provided $u(0) \neq 0$, and that $u(x)$ satisfies the equation

$$\frac{u(x)}{u(0)} = \frac{(1 + u'^2)^2}{4u'^3} .$$

6. Show that, for every integrand $F(x, u, u')$ of the form $F = H(x, u)(1 + u'^2)^{1/2}$ the

transversality condition associated with the minimization of $K = \int_a^{\hat{x}} F(x, u, u') \, dx$

subject to $u(a) = \alpha$ and $u(\hat{x}) = f(\hat{x})$ becomes the condition that the minimizing curve $y = \bar{u}(x)$ is orthogonal to $y = f(\hat{x})$ at $x = \hat{x}$.

7. A body of mass m travelling with constant speed U_1 along the x axis is to be transferred so as to move with constant speed U_2 along the line $y = h$ by the action of a force of constant magnitude ma acting over the time interval $0 \leqslant t \leqslant T$. If $v(t)$ denotes the speed of the body in the y direction over the interval $0 \leqslant t \leqslant T$ show that when h takes its maximum value

$$v(t) = \tfrac{1}{2}a\{[(2t - T)^2 + 4\lambda^2]^{1/2} - [T^2 + 4\lambda^2]^{1/2}\} ,$$

where λ satisfies the equation $2\lambda \sinh\{(U_2 - U_1)/2a\lambda\} = T$. (*Hint.* Since the acceleration in the x direction is $(a^2 - v'^2)^{1/2}$ then $h = \int_0^T v \, dt$ is to be maximized subject to the constraint $U_2 - U_1 = \int_0^T (a^2 - v'^2)^{1/2} \, dt$.)

8. A heavy uniform chain of length l and mass per unit length σ is fixed at one end to the point $(0, 0)$ and the other end slides on a vertical wire at $x = a$. The sliding end hangs from a spring in which the tension is $-ku(a)$ where k is the spring stiffness and $u(x)$ is the displacement of the chain in the positive y direction (see example 8, §8.2). The potential energy of the spring is $\tfrac{1}{2}k[u(a)]^2$ and the total potential energy $P[u]$ of the system is

$$P[u] = \int_0^a \sigma g u(x) \{1 + [u'(x)]^2\}^{\frac{1}{2}} \, dx + \tfrac{1}{2} k \, [u(a)]^2 \, ,$$

where $u(0) = 0$ and $\int_0^a \{1 + [u'(x)]^2\}^{\frac{1}{2}} \, dx = l$. Determine the natural boundary condition at $x = a$ and the equilibrium shape of the chain.

9. A uniform elastic cantilever of length l is built-in at the end $x = 0$ and free at the end $x = l$. The cantilever supports a distributed load $q(x)$ and its bending rigidity is EI. If $u(x)$ is any displacement satisfying the built-in conditions $u(0) = u'(0) = 0$, the potential energy $P[u]$ is given by

$$P[u] = \tfrac{1}{2} EI \int_0^l [u''(x)]^2 \, dx - \int_0^l q(x) u(x) \, dx \, .$$

Derive the Euler–Lagrange equation and the natural boundary conditions at the free end.

10. *Hamilton's principle* for a dynamical system acted upon by conservative forces states that the motion of the system between any two times t_1 and t_2 is such as to render stationary the functional

$$I = \int_{t_1}^{t_2} (T - V) \, dt \, ,$$

where T is the kinetic energy and V is the potential energy of the system.

A double pendulum consists of a heavy bob of mass m_1 attached by a light string of length l_1 to another bob of mass m_2 which in turn is attached to a fixed point by a string of length l_2. If $\theta_1(t)$ and $\theta_2(t)$ denote the angles that the respective strings make with the downward vertical then for small motions

$$T = \tfrac{1}{2} m_1 (l_1 \dot\theta_1 + l_2 \dot\theta_2)^2 + \tfrac{1}{2} m_2 l_2^2 \dot\theta_2^2 \, ,$$
$$V = \tfrac{1}{2} m_1 g (l_1 \theta_1^2 + l_2 \theta_2^2) + \tfrac{1}{2} m_2 g l_2 \theta_2^2 \, .$$

Obtain the Euler–Lagrange equations for the motion.

11. An elastic string of length l and mass per unit length σ is fixed at its two ends $x = 0$ and $x = l$ and is undergoing transverse vibrations in a horizontal plane. If $u(x, t)$ is the displacement of the point x at the time t, the potential energy V and kinetic energy T are given by the expressions

$$V = \tfrac{1}{2} EA \int_0^l \left(\frac{\partial u}{\partial x}\right)^2 \, dx, \qquad T = \tfrac{1}{2} \sigma \int_0^l \left(\frac{\partial u}{\partial t}\right)^2 \, dx \, ,$$

where E is the Young's modulus and A the area of cross-section of the string. Derive the equation of motion from Hamilton's principle. (See problem 10.)

12. The free vibrations of a body attached to a fixed point by means of a non-linear spring are such as to minimize the functional

$$I[x] = \int_0^\tau \tfrac{1}{2}\left\{ \left(\frac{dx}{dt}\right)^2 - kx^2(1 + \tfrac{1}{2}\mu x^2) \right\}\, dt \; .$$

In this expression k and μ are constants, τ is the period of the vibration and $x(t)$ is the displacement of the body with $x(0) = x(\tau) = 0$. Use the test function $x_1(t) = C_1 \sin 2\pi t/\tau$ to obtain an approximate solution for $x(t)$.

13. The potential energy of a beam of length l, simply supported at the two ends $x = 0$ and $x = l$ and carrying a distributed load qx^2/l^2 is given by

$$P[u] = \int_0^l \left\{ \tfrac{1}{2}EI(u'')^2 - \frac{qx^2 u}{l^2} \right\}\, dx \; ,$$

where EI is the bending rigidity, $u(x)$ is the displacement and $u(0) = u'(0) = 0$, $u(l) = 0$. Find values of the constants C_1, C_2, C_3, so that the displacement

$$u_3(x) = \begin{cases} C_1 x^2/l^2 & \text{for } 0 \leqslant x \leqslant l/3 \; , \\ C_2(3x - l)(3x - 2l)/ql^2 + C_3(3x - l)/9l - C_1(3x - 2l)/9l \\ & \text{for } l/3 < x \leqslant 2l/3 \; , \\ C_3(l - x)^2/l^2 & \text{for } 2l/3 < x \leqslant l \; , \end{cases}$$

gives the minimum of $P[u_3]$.

14. The whirling deflection $u(x)$ of a shaft of length l and bending rigidity EI under an end thrust P, is obtained by minimizing

$$I[u] = \int_0^l \tfrac{1}{2}\{EI(u'')^2 - P(u')^2 - 4\pi^2\omega^2\sigma u^2\}\, dx \; ,$$

where σ is the mass per unit length of the shaft and ω is the whirling frequency. Derive and solve the Euler–Lagrange equation and show that ω satisfies the equation

$$Pl^2 + 4\sigma\omega^2 l^4 = \pi^2 EI \; ,$$

when $u(x)$ satisfies the boundary conditions $u(0) = u''(0) = u(l) = u''(l) = 0$, which correspond to the shaft running in short bearings.

15. Use the displacement $u_1(x) = C_1 x(x - l)(x^2 - xl - l^2)$ to obtain an approximate equation for the whirling frequency ω of problem 14.

16. The deflection $u(x, y)$ of an elastic membrane clamped along its boundary curve C and supporting a distributed load $w(x, y)$ is such as to minimize the potential energy

$$P[u] = \tfrac{1}{2}\iint \left\{ T\left[\left(\frac{\partial u}{\partial x}\right)^2 + \left(\frac{\partial u}{\partial y}\right)^2 \right] - 2wu \right\}\, dx\, dy \; ,$$

where T is the tension in the membrane and $u(x, y) = 0$ on C. Use the displacement $u_1(x, y) = C_1 \cos \pi x/2a \cos \pi y/2a$ to obtain the approximate solution for the deflection of a square membrane $x = \pm a$, $y = \pm a$, under a load $w(x, y) = k(x^2 - a^2)$.

BIBLIOGRAPHY

[1] Craggs, J. W., *Calculus of Variations*, Allen & Unwin, London (1973).
[2] Forray, M. J., *Variational Calculus in Science and Engineering*, McGraw-Hill, New York (1968).
[3] Courant, R., and D. Hilbert, *Methods of Mathematical Physics*, Vol. 1, Interscience, New York (1965).
[4] Kline, M., *Mathematical Thought From Ancient to Modern Times*, Oxford Univ. Press, New York (1972).
[5] Zienkiewicz, O. C., *The Finite Element Method in Engineering Science*, McGraw-Hill, London (1971).

Appendix

TABLE A1: SOME UPPER CRITICAL VALUES OF THE STANDARDIZED NORMAL DISTRIBUTION $N(0, 1)$

Values of z_α^* where $P\{Z > z_\alpha^*\} = \alpha$
$[P\{|Z| > z_\alpha^*\} = 2\alpha, \qquad \alpha = 1 - F(z_\alpha^*)$ where F is the c.d.f.$]$

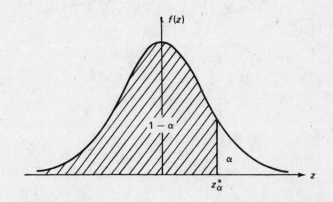

α	0.500	0.3085	0.1587	0.0668	0.0228	0.0062	0.0013
z_α^*	0.0	0.5	1.0	1.5	2.0	2.5	3.0

α	0.250	0.100	0.050	0.025	0.010	0.005	0.001
z_α^*	0.675	1.282	1.645	1.960	2.326	2.576	3.090

TABLE A2: SOME UPPER CRITICAL VALUES OF STUDENT'S t DISTRIBUTION

Values of $t_{[\nu]\alpha}^{*}$ where
$$P\{t_{[\nu]} > t_{[\nu]\alpha}^{*}\} = \alpha$$
$$[P\{|t_{[\nu]}| > t_{[\nu]\alpha}^{*}\} = 2\alpha]$$

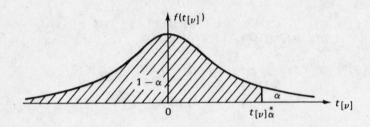

| | α | |
ν	0.05	0.025
1	6.31	12.71
2	2.92	4.30
3	2.35	3.18
4	2.13	2.78
5	2.02	2.57
6	1.94	2.45
7	1.89	2.36
8	1.86	2.31
9	1.83	2.26
10	1.81	2.23
12	1.78	2.18
14	1.76	2.14
16	1.75	2.12
18	1.73	2.10
20	1.72	2.09
25	1.71	2.06
30	1.70	2.04
60	1.67	2.00
∞	1.64	1.96

Tables A2 and A3 have been respectively extracted from Tables 12 and 8 of *Biometrika Tables for Statisticians*, Vol. I (3rd edition, 1966), Cambridge University Press, with kind permission of the Biometrika trustees.

TABLE A3: SOME UPPER CRITICAL VALUES OF THE CHI-SQUARE DISTRIBUTION

Values of $\chi^2_{[\nu]\alpha}{}^*$ where
$$P\{\chi^2_{[\nu]} > \chi^2_{[\nu]\alpha}{}^*\} = \alpha$$

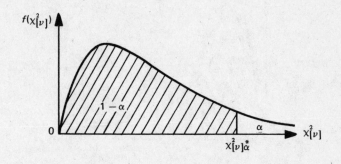

	α	
ν	0.05	0.01
1	3.84	6.63
2	5.99	9.21
3	7.81	11.34
4	9.49	13.28
5	11.07	15.09
6	12.59	16.81
7	14.07	18.48
8	15.51	20.09
9	16.92	21.67
10	18.31	23.21
11	19.68	24.73
12	21.03	26.22
13	22.36	27.69
14	23.68	29.14
15	25.00	30.58
16	26.30	32.00
17	27.59	33.41
18	28.87	34.81
19	30.14	36.19
20	31.41	37.57
22	33.92	40.29
24	36.42	42.98
26	38.89	45.64
28	41.34	48.28
30	43.77	50.89
40	55.76	63.69
50	67.50	76.15

TABLE A4: SOME UPPER CRITICAL VALUES OF THE F DISTRIBUTION (VARIANCE RATIO)

Values of $F_{[\nu_1,\nu_2]\alpha}^*$ where $P\{F_{[\nu_1,\nu_2]} > F_{[\nu_1,\nu_2]\alpha}^*\} = \alpha$ for $\alpha = 0.05$ and $\alpha = 0.025$

ν_1 is the number of degrees of freedom associated with the numerator.

ν_2 is the number of degrees of freedom associated with the denominator.

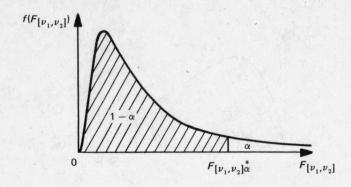

$\alpha = 0.05$

ν_1 / ν_2	1	2	3	4	5	6	8	12	24	∞
2	18.51	19.00	19.16	19.25	19.30	19.33	19.37	19.41	19.45	19.50
3	10.13	9.55	9.28	9.12	9.01	8.94	8.85	8.74	8.64	8.53
4	7.71	6.94	6.59	6.39	6.26	6.16	6.04	5.91	5.77	5.63
5	6.61	5.79	5.41	5.19	5.05	4.95	4.82	4.68	4.53	4.36
6	5.99	5.14	4.76	4.53	4.39	4.28	4.15	4.00	3.84	3.67
7	5.59	4.74	4.35	4.12	3.97	3.87	3.73	3.57	3.41	3.23
8	5.32	4.46	4.07	3.84	3.69	3.58	3.44	3.28	3.12	2.93
9	5.12	4.26	3.86	3.63	3.48	3.37	3.23	3.07	2.90	2.71
10	4.96	4.10	3.71	3.48	3.33	3.22	3.07	2.91	2.74	2.54
12	4.75	3.89	3.49	3.26	3.11	3.00	2.85	2.69	2.51	2.30
14	4.60	3.74	3.34	3.11	2.96	2.85	2.70	2.53	2.35	2.13
16	4.49	3.63	3.24	3.01	2.85	2.74	2.59	2.42	2.24	2.01
18	4.41	3.55	3.16	2.93	2.77	2.66	2.51	2.34	2.15	1.92
20	4.35	3.49	3.10	2.87	2.71	2.60	2.45	2.28	2.08	1.84
25	4.24	3.39	2.99	2.76	2.60	2.49	2.34	2.16	1.96	1.71
30	4.17	3.32	2.92	2.69	2.53	2.42	2.27	2.09	1.89	1.62
60	4.00	3.15	2.76	2.53	2.37	2.25	2.10	1.92	1.70	1.39
∞	3.84	3.00	2.60	2.37	2.21	2.10	1.94	1.75	1.52	1.00

$\alpha = 0.025$

v_1 v_2	1	2	3	4	5	6	8	12	24	∞
2	38.51	39.00	39.17	39.25	39.30	39.33	39.37	39.41	39.46	39.50
3	17.44	16.04	15.44	15.10	14.88	14.73	14.54	14.34	14.12	13.90
4	12.22	10.65	9.98	9.60	9.36	9.20	8.98	8.75	8.51	8.26
5	10.01	8.43	7.76	7.39	7.15	6.98	6.76	6.52	6.28	6.02
6	8.81	7.26	6.60	6.23	5.99	5.82	5.60	5.37	5.12	4.85
7	8.07	6.54	5.89	5.52	5.29	5.12	4.90	4.67	4.42	4.14
8	7.57	6.06	5.42	5.05	4.82	4.65	4.43	4.20	3.95	3.67
9	7.21	5.71	5.08	4.72	4.48	4.32	4.10	3.87	3.61	3.33
10	6.94	5.46	4.83	4.47	4.24	4.07	3.85	3.62	3.37	3.08
12	6.55	5.10	4.47	4.12	3.89	3.73	3.51	3.28	3.02	2.72
14	6.30	4.86	4.24	3.89	3.66	3.50	3.29	3.05	2.79	2.49
16	6.12	4.69	4.08	3.73	3.50	3.34	3.12	2.89	2.63	2.32
18	5.98	4.56	3.95	3.61	3.38	3.22	3.01	2.77	2.50	2.19
20	5.87	4.46	3.86	3.51	3.29	3.13	2.91	2.68	2.41	2.09
25	5.69	4.29	3.69	3.35	3.13	2.97	2.75	2.51	2.24	1.91
30	5.57	4.18	3.59	3.25	3.03	2.87	2.65	2.41	2.14	1.79
60	5.29	3.93	3.34	3.01	2.79	2.63	2.41	2.17	1.88	1.48
∞	5.02	3.69	3.12	2.79	2.57	2.41	2.19	1.94	1.64	1.00

TABLE A5: LAPLACE TRANSFORMS

$$f(t) \qquad\qquad \bar{f}(s) = \int_0^\infty e^{-st} f(t)\, dt$$

General Properties of Laplace Transforms

$e^{at} f(t)$		$\bar{f}(s - a)$
$f(t - a)H(t - a)$	$(a > 0)$	$e^{-as}\bar{f}(s)$
$f(at)$	$(a > 0)$	$a^{-1}\bar{f}(a^{-1}s)$
$\displaystyle\int_0^t f(\tau)\, d\tau$		$s^{-1}\bar{f}(s)$
$t^n f(t)$	$(n = 1, 2, 3, \ldots)$	$(-1)^n \bar{f}^{(n)}(s)$
$t^{-1} f(t)$		$\displaystyle\int_s^\infty \bar{f}(\sigma)\, d\sigma$
$\displaystyle f(t)*g(t) \equiv \int_0^t f(\tau)g(t - \tau)\, d\tau$		$\bar{f}(s)\bar{g}(s)$
$f^{(n)}(t)$		$\displaystyle s^n \bar{f}(s) - \sum_{r=1}^n s^{n-r} f^{(r-1)}(0)$
$\displaystyle\sum_{n=0}^{[t/a]} r^n f(t - na)$	$(a > 0)$	$(1 - re^{-as})^{-1}\bar{f}(s)$

Table of Laplace Transform Pairs

$$f(t) \qquad\qquad \bar{f}(s) = \int_0^\infty e^{-st} f(t)\, dt$$

$\delta(t - a)$	$(a > 0)$	e^{-as}
$H(t - a)$	$(a > 0)$	$s^{-1} e^{-as}$
$r^{[t/a]}$	$(a > 0)$	$s^{-1}(1 - re^{-as})^{-1}(1 - e^{-as})$
$(-1)^{[t/a]}$	$(a > 0)$ (square wave)	$s^{-1} \tanh(\tfrac{1}{2}as)$
t^n	$(n = 0, 1, 2, \ldots)$	$n!s^{-n-1}$
t^ν	$(\nu > -1)$	$\Gamma(\nu + 1)s^{-\nu-1}$
$t^{-1}H(t - a)$	$(a > 0)$	$E_1(as)$
e^{kt}		$(s - k)^{-1}$
$\exp(-\tfrac{1}{4}a^{-1}t^2)$	$(a > 0)$	$\pi^{1/2}a^{1/2}\exp(as^2)\,\text{erfc}(a^{1/2}s)$
$t^{-3/2}e^{-a/t}$	$(a > 0)$	$\pi^{1/2}a^{-1/2}\exp(-2a^{1/2}s^{1/2})$
$t^{-1}(e^{\alpha t} - e^{\beta t})$		$\log(s - \beta) - \log(s - \alpha)$
$\sinh kt$		$k(s^2 - k^2)^{-1}$
$\cosh kt$		$s(s^2 - k^2)^{-1}$

Table A5: Laplace Transform Pairs (cont)

$\sin kt$	$k(s^2 + k^2)^{-1}$
$\cos kt$	$s(s^2 + k^2)^{-1}$
$t \sin kt$	$2ks(s^2 + k^2)^{-2}$
$t \cos kt$	$(s^2 - k^2)(s^2 + k^2)^{-2}$
$t^{-1} \sin kt$	$\tan^{-1} ks^{-1}$
$t^{-1}(1 - \cos kt)$	$\frac{1}{2} \log(1 + k^2 s^{-2})$
$t^{-\frac{1}{2}} \cos kt^{\frac{1}{2}}$	$\pi^{\frac{1}{2}} s^{-\frac{1}{2}} \exp(-\frac{1}{4}k^2 s^{-1})$
$J_0(kt)$	$(s^2 + k^2)^{-\frac{1}{2}}$
$J_0(kt^{\frac{1}{2}})$	$s^{-1} \exp(-\frac{1}{4}k^2 s^{-1})$
$I_0(kt)$	$(s^2 - k^2)^{-\frac{1}{2}}$
$I_0(kt^{\frac{1}{2}})$	$s^{-1} \exp(\frac{1}{4}k^2 s^{-1})$
$\text{erf}(kt^{\frac{1}{2}})$	$ks^{-1}(s + k^2)^{-\frac{1}{2}}$
$\text{erfc}(kt^{-\frac{1}{2}})$ $\quad (k > 0)$	$s^{-1} \exp(-2ks^{\frac{1}{2}})$
$E_1(t)$	$s^{-1} \log(s + 1)$
$\text{Ci}(t)$	$-\frac{1}{2}s^{-1} \log(s^2 + 1)$
$\text{Si}(t)$	$s^{-1} \cot^{-1} s$

TABLE A6: FOURIER TRANSFORMS

$$f(x) \qquad\qquad\qquad F(\xi) = \int_{-\infty}^{\infty} e^{-i\xi x} f(x)\, dx$$

General Properties of Fourier Transforms

$e^{iax} f(x)$		$F(\xi - a)$
$f(x - a)$		$e^{-ia\xi} F(\xi)$
$x^n f(x)$	$(n = 1, 2, 3, \ldots)$	$i^n F^{(n)}(\xi)$
$f(x)*g(x) \equiv \displaystyle\int_{-\infty}^{\infty} f(x - u)g(u)\, du$		$F(\xi)G(\xi)$
$f^{(n)}(x)$		$(i\xi)^n F(\xi)$

Table of Fourier Transform Pairs

$\delta(x - a)$		$e^{-ia\xi}$
$H(x + a) - H(x - a)$		$2\xi^{-1} \sin(a\xi)$
x^{-1}		$-i\pi\, \mathrm{sgn}\, \xi$
$x^{-1}(x^2 + a^2)^{-1}$	$(a > 0)$	$-i\pi a^{-2}(1 - e^{-a|\xi|})\, \mathrm{sgn}\, \xi$
$x^{-1} e^{-k|x|}$		$-2i \tan^{-1}(k^{-1}\xi)$
$e^{-k|x|}$	$(k > 0)$	$2k(\xi^2 + k^2)^{-1}$
$\exp(-kx^2)$	$(k > 0)$	$\pi^{1/2} k^{-1/2} \exp(-\tfrac{1}{4} k^{-1}\xi^2)$

TABLE A7: COSINE TRANSFORMS

$$f(x) \qquad\qquad F_c(\xi) = \int_0^\infty \cos \xi x\, f(x)\, dx \quad (\xi > 0)$$

General Properties of Cosine Transforms

$f''(x)$ $\qquad\qquad -\xi^2 F_c(\xi) - f'(0)$

$x^{2n} f(x)$ $\qquad (n = 1, 2, 3, \ldots)$ $\quad (-1)^n F_c^{(2n)}(\xi)$

Table of Cosine Transform Pairs

$\delta(x - a)$	$(a > 0)$	$\cos a\xi$
$H(x) - H(x - a)$	$(a > 0)$	$\xi^{-1} \sin a\xi$
$x^{-1} H(x - a)$	$(a > 0)$	$-\text{Ci}(a\xi)$
$x^{-\frac{1}{2}}$		$(\tfrac{1}{2}\pi)^{\frac{1}{2}} \xi^{-\frac{1}{2}}$
$(x^2 + a^2)^{-1}$	$(a > 0)$	$\tfrac{1}{2}\pi a^{-1} e^{-a\xi}$
$(a^2 - x^2)^{-1}$	$(a > 0)$	$\tfrac{1}{2}\pi a^{-1} \sin a\xi$
$(a^2 - x^2)^{-\frac{1}{2}}\{H(x) - H(x - a)\}$	$(a > 0)$	$\tfrac{1}{2}\pi J_0(a\xi)$
$x(a^2 - x^2)^{-1}$	$(a > 0)$	$\cos a\xi\, \text{Ci}(a\xi) + \sin a\xi\, \text{Si}(a\xi)$
e^{-kx}	$(k > 0)$	$k(\xi^2 + k^2)^{-1}$
xe^{-kx}	$(k > 0)$	$(k^2 - \xi^2)(k^2 + \xi^2)^{-2}$
$x^{-1}(e^{-\alpha x} - e^{-\beta x})$	$(\alpha, \beta > 0)$	$\tfrac{1}{2}\log(\xi^2 + \beta^2) - \tfrac{1}{2}\log(\xi^2 + \alpha^2)$
$\exp(-kx^2)$	$(k > 0)$	$\tfrac{1}{2}\pi^{\frac{1}{2}} k^{-\frac{1}{2}} \exp(-\tfrac{1}{4}k^{-1}\xi^2)$
$\cosh \alpha x\, \text{sech}\, \beta x$	$(\lvert \alpha \rvert < \beta)$	$\dfrac{\pi\beta^{-1} \cos \tfrac{1}{2}\pi\beta^{-1}\alpha \cosh \tfrac{1}{2}\pi\beta^{-1}\xi}{\cos \pi\beta^{-1}\alpha + \cosh \pi\beta^{-1}\xi}$
$x^{-2} \sin^2 kx$	$(k > 0)$	$\tfrac{1}{4}\pi(2k - \xi)\{1 - H(\xi - 2k)\}$

TABLE A8: SINE TRANSFORMS

$$f(x) \qquad\qquad F_s(\xi) = \int_0^\infty \sin \xi x\, f(x)\, dx \qquad (\xi > 0)$$

General Properties of Sine Transforms

$f''(x)$		$-\xi^2 F_s(\xi) + \xi f(0)$
$x^{2n} f(x)$	$(n = 1, 2, 3, \ldots)$	$(-1)^n F_s^{(2n)}(\xi)$

Table of Sine Transform Pairs

$\delta(x - a)$	$(a > 0)$	$\sin a\xi$
$H(x) - H(x - a)$	$(a > 0)$	$\xi^{-1}(1 - \cos a\xi)$
x^{-1}		$\tfrac{1}{2}\pi$
$x^{-1}\{H(x) - H(x - a)\}$	$(a > 0)$	$\mathrm{Si}(a\xi)$
$x^{-\frac{1}{2}}$		$(\tfrac{1}{2}\pi)^{\frac{1}{2}} \xi^{-\frac{1}{2}}$
$x^{-1}(x^2 + a^2)^{-1}$	$(a > 0)$	$\tfrac{1}{2}\pi a^{-2}(1 - e^{-a\xi})$
$(a^2 - x^2)^{-1}$	$(a > 0)$	$a^{-1}\{\sin a\xi\, \mathrm{Ci}(a\xi) - \cos a\xi\, \mathrm{Si}(a\xi)\}$
$x(a^2 - x^2)^{-1}$	$(a > 0)$	$-\tfrac{1}{2}\pi \cos a\xi$
e^{-kx}	$(k > 0)$	$\xi(\xi^2 + k^2)^{-1}$
$x^{-1} e^{-kx}$	$(k > 0)$	$\tan^{-1}(k^{-1}\xi)$
$x^{-1} \exp(-kx^2)$	$(k > 0)$	$\tfrac{1}{2}\pi\, \mathrm{erf}(\tfrac{1}{2} k^{-\frac{1}{2}} \xi)$
$x^{-1} \sinh \alpha x\, \mathrm{cosech}\, \beta x$	$(|\alpha| < \beta)$	$\tan^{-1}(\tan \tfrac{1}{2}\pi\beta^{-1}\alpha \tanh \tfrac{1}{2}\pi\beta^{-1}\xi)$

Answers to Exercises and Problems

Chapter 1

Exercises

§1.2

1.

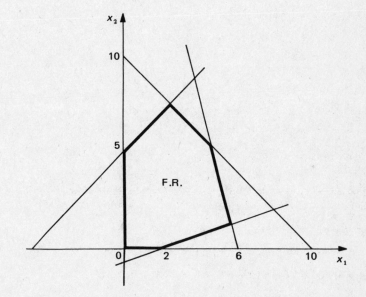

2. $7.5, 5\frac{9}{13}, 19\frac{1}{3}, 4\frac{6}{13}$.

3. 10, along the line $x_1 + x_2 = 10$ within the range $2\frac{1}{2} \leqslant x_1 \leqslant 4\frac{2}{3}$.

4. (a) ∞ (b) 6 .

5. 1.5

6. $x_A = 25$, $x_B = 5$; $x_A = 2.5$, $x_B = 12.5$.

7. Example 1: 4,350 at $x_A = 600$, $x_B = 150$, $x_C = 600$.

Example 3: $x_1 = 5\frac{5}{9}$, $x_2 = 1\frac{5}{9}$.

§1.3

1. $4(1, 1, 1, 1)^T - (1, 1, 1, 0)^T - (1, 1, 0, 0)^T - (1, 0, 0, 0)^T$

2. $(0, \frac{3}{4}, \frac{1}{4}, \frac{1}{4}), (\frac{9}{8}, 0, -\frac{1}{8}, \frac{1}{2}), (\frac{3}{4}, \frac{1}{4}, 0, \frac{1}{4}), (\frac{3}{8}, \frac{1}{2}, \frac{1}{8}, 0)$

§1.4

1. $(0, 0, 6, 4), (0, 3, 0, 1), (4, 0, 2, 0), (2, 2, 0, 0), 9$.

§1.5

1.   6,500 at $x_1 = 0$, $x_2 = 300$, $x_3 = 100$.

2. $19\frac{1}{3}$ at $x_1 = 4\frac{2}{3}$, $x_2 = 5\frac{1}{3}$.

3.   2.5 at $x_1 = 7.5$, $x_2 = 2.5$.

4.   See exercise 7 of §1.2.

§1.6

1.   O.F. $= 22\frac{1}{2} - 9\frac{1}{2}\delta$ for increasing values of δ.

Problems

1. $714\frac{2}{7}$ of model A, 0 of model B, $428\frac{4}{7}$ of model C. Spare capacity in the body division.

2.   Two equal optimal solutions

      $AM = 0$, $AN = 2000$, $BM = 4000$, $BN = 1000$ or

      $AM = 2000$, $AN = 0$, $BM = 2000$, $BN = 3000$

      Any solution of the type

      $AM = x_1$, $AN = 2000 - x_1$, $BM = 4000 - x_1$, $BN = 1000 + x_1$

      for $0 \leqslant x_1 \leqslant 2000$ is an optimum.

3. $x_A = 0.1$, $x_B = 0.5$, $x_C = 0.4$

4. $x_{11} = 0$, $x_{12} = 300$, $x_{13} = 0$, $x_{21} = 150$, $x_{22} = 50$, $x_{23} = 320$.

5. $x_A = 600$, $x_B = 150$, $x_C = 600$.

      When thermal requirements $= 2700 + \phi$ units then

      $x_A = 600$, $x_B = 150 + \frac{1}{2}\phi$, $x_C = 600$ for $\phi \leqslant 900$

      $x_A = 600$, $x_B = \phi - 300$, $x_C = 1500 - \phi$ for $900 \leqslant \phi \leqslant 1500$.

6. (a) When engine production capacity $= 9000 + \phi$ units then

$x_A = (5000 + \phi)/7$, $x_B = 0$, $x_C = (9000 - \phi)/21$ for $0 \leqslant \phi \leqslant 2000$.

For $\phi \geqslant 2000$, profit remains at $\frac{1}{3}10^5$.

(b) For $0 \leqslant \phi \leqslant 111\frac{1}{9}$, $x_A = \frac{1}{21}(15{,}000 - 2\phi)$, $x_B = 0$, $x_C = \frac{1}{7}(3000 + \phi)$

For $\phi \geqslant 111\frac{1}{9}$, profit $= \frac{1}{3}(10^5 - 40\phi)$. Next change at $\phi = 375$.

7. 40 cans of sausages, 120 cans of sausages and beans, 30 cans of beans. Shadow prices $0, 4, 0, -5, 0$.

8. $x_1 = 650$, $x_2 = 225$, $x_3 = 150$.

Shadow prices $1, 0, \frac{1}{2}, -2\frac{1}{2}$.

Range $-150 < \phi < 650$.

New optimum $x_1 = 400$, $x_2 = 200$, $x_3 = 200$.

9. Maximum profit $= £150$ per week; 14 of A on machine 1, 16 of A on machine 2, B and C not produced. After replacement, the optimum policy is 32 of A, 0 of B, 0 of C. Overall increase in profit is £8 per week.

Chapter 2

Exercises

§2.2

1. (a) 140 at $s = 5$, (b) 2.2874 at $s = 1$, (c) 1.1585 at $s = 1.29$

2. 11.12 at $s = 0.8$ 3. 0.4587 at $s = 0.53$ 4. $(0.47, 0.50)$

§2.3

1. $(4.167, 0.366)$ 2. 18.33 at $(3.33, 2.67)$

3. $(1.444, 1.083)$, $(1.443, 1.082)$

4. 7.11 at $(1.33, 1.33)$ 5. Put $x_1 = 4 - 2x_2 - y_1^2$

§2.4

1. (a) -0.9246 at $x_1 = 1.8320$, $x_2 = 0$, $x_3 = 0.7010$

(b) -2 at $x_1 = 1$, $x_2 = 0$, $x_3 = 1$

2. 76.33 at $(9, 0, 0)$.

3. Jan. sell 25 buy 0, Feb. sell 0 buy 100, Mar. sell 100 buy 50

4. $x_1 = 5.6$, $x_2 = 12.4$, $x_3 = 12$.

Problems

1. 0.6160 at $x = 0.4687$ 2. 1.9725 at $x = 0.14$

3. 4.3872 at $x = 0.4077$ 4. 3.0517 at $x = 0.6566$

5. 0.5 at $(0.5, 2.0)$ 6. 0 at $(0, 2, 4)$

7. 0.5083 at $(0.39, -1.11)$ 8. 0.9988 at $(0.619, -0.929)$

9. 4 at $(2, 2, 0)$ 10. $(1, 1, 0)$, 1.25 at $(0.5, 0.25, 0)$

11. 12.25 at $(2, 3.5, 1.75)$ 12. 0.0188 at $(0.9375, 1.9625)$

13. 6.6957 at $(0.5652, -0.7391)$ 14. $(0.44, -0.29)$

15. 4.9232 at $(3.3174, 1.6058)$ 16. -5.375 at $(1.5, 1.25)$

17. 27 at $(3, 0)$

18. d_5 d_4 d_3 d_2 d_1

         ↗ retain → replace → retain → overhaul

    retain ↘ overhaul → retain → retain → replace

19. (a)   46.94 at $(0, 0, 2.17)$

     (b)   40 at $(0, 0, 2)$, 25 at $(5, 0, 0)$

20. 1 of A, 1 of B, 1 of D. 2 of B, 1 of C

Chapter 3

Exercises

§3.1

2. $\text{s.e.}(p_1) = \left\{ \dfrac{p(1-p)}{n_1 + n_2} \right\}^{\frac{1}{2}} < \frac{1}{2} \left\{ p(1-p) \left(\dfrac{1}{n_1} + \dfrac{1}{n_2} \right) \right\}^{\frac{1}{2}} = \text{s.e.}(p_2).$

§3.2

2. $\beta = 0.295, 0.313, 0.821.$

§3.3

3. $\dfrac{(0.5 - x) - 0.5}{\{(0.5 \times 0.5)/n\}^{\frac{1}{2}}} = -1.96, \quad \dfrac{(0.5 - x) - 0.4}{\{(0.4 \times 0.6)/n\}^{\frac{1}{2}}} = 1.645 .$

§3.4

3. $t_{[\nu]\frac{1}{2}\alpha}^{*\prime} > t_{[\nu]\alpha}^{*} > z_{\alpha}^{*}.$

     $t_{[40]0.05}^{*} = 1.68, \quad t_{[\infty]0.02}^{*\prime} \equiv z_{0.02}^{*} = 2.05 .$

§3.5

3. $\chi^2_{[1]} = 1.80 = 1.34^2 = z^2$, as calculated in example 3 of §3.3.

§3.6

1. $F_{[\nu_1, \nu_2]\frac{1}{2}\alpha}^{*} > F_{[\nu_1, \nu_2]\alpha}^{*} > F_{[\nu_1, \nu_2 + 1]\alpha}^{*}$ (if $\alpha \leqslant 10\%$).

   (If ν_2 is not *very* small, $F_{[\nu_1, \nu_2]\alpha}^{*} > F_{[\nu_1 + 1, \nu_2]\alpha}^{*}$.)

2. $F_{[7, 15]0.05}^{*} = 2.71$, $F_{[15, 7]0.05}^{*} = 3.51$, $F_{[10, 10]\,0.025}^{*} = 3.72$.

3. $F_{[5, \infty]0.025}^{*} = 2.57$, $F_{[5, \infty]0.975}^{*} = 0.17$.

§3.7

4. $a_0 n + a_1 \Sigma x_{1i} + a_2 \Sigma x_{1i} x_{2i} = \Sigma y_i$

   $a_0 \Sigma x_{1i} + a_1 \Sigma x_{1i}^2 + a_2 \Sigma x_{1i}^2 x_{2i} = \Sigma x_{1i} y_i$

   $a_0 \Sigma x_{1i} x_{2i} + a_1 \Sigma x_{1i}^2 x_{2i} + a_2 \Sigma x_{1i}^2 x_{2i}^2 = \Sigma x_{1i} x_{2i} y_i$ $\Sigma \equiv \sum\limits_{i=1}^{n}$

5. $|t| = 6.78 > 2.31 = t_{[8]0.05}$. The values are positively correlated.

§3.8

1.   (a) $n = 5$,

   (b) $n = 6$,

n	5	6	7	8	9
(a)	0	0	0	0, 1	0, 1
(b)	–	0, 6	0, 7	0, 8	0, 1, 8, 9

   $(r - s)/\sqrt{n} \simeq N(0, 1)$.

Problems

   Wherever applicable α has been given the value 0.05.

2.   Sample size is not to be less than about 1218.

3. $|z| = 2.06$; breakage rate is significantly greater than 4%.

4. $|z| = 0.45$; evidence is not significant. (Alternatively evaluate $\chi^2_{[1]} = 0.20$.)

5. $|z| = 2.38$; evidence signifies a decrease;
   95% confidence interval for the new mileage is (9945, 10355).

6. $|z| = 2.07$; second valley is significantly wetter.

7. $t_{[7]} = 1.84 < 1.89 = t_{[7]0.05}^{*}$; result is not significant.

8.   Variance ratio $= 2.07 < 4.03 = F_{[9, 9]0.025}$. Pooling gives $s = 0.247$;
   $|t_{[18]}| = 1.98 < 2.10 = t_{[18]0.05}$; difference is not significant.

9. (a) Paired t test: $|t| = 1.32 < 2.36 = t_{[7]0.05}$.

   (b) Sign test with $p = \frac{1}{2}$: Probability of 6, 7 or 8 all of one sign is $37/2^7 > 0.05$.

10. $\hat{\lambda} = \bar{x} = 1.7$. $\chi^2_{[3]} = 0.67 < 7.81 = \chi^{2*}_{[3]0.05}$. Poissonian hypothesis is acceptable.

11. $\chi^2_{[1]} = 0.55 < 3.84 = \chi^{2*}_{[1]0.05}$; there is no significant difference. (Alternatively $|z| = 0.74$.)

12. $\chi^2_{[2]} = 6.06 > 5.99 = \chi^{2*}_{[2]0.05}$. The main difference is the proportion of neutrals.

13. $F_{[5,\infty]} = 1.20 < 2.21 = F_{[5,\infty]0.05}^{*}$; change is not significant.

14. $E_1 = 49.95 \times 10^{10}$ N/m^2, $E_2 = 10.05 \times 10^{10}$ N/m^2 .

15. (a) $y + 0.0096x = 63.2$;   (b) $y + 0.0121x = 67.2$.
    (1) 3490 mm;   (2) 57.5%.

16. Linear: $y = 20.3 - 0.0947x$. When $x = 125$ km/hr, $y = 8.5$ km/l.
    Quadratic: $y = 15.8 + 0.0272x - 0.000762x^2$. When $x = 125$, $y = 7.3$.

Chapter 4

Exercises

§4.2

1. (a) $(a_1^2 - b_1^2 + 3a_2 + 1) + i(2a_1b_1 + 3b_2)$

   (b) $2(a_1a_2 + b_1b_2) + 0i$

   (c) $\{(a_1 + a_2)^3 - 3(a_1 + a_2)(b_1 - b_2)^2\} + i\{3(a_1 + a_2)^2(b_1 - b_2) - (b_1 - b_2)^3\}$

   (d) $\left(\dfrac{a_1a_2 - 1 + a_2 - a_1 + b_1b_2}{a_2^2 - 2a_2 + 1 + b_2^2}\right) + i\left(\dfrac{-a_1b_2 + b_2 + b_1a_2 - b_1}{a_2^2 - 2a_2 + 1 + b_2^2}\right)$.

2. $\omega = \pm\left(\dfrac{L - CR_1^2}{L^2C - LR_2^2C^2}\right)^{1/2}$.

3. (a) $2\exp\{i\pi(2k + \frac{1}{3})\}$ all integer k

   (b) $2\exp\{i\pi(2k + \frac{5}{3})\}$ all integer k

   (c) $\sqrt{2}\exp\{i(\theta + 2k\pi)\}$ all integer k, where $\sin\theta = \dfrac{-7}{\sqrt{50}}$, $\cos\theta = \dfrac{-1}{\sqrt{50}}$

   (d) $4\exp\{i\pi(2k + 1)\}$ all integer k

   (e) $9^{1/3}\exp\{i(\frac{4}{3}\theta + 2k\pi)\}$ for $k = 0, 1, 2$, where $\sin\theta = \sqrt{\frac{1}{3}}$, $\cos\theta = \sqrt{\frac{2}{3}}$.

5. (a) Upper arc of the circle radius $\sqrt{10}$ passing through $z = 3$ and $z = i$.

   (b) ellipse with foci at $z = \pm 2i$; equation $x^2/a^2 + y^2/b^2 = 1$, where $a = 3/2$, $b = 5/2$.

(c) The portion $x < 0$ of the hyperbola $x^2/a^2 - y^2/b^2 = 1$, where $a = 3/2$, $b = \sqrt{7}/2$.

6. (a) annulus composed of region between the circles with centre at $z = -2$ and radii 1 and 2.

(b) annulus composed of the interior of the circle with centre $z = i$ and radius 1 except the point $z = i$.

(c) Interior of an ellipse with foci at $z = \pm 2$.

(d) the regions $x > (2 + y^2)^{\frac{1}{2}}$ and $x < -(2 + y^2)^{\frac{1}{2}}$.

§4.3

1. (a) $e^{-3y}(\cos 3x + i \sin 3x)$

(b) $(x \cos x \cosh y + y \sin x \sinh y) + i(y \cos x \cosh y - x \sin x \sinh y)$

(c) $\sin 2x \cosh 2y + i \cos 2x \sinh 2y$

(d) $e^{2x}[\{(x^2 - y^2)\cos 2y - 2xy \sin 2y\} + i\{(x^2 - y^2)\sin 2y + 2xy \cos 2y\}]$

(e) $\sinh 2x \cos 2y + i \cosh 2x \sin 2y$.

4. The rectangular hyperbolae $x^2 - y^2 = u_0$ and $xy = \frac{1}{2}v_0$.

7. $\exp(-\frac{3}{2}\pi - 2k\pi)$ for $k = 0, \pm 1, \pm 2, \ldots$

8. (a) $z = \pm 3$ (b) $z = \pm 2$.

§4.4

1. (a) $-3 + 6i$ (b) 1   (c) $\frac{1}{3}$.

2. (a) $z = (25)^{\frac{1}{5}} \exp\{\frac{1}{5}i\pi(1 + 2k)\}$ for $k = 0, 1, 2, 3, 4$.

(b) $z = 0$ and $z = (2n + 1)\pi/2$ for $n = 0, \pm 1, \pm 2, \ldots$

(c) $z = \pm\sqrt{2}i$ and $z = i(2n + 1)\pi/2$ for $n = 0, \pm 1, \pm 2, \ldots$

4. $v(x, y) = e^x(x \sin y + y \cos y) + \text{const.}$

$f(z) = ze^z + iK$ where K is a real constant.

5. (a) $z = \pm i, z = \pm 1$

(b) branch point at $z = -2i$, double pole at $z = 0$.

(c) branch points at $z = 0$ and $z = \pm(-a)^{\frac{1}{2}}$.

(d) branch point at $z = 0$, simple pole at $z = -1$.

(e) simple poles at $z = i(2n + 1)\pi/2$ for $n = 0, \pm 1, \pm 2, \ldots$

(f)   triple pole at $z = 0$, simple poles at $z = n\pi$ for $n = \pm1, \pm2, \ldots$ and simple poles at $z = in\pi$ for $n = \pm1, \pm2, \ldots$.

(g)   removable singularity at $z = 0$.

6. $-6 + 7i$

§4.5

1.   (a) $\tan z = z + \frac{1}{3}z^3 + \ldots$, convergent in $|z| < \frac{1}{2}\pi$

$\sec z = 1 + \frac{1}{2}z^2 + \ldots$, convergent in $|z| < \frac{1}{2}\pi$

(b) $\tan z = \sqrt{3} + 4(z - \frac{1}{3}\pi) + \ldots$, convergent in $|z - \frac{1}{3}\pi| < \frac{1}{6}\pi$.

$\sec z = 2 + 2\sqrt{3}(z - \frac{1}{3}\pi) + \ldots$, convergent in $|z - \frac{1}{3}\pi| < \frac{1}{6}\pi$.

2.   (a) $e^{-6}\{(z + 2)^{-2} + 3(z + 2)^{-1} + 9/2! + \ldots\}$, convergent in $0 < |z + 2| < \infty$, double pole, residue $3e^{-6}$.

(b) $1/3! - z^2/5! + \ldots$, convergent in $|z| < \infty$. Removable singularity, no residue.

(c) $(z - 1) + 2 + \frac{3}{2}(z - 1)^{-1} + \frac{2}{3}(z - 1)^{-2} + \frac{5}{24}(z - 1)^{-3} + \ldots$, convergent in $0 < |z - 1| < \infty$, essential singularity, residue $\frac{3}{2}$.

(d)   (i) $\frac{2}{27}(z^{-1} + \frac{1}{2} + \frac{1}{6}z + \ldots)$, convergent in $0 < |z| < 2$, simple pole, residue $\frac{2}{27}$.

(ii) $\frac{1}{3}\{(z - 3)^{-3} + \frac{2}{3}(z - 3)^{-2} - \frac{2}{3}(z - 3)^{-1} + \frac{2}{27} - \frac{2}{81}(z - 3) + \ldots\}$
convergent in $0 < |z - 3| < 1$, triple pole, residue $-\frac{2}{27}$.

3.   (a) $-6\pi i/25$

(b) 0

(c) $3\pi i$

(d) $2\pi i (1 - 2 \cosh \pi + 2 \cosh 2\pi)$

4.   (a) $\pi 5^{-\frac{1}{2}}(3 - 5^{\frac{1}{2}})$

(b) $\frac{1}{4}\pi$

(c) $\frac{1}{2}\pi e^{-3}$

(d) $\frac{1}{2}\pi$

Problems

2. $z_k = \exp\{\frac{1}{7}i\pi(1 + 2k)\}$ for $k = 0, 1, 2, 3, 4, 5, 6$.
$w_k = -i \cot\{\frac{1}{7}\pi(\frac{1}{2} + k)\}$ for $k = 0, 1, 2, 3, 4, 5, 6$.
roots are $x_k = -i \cot\{\frac{1}{7}\pi(\frac{1}{2} + k)\}$ for $k = 0, 1, 2, 4, 5, 6$.
(n.b. when $k = 3, x_3 = 0$ which is *not* a solution.)

3. $e^{ix}(1 - ix) + \text{const.}$

4. $e^{ax}(a^2 + b^2)^{-1}\{(a - ib)(\cos bx + i \sin bx)\} + \text{const.}$
    $e^{ax}(a^2 + b^2)^{-1}(a \cos bx + b \sin bx) + \text{const.}$
    $e^{ax}(a^2 + b^2)^{-1}(a \sin bx - b \cos bx) + \text{const.}$

5. $\exp(2ki\pi/n)$ for $k = 0, 1, \ldots, n - 1$.

6. $z = 1 \pm i$ and $z = -1 \pm \sqrt{3}$.

7. $z = m\pi$ for $m = 0, \pm 1, \pm 2, \ldots$.

8. The region $P'O'Q'S'$ in Fig. 4.9 reflected in the u axis.

10. The rectangle $\text{Log } \alpha \leqslant u \leqslant \text{Log } \beta$ and $0 \leqslant \theta < 2\pi$ in the w plane.

13. $v(r, \theta) = \theta + \text{const}, f(z) = \log z + \text{const}.$

14. $z = 0$ is a critical point.

15. $6\pi i e^{-6}$

18. (i) $2\pi(1 - a^2)^{-1}$ (ii) $2\pi(a^2 - 1)^{-1}$

19. (a) $v(x, y) = -\cosh x \cos y + K, f(z) = -i \cosh z + iK$ where K is a real constant.

    (b) $z = \pm i$ are triple poles
    $$2^{-3}e^{-m}\{i(z - i)^{-3} - (m + \tfrac{3}{2})(z - i)^{-2} - i(\tfrac{1}{2}m^2 + \tfrac{3}{2}m + \tfrac{3}{2})(z - i) + \ldots\},$$
    convergent in $0 < |z - i| < 2$; $\pi e^{-m}2^{-4}(m^2 + 3m + 3)$

21. $-1 + i$. The function is not analytic within and on C.

22. (a)   The interior of the rectangle with vertices at $\pm i, -2 \pm i$.

    (b)   The region between $v = 0$ and the parabolae
    $$v^2 = 4(u + 1), v^2 = 4(1 - u) \text{ and } v^2 = 16(4 - u).$$

23. $G(z) = -i\pi^{-1}\text{Log}\{(1 + iz)(i + z)^{-1}\}.$

24. (a) $v(x, y) = -e^{-2xy} \cos(x^2 - y^2) + K$
    $f(z) = -i \exp(iz^2) + iK$, where K is a real constant

    (b) $x = \cosh u \cos v, y = \sinh u \sin v$, critical point at $z = (1, 0)$.

25. (a) $W(z) = Vze^{-i\alpha}, \Phi(x, y) = Vx \cos \alpha + Vy \sin \alpha, \Psi(x, y) = -Vx \sin \alpha + Vy \cos \alpha$
    stream lines $-Vx \sin \alpha + Vy \cos \alpha = \psi$
    equipotential lines $Vx \cos \alpha + Vy \sin \alpha = \phi$

    (b) $W(z) = V\left(z + \dfrac{1}{z}\right)$

26. (a) $A = \pi^{-1}(t_1 - t_0), B = \pi^{-1}(t_2 - t_1), C = \tfrac{1}{2}(t_0 + t_2)$

    (b) $\Theta(x, y) = \dfrac{\lambda}{\pi}\left\{-\tan^{-1}\left(\dfrac{\cosh \tfrac{1}{2}\pi x \sin \tfrac{1}{2}\pi y + 1}{\sinh \tfrac{1}{2}\pi x \cos \tfrac{1}{2}\pi y}\right)\right.$

    $\left. + 2 \tan^{-1}\left(\dfrac{\cosh \tfrac{1}{2}\pi x \sin \tfrac{1}{2}\pi y - 1}{\sinh \tfrac{1}{2}\pi x \cos \tfrac{1}{2}\pi y}\right) + \dfrac{3\pi}{2}\right\}$

Chapter 5

Exercises

§5.2

2.   (a) $\pi^{1/2}s^{-1/2}$,   (b) $\frac{3}{4}\pi^{1/2}s^{-5/2}$

3. $\{\Gamma(\alpha)\}^{-1}\displaystyle\int_0^t \tau^{\alpha-1}f(t-\tau)\,d\tau$

4. $(s^2-1)^{-1/2}$

5. $s^{-1}(s+1)^{-1/2}$

§5.3

1.   (a) $\frac{3}{4}e^{2t}-\frac{1}{4}e^{-2t}+\frac{1}{2}\cos 2t - \sin 2t$,   (b) $\frac{1}{2}\omega^{-1}\sin\omega t$

3. $\frac{1}{2}\pi^{-1/2}t^{-3/2}(e^{bt}-e^{at})$

§5.4

2. $f(t)\sim\pi^{-1/2}\displaystyle\sum_{n=0}^{\infty}\frac{(-1)^n(a/t)^{n+1/2}}{2^{2n}(2n+1)n!}$

4. $f(t)\to\frac{1}{2}a$ as $t\to 0$,

$$f(t)\sim\frac{e^{at}}{(2\pi at^3)^{1/2}}\left\{1-\frac{3}{8at}-\frac{15}{2(8at)^2}+\ldots\right\}\text{ as } t\to\infty$$

§5.5

2. $\pi a^{-1}e^{-a|\xi|}$

3. $-\frac{1}{2}i\pi^{1/2}\xi\exp(-\frac{1}{4}\xi^2)$

4. $\frac{1}{2}\pi^{1/2}\exp(-\frac{1}{4}\xi^2)$, $\frac{1}{4}\pi^{1/2}\xi\exp(-\frac{1}{4}\xi^2)$

5. $F(\omega)=2(1-\omega^2)^{-1}\cos\frac{1}{2}\pi\omega$, $c_n=\pi^{-1}(1-n^2)^{-1}\cos\frac{1}{2}\pi n$

§5.6

2. $\dfrac{T}{\pi}\left\{\tan^{-1}\dfrac{x+a}{y}+\tan^{-1}\dfrac{x-a}{y}-\tan^{-1}\dfrac{x+b}{y}-\tan^{-1}\dfrac{x-b}{y}\right\}$

3. $\Theta(\xi, y) = \Theta_0(\xi) \operatorname{cosech} \xi h \sinh \xi(h - y),$

$$\phi = h^{-1} \sum_{n=1}^{\infty} (-1)^{n+1} e^{-n\pi|x|/h} \sin n\pi(1 - y/h),$$

$$\theta = h \sum_{n=1}^{\infty} (-1)^{n+1} (n^2 \pi^2 + h^2)^{-1} \sin n\pi(1 - y/h) f(n, x)$$

where

$$f(n, x) = \begin{cases} 2 \exp(-\tfrac{1}{2} n\pi^2 h^{-1}) \cosh n\pi h^{-1} x, & |x| < \tfrac{1}{2}\pi, \\ \exp\{n\pi h^{-1}(\tfrac{1}{2}\pi - |x|)\}, & |x| > \tfrac{1}{2}\pi \end{cases}$$

4. $\bar{\theta}(x, s) = Ts^{-1} \operatorname{sech} \kappa^{-\frac{1}{2}} s^{\frac{1}{2}} \cosh \kappa^{-\frac{1}{2}} s^{\frac{1}{2}} (1 - x),$

$$\theta = T \left[1 - 2\pi^{-1} \sum_{n=1}^{\infty} (n + \tfrac{1}{2})^{-1} \sin(n + \tfrac{1}{2})\pi x \exp\{-(n + \tfrac{1}{2})^2 \pi^2 \kappa t\} \right]$$

5. $\sigma_x = \dfrac{P}{\pi} \left\{ \tan^{-1} \dfrac{x + a}{y} - \tan^{-1} \dfrac{x - a}{y} - \dfrac{(x + a)y}{(x + a)^2 + y^2} + \dfrac{(x - a)y}{(x - a)^2 + y^2} \right\},$

$\sigma_y = \dfrac{P}{\pi} \left\{ \tan^{-1} \dfrac{x + a}{y} - \tan^{-1} \dfrac{x - a}{y} + \dfrac{(x + a)y}{(x + a)^2 + y^2} - \dfrac{(x - a)y}{(x - a)^2 + y^2} \right\},$

$\tau_{xy} = P\pi^{-1} y^2 [\{(x + a)^2 + y^2\}^{-1} - \{(x - a)^2 + y^2\}^{-1}]$

Problems

1. (a) $a^{-\frac{1}{2}} e^{at} \operatorname{erf}(at)^{\frac{1}{2}},$

    (b) $\tfrac{1}{3} a^{-2} \{e^{-at} - e^{\frac{1}{2}at}(\cos \tfrac{1}{2}\sqrt{3}at - \sqrt{3} \sin \tfrac{1}{2}\sqrt{3}at)\}$

2. (a) $a + 2b\pi^{-2} \sum_{n=1}^{\infty} (-1)^n (n - \tfrac{1}{2})^{-\frac{1}{2}} \sin(n - \tfrac{1}{2})\pi ab^{-1} \cos(n - \tfrac{1}{2})\pi b^{-1} t,$

    (b) $\sum_{n=0}^{\infty} (-1)^n [\{t - (2n + 1)b + a\} H\{t - (2n + 1)b + a\}$
    $\qquad\qquad\qquad\qquad - \{t - (2n + 1)b - a\} H\{t - (2n + 1)b - a\}]$

3. $f(t) \sim \dfrac{1}{\pi^{\frac{1}{2}} a^{\frac{1}{2}} t^{\frac{3}{2}}} \left\{ 1 - \dfrac{3}{4at} - \dfrac{15}{32a^2 t^2} + \dots \right\}, \quad t \to \infty,$

    $f(t) \sim \tfrac{1}{4} a, \quad t \to 0$

4. $\tfrac{1}{4}(t + 2\pi)\{H(t + 2\pi) - H(t)\} - \tfrac{1}{4}(t - 2\pi)\{H(t) - H(t - 2\pi)\};$

    (a) $\tfrac{1}{4}(t - 4n\pi + 2\pi)\{H(t - 4n\pi + 2\pi) - H(t - 4n\pi)\}$
    $\qquad - \tfrac{1}{4}(t - 4n\pi - 2\pi)\{H(t - 4n\pi) - H(t - 4n\pi - 2\pi)\}, \quad -2\pi \leqslant t - 4n\pi \leqslant 2\pi,$

(b) $\frac{1}{6}(t - 6n\pi + 2\pi)\{H(t - 6n\pi + 2\pi) - H(t - 6n\pi)\}$

   $\quad - \frac{1}{6}(t - 6n\pi - 2\pi)\{H(t - 6n\pi) - H(t - 6n\pi - 2\pi)\}, \quad -3\pi \leqslant t - 6n\pi \leqslant 3\pi$

5. $s^{-1} \operatorname{cosech} d(\alpha^2 + s)^{1/2} \{T_0 \sinh(d - x)(\alpha^2 + s)^{1/2} + T_1 \sinh x(\alpha^2 + s)^{1/2}\};$

   $T_0 f(d - x, t) + T_1 f(x, t), \quad$ where

   $$f(x, t) = \frac{\sinh \alpha x}{\sinh \alpha d} + 2\pi \sum_{n=0}^{\infty} \frac{(-1)^n n \sin n\pi d^{-1} x \exp\{-(\alpha^2 + n^2 \pi^2 d^{-2})t\}}{n^2 \pi^2 + \alpha^2 d^2}$$

6. $\dfrac{bp_1 \sinh(r - a)c^{-1}s}{r(s + \lambda) \sinh(b - a)c^{-1}s},$

   $$\frac{bp_1}{r} \sum_{n=0}^{\infty} \left[\exp\left\{-\lambda\left(t - \frac{2n(b - a) + b - r}{c}\right)\right\} H\left(t - \frac{2n(b - a) + b - r}{c}\right)\right.$$

   $$\left. - \exp\left\{-\lambda\left(t - \frac{(2n + 1)(b - a) + r - a}{c}\right)\right\} H\left(t - \frac{(2n + 1)(b - a) + r - a}{c}\right)\right]$$

7. $\Theta(\xi, y) = T_0 \operatorname{sech} \xi h \cosh \xi(h - y),$

   $$\theta(x, y) = \frac{T_0 \cosh \frac{1}{2}\pi h^{-1} x \sin \frac{1}{2}\pi h^{-1} y}{h(\cosh \pi h^{-1} x - \cos \pi h^{-1} y)}$$

8. $2\lambda\pi^{-1}[2 \tan^{-1}\{\tanh \frac{1}{4}\pi x \tan \frac{1}{4}\pi(1 + y)\} + \tan^{-1}\{\tanh \frac{1}{4}\pi x \tan \frac{1}{4}\pi(1 - y)\}]$

   (Note that this expression differs from that given as the answer to problem 26(b) of Chapter 4, although the two problems are identical. However, it can be shown that the two expressions are equal.)

Chapter 6

Exercises

§6.2

1. $W(x) = -\frac{1}{2}(3x^2 + 4x + \frac{4}{3})(1 + x)^{-1/2}$

2. (a) $-\frac{9}{4}(x^2 - \frac{4}{3})$,   (b) $-3(x^2 - \frac{4}{3})$,   (c) $\dfrac{\sqrt{3}}{4}(x^2 - \frac{4}{3})$

4. (a) $-\dfrac{3(1 + 3\sqrt{3})}{2(6\sqrt{3} + 1)}(x^2 - \frac{4}{3}) + \dfrac{6\sqrt{3}}{(6\sqrt{3} + 1)}(1 + x)^{1/2},$

   (b) $-\frac{5}{2}(x^2 - \frac{4}{3})$,   (c) 0,   (d) $c_1(x^2 - \frac{4}{3})$

§6.3

1. $c_1 x + c_2(1 - x^2) + 2x \tan^{-1} x - x^2 - \frac{1}{2}(1 - x^2) \log(1 + x^2)$

2. (a) $c_1 = 0, c_2 = 0$,   (b) $c_1 = \dfrac{\pi}{2} - 1, c_2 = \frac{1}{2}(5 + \log 2)$,

   (c) $c_1 = 1 - \dfrac{\pi}{2}, c_2 = 2$,   (d)   no solution possible

3. $c_1 x + c_2(1 + x^2)^{\frac{1}{2}} + x \log\{x + (1 + x^2)^{\frac{1}{2}}\} - \frac{1}{2}(1 + x^2)^{\frac{1}{2}} \log(1 + x^2)$

§6.4

1. $1 + x - \dfrac{x^3}{3!} - \dfrac{2x^4}{4!} + \dfrac{4x^6}{6!} + \dfrac{10x^7}{7!} - \ldots + (-1)^k 1 \times 4 \times 7 \times \ldots \times (3k - 2)\dfrac{x^{3k}}{(3k)!} +$

   $+ (-1)^k 2 \times 5 \times 8 \times \ldots \times (3k - 1)\dfrac{x^{3k+1}}{(3k+1)!} + \ldots$

2. $a_0 \left\{ 1 + \displaystyle\sum_{k=1}^{\infty} (-1)^k (3k - 2)(3k - 5) \ldots 4 \times 1 \dfrac{x^{3k}}{(3k)!} \right\} +$

   $+ a_1 \displaystyle\sum_{k=0}^{\infty} (-1)^k (3k - 1)(3k - 4) \ldots 5 \times 2 \dfrac{x^{3k+1}}{(3k+1)!}$

   Both series convergent for all finite x

3. $2(r + 2)(r + 1)a_{r+2} + (r + 1)ra_{r+1} - (r - 4)a_r = 0, \quad r \geqslant 1$

   $1 - x^2 + \dfrac{x^3}{6} + \dfrac{x^4}{24} - \dfrac{x^5}{60} + \ldots, \quad x - \dfrac{x^3}{4} + \dfrac{x^4}{16} - \dfrac{x^5}{80} + \dfrac{x^6}{240} + \ldots$

4. $1 + \dfrac{x^4}{6} - \dfrac{13x^6}{180} + \ldots, \quad a_{n+2} = -\dfrac{\{(3n + 1)a_n - a_{n-2}\}}{(n + 2)(n + 1)}$.

§6.5

1. (a)   No,   (b)   yes,   (c)   yes

2. (a) $2p^2 - 5p - 1 = 0$,

   $\{2(r + p)^2 - 5(r + p) - 1\}a_r + \{(r + p)^2 - 3(r + p) + 3\}a_{r-1} = 0$,

   (b) $p(3p - 2) = 0, \quad (p + r)(2p + 2r - 5)a_r + a_{r-1} = 0$

3. $a_0 \left\{ 1 + \dfrac{x}{3} + \dfrac{x^2}{6} - \dfrac{x^3}{18} + \ldots + \dfrac{(-1)^r}{3} \dfrac{x^r}{r!} \dfrac{1}{(2r - 5)(2r - 8) \ldots 3 \times 1} + \ldots \right\}$

   $+ a_1 x^{5/2} \left\{ 1 - \dfrac{x}{7} + \dfrac{x^2}{126} - \ldots + (-1)^r \dfrac{x^r}{r!} \dfrac{1}{(2r + 5)(2r + 3) \ldots 9 \times 7} + \ldots \right\}$

§6.6

1. $u = y - 1 - 3x, \quad u'' + 2u' + 5u = -15x - 11$

3. $\lambda_n = n^2 \pi^2, \quad \varphi_n(x) = \sin n\pi x, \quad n = 1, 2, \ldots$

§6.7

1. $e^{-2t} + \epsilon \left[-\dfrac{e^{2t}}{68} + e^{-2t} \left\{ \dfrac{4}{17} \cos t - \dfrac{1}{17} \sin t - \dfrac{1}{4} \right\} \right]$

2. $\sin t + \dfrac{\epsilon}{32} \{ (1 + 12t) \cos t - 12 \sin t - \cos 3t \}$

3. $\pi^2 + 2\epsilon\pi \left(1 - \dfrac{\pi}{8} \right)$

§6.8

1. Unique for all (x_0, y_0)

2. $y = 0, \quad 4\sqrt{y} = x^2 + C$

3. $\dfrac{dx}{dt} = y, \quad \dfrac{dy}{dt} = -x(1 - \epsilon x^2), \quad y^2 + x^2 \left(1 - \dfrac{\epsilon x^2}{2} \right) = K$

4. $(0, 0)$: Stable node for $p^2 \leqslant \tfrac{1}{4}k^2$, stable focus for $p^2 > \tfrac{1}{4}k^2$
   $(1, 0)$: Saddle point

Problems

1. $-8(3x + 2) + \dfrac{21}{(1 - x)}$

2. $-8(3x + 2) + \dfrac{21}{(1 - x)} + x(3x + 2) + \dfrac{x(2x^2 - x - 4)}{2(1 - x)}$

3. $c_1 (x^2 + 2) + c_2 \sqrt{x} + \dfrac{9x^4}{7} - 2x^2$

4. $u = (x - 1)(x + 1)^{1/2}$

5. $1 + \displaystyle\sum_{k=1}^{\infty} (-1)^k \dfrac{\{(2k - 2)^2 - 3\}\{(2k - 4)^2 - 3\} \ldots \{-3\}x^{2k}}{(2k)!}$,

   $x \left[1 + \displaystyle\sum_{k=1}^{\infty} (-1)^k \dfrac{\{(2k - 1)^2 - 3\}\{(2k - 3)^2 - 3\} \ldots \{(1)^2 - 3\}x^{2k}}{(2k + 1)!} \right]$

6. $1 + \sum_{k=1}^{\infty} \{(2k-2)(2k-1) - \alpha(\alpha+1)\}\{(2k-4)(2k-3) - \alpha(\alpha+1)\} \dots$

    $$\dots \{-\alpha(\alpha+1)\} \frac{x^{2k}}{(2k)!},$$

    $$x \left[1 + \sum_{k=1}^{\infty} \{(2k-1)2k - \alpha(\alpha+1)\}\{(2k-3)(2k-2) - \alpha(\alpha+1)\} \dots \right.$$

    $$\left. \dots \{2 - \alpha(\alpha+1)\} \frac{x^{2k}}{(2k+1)!} \right]$$

8. $1 + x + x^2 + x^3 + \dots + x^n + \dots = (1-x)^{-1}$

9. $a_0 \left(1 + \frac{x^2}{2}\right) + a_1 x^{\frac{1}{2}}$

10. $a_0 x \left\{1 + \sum_{r=1}^{\infty} \frac{(-2x)^r}{r!(3r+2)(3r-1)\dots 5}\right\} + a_1 x^{\frac{1}{3}} \left\{1 + \sum_{r=1}^{\infty} \frac{(-2x)^r}{r!(3r-2)(3r-5)\dots 1}\right\}$

11. Singular point at $x = 0$ is not regular.

12. $x^{\frac{1}{2}} J_\alpha(x), \ x^{\frac{1}{2}} J_{-\alpha}(x)$.

13. $1 + \sum_{k=1}^{\infty} \frac{(-1)^k \left(\frac{x}{2}\right)^{2k}}{(k!)^2}$

16. $2p = -\frac{Kn^2\pi^2}{L^2} \pm \left(\frac{K^2 n^4 \pi^4}{L^4} - \frac{4n^2 \pi^2 c^2}{L^2}\right)^{\frac{1}{2}}$

17. $x - \frac{\epsilon x^3}{3!} + \frac{\epsilon^2 x^5}{5!} - \dots + (-1)^r \frac{\epsilon^r x^{2r+1}}{(2r+1)!} + \dots = \frac{1}{\sqrt{\epsilon}} \sin x \sqrt{\epsilon}$

18. $\cos 2x + \frac{\epsilon}{12}(2\sin 2x - \sin 4x) - \epsilon^2 \left(\frac{23}{1152}\cos 2x + \frac{x \sin 2x}{48} - \frac{\cos 4x}{36} + \frac{\cos 6x}{128}\right)$

20. $\pi^2 \{1 + \frac{3}{4}\epsilon B_0^2\}$ where $y_0 = B_0 \sin \pi x$

21. (a) $y = \frac{2}{3}x - \frac{2}{9} + Ce^{-3x}$, (b) $y = 1 + cx$

22. $y = \frac{3}{2}x, \quad y = -x$

23. $y = \sin(x + c)$

25. $R^2 C_0 < 4L$ stable focus, $\quad R^2 C_0 \geqslant 4L$ stable node

26. $(0,0): k \geqslant 2$ stable node, $0 < k < 2$ stable focus, $k = 0$ centre,
    $\qquad -2 < k < 0$ unstable focus, $k \leqslant -2$ unstable node
    $\left(\frac{1}{\sqrt{\mu}}, 0\right)$: saddle point, unstable, $\quad \left(-\frac{1}{\sqrt{\mu}}, 0\right)$: saddle point, unstable

27. $(0,0)$: stable focus, $\quad (1,0)$: saddle point, $\quad (-1,0)$: saddle point

Chapter 7

Exercises

§7.2

1.   0.4054, 0.8441

2.   0.5321, 0.6382

§7.3

1.   1.415506, 1.415522

2.   1.111, 1.253

3.   1.041

§7.4

1.   1.2925, 1.4654, 1.6585

2.   2.014, 2.282

3.   1.1379, 1.2925, 1.4655, 1.6586

§7.5

1.   0.2769, 0.5429, 0.7871

2.   0.009, 0.259, 0.546, 0.864

§7.6

1.   Exact solution $u = \dfrac{8}{\pi} \displaystyle\sum_{n=1}^{\infty} \dfrac{e^{-n^2\pi^2 t} \sin n\pi x}{(2n+1)[(2n+1)^2 - 4]}$ which gives

t	$x =$ 0.1	0.2	0.3	0.4	0.5
0	0.0955	0.3455	0.6545	0.9045	1.0000
0.001	0.1110	0.3515	0.6485	0.8888	0.9806
0.01	0.1790	0.3857	0.6026	0.7724	0.8369
0.05	0.1585	0.3027	0.4186	0.4940	0.5202
0.1	0.0977	0.1859	0.2559	0.3009	0.3164

2.   Using a finite difference mesh similar to Fig. 7.2 the values are

on $y = 0.75$	1.4331	1.4675	1.5780	1.7904	2.1678
on $y = 0.50$	1.7974	1.8590	2.0541	2.4159	3.0064
on $y = 0.25$	2.0385	2.1170	2.3636	2.8120	3.5227
on $y = 0$	2.1227	2.2068	2.4706	2.9484	3.6978

Problems

1. 1.224, 1.515, 1.906, 2.437, 3.155

2. $(1.0204, 0.0200), (1.0866, 0.0802), (1.2145, 0.1820)$

3. 0.80, 1.20, 1.39

4. $\left(1 - \dfrac{1}{2i}\right)u_{i-1,j} + \left(1 + \dfrac{1}{2i}\right)u_{i+1,j} - 2\left(1 + \dfrac{1}{(i\delta\theta)^2}\right)u_{i,j}$

$$+ \dfrac{1}{(i\delta\theta)^2}u_{i,j-1} + \dfrac{1}{(i\delta\theta)^2}u_{i,j+1} = 0$$

5. 0.387, 0.713, 1.028, 1.338, 1.646, 1.952, 2.257, 2.561, 2.865

6. Analytic solution is $y = \sin x$

7. 1.1985, 1.3872, 1.5535

8. For $\epsilon = 0.2$ and $x = 0.2(0.2)1$, $y = 0.9221, 0.7038, 0.3818, 0.0046, -0.3732$
   For $\epsilon = 2$ and $x = 0.2(0.2)1$, $y = 0.9304, 0.7585, 0.5270, 0.2633, -0.0141$

9. For $x = 0(0.1)0.5$, $u(x, 0.1) = 0.8462, 0.8322, 0.8210, 0.8129, 0.8079, 0.8063$

Chapter 8

Exercises

§8.2

1. (a) $\bar{u} = 2x$, (b) $\bar{u} = 2\dfrac{\sinh x}{\sinh 1}$, (c) $\bar{u} = (x^5 + 79x)/40$

2. $p(x^2 + y^2) + 2x - 2y(p + 1) = 0$

3. $\bar{u} = A^{-1}\cosh Ax$ where $2A = \cosh A$. Two roots $A = 0.589, A = 2.127$, first root gives least area.

4. $x = -1, y = 0$.

§8.3

1. $C_1 = 0, C_2 = -45/2\pi^3, I = 2.5882$

2. $C_1 = -(9 + 2\pi)/3\pi^2, C_2 = 1/15\pi, I = 2.4566, \bar{I} = 2.4540$

3. $-5/4(a^2 + b^2)$

4. $C_2 = 0 \quad \lambda = 1 + \pi^2, \qquad C_1 = 0 \quad \lambda = 1 + 4\pi^2$

Problems

1. $(x - \frac{1}{2})^2 + (y - k^{-1})^2 = \frac{1}{4} + k^{-2}$

8. $\sigma g(u + \lambda)u' - ku(1 + u'^2)^{\frac{1}{2}} = 0, \quad \lambda = c \cosh b/c$

    $\bar{u} = c\{\cosh (x + b)/c - \cosh b/c\}$ where b and c satisfy
    $c\{\sinh (a + b)/c - \sinh b/c\} = l$, $\sigma g c \sinh (a + b)/c - k \cosh (a + b)/c = 0$

9. $Elu^{(iv)} - q = 0, u'' = u''' = 0$ at $x = l$

10. $l_1 \ddot{\theta}_1 + l_2 \ddot{\theta}_2 + g\theta_1 = 0, \; m_1 l_1 \ddot{\theta}_1 + (m_1 + m_2)l_2 \ddot{\theta}_2 + (m_1 + m_2)g\theta_2 = 0$

11. $EA \dfrac{\partial^2 u}{\partial x^2} - \sigma \dfrac{\partial^2 u}{\partial t^2} = 0$ 12. $C_1^2 = \dfrac{4}{3\mu}\left(\dfrac{4\pi^2}{k\tau^2} - 1\right)$

13. $C_1 = \dfrac{-67}{19440} \dfrac{ql^4}{EI}, \quad C_2 = \dfrac{23}{19440} \dfrac{ql^4}{EI}, \quad C_3 = \dfrac{-187}{19440} \dfrac{ql^4}{EI}$

15. $Pl^2 + 4\omega^2 \sigma l^4 \dfrac{93\pi^2}{918} = EI \dfrac{168}{17}$

16. $C_1 = \dfrac{-256ka^4}{\pi^6 T}$

Index